FUNCTIONAL ANALYSIS

A Blaisdell Book in the Pure and Applied Sciences

GEORGE SPRINGER, *University of Kansas*

CONSULTING EDITOR

FUNCTIONAL ANALYSIS

Albert Wilansky

LEHIGH UNIVERSITY

BLAISDELL PUBLISHING COMPANY

A Division of Ginn and Company

NEW YORK · TORONTO · LONDON

TO

Ruth

MY COMPANION IN THE GREAT ADVENTURE

PREFACE

It is now 32 years since the appearance of Banach's famous treatise. During this period the place of functional analysis in the pure mathematics curriculum has become secure. In the applied mathematics and engineering curricula, it is assuming an ever-increasing importance to the extent that it is strongly suggested for graduate students in these fields. In the *Curricula in Solid Mechanics*,[1] the following statements are made:

"The subject matter [of functional analysis] includes the study of abstract spaces of functional operators, transformations of these spaces and spectral theory, and provides a general framework for the study of the boundary value problems and eigenvalue problems of partial differential and integral equations. This is an aspect of modern mathematical analysis which is very much in vogue and with which we should become familiar. For one thing, unless we do, we will soon be unable to converse with mathematicians about topics which really concern us, such as the theory of differential equations, due to the introduction of much new terminology as well as new concepts. For another thing, the emphasis in functional analysis on the operators and their abstract properties is closely related to, and, in fact, was in large part inspired by the problems of quantum mechanics in physics.

Thus we have here a promising new level of interplay between mathematical and physical ideas which may well provide a key to a deeper understanding of both, just as did calculus in a previous era.

A study of functional analysis in itself frequently provides new insight and understanding into the processes and techniques of elementary analysis which we are accustomed to use in our everyday calculations. By shifting from the particular to the general in the operations of analysis we are provided with powerful tools. These replace the special tricks of an earlier day when we are out to prove convergence or find a solution, or even to formulate a proper problem."

This book is written to serve as a senior or beginning graduate text. Although the student should not expect to learn the value of a subject at the time that he is

---

[1] Reprinted from H. Liebowitz and J. M. Allen, *CURRICULA IN SOLID MECHANICS*, 1961, with permission of the University of Colorado, Boulder, Colorado, and Prentice-Hall, Inc., Englewood Cliffs, New Jersey.

learning the subject itself, we have tried to give, in problems and examples, some of the applications of functional analysis. To mention only two, a proof is given of a version of the Riemann mapping theorem, as is a proof of the existence of a continuous function whose Fourier series diverges.

Approximately 2000 problems, most of them quite easy, allow the book to be used as a problem course for independent study. An introductory essay on the subject of functional analysis is given in Section 1.6. The knowledge prerequisite to the study of this book is outlined in Section 1.1.

The first eight chapters of the book are more elementary than the last six. Topology is introduced in Chapter 9 and linear topology in Chapter 10. The first eight chapters go only so far into topology as metric space and only so far into linear topology as Fréchet, Banach, and Hilbert space; this is far enough to present the uniform-boundedness principle and the Hahn-Banach theorem. The deeper, and perhaps, more useful, closed-graph theorem is postponed until Chapter 11.

A leisurely one-semester course could cover the first eight chapters, omitting Chapter 3. Instructors intending to cover the entire book in a year should attempt to finish Chapter 9 in the first semester. For alumni of strong courses in algebra and topology, a year should be more than adequate to cover the book.

The purpose of a text is to prepare the student for study of the periodical literature, hence notation and terminology must be standard. In cases where there is no fixed standard, the text must make a decision and occasionally, when fully justified, introduce a new term. This procedure has been followed. The outstanding example is the words "norm" and "seminorm," which, most usually, denote positively homogeneous functions (with some other properties). However, in a substantial body of the literature, a norm need not be positively homogeneous. In this book, a norm p is always positively homogeneous. A new name and notation are introduced for the function which has all the properties of a norm save this one. It is called a paranorm. The norm of a vector x is denoted by $\|x\|$ according to standard usage; we shall denote the paranorm of x by $!x!$ to avoid the ambiguity of $\|x\|$ and the confusion of $|x|$.

Other new words and terminology used in the book are "balloon," the t and b properties, the symbol $w(A, \Phi)$, and the word "finalizing." The last of these is an attempt to fill a gap in the terminology of almost every published attempt to define a subnet. In problems a few other new words such as "true subset" and "crisscross theorem" are used, but only temporarily. In defining polars, I have followed Nakano rather than Bourbaki, the complex case seems, thereby, a little easier to cover. A glossary of the terminology used in the periodical literature is given at the end of the book.

Following a popular trend to avoid redundant separation assumptions, strongly noticeable in *General Topology* by J. L. Kelley, this book deals with semimetric spaces. The extra generality is usually not needed and, if a lecturer wishes to make the extra assumption that the semimetrics are metrics, he may do so. He will have to be cautious in dealing with non-Hausdorff spaces in and after Chapter 9, and will find himself unable to cover Section 12.3 in which the properties of a seminormed space are essential.

Some examples of the convenience of using semimetrics are (a) the possibility of defining the topology generated by a family of seminorms in terms of the individual semimetric topology generated by each seminorm; (b) the most general linear topology for a finite-dimensional space is a semimetric topology; (c) theorems proved about the Fréchet combination remain true if there are only finitely many seminorms, since almost all the seminorms may be set equal to zero; (d) as mentioned above, our proof of the uniform-boundedness principle in linear topological space uses seminormed spaces.

The hypotheses of almost every theorem are minimal to the extent consistent with a unified treatment. Examples and problems are given in almost every case to show that hypotheses cannot be omitted.

ACKNOWLEDGMENTS

Functional analysis was founded by S. Banach, M. Fréchet, H. Hahn, F. Hausdorff, D. Hilbert, S. Mazur, J. von Neumann, F. Riesz, M. H. Stone, and others. Their very names are synonymous with the tools of the subject.

In many years of study, during some of which I was not aware that my studies would culminate in the publication of a book, I consulted innumerable research articles and books to the extent that it is no longer possible for me to identify the source of much material in my book. I make no claim of originality for the material used here and I acknowledge that this material was culled from the publications of many mathematicians, some of whom are now listed:

R. F. Arens, G. Birkhoff, N. Bourbaki, R. C. Buck, P. Civin, M. M. Day, J. Dieudonne, J. Dixmier, N. Dunford, W. F. Eberlein, B. R. Gelbaum, H. H. Goldstine, M. Henriksen, E. Hewitt, E. Hille, J. Hotta, R. C. James, R. V. Kadison, S. Karlin, J. L. Kelley, H. Kober, M. Krein, L. H. Loomis, E. R. Lorch, G. G. Lorentz, H. Löwig, G. W. Mackey, W. Meyer-König, F. J. Murray, M. A. Naimark, H. Nakano, W. F. Newns, J. C. Oxtoby, B. J. Pettis, R. A. Raimi, C. E. Rickart, J. T. Schwartz, F. Smithies, V. Smulian, A. E. Taylor, J. V. Wehausen, E. S. Wolk, B. Yood.

A few mathematicians not listed above are mentioned in the text. Their names are listed in the Index.

I have had the privilege of examining the manuscript of *Linear Topological Spaces* by J. L. Kelley and I. Namioka before its publication. This proved most helpful.

Next I mention those persons whose contributions came through personal contact. Above all I am irrevocably indebted to J. A. Schatz and Karl Zeller. Their shared genius in conversation, seminar, and collaboration, I count as my greatest and least deserved good fortune.

I wish to acknowledge with thanks conversations, correspondence, and seminars in functional analysis in which I benefitted; these involved I. D. Berg, V. F. Cowling, D. J. Foulis, S. Gulden, G. Laison, G. Rayna, G. A. Stengle, L. J. Wallen, H. H. Wicke, J. Woll, and T. Yen.

For skillful help with the manuscript and problems, I thank A. K. Snyder. His keen eye has reduced considerably the number of blemishes. I wish to thank Laura Sue Wilansky for assistance with the index. Harry M. Paton assisted generously in the preparation of an earlier version of the manuscript.

The book would have been impossible to write without the assistance of Mrs. Helen Farrell who typed the manuscript with unbelievable speed and accuracy. My deepest thanks go to her for her assistance.

The administration of Lehigh University has viewed my project with approval and sympathetic consideration. I wish to thank the officers of the University for taking every opportunity to smooth my path.

My thanks go to the staff of Blaisdell Publishing Company for their friendly and efficient treatment of this book and its author.

A. WILANSKY

May, 1964

CONTENTS

1. INTRODUCTION

1.1	Explanatory notes	1
1.2	The table of spaces	3
1.3	Special functions	4
1.4	Inequalities	5
1.5	Partially ordered sets	9
1.6	Functional analysis	11

2. LINEAR SPACE

2.1	Linear space	13
2.2	Linear dependence and span	14
2.3	Hamel dimension	16
2.4	Linear maps	18
2.5	Arithmetic	22
2.6	Convex and affine sets	26
2.7	Balloons and cones	30
2.8	Quotient space	32
2.9	Finite dimensional space	35
2.10	Maximal subspaces and hyperplanes	37
2.11	Real versus complex	42
2.12	Distributions, linear theory	43

3. SEPARATION

3.1   Support   46
3.2   Separation   49

4. PARANORMS AND SEMINORMS

4.1   Paranorms   52
4.2   Seminorms   56
4.3   Semimetric space   60
4.4   Seminormed space   64

5. SEMIMETRIC SPACE

5.1   Semimetric space   72
5.2   Cardinality and structure   75
5.3   Completeness   76

6. LINEAR SEMIMETRIC SPACE

6.1   Linear semimetric space   81
6.2   Series in linear semimetric space   84
6.3   Basis   86
6.4   Representation of functionals   90
6.5   Quotient space   96

7. BANACH SPACE

7.1   The adjoint operation   98
7.2   The second conjugate   100
7.3   Finite dimensional space   105
7.4   Rotundity   107
7.5   Pathology   112
7.6   Uniform boundedness   116

8. HILBERT SPACE

8.1 Inner products 120

8.2 The conjugate space 123

8.3 Inner product norms 124

8.4 Orthonormal sets in an inner product space 126

8.5 Orthonormal sets in Hilbert space 129

8.6 Operators 132

9. TOPOLOGY AND NETS

9.1 Topological space 136

9.2 Nets 143

9.3 Sup, weak, and product topologies 148

9.4 Subnets 156

9.5 Compact sets 160

9.6 Universal nets 164

10. LINEAR TOPOLOGY

10.1 Linear topological space 167

10.2 Arithmetic 173

10.3 Bounded sets 178

10.4 Metrization 182

10.5 Continuity and equicontinuity 186

10.6 Finite-dimensional space 191

10.7 Uniformity 193

11. THE CLOSED GRAPH THEOREM

11.1 Closed functions 195

11.2 The closed-graph theorem 198

11.3   *FH* spaces   202
11.4   The basis in Fréchet space   207

12.   LOCAL CONVEXITY

12.1   Seminorms   215
12.2   Separation   219
12.3   Uniform boundedness   223
12.4   Locally convex *FK* spaces   226

13.   DUALITY

13.1   Duality   233
13.2   Polars   236
13.3 σ topologies   239
13.4   Normed space   243
13.5   Two more topologies   246

14.   BANACH ALGEBRA

14.1   Algebra   251
14.2   Banach algebra   259
14.3   Applications   267
14.4 B^* algebras   272
14.5   Unfinished business   275

       APPENDIX   279
       GLOSSARY   281
       INDEX   283
       TABLE   289

FUNCTIONAL ANALYSIS

1
INTRODUCTION

1.1 Explanatory

This section explains some of the conventions of which constant use will be made. Although some of the later sections of this chapter may be glanced over and referred to as needed, the present section must be thoroughly assimilated.

The usual notations of elementary set theory are used. As examples, $\{x: f(x) > 0\}$ means the set of all x for which $f(x)$ is positive, $\{a\}$ is the set whose only member is a,

$$A \setminus B \text{ means } \{a: a \in A \text{ and } a \notin B\};$$

when a set X has been specified and $A \subset X$, the set $X \setminus A$ is denoted by $\tilde{A}$ when no confusion can result.

The notation $A \not\cap B$ (read: A does not meet B) stands for $A \cap B = \emptyset$, that is, A, B are disjoint.

The usual $f: X \rightarrow Y$ means that f is a function (synonymous with map) with domain X and range $f[X]$, with $f[X] \subset Y$. In this case, f is a function *on* X or *from* X *into* Y. If $f[X] = Y$, f is said to be *onto*. If $f: X \rightarrow Y$ and $S \subset X$, then $f|S$ is the restriction of f to S; that is, $g \equiv f|S$ satisfies $g: S \rightarrow Y$, $g(x) = f(x)$ for $x \in S$.

We occasionally write $f(x)$ as fx.

If f is a function, the abbreviations $(f < 0)$, $(|f| < 1)$, $(f = 4)$ are used, respectively, for $\{x: f(x) < 0\}$, $\{x: |f(x)| < 1\}$, $\{x: f(x) = 4\}$, and other, similar abbreviations are used.

For $f: X \rightarrow Y$, $g: Y \rightarrow Z$, $g \circ f: X \rightarrow Z$ is defined by $g \circ f(x) = g[f(x)]$.

The letter R always denotes the set of real numbers with all its structure, namely algebraic operations, order, open and closed sets. ω is the set of positive integers, E is the set of complex numbers, each with its structure.

If f is a *complex function*, that is, $f: X \rightarrow E$ for some X, Rf denotes the real part of f.

As usual $[a, b] = \{x \in R: a \leq x \leq b\}$, $(a, b) = \{x \in R: a < x < b\}$, $[a, b) = \{x \in R: a \leq x < b\}$, similarly $(a, b]$. For $S \subset R$, $x = \sup S$ means $x \geq y$ for all $y \in S$, and, for any $\epsilon > 0$, $y > x - \epsilon$ for some $y \in S$; $\inf S$ has a dual definition.

For $z \in E$, $z = |z|e^{i\theta}$, sgn z is, by definition, $e^{-i\theta}$ so that z sgn $z = |z|$, sgn $0 = 0$.

The sentence "x is a *sequence*" will mean, "$x = \{x_n\} = (x_1, x_2, \ . \ . \ .)$, where each x_n is a complex number." Thus if x is a sequence, $x: \omega \rightarrow E$. A *real sequence* x is one in which each x_n is a real number.   Occasionally, and with explicit mention, a sequence x may be $(x_0, x_1, x_2, \ . \ . \ .)$.

A *null* sequence is one which converges to 0.

To say that x_n satisfies a certain condition for *almost all n* means that x_n satisfies the condition for all but finitely many n.   On a few occasions, indicated by the context, almost all will mean all but a set of measure zero.

Such words as "includes" and "increasing" are never used in the strict sense.   Thus "$A \supset A$" is correct, the largest integer function $[\cdot]$ is an increasing function.   Such a function as the exponential is said to be *strictly* increasing, and $A \supset B$ *strictly* if $A \supset B$ and $A \neq B$.

PROOF BRACKETS.   When part of a discussion is enclosed in square brackets, this means that the statement immediately preceding the brackets is being proved.   As an example, suppose the text reads, "Since x is not zero ⟦if $x = 0$, it follows that $\cos x = 1$ contradicting the hypothesis⟧, we may cancel x from both sides."   The reader should first absorb "since x is not zero, we may cancel x from both sides."   He may then proceed with the text, or, if desired, return to the proof in brackets.

PROBLEMS.   In general, the problems are very easy and should be worked to demonstrate mastery of the text.

STARRED PROBLEMS AND EXAMPLES.   Problems marked with a star ★ must be done. They form part of the development of the text and, in extreme cases, are used later without citation.   They are easy or are supplied with hints.   Difficult problems are indicated by the symbol ▲.

The same remark applies to Examples marked with ★ and ▲.   *Note: unmarked Problems and Examples may be omitted without disturbing the continuity of the text.*   Sections and theorems marked ▲ are not important for the continuity of the book, and may be incomplete.

ITALICS.   A word in italics is being used for the first time.   It is defined by the sentence in which it occurs.

END OF PROOF.   The end of the proof of a theorem is indicated by the sign $//$.

INTERNAL REFERENCES.   References will be of the form, Section 4.5, Theorem 2, referring to Chapter 4, Section 5, Theorem 2.   The reference, Section 5, Theorem 2 refers to the same chapter as the one in which the reference occurs; the reference Theorem 2 is to the same section.

PREREQUISITES.   A few algebraic and analytic results will be used without proof.   Examples are the facts that a system of n linear equations in $n + 1$ unknowns has a solution, and that R is connected (that is, R is not the union of two disjoint nonempty open sets).   One application is made of the Cantor-Bernstein theorem, which says that if each of two sets allows a one-to-one map into the other, the sets are of equal cardinality; at the same point a simple use is made of cardinal numbers.   In examples, the Weierstrass approximation theorem is cited, but it is not used in the text.   In one example, the identity $\Sigma 1/n^2 = \pi^2/6$ is used.   Mention of the Lebesgue integral occurs in examples but not in the text.   In Section 6.4, Example 8, a simple type of measure and integral is developed.   There is an application of Liouville's theorem on bounded analytic functions in Chapter 14. Otherwise the book is self contained for readers with a background including advanced calculus.

Problems 1.1

★1. Let u, v be real functions on a set A. Show that sup $\{u(x) + v(x): x \in A\} \leq$ sup $u(x) +$ sup $v(x)$ and that inequality may hold. What is the corresponding result for inf?

★2. Let u, v be real functions on sets A, B, respectively. Show that sup $\{u(x) + v(y): x \in A, y \in B\} =$ sup $\{u(x): x \in A\} +$ sup $\{v(x): x \in B\}$.

★3. For $S \subset R$, show that sup $S = -$ inf $(- S)$.

1.2 The table of spaces

In the Table of Spaces (at the end of the book) are listed the spaces which will be used to illustrate the theoretical developments of the text. For easy reference they are all listed in one place, together with some relevant formulas which are explained in later chapters. The table need not be memorized, or studied carefully; it may be consulted each time it is needed. If, for example, the text should say "for $x \in m$, set $p(x) = \cdots$," the reader should, by consulting the Table of Spaces, learn that $x \in m$ means that x is a bounded sequence.

★*Example 1.* Each member $(x_1, x_2, \ldots, x_n)$ of E^n will be identified with the *finite sequence* $(x_1, x_2, \ldots, x_n, 0, 0, \ldots)$, so that we may write, for example, $E^4 \subset E^7 \subset E^\infty$.

★*Example 2.* $s = F[\omega]$, since a sequence is, by definition, a function on ω. Also $E^n = F[(1, 2, 3, , \ldots, n)]$.

Example 3: Summability. Let $A = (a_{nk})$, n, $k = 1, 2, \ldots$, be a matrix of complex numbers. For any sequence x, let $(Ax)_n = \Sigma_{k=1}^\infty a_{nk}x_k$, $n = 1, 2, \ldots$. Finally, let the sequence $\{(Ax)_n\}$ be denoted by Ax. Thus Ax may be thought of as the ordinary matrix product of A with the column vector x. The *domain* of the matrix A, written d_A, is the set of all x such that Ax exists. The Table may now be consulted for the meaning of c_A, m_A, r_A.

Finally we introduce the important concept of product. Let B be a set and, for each $\beta \in B$, let A_β be a set. Then $\pi\{A_\beta: \beta \in B\}$, or, simply, πA_β, is the set of all functions $f: B \to \cup\{A_\beta: \beta \in B\}$ satisfying $f(\beta) \in A_\beta$ for each $\beta \in B$. The spaces A_β are called *factors* of the product. Here B is being used as an indexing set. If we are dealing with finitely or countably many sets A_β, we shall take B to be $(1, 2, \ldots, n)$ or ω and write $A_1 \times A_2 \times \cdots \times A_n$ or $A_1 \times A_2 \times \cdots$. Sometimes we shall do without indices, for example, $A \times D$. The phrase *countable product* refers to the product of a countable number of sets; similarly for the phrase *finite product*. If A_β is the same for all $\beta \in B$, say $A_\beta = A$, then $\pi\{A_\beta: \beta \in B\}$ is written A^B. Thus A^B is the set of all functions from B to A.

Problems 1.2

★1. Show that $R^n \subset E^n \subset E^\infty \subset l^p \subset l^{p+\epsilon} \subset c_0 \subset m \subset s$, (here $\epsilon > 0$), and that none of these inclusions can be replaced by equality.

2. Is it true or false that $\cup_{n=1}^\infty l^n \neq c_0$?

3. Show that $s = C[\omega]$.

4. Show that $m = C_1[\omega]$.

5. Show that, with a suitable interpretation of the symbols, $c = C[\omega \cup \{\infty\}]$.

6. If $\epsilon > 0$, $L^{p+\epsilon} \subset L^p$.   (Compare Problem 1.)   Prove this and show that the inclusion cannot be replaced by equality.

7. Show that $R^3 = R^B$ where $B = \{1, 2, 3\}$.

8. Show that $s = E^\omega$, and that $E^\infty = E^{(\omega)}$.

9. Show that $F[X] = E^X$.

10. The symbol 2^B is often used to denote the class of all subsets of a set B.   Show that there is a one-to-one correspondence between 2^B and A^B, where A is a set, for example $\{1, 2\}$, with 2 elements.

11. Suppose a sequence a has the property that $\Sigma a_n b_n$ is convergent for each $b \in c_0$.   Show that $a \in l$.

12. In Problem 11, replace c_0 by l and l by m.

13. In Problem 11, replace c_0 by l^p where p is some number greater than 1.   What conclusion can now be drawn in place of $a \in l$?

14. Show that $c_I = c$, I being the identity matrix.

15. Show that a matrix A is *row-finite*, that is, each row of $A \in E^\infty$, if and only if $d_A = s$.

16. Show that a matrix A is *column-finite*, that is, each column $\in E^\infty$, if and only if $A[E^\infty] \subset E^\infty$.

17. Show that a matrix A is *conservative*, that is, $c_A \supset c$, if and only if it satisfies the famous L. L. Silverman–0. Toeplitz conditions.

$$\|A\| \equiv \sup_n \sum_{k=1}^{\infty} |a_{nk}| < \infty,$$

$a_k \equiv \lim_n a_{nk}$ exists for each k, and $\lim_n \Sigma_k a_{nk}$ exists.

18. Show that a matrix A is *regular*, that is, $\lim_A x \equiv \lim Ax = \lim x$ for all $x \in c$, if and only if it is conservative, $a_k = 0$ for each k, and $\lim_n \Sigma_k a_{nk} = 1$.

19. A *triangle* is a matrix A satisfying $a_{nk} = 0$ for $k > n$, $a_{nn} \neq 0$ for all n.   Let A, B be triangles. Show that $c_A \supset c_B$ if and only if AB^{-1} is conservative, and that $\lim_{n \to \infty} (Ax)_n = \lim_{n \to \infty} (Bx)_n$ whenever the latter exists, if and only if AB^{-1} is regular.

20. Suppose that a conservative matrix A has a conservative right inverse.   Show that $c_A = c \oplus A^\perp$. $[\![x = [x - B(Ax)] + B(Ax).]\!]$

21. Use Problem 20 to show that if $\{2x_n - x_{n+1}\}$ is convergent, then $x_n = u_n + t2^n$ where $u \in c$, and t is a number.

22. Use Problem 20 to show that if $\{x_n - 2x_{n+1}\}$ is convergent, then x is convergent.

23. Let $a_{1k} = 1$, for all k; and, for $n > 1$, let $a_{nk} = 1$ if $k = n$, 0 otherwise.   Show that $E^\infty \subset r_A$, and $\{1\} \notin r_A$.

1.3   Special functions

The sequence $\{1, 1, 1, \ldots\}$ will be denoted by 1 whenever no confusion will result. For example $1 \in c$.   Similarly, in the formula $1 \in C$, 1 stands for the function which is identically 1.   The sequences $\{1, 0, 0, \ldots\}$, $\{0, 1, 0, 0, \ldots\}$, $\{0, 0, 1, 0, 0, \ldots\}$ and so on, are written δ^1, δ^2, δ^3, $\ldots$.   Thus δ^n_k, the kth term of δ^n, is 1 if $k = n$, 0 if $k \neq n$. (This is the Kronecker delta.)

We now define the *coordinate functions*.   For each integer $k > 0$, define $P_k : s \to E$ by $P_k a = a_k$.   Thus $a = \{a_n\} \in s$ and $P_k a = a_k$ is the kth term or kth coordinate of a.   Clearly the coordinate functions are defined on all sequence spaces.   The coordinate functions are often referred to as *the coordinates;* for example one says that on c the coordinates are additive, meaning that $P_k(a + b) = P_k a + P_k b$.

The same idea may be applied to function spaces.   For a given t, $0 \leq t \leq 1$, we define $P_t : F \to E$ by $P_t(f) = f(t)$.   For example $P_0 \cos = \cos 0 = 1$.   More generally, given a set H, and $h \in H$, $P_h: F[H] \to E$ is defined by $P_h f = f(h)$. Still more generally, given sets A, B, and $t \in B$, define $P_t: A^B \to A$ by $P_t f = f(t)$. With $A = E$, $B = H$ this includes the preceding definition since $A^B = E^H = F[H]$. In this context, P_t is called the *evaluation map* at t. It is also referred to as a *point;* for example one says that on C the points are additive, meaning that $P_t(f + g) = P_t f + P_t g$. Clearly the evaluation maps are defined on all function spaces. Notice that the coordinates are a special case since $s = E^\omega$. Turning again to products, consider for each $t \in B$, $P_t: \pi\{A_\beta: \beta \in B\} \to A_t$ given by $P_t f = f(t)$. Now P_t is called the *projection* on A_t. The evaluation map is a special case. [Taking $A_\beta = A$ for all β, we have $P_t: A^B \to A$ is given by $P_t f = f(t)$. This is the evaluation map.]

For an example in which "projection" is the natural word, consider $R^3 = R^A$ if $A = (1, 2, 3)$. Then $P_2(x, y, z) = y$, the projection onto the y axis!

Some further functions of interest are $\lim: c \to E$ defined by $\lim a = \lim_{n \to \infty} a_n$, $\lim_A: c_A \to E$ defined by $\lim_A x = \lim Ax$; here A is a matrix.

Finally, if f is a real or complex function defined on a set A, $f^\perp = f^{-1}[\{0\}]$ is defined to be $\{a \in A: f(a) = 0\}$. It is pronounced, "f perp," and called the *annihilator* of f, or *kernel* of f.

Problems 1.3

★1. Show that $(\{P_n\}\{\delta^n\})$ is a *biorthogonal* system: that is, $P_n(\delta^k) = 1$ if $n = k$, 0 if $n \neq k$.

★2. For $a \in E^n$, show that $a = \Sigma_{k=1}^n P_k(a) \delta^k$.

★3. Define $f \in C$ by $f(x) = 4x^2 + 3$. Show that $P_{\frac{1}{2}} f = 4$.

4. Show that if k, m, n are distinct integers, $P_k \neq P_m + P_n$. More generally, no complex numbers s, t, exist such that $P_k = sP_m + tP_n$. In this problem the domain of these functions may, for definiteness, be taken as c_0.

5. Extend Problem 4 to a result concerning any finite set of integers.

6. Show that there exists no $a \in s$ such that for all $x \in c$, $\lim x = \Sigma a_k x_k$.

7. Show that if r, s, t are distinct numbers in $[0, 1]$, $P_r \neq P_s + P_t$. (Take C as domain.) Generalize as in Problems 4 and 5.

8. Define $I: C \to R$ by $If = \int_0^1 f$. Show that there is no number t such that $I = P_t$.

9. Extend Problem 8 by showing that there is no finite collection t_1, t_2, . . . , t_n such that I is a linear combination of P_{t_1}, P_{t_2}, . . . , P_{t_n}.

10. Show that

$$\bigcup_{m=1}^{\infty} \bigcap_{n=m}^{\infty} P_n^\perp = E^\infty.$$

1.4 Inequalities

In applications of functional analysis, several standard inequalities occur frequently. Proofs of these will now be sketched.

Let $f(x) = -\ln x$ for $x > 0$. Since $f''(x) > 0$ for all x, f is convex. This means that for all a, b, θ with $0 < a < b$, $0 < \theta < 1$, we have

(1) $$f[\theta a + (1 - \theta)b] \leq \theta f(a) + (1 - \theta)f(b).$$

[Let $x = \theta a + (1 - \theta)b$. Then

$$\frac{f(x) - f(a)}{x - a} = \frac{1}{x - a} \int_a^x f' \leq f'(x) \leq \frac{1}{b - x} \int_x^b f' = \frac{f(b) - f(x)}{b - x}.$$

Solving this inequality for $f(x)$ yields equation (1).]

Hence $\ln \left[\theta a + (1 - \theta)b \right] \geq \theta \ln a + (1 - \theta) \ln b$ and so

$$(2) \qquad\qquad a^\theta b^{1-\theta} \leq \theta a + (1 - \theta)b.$$

By symmetry, equation (2) holds for all positive a, b.

Now, consider two sequences $\{a_n\}$, $\{b_n\}$ of nonnegative real numbers with $A = \Sigma a_n < \infty$, $B = \Sigma b_n < \infty$. For example, the sequences may be finite, in which case we declare them to be ordinary infinite sequences by defining $a_n = 0$, $b_n = 0$ for any n larger than the maximum n for which they are already defined. By equation (2) we have, for any θ satisfying $0 < \theta < 1$,

$$\Sigma \left(\frac{a_n}{A} \right)^\theta \left(\frac{b_n}{B} \right)^{1-\theta} \leq \frac{\theta}{A} \Sigma a_n + \frac{1-\theta}{B} \Sigma b_n = 1.$$

This shows in particular that the first series converges. Multiplying both sides by $A^\theta B^{1-\theta}$ yields

$$(3) \qquad\qquad \Sigma a_n^\theta b_n^{1-\theta} \leq (\Sigma a_n)^\theta (\Sigma b_n)^{1-\theta}.$$

Let us now choose arbitrary numbers p, q, satisfying $p > 1$, $1/p + 1/q = 1$. Then $q > 1$, also. Let $\{u_n\}$, $\{v_n\}$ be arbitrary sequences of complex numbers satisfying $\Sigma |u_n|^p < \infty$, $\Sigma |v_n|^q < \infty$. Let $\theta = 1/p$, $a_n = |u_n|^p$, $b_n = |v_n|^q$. The inequality (3) now reads

$$(4) \qquad\qquad \Sigma |u_n v_n| \leq (\Sigma |u_n|^p)^{1/p} (\Sigma |v_n|^q)^{1/q} \qquad (\textit{Hölder's inequality}).$$

This inequality holds for all complex $\{u_n\}$, $\{v_n\}$ such that the right-hand side is meaningful, in which case we also have the convergence of the series on the left, and for all p, q with $p > 1$, $1/p + 1/q = 1$. Taking account of the fact that $|\Sigma u_n v_n| \leq \Sigma |u_n v_n|$, we may replace the left hand side of inequality (4) by $|\Sigma u_n v_n|$.

Next, let $p > 1$ and let $\{u_n\}$, $\{v_n\}$ be sequences of nonnegative real numbers such that $\Sigma u_n^p < \infty$, $\Sigma v_n^p < \infty$. In the following argument we shall write $\Sigma (u_n + v_n)^p$. That this series converges will be evident; for we can apply the following argument with $\Sigma_{n=1}^m$ in place of Σ and, at the end, let $m \to \infty$. We have

$$\begin{aligned}
\Sigma (u_n + v_n)^p &= \Sigma (u_n + v_n)(u_n + v_n)^{p-1} \\
&= \Sigma u_n (u_n + v_n)^{p-1} + \Sigma v_n (u_n + v_n)^{p-1} \\
&\leq (\Sigma u_n^p)^{1/p} [\Sigma (u_n + v_n)^{(p-1)q}]^{1/q} + (\Sigma v_n^p)^{1/p} [\Sigma (u_n + v_n)^{(p-1)q}]^{1/q}
\end{aligned}$$

by Hölder's inequality, where q is given by $1/p + 1/q = 1$. Now $(p - 1)q = p$, so if we divide the first and last terms by $[\Sigma (u_n + v_n)^p]^{1/q}$, we obtain

$$(5) \qquad\qquad [\Sigma (u_n + v_n)^p]^{1/p} \leq (\Sigma u_n^p)^{1/p} + (\Sigma v_n^p)^{1/p}.$$

Since for complex numbers u, v we have $|u + v| \leq |u| + |v|$, we immediately obtain from inequality (5),

$$(6) \qquad (\Sigma |u_n + v_n|^p)^{1/p} \leq (\Sigma |u_n|^p)^{1/p} + (\Sigma |v_n|^p)^{1/p} \qquad (\textit{Minkowski's inequality}).$$

This inequality holds for all complex $\{u_n\}$, $\{v_n\}$ such that the right-hand side is meaningful, in which case we have the convergence of the series on the left, and for all p with $p \geq 1$. The argument assumed $p > 1$, but inequality (6) is clearly true for $p = 1$.

The inequality (6) fails if $0 < p < 1$. Let us assume that $0 < p < 1$. Then since $1/p > 1$, we have, from inequality (6),

(7) $$(\Sigma |u_n + v_n|^{1/p})^p \leq (\Sigma |u_n|^{1/p})^p + (\Sigma |v_n|^{1/p})^p, \qquad 0 < p < 1.$$

Let a, b be any complex numbers, and, in inequality (7) make the substitution

$$u_1 = |a|^p, u_2 = u_3 = \cdots = 0, v_1 = 0, v_2 = |b|^p, v_3 = v_4 = \cdots = 0.$$

We obtain

(8) $$(|a| + |b|)^p \leq |a|^p + |b|^p, \text{ hence clearly}$$

(9) $$|a + b|^p \leq |a|^p + |b|^p, \qquad 0 < p < 1.$$

Observe that if $1/p$ is a positive integer, inequality (9) is a trivial consequence of the binomial theorem.

Inequality (10), which for $0 < p < 1$ plays the same role as Minkowski's inequality, follows easily after insertion of subscripts in inequality (9) and summation:

(10) $$\Sigma |u_n + v_n|^p \leq \Sigma |u_n|^p + \Sigma |v_n|^p, \qquad 0 < p < 1.$$

Suppose that $r > s > 0$. Then if $\Sigma |u_n|^s < \infty$, it follows that $\Sigma |u_n|^r < \infty$; [for $|u_n| < 1$ for almost all n, and so $|u_n|^r \leq |u_n|^s$ for almost all n]. But more is true; indeed, we have the following result, known as *Jensen's inequality:*

(11) $$(\Sigma |u_n|^p)^{1/p} \text{ is a decreasing function of p for p} > 0.$$

This result may be interpreted in the (wide) sense that the expression may be infinite for some p but if for some p it is finite, then it is finite for all larger p.

To prove Jensen's inequality, let $r > s > 0$. Let $m = (\Sigma |u_n|^r)^{1/r}$. Then $|u_n|/m \leq 1$ for each n, and so $(|u_n|/m)^s \geq (|u_n|/m)^r$ for each n. Making use of this we have

$$\frac{1}{m} (\Sigma |u_n|^s)^{1/s} = \left[\Sigma \left(\frac{|u_n|}{m} \right)^s \right]^{1/s} \geq \left[\Sigma \left(\frac{|u_n|}{m} \right)^r \right]^{1/s} = 1,$$

and inequality (11) follows.

It follows from inequality (11) that the limit as $p \to +\infty$ of the given expression exists. Its value will now be given.

Let $\{u_n\}$ be a complex sequence such that for some p > 0, t(p) $\equiv (\Sigma |u_n|^p)^{1/p} < \infty$. Then

(12) $$\lim_{p \to +\infty} t(p) = \inf_{p>0} t(p) = \max |u_n|.$$

Let $m = \max |u_n|$ and assume $m > 0$. (The result is trivial if $m = 0$.) There is at least one term of the sequence $\{|u_n|\}$ which is equal to m since $u_n \to 0$, thus $t(p) \geq (m^p)^{1/p} = m$, from which

(13) $$\lim t(p) \geq m.$$

Should there exist k such that $u_n = 0$ for $n > k$, we would have $t(p) \leq (km^p)^{1/p} = k^{1/p}m \to m$ and, with inequality (13), the proof of equation (12). In general, we require a slightly more delicate argument.

Let s be some number such that $t(s) < \infty$, let $p > s$, and let R be a positive integer.   Then

$$(14) \qquad t(p) = (\sum_{n=1}^{R} + \sum_{n=R+1}^{\infty} |u_n|^p)^{1/p} \le (\sum_{n=1}^{R} |u_n|^p)^{1/p} + (\sum_{n=R+1}^{\infty} |u_n|^p)^{1/p}$$

by inequality (9), since $0 < 1/p \le 1$.

Applying Jensen's inequality to $\{0, 0, \ldots, 0, u_{R+1}, u_{R+2}, \ldots\}$, we obtain

$$(\sum_{n=R+1}^{\infty} |u_n|^p)^{1/p} \le (\sum_{n=R+1}^{\infty} |u_n|^s)^{1/s}.$$

Also,

$$(\sum_{n=1}^{R} |u_n|^p)^{1/p} \le (Rm^p)^{1/p} = R^{1/p}m.$$

Applying these to inequality (14) yields

$$t(p) \le R^{1/p}m + (\sum_{n=R+1}^{\infty} |u_n|^s)^{1/s},$$

from which it follows that

$$\lim t(p) \le m + (\sum_{n=R+1}^{\infty} |u_n|^s)^{1/s}.$$

Since R is arbitrary, we have $\lim t(p) \le m$.   With (13), this completes the proof of equation (12).

Problems 1.4

1. Prove that

$$\sum_{n=1}^{m} |u_n| \le m^{1-1/p} (\sum_{n=1}^{m} |u_n|^p)^{1/p} \qquad \text{if } p > 1.$$

2. Let $r > s > 0$.   In problem 1, let $u_n = |a_n|^s$, $p = r/s$, and deduce that for each m, $(1/m \sum_{n=1}^{m} |a_n|^p)^{1/p}$ is an increasing function of p for $p > 0$.

3. Show that inequality (4) becomes an equality if and only if there exists a constant C such that $|v_n|^q = C|u_n|^p$ for all n.

4. Prove Hölder's inequality for integrals,

$$|\smallint fg| \le (\smallint |f|^p)^{1/p}(\smallint |g|^q)^{1/q}.$$

5. Let $r > s > 0$.   In Problem 4, let $f = |h|^s$, $g = 1$, $p = r/s$, and deduce that $\left(1/(b-a) \int_a^b |h|^p\right)^{1/p}$ is an increasing function of p, for $p > 0$.   (Compare this with Jensen's inequality.)

6. Prove that

$$(\sum |u_n - v_n|^p)^{1/p} \ge |(\sum |u_n|^p)^{1/p} - (\sum |v_n|^p)^{1/p}, \qquad \text{if } p \ge 1.$$

7. For sequences x, y, and $p > 1$.   Let

$$d(x, y) = (\sum |x_n - y_n|^p)^{1/p}.$$

Show that $d(x, z) \le d(x, y) + d(y, z)$.

8. Show that equality holds in (5) if and only if there exists a constant C such that $u_n = Cv_n$ for all n.

9. Show that equality holds in (6) if and only if there exists a nonnegative real constant C such that $u_n = Cv_n$ for all n.

10. Show that Minkowski's inequality (6) is false for $0 < p < 1$.

11. Show that if $p > 1$, the inequality (8) is reversed.

12. Show that if $0 < p < 1$, the inequality (5) is reversed. We are assuming that $u_n \geq 0$, $v_n \geq 0$.

13. If a, b are members of l^2, the sequence $\{a_n b_n\}$ is a member of l.

14. Let $p \to 1 +$ in Hölder's inequality. What is the resulting inequality? Prove it independently. What is the necessary and sufficient condition for equality?

15. Let $f \in C$. Show that

$$\lim_{p \to +\infty} \left(\int_0^1 |f|^p \right)^{1/p} = \max |f|.$$

16. Show that $t(p)$, given before equation (12), is a continuous function of p. What other properties, such as convexity, differentiability, does it have?

1.5   Partially ordered sets

A partially ordered set, for short, a *poset*, is a set for which a transitive and reflexive binary relation is defined. To explain what this means, we shall write $a \geq b$ to denote that (a, b) is in the relation, and our definition requires that if $a \geq b$, and $b \geq c$, then $a \geq c$ (*transitivity*), and that $a \geq a$ for all a (*reflexivity*). Finally, $a \leq b$ shall mean $b \geq a$. The most obvious example is R, taking $a \geq b$ with its usual meaning.

Example 1. R^2, $(x, y) \geq (u, v)$ means $x \geq u$ and $y \geq v$.

★*Example 2.* R^2, $(x, y) \geq (u, v)$ means $x \geq u$, or $x = u$ and $y \geq v$. This is the *lexicographic order*. For example, $(2, 9) \leq (8, 1) \leq (8, 2)$.

From Example 1 we see that a poset may have noncomparable elements; $(5, 2)$ and $(4, 3)$ are noncomparable. (We call a, b *comparable* if either $a \geq b$ or $b \geq a$; otherwise, they are *noncomparable*.)

A poset is called *totally ordered* if the ordering is *antisymmetric* (that is, $a \geq b$ and $b \geq a$ together imply $a = b$) and all elements are comparable. The poset of Example 2 is totally ordered. At the opposite extreme is the *trivial order* which may be put on an arbitrary set, namely, $a \geq b$ if and only if $a = b$.

★*Example 3.*   (*Very important.*)   Let A be a collection of subsets of a set B. For $x \in A$, $y \in A$ (that is, x, y are subsets of B) let $x \geq y$ mean $x \subset y$. This ordering will be called *ordering by inclusion*.

★*Example 4.*   (*Very important.*)   Same as Example 3 except $x \geq y$ means $x \supset y$. This ordering will be called *ordering by containment*.

A *directed set* is a poset which satisfies the condition that given a, b, there is an element c satisfying $c \geq a$ and $c \geq b$. We say that the set is directed by the relation $\geq$. An unimportant example is provided by a poset with a maximum element. More important are the set ω, and the class of all finite subsets of a given set ordered by containment. A directed set used in integration is the set of partitions of an interval, ordered by refinement.

A *chain* is a totally ordered subset of a poset. For example, in R, any set is a chain. In Example 1, the set $\{(n, n): n = 1, 2, 3, \ldots\}$ is a chain, also $\{(t, t + 1): t \in R\}$. In the trivial order (on a nonempty set) all chains have one element.

A *maximal* chain is one not properly included in any chain. The chain $\{(n, n)\}$ just mentioned is not maximal since it is properly included in $\{(t, t) : t \in R\}$. This latter chain is maximal. The chain $\{(t, t+1) : t \in R\}$ is maximal in Example 1. These two maximal chains are noncomparable (neither includes the other), thus neither is a *maximum* (or largest) chain.

AXIOM OF TRANSFINITE INDUCTION. *Every poset includes a maximal chain.*

Clearly a finite poset includes a maximal chain [one picks an element at random, then, if possible, another comparable with the first, another comparable with both, and so on until no further choice is possible]. In the case of an infinite poset, the result is postulated. We shall never refer to this axiom by name, but merely use its result, mostly in the form expressed in Theorem 1.

THEOREM 1. *Every chain is included in a maximal chain.*

Let A be a poset and C a nonempty chain in A. Let B be the subset of A consisting of elements comparable with all the elements of C; clearly $C \subset B$. Also B is a poset with the ordering it inherits from A. Hence B includes a maximal chain. This includes C [for if not we could enlarge it by adjoining C to it] and is maximal in A since any larger chain would, by definition of B, be included in B.//

We give one application, not important in itself, to illustrate the use of the axiom. Let $f : A \to B$, where A, B are sets, and suppose that f is onto. We shall prove that A has a subset S such that $f : S \to B$ is one to one and onto. The obvious procedure is to choose one member of $f^{-1}[\{b\}]$ for each $b \in A$. This infinite task is avoided by considering the set P of all subsets of A on which f is one to one. Each subset of A with exactly one element belongs to P. Order P by containment, choose a maximal chain C and let S be the union of all the sets in C. It is seen that f is one to one on S. [If $x, y \in S$, $x \neq y$, let X, Y be members of C containing x, y, respectively. Since C is a chain, one of them, say Y, includes the other. Thus $x, y \in Y$ and so $f(x) \neq f(y)$ since f is one to one on Y.] Finally $f|S$ is onto B [for if $b \in B \backslash f[S]$ we may choose an element $a \in f^{-1}[\{b\}]$ and adjoin $S \cup \{a\}$ to C to get a larger chain than C].//

Problems 1.5

★1. Let A, B be directed sets. Order $A \times B$ by defining $(a, b) \geq (a', b')$ to mean $a \geq a'$ and $b \geq b'$. Show that this makes $A \times B$ a directed set.

★2. Let S be a nonempty finite set in a directed set A. Show that there exists $a \in A$ such that $a \geq x$ for each $x \in S$.

3. Verify that the posets given in Examples 1 through 4 are directed.

4. (a) In Example 1, (b) in Example 2, arrange in increasing order (if possible) the points $(1, 7)$, $(2, 6)$, $(3, 7)$ $(2, 8)$, $(1, 8)$, $(4, 3)$, $(4, 2)$. If this is not possible, make up a diagram showing all the relationships.

★5. *The dense cone.* For $a, b \in R^\infty$, define $b > a$ to mean that $b \neq a$ and the last nonzero term of $b - a$ is positive; and $b \geq a$ to mean $b > a$ or $b = a$. Verify that R^∞ is a totally ordered poset. (The set in R^∞ given by $\{a : a \geq 0\}$ is called the *dense cone.*)

6. A set S in a poset A is called *cofinal* if for each $a \in A$, there exists $x \in S$ with $x \geq a$. Give an example of a maximal chain which is not cofinal. (The space of Example 1 has some.)

7. Let A, B be sets, and $f\colon A \to B$. If there exists $g\colon B \to A$ such that $f[g(b)] = b$ for all $b \in B$, we call g a *right inverse* for f. While if $g[f(a)] = a$ for all $a \in A$, g is a *left inverse*. Show that if f is one to one, any right inverse is a left inverse.

8. A function has a right inverse if and only if it is onto, a left inverse if and only if it is one to one.

▲9. Show that πA_β is not empty if each A_β is not empty. Thus (as pointed out by Bertrand Russell) when the number of settled worlds is infinite we shall be able to elect a parliament (provided that the Constitution of the Universe includes the Axiom).

▲10. Let A be a set. Let p be a property of certain subsets of A, and for any subsets S of A assume that S has property p if and only if every finite subset of S has property p. Show that A includes a maximal subset with property p.

11. If in Problem 10 we replace "finite subset" by "finite proper subset," we can get the result of Problem 10 without use of the Axiom.

▲12. Let P be a poset and assume that every chain in P has an upper bound in P. Show that P has a maximal element.

13. For a finite poset, the Axiom can be proved.

▲14. Show that there exists a set A of real numbers such that $A + x$ meets A if and only if x is irrational. (Thus A has an infinite number of disjoint translates and cannot be measurable.)

15. Let P be a poset with a maximum element u. Let A, B be sets in P which contain u and such that every subset of A (and B) has a greatest lower bound in A (in B). For any $x \in P$, let Ax be the greatest lower bound of $y \in A$ satisfying $y \geq x$, similarly for Bx. (For example, if P is the class of subsets of R and A is the class of closed sets, Ax is the closure of x.) Suppose that $Ba \in A$ for all $a \in A$. Let $C = A \cap B$. Show that $Cx = BAx$ for all $x \in P$ but that $Cx = ABx$ is not necessarily true.

16. Give an example of an uncountable family F of sets, no two equal, such that F is totally ordered by inclusion, and the union of all the sets in F is countable. (Hint: This is easy.)

17. Give an example of a poset that has no cofinal chain. (One is given in Section 10.4, Problem 9.)

1.6 Functional analysis

A classical tradition in mathematics is that of working with individual objects. For example, every differentiable function is continuous. This is proved by considering *one* function f, assuming it differentiable, and proving it continuous. Perhaps the first break with this tradition came in the year 1874, when George Cantor proved the existence of a transcendental number by showing that R is uncountable, while the set of algebraic numbers is countable. This is reasoning with classes of objects, rather than with individual objects. Functional analysis similarly deals with classes of objects; the classes are called spaces, and are usually endowed with some sort of structure.

It seemed at first an inherent defect in the subject that it could prove only the existence of an object, never exhibit it explicitly. (For example, Cantor's proof shows no transcendental number explicitly.)

Partly for this reason, functional analysis was disparagingly dubbed "soft analysis" by the practitioners in the classic tradition, their own work being called "hard analysis."

During the period since 1930, functional analysis has fully repudiated any such epithet by the grandeur and depth of its accomplishments. With local maxima in Banach's book (1932), the work of von Neumann, (1935), and Gelfand's introduction of Banach algebra (1941), functional analysis has established itself during this period as a powerful and pervading tool in almost all branches of mathematics. (C.f. Preface, p. vii.)

As an example of the "space" approach, consider the result: "Suppose that an infinite matrix A has the property that the sequence $\{\Sigma_{k=1}^{\infty}a_{nk}x_k\}$ is convergent for all $x \in c$. Then it follows that $\{\Sigma_{k=1}^{\infty}|a_{nk}|\}$ is a bounded sequence." This was proved by O. Toeplitz in 1911 by the "hard analysis" approach of assuming the conclusion false, and constructing a sequence $x \in c$ for which $\{\Sigma_{k=1}^{\infty}a_{nk}x_k\}$ is a divergent sequence. In Banach's book, in 1932, the theorem is shown to be a trivial special case of the uniform boundedness principle, applied to a sequence of functions *on the space c.* (See Section 7.6, Application 2, for details.) Furthermore, the same principle yields innumerable other useful results of this nature. Although a startling feat in 1932, such announcements that lengthy proofs, already in print, can be abbreviated to a few lines, no longer are news. The uniform boundedness principle is like the slide rule—it is worth mastering the technique of its use for the ultimate gain in power and speed.

Theorems of the type "Every thing with property B also has property A" are proved by considering the subset $A \cap B$ of B, and showing that this subset has some property sufficient to make it occupy the whole of B. (We are denoting by B, the set of things with property B.) An example of this is Corollary 7 of Section 11.3, which says that if $A \cap B$ is of second category in B, it is all of B. (John Stuart Mill complained in 1848 that the syllogism "All men are mortal, Socrates is a man, hence Socrates is mortal" is useless because we could not know that all men are mortal without first checking the case of Socrates. If we could prove that the set of mortal men is of second category in the space of men, and the above mentioned corollary, this objection would disappear. The author confesses that this project appears to be beyond the reach of our subject.)

A similar technique yields results of the type, there exists at least one object with property A which does not have property B, by showing that $A \cap B$ could not be all of A. An example of this is given in Section 11.3, Example 7, which yields the result that there must be a null sequence x such that $\Sigma|x_n|^p$ is divergent for every $p > 0$. (This is, of course, a trivial result.)

One of the outstanding examples of the method of examining sets is I. M. Gelfand's proof (Section 14.3, Application 1) of N. Wiener's theorem that under certain hypotheses on f, $1/f$ has a certain type of expansion. This might be proved by examining one function with the given properties. The functional analytic proof consists of finding the form of an ideal in a certain algebra.

Functional analysis thus provides a quick method of establishing certain classical results. Soon one obtains new results! In addition, when the same technique produces results in two unrelated fields, it becomes clear that the two fields are being unified in a way that will enrich each.

Although studied for its applications at first, functional analysis soon became an object of interest for its own sake. Questions about the structure of the spaces used were asked without regard to possible applications, and a generation of mathematicians has developed whose major interest lies in developing structure and representation theorems, and characterizing among axiomatic systems those whose only realizations are spaces of some special type, such as the space of continuous functions on some topological space.

Questions arise naturally in such purely abstract discussions, which, when specialized to some classical situation, demand the full resources of classical analysis to answer.

The abstract, yet powerful, nature of the subject, with its command of vast vistas, and its enormous diversity of possible specializations, makes it esthetically satisfying and rewarding to all its practitioners.

2

LINEAR SPACE

2.1 Linear space

The elements of any one of the sequence and function spaces of Chapter 1 may be added [Definition: $f + g$ is that function whose value at a is $f(a) + g(a)$] and the space becomes a commutative group. Also they may be multiplied by constants [Definition: $(tf)(a) = tf(a)$, t being constant]. With these operations each space becomes a linear space, a concept whose definition we now give. When the word *scalar* occurs, it stands for complex number; however, when we speak of a *real linear space* we shall understand that in the following definition the scalars are real numbers. Along with every definition involving linear spaces, a parallel definition will be assumed in which the scalars are real.

DEFINITION 1. *A linear space* A *is a set for which are defined an addition, making* A *a commutative group, and multiplication by scalars, satisfying the distributive laws* $t(a + b) = ta + tb$ *and* $(s + t)a = sa + ta$, *where* s, t, *are scalars,* a, b $\in$ A, *and satisfying* $(st)a = s(ta)$, *and* $1a = a$.

The elements of A will be called *vectors*, or *points*. The additive inverse of a is written $-a$; $a - b$ means $a + (-b)$. We make the usual conventions that $a + tb = a + (tb)$ and that in a complex expression like $-x + y - z - w$ we work from left to right; that is, the given expression is $[(-x + y) - z] - w$, just as in elementary arithmetic $8 - 5 + 2$ is not $8 - 7$ (right to left) but is $3 + 2$ (left to right).

A *linear subspace*, or simply *subspace*, of a linear space is a subset which, with the same operations and scalars, is a linear space. For example, $\{(t, 0): t \in R\}$ is a subspace of R^2, since sums and scalar multiples of its elements are in it. For example, $2 \cdot (4, 0) + (1, 0) = (9, 0)$. See problem 20 for the principal idea.

THEOREM 1. *The intersection* I *of any family* Φ *of linear subspaces of a linear space* A *is a linear subspace of* A.

Let, $a, b \in I$, and let t be a scalar. Let $S \in \Phi$. Then $a, b \in S$; hence $ta + b \in S$. Since S is arbitrary, $ta + b \in I.//$

Problems 2.1

These problems refer to a linear space A; a, b, c are vectors, t, u, v are scalars.   The first 16 problems have been arranged so that their solutions form a sequential development.   To avoid circular reasoning, each problem should use only the results of earlier problems.   Whenever no scalar is mentioned, we have a problem in group theory, as in the first nine problems.

★1. $-(-a) = a$.
★2. $a - a = 0$.
★3. $0 - a = -a$.
★4. $(a + b) - c = a + (b - c)$.
★5. $(a - b) + b = a$.
★6. $-(a - b) = b - a$.
★7. $-(a + b) = -a - b$.
★8. $(a - b) - c = a - (b + c)$.

★9. $(a - b) + c = a - (b - c)$.
★10. $0a = 0$.
★11. $(-1)a = -a$.
★12. $t(-a) = (-t)a = -ta$.
★13. $t(a - b) = ta - tb$.
★14. $(u - v)a = ua - va$.
★15. $t0 = 0$.
★16. $a + a + a + a = 4a$, generalize.

★17. If $a + b = a + c$, then $b = c$.
 18. If $ua = va$ and $a \neq 0$, then $u = v$.
 19. Show that the following are linear spaces:

(a) s,
(b) c,
(c) c_0,
(d) C,
(e) Real F,
(f) l^p, $p > 0$,
(g) L^p, $p > 0$,
(h) c_A.

★20. A nonempty set S in a linear space is a subspace if and only if $ta + b \in S$ for every scalar t, and a, $b \in S$.
 21. Show that the only linear subspaces of R^2 are $\{0\}$, R^2, and straight lines passing through 0.
 22. Show that $\{f: f(\tfrac{1}{2}) = 0\}$, and $\{f: \int_0^1 f = 0\}$ are subspaces of C.
 23. Show that the sets mentioned in Problem 22 are subspaces of $R^{[0,1]}$.
 24. Show that $\{f: f(\tfrac{1}{2}) = 1\}$ is not a subspace of C.
 25. Must the union of two subspaces be a subspace?
 26. Let A be a linear space and B a set.   Show that $Al^{(B)}$ is a subspace of A^B.
 27. Show that the set of solutions of a linear homogeneous differential equation is a subspace of C.

2.2 Linear dependence and span

DEFINITION 1.   *Let* S *be a subset of a linear space* A.   *A linear combination of* S *is an element* $\sum_{k=1}^n t_k a_k$ *where* t_1, t_2, . . . , t_n *are scalars, and* a_1, a_2, . . . , a_n *are distinct members of* S.

Observe that S may be an infinite set, but only finite sums are meaningful.   Of course an element of A may be expressable as a linear combination of S in two different ways; we abuse the language slightly and say that two different linear combinations are equal.   For example, let $A = R^2$, let $a = (1, 1)$, $b = (1, 2)$ and let $S = \{a, b, \delta^1, \delta^2\}$.   Then $a + b = (2, 3) = 2\delta^1 + 3\delta^2$, thus $(2, 3)$ is a linear combination of S in at least two ways.   We shall not count the combination $a + b + 0 \cdot c$ as different from $a + b$.

Any linear combination with at least one nonzero scalar coefficient is called *nontrivial;* 0 is the *trivial* linear combination of every set (for the empty set, this is taken as a convention).

DEFINITION 2.   *A subset* S *of a linear space is called linearly dependent if* 0 *is a nontrivial linear combination of* S.   *Otherwise it is called linearly independent.*

In other words, S is linearly independent if and only if, whenever $a_1, a_2, \ldots, a_n$ are members of S, $t_1, t_2, \ldots, t_n$ are scalars, and $\Sigma t_k a_k = 0$, then $t_1 = t_2 = \cdots = t_n = 0$. It is inherent in the very definition that a set is linearly independent if and only if each finite subset is, and that every subset of a linearly independent set is linearly independent, provided we agree, as is usual, that the empty set is linearly independent. In the example just given, S is linearly dependent since $a + b - 2\delta^1 - 3\delta^2 = 0$. However $\{a, b\}$ is linearly independent since if s, t are scalars with $sa + tb = 0$ we have $0 = s(1, 1) + t(1, 2) = (s, s) + (t, 2t) = (s + t, s + 2t)$, hence $s + t = s + 2t = 0$ and so $s = t = 0$. Sometimes "$\{x, y, z, \ldots\}$ is linearly independent" is written "$x, y, z, \ldots$ are linearly independent."

DEFINITION 3. *The set of all linear combinations of a set is called its span. A set S is said to span a set* T *if the span of S includes* T. *The real span is the set of all real linear combinations.*

THEOREM 1. *If two linear combinations of a linearly independent set S are equal, they must contain the same vectors and scalar coefficients, the only possible difference being the order.*

Otherwise the span of S contains two essentially different but equal linear combinations. Suppose that a is a vector that occurs in one but not the other, or occurs in both but with different coefficients. In either case we have $ta + b = sa + c$ with $t \neq s$, and b, c are linear combinations of S, neither of which involves a. From this, $(t - s)a + b - c = 0$. This is a nontrivial linear combination of S, contradicting the hypothesis.//

COROLLARY 1. *No element of a linearly independent set is a linear combination of the rest of the set.*

THEOREM 2. *The span S' of a set S is the smallest linear subspace which includes S. This means that S' is a linear subspace, and if* T *is a linear subspace including* S, T *also includes S'.*

Notice, of course, that all this is taking place in some fixed linear space. It is clear that S' is a linear subspace since a linear combination of two linear combinations of S is a linear combination of S. Next we show that T includes S'. Let $a \in S'$. Then, by definition, a is a linear combination of S. Since $T \supset S$, a is a linear combination of T, hence $a \in T$ since T is a linear subspace.//

DEFINITION 4. *If* S, T *are subsets of a linear space,* S $\oplus$ T *is the span of* S $\cup$ T.

As usual, $\{a\} \oplus S$ will be abbreviated to $a \oplus S$.

Problems on linear space 2.2

1. Describe the span of $\{(1, 2, 1), (2, 1, 0)\}$ in R^3. Does it contain $(1, 1, 1)$? $(0,3,2)$?
2. No linearly independent set in R^2 has more than two members.
3. No linearly independent set contains 0.
4. Define $f, g, h, k \in C$ by $f(t) = e^t$, $g(t) = e^{-t}$, $h(t) = \cosh t$, $k(t) = \sinh t$. Which of the following sets are linearly independent: $\{f, g, h, k\}$, $\{f, g, h\}$, $\{f\}$, $\{h, k\}$?
5. If a set S is linearly dependent, it must contain a vector a such that the span of $s \setminus \{a\}$ is the same as the span of S.

6. Show that $\{\delta^n: n \in \omega\}$ is a linearly independent set in c_0.

7. The linear span in s of $\{\delta^n: n \in \omega\}$ is E^∞.

8. Define $x \in c_0$ by $x_n = 1/n$. Show that $\{x, \delta^1, \delta^2, \delta^3, \ldots\}$ is linearly independent in c_0.

9. For $n = 0, 1, 2, \ldots$, define $f_n \in C$ by $f_n(t) = t^n$ for $0 \leq t \leq 1$. Show that $\{f_n\}$ is linearly independent.

★10. Let $g \in C$ be defined by $g(t) = (2 - t)^{-1}$. Show that $\{g, f_0, f_1, f_2, \ldots\}$ is linearly independent, the f_n being given in Problem 9. This, and the fact that $g(t) = \Sigma 2^{-n-1} f_n(t)$, the series being uniformly convergent on $[0, 1]$, constitute a succint comment on Corollary 1.

11. The linear span in C of $\{f_n: n = 0, 1, 2, \ldots\}$, (see Problem 9) is the set of polynomials.

12. The span of a set is the intersection of the family of all linear subspaces including the set.

13. The rows of an $n \times k$ matrix are linearly dependent in R^k if and only if the rank of the matrix is less than n. In particular, this must be true if $n > k$.

★14. Let S, T be subspaces of a linear space. Show that $S \oplus T = \{a + b: a \in S, b \in T\}$.

2.3   Hamel dimension

DEFINITION 1.   *A Hamel basis for a linear space* A *is a linearly independent set which spans* A.

Spaces such as R^n which have a finite Hamel basis, in this case $\{\delta^1, \delta^2, \ldots, \delta^n\}$, are said to be *finite dimensional*. All others are *infinite dimensional*. If our only interest lay in finite-dimensional spaces we should have omitted the designation, Hamel. However, we shall be interested in another type of basis which, in the finite-dimensional case, is the same as a Hamel basis, but in general, is different. Hence the need to distinguish between them.

An example of an infinite Hamel basis is $\{\delta^n: n \in \omega\}$ in E^∞. This set is not a Hamel basis for c_0 however, since its span, E^∞, is a proper subset.

In the proof of Theorem 1 it may be assumed that the linear space A has at least one nonzero element. If $A = \{0\}$, the family P mentioned in the proof will have just one member, the empty set. This is a Hamel basis for A, since the span of the empty set is $\{0\}$. If this disturbs the student, he may ignore the difficulty and apply Theorem 1 only to linear spaces with more than one element. Similar remarks are appropriate wherever some trivial special case seems to form an exception.

THEOREM 1.   *Every linear space has a Hamel basis.*

Let A be a linear space and let P be the family of all linearly independent subsets of A. Order P by containment, making P a poset. Let C be a maximal chain in P. Finally, let H be the union of all the sets in C. Then H is a Hamel basis for A, as we now show. The set H is linearly independent. ⟦$\{h_1, h_2, \ldots, h_n\}$ be a definite subset of H. Each $h_k, k = 1,$ $2, \ldots, n$ belongs to some member S_k of C. Since C is a chain, the sets $S_1, S_2, \ldots, S_n$ are comparable, thus there is a largest, call it S. Since all $h_1, h_2, \ldots, h_n \in S$ and since S is linearly independent it follows that $\{h_1, h_2, \ldots, h_n\}$ is linearly independent.⟧ The set H is a maximal linearly independent set. ⟦If not, there would be a larger one, that is, one properly including H. Adjoining this to C would yield a chain larger than C. But C is maximal.⟧ The set H spans A. ⟦Let x be an arbitrary vector not in H. We have just proved that H is a maximal linearly independent set; hence, $H \cup \{x\}$ is linearly dependent, being larger than H. Thus for some scalars $t, t_1, t_2, \ldots, t_n$, not all zero, and some members h_1, h_2, . . . , h_n of H, we have $tx + \Sigma t_k h_k = 0$. Clearly $t \neq 0$ since H is linearly independent and so $x = \Sigma(-t_k/t)h_k.$]//

Remark. If H is a Hamel basis for A, every vector of A is a linear combination of H. We write $x = \Sigma\{th\colon h \in H\}$ and, realizing that this means $\Sigma t_n h_n$ for a certain finite subset of H and finite set of scalars, we shall still understand that the summation Σth is carried over all of H with zero coefficients for all but a finite number of the h. The advantage of this convention is that if $x = \Sigma sh$ and $y = \Sigma th$, then $x + y = \Sigma(s + t)h$ without regard to the set of h used by x, y separately. For example, taking $A = R^2$, $H = \{\delta^1, \delta^2\}$, $x = \delta^1$, $y = 2\delta^1 + 5\delta^2$, we have $x = \delta^1 + 0\delta^2$ and so $x + y = (1 + 2)\delta^1 + (0 + 5)\delta^2$.

The student who is unfamiliar with arguments using transfinite cardinal numbers may omit the rest of the section, although he is urged to read the statement of Theorem 2 and attempt its proof.

THEOREM 2. *Any two Hamel bases of a linear space are in one-to-one correspondence.*

Let the bases be B and H. It is possible that B is finite. Let us dispose of this case first. Suppose that $B = \{b_1, b_2, \ldots, b_n\}$. Any set of $n + 1$ vectors is linearly dependent. [If $A = \{a_1, a_2, \ldots, a_{n+1}\}$ is such a set, each a_k is a linear combination of B, say $a_k = \Sigma_{r=1}^{n} t_{kr} b_r$, $k = 1, 2, \ldots, n$. We are going to show that $\Sigma s_k a_k = 0$ for some set of scalars $s_1, s_2, \ldots, s_{n+1}$, not all 0. Substituting the expression of each a_k as a linear combination of B into this equation leads to the equation $\Sigma_{k=1}^{n} b_r \Sigma_{k=1}^{n+1} t_{kr} s_k = 0$ and to achieve this it is sufficient (we are not using the linear independence of B) to find a nontrivial solution of the system $\Sigma_{k=1}^{n+1} t_{kr} s_k = 0$, $r = 1, 2, \ldots, n$, of n equations in $n + 1$ unknowns $s_1, s_2, \ldots, s_{n+1}$. This is always possible.]

Thus any set with more than n vectors is linearly dependent; it follows that H has at most n members. It cannot have less than n for we may interchange B and H in the above argument.

Next we turn to the case in which B is infinite. Each $b \in B$ is a linear combination of H, hence there is a finite subset H_b of H such that b is a linear combination of H_b. Every member of H occurs in at least one H_b; that is, $\cup\{H_b\colon b \in B\} = H$. [If, on the contrary, we could find h, a member of H not in any H_b we should arrive at the following absurdity: h is a linear combination of B, say $h = \Sigma_{k=1}^{n} t_k b_k$. Each b_k is a linear combination of H_{b_k}, so each b_k is a linear combination of $\cup\{H_b\colon b \in B\}$, and hence h is a linear combination of this set. This makes h a linear combination of $H \setminus \{h\}$, contradicting the linear independence of H.]

We have now proved that H is the union of a class of finite sets, one set for each element of B. (*A priori*, two different members of B might lead to the same set H_b but this is immaterial.) Denoting by $|H|$ the cardinal number of H we have $|H| \leq |B| \cdot \aleph_0$ (since each H_b is finite, $|H_b| < \aleph_0$). Since B is infinite, $|B| \cdot \aleph_0 = |B|$ and so $|H| \leq |B|$. By symmetry, $|B| \leq |H|$. The student may now be willing to draw the conclusion that $|B| = |H|$.

We do this by referring to the Cantor-Bernstein theorem, quoted in Section 1.1.//

In view of Theorem 2 we may define the *Hamel dimension* of a linear space to be the cardinality of its Hamel basis. The *Hamel dimension* of a set in a linear space is defined to be the Hamel dimension of its span.

The concept of Hamel dimension is not as important as one might expect in functional analysis because of the difficulty of relating the Hamel basis to the topological structure. For example, if H is a Hamel basis for an infinite-dimensional linear space A, and h is a member of H, we may define a scalar-valued function f on A by defining $f(a)$ to be the coefficient of h in the expression of a as a linear combination of H. It turns out that in any reasonable situation we are unable to prove that f is continuous. This illustrates the fact that the chief use of the Hamel basis is for constructing couterexamples.

Example 1.   Earlier in this section we saw that Hamel dimension of E^∞ is countable. The Hamel dimension of c_0 is the cardinality of the continuum. [If we define for each t, $0 < t < 1$, the sequence $x^t \in c_0$ by $x_n^t = t^n$, $n = 1, 2, \ldots$, we may verify that $H \equiv \{x^t: 0 < t \leq 1\}$ is linearly independent. This follows from the fact that if a polynomial is zero, its coefficients are zero. Thus c_0 includes a linearly independent set with a continuum of members. The set H is not a Hamel basis for c_0 since, for example, each $x^t \in l$, thus the span of H is included in l. However c_0 has only a continuum of elements altogether (for, $c_0 \subset s = E^\omega$; thus $|c_0| \leq |s| = c^{\aleph_0} = c$; here c stands for the cardinality of the continuum).]

Problems on linear space 2.3

    1. Find all Hamel bases for E^2 and R^2.

★2. Show that $\{\delta^n: n \in \omega\}$ is a Hamel basis for E^∞.

    3. A maximal linearly independent set is a Hamel basis.

    4. A minimal spanning set is a Hamel basis; however, the intersection of a chain of spanning sets need not span the space. (Give an example in R.)

★5. Any linearly independent set can be extended to (is a subset of) a Hamel basis.

    6. Any spanning set can be reduced to a Hamel basis.

★7. Suppose that A, B are two linear spaces of the same finite dimension and that $A \subset B$. Show that $A = B$.

    8. Find the Hamel dimension of

(a) l^p,	(c) m,	(e) C,	(g) I^I where $I = [0, 1]$,	(i) A_c,
(b) c,	(d) s,	(f) L^p,	(h) $I^{(I)}$,	(j) E_c.

    9. Show that the set H defined in Example 1 is not a Hamel basis for l.

    10. Let A be a linear space with Hamel basis H. Set up the very natural one-to-one correspondence between A and $E^{(H)}$ given by associating each $a \in A$ with the set of (scalar) coefficients of the expression of a as a linear combination of H. (More precisely, with the function $f: H \to E$ given by $a = \Sigma\{f(h)h: h \in H\}$.) Compare Section 4, Problem 13.

    11. Construct a linear space of any preassigned Hamel dimension. [Hint: See Problem 26 of Section 1, and Problem 10, above. Another solution is given in Section 4, Problem 14.]

    12. Show that there exists a subset H of R with the property that every real number is a unique linear combination of H with rational coefficients.

    13. For $n = 1, 2, \ldots$, let S_n be an n-dimensional subspace of a linear space A such that $S_n \subset S_{n+1}$ for each n, and $A = \bigcup S_n$. If $x_n \in S_n \setminus S_{n-1}$ for each n, show that $\{x_n\}$ is a Hamel basis for A.

2.4   Linear maps

    An *additive* function f is one satisfying $f(a + b) = f(a) + f(b)$ for all a, b. A *linear* function f is an additive function satisfying $f(ta) = tf(a)$ for scalar t, vector a. In these definitions, f is a map from a linear space to a linear space. A linear map is also called a *homomorphism*.

A one-to-one linear map is called an *isomorphism into*. For example, if S is a linear subspace of A, the *inclusion map* $i: S \to A$, given by $ia = a$, is an isomorphism into. If $S = A$, i is called the *identity* map.

We say that two linear spaces are *isomorphic* if there is an isomorphism from each onto the other.

As an example, let P be the linear space of polynomials, then $D: P \to P$, the differentiation operator, is linear. As another example, for $x \in m$ let $f(x) = \{x_n/n\}$, then $f: m \to c_0$ is linear. The function g given by $g(x) = \{x_n^2\}$ is an example of a nonlinear function from c_0 to c_0. Further examples of linear maps are furnished by the functions of Section 1.3. These are P_t when defined on a linear space to its scalars, for example $P_t: C \to E$, $P_n: s \to E$.

Maps from a linear space to the set of scalars occur frequently. Such a map is called a *functional*. A linear functional on c is given by the limit; that is, $\lim x$ is the ordinary limit of the convergent sequence x. Also the functions P_t just mentioned are functionals.

THEOREM 1. *An additive function* f *is rational homogeneous; that is,* f(ta) = tf(a) *for rational* t, *vector* a.

$$(1) \qquad\qquad\qquad f(0) = 0,$$

⟦for, $f(0) + f(0) = f(0 + 0) = f(0)$⟧.

$$(2) \qquad\qquad\qquad f(-a) = -f(a),$$

⟦for, $f(a) + f(-a) = f(a - a) = f(0) = 0$⟧.

$$(3) \qquad\qquad\qquad f(na) = nf(a) \qquad \text{for integer } n.$$

⟦If n is positive, this is trivial. If $n = 0$, it is (1). If n is negative it follows from (2) and $f[(-n)a] = (-n)f(a)$.⟧

Finally if $t = m/n$, m, n integers, we have, for each a, $nf(ta) = f(nta) = f(ma) = mf(a)$ from (3), and so $f(ta) = tf(a)$. //

As we shall see, much of the representation theory and many applications will depend on there being defined enough functions of a certain type to satisfy certain requirements. A typical result would be that given a certain set, there exists a function, not identically zero, which vanishes on it. The function might be required to be linear, or continuous, or bounded. It is too early to develop this theory extensively; it will be carried to fruition in Chapters 4, 6, and 12. For the present we obtain evidences of a rich supply of linear functionals, but purposely limit our investigations to avoid later duplication.

THEOREM 2. *Let* S *be a subspace of a linear space* A *and* a *a vector not in* S. *Then there exists a linear functional* f *on* A *with* f(a) = 1, f(x) = 0 *for* x $\in$ S.

Choose a Hamel basis B for S. Then $B \cup \{a\}$ is linearly independent and so can be extended to a Hamel basis H for A. ⟦Section 3, Problem 5.⟧ Every $b \in A$ has a unique expansion $\Sigma\{th: h \in H\}$. Define $f(b)$ to be the coefficient of a in this expansion. Then f is linear. ⟦For example, if $b = f(b)a + \Sigma sh$, $tb = tf(b)a + t\Sigma sh$ and so $f(tb) =$ coefficient of $a = tf(b)$.⟧ Also $f(a) = 1$, and for $x \in S$, $f(x) = 0$ ⟦since x is a linear combination of B, and $a \notin B$⟧.//

See Problem 9 for an alternative construction of f.

THEOREM 3. *Let* A, A₁ *be linear spaces, let* S *be a subspace of* A, *and* f: S $\rightarrow$ A₁ *a linear function. Then* f *can be extended linearly to all of* A; *that is, there exists a linear function* F: A $\rightarrow$ A₁ *such that* F = f *on* S.

Choose Hamel bases B for S, and H for A with $B \subset H$. We may assign F arbitrarily on $H \setminus B$; let us, for definiteness define F to be 0 on $H \setminus B$. Now define $F = f$ on B and *extend F linearly*. This means that for any $a \in A$, $a = \Sigma\{th: h \in H\}$ we define $F(a) = \Sigma t F(h)$. This sum is finite, of course. Then F is linear ⟦$F(ua + b) = F(u\Sigma sh + \Sigma th) = F[\Sigma(us + t)h]$. By definition, this is $\Sigma(us + t)F(h) = u\Sigma sF(h) + \Sigma tF(h) = uF(a) + F(b)$.⟧

Finally, it is obvious that $F = f$ on S since $F - f$ is linear and vanishes (equals 0) on B.//

THEOREM 4. *Two linear spaces with the same Hamel dimension are isomorphic. The same result holds for real linear spaces.*

Although this follows easily from Section 3, Problem 10, we shall give a self-contained proof. Suppose the spaces are A and A_1 with Hamel bases H, H_1 in one-to-one correspondence. Let $f: H \rightarrow H_1$ be one to one and onto. Then f may be extended linearly to the whole of A exactly as in the proof of Theorem 3. Then f is one to one. ⟦If $f(a) = 0$, let $a = \Sigma th$, then $0 = f(a) = \Sigma tf(h)$, thus all the t are zero because the $f(h)$ are distinct members of the linearly independent set H_1. Now see Problem 1, below.⟧ It is also true that f is onto. ⟦Let $b \in A_1$ be given. Then $b = \Sigma th_1$, the expression of b as a linear combination of H_1. Let $a = \Sigma tf^{-1}(h_1)$, this is meaningful since $f: H \rightarrow H_1$ is a one-to-one correspondence. Then $f(a) = \Sigma tff^{-1}(h_1) = \Sigma th_1 = b$.⟧//

DEFINITION 1. *A set Φ of functions defined on a set* S *is called separating (or, separating over* S*) if given* a, b $\in$ S *with* a $\neq$ b*, there exists* f $\in \Phi$ *with* f(a) $\neq$ f(b).

For example, let $\Phi = \{P_t: 0 \leq t \leq 1\}$, each P_t: $C \rightarrow E$ being defined by $P_t(f) = f(t)$ (Section 1.3). Then Φ is separating. ⟦Given f, g with $f \neq g$, there exists $t \in [0, 1]$ such that $f(t) \neq g(t)$. For this t, $P_t(f) \neq P_t(g)$.⟧

DEFINITION 2. *A set Φ of functions from a linear space* A *to a linear space is total (or, total over* A*) if given* a $\in$ A, a $\neq$ 0*, there exists* f $\in \Phi$ *such that* f(a) $\neq$ 0.

This could also be phrased, $f(a) = 0$ for all $f \in \Phi$ implies $a = 0$.

Clearly a family of functions from one linear space to another is total if it is separating. However, the converse is not true ⟦let $\Phi = \{f\}$, $f(x, y) = (x^2 + y^2)^{1/2}$ for $(x, y) \in R^2$⟧. For linear maps, the concepts are equivalent ⟦since $f(a) \neq f(b)$ if and only if $f(a - b) \neq 0$⟧

DEFINITION 3. A# *is the set of all linear functionals on* A.

$A^{\#}$ is pronounced A sharp. It is a linear subspace of E^A.

COROLLARY 1. $A^\#$ *is total over* A.

This is proved by taking $S = \{0\}$ in Theorem 2.//

Of course, it follows that $A^\#$ is separating over A, since its members are linear.

Problems on linear space 2.4

★1. A linear map f is one to one if and only if $f(x) = 0$ implies $x = 0$.

★2. A map f is linear if and only if $f(tx + y) = tf(x) + f(y)$ for all vectors x, y, and scalar t.

★3. $P_{\frac{1}{2}}$ is a linear functional on C; P_2 is a linear functional on c.

★4. A linear functional which is not identically zero is onto the scalars.

5. Given distinct vectors x, y, there exists a linear functional f with $f(x) \neq f(y)$.

6. Given linearly independent vectors x, y, there exists a linear functional f with $f(x) = f(y) \neq 0$.

7. Find all linear functionals on E, R, E^2, R^2 and E^3.

8. A linear map from E^m to E^n is given by a matrix.

9. Use the following construction to prove Theorem 2.   Define $f(a) = 1$, $f(b) = 0$ for $b \in B$, $f(h) =$ anything (say, 0) for $h \in H \setminus B$, $h \neq a$, and $f(x) = \Sigma tf(h)$ if $x = \Sigma th$.

10. Define $f \colon m \rightarrow c_0$ by $f(a) = \{a_n/n\}$.   Show that f is not onto, but is an isomorphism into.

11. Define $f \colon c \rightarrow c_0$ by $f(a) = \{\lim a, a_1 - \lim a, a_2 - \lim a, \ldots\}$.   Show that f is an isomorphism onto and give the inverse map.

12. Suppose that f, g are linear functionals and that $g(x) = 0$ for each x such that $f(x) = 0$.   Show that g is a scalar multiple of f.

13. Let A be a linear space with Hamel basis H.   Set up the very natural isomorphism between $A^\#$ and E^H given by associating each $f \in A^\#$ with $f|H$.   Compare Section 3, Problem 10.

14. Let S be a set.   For each $x \in S$, let $f_x \colon R^S \rightarrow R$ be given by $f_x(g) = g(x)$ for each $g \in R^S$. Show that the linear subspace of $(R^S)^\#$ spanned by $H \equiv \{f_x \colon x \in S\}$ has H as a Hamel basis, hence has Hamel dimension equal to $|S|$.   This is another solution of Section 3, Problem 11.

15. Suppose that for $n = 1, 2, \ldots$, $a_n \in A$, $f_n \in A^\#$ and $(\{a_n\}, \{f_n\})$ is a biorthogonal system. Show that $\{a_n\}$ is linearly independent.

16. Let A, B be sets, B having at least two members.   Show that B^A is separating over A.

★17. Let f be a linear functional which is bounded on a subspace S.   (That is, $f[S]$ is a bounded set in E.)   Show that f is 0 on S.   〖Problem 4.〗

18. Show that the correspondence in Section 3, Problem 10 is an isomorphism.

▲19. Let $f \colon R \rightarrow R$ be additive.   Then $f(rx) = rf(x)$ for rational r 〖Theorem 1〗.   Show that if f is continuous, $f(x) = Kx$ for all x; where $K = f(1)$.   However if f is not continuous, show that the graph of f is dense in the plane.   Use Section 3, Problem 12 to construct a discontinuous solution.

20. Show that $\{P_t \colon 0 \leq t \leq 1\}$ is a linearly independent set in $C^\#$.

21. Prove the crisscross theorem for isomorphism; that is, two linear spaces are isomorphic if each is isomorphic into the other.

★22. Let S be a set in a linear space.   Let f be a functional defined on S with the property that whenever $(t_1, t_2, \ldots, t_n)$ is a set of scalars and $(a_1, a_2, \ldots, a_n)$ is a subset of S satisfying $\Sigma t_k a_k = 0$, it follows that $\Sigma t_k f(a_k) = 0$.   Show that f can be extended to a linear functional defined on the whole space.   In particular, if S is linearly independent, any f on S can be so extended.   〖Extend f linearly as in the proof of Theorem 3.〗

23. The dual of problem 22 is false.   Prove this in the countable case under the following form: if $\{f_k\}$ is a sequence of points of $A^\#$, $\{u_k\}$ is a sequence of scalars, and $\Sigma t_k f_k = 0$ implies $\Sigma t_k u_k = 0$; there may not exist a vector a such that $f_k(a) = u_k$ for $k = 1, 2, \ldots$.   〖Example: $P_k(a) = 1$ for all k is impossible for $a \in E^\infty$.   In general, let H be a Hamel basis, $\{a_n\} \subset H$; define $f_n(a_n) = 1$, $f_n(H \setminus \{a_n\}) = 0$.   Then $f_n(a) = 1$ for all n is impossible.〗

24. The dual of Problem 22, as spelled out in Problem 23, is true if S is finite.

25. A real function f is called *subadditive* if $f(a + b) \leq f(a) + f(b)$ for all a, b. Let g be a bounded real function, say $|g(a)| \leq M$ for all a. Show that $g + 3M$ is subadditive. (Thus, a subadditive function may have quite bad behaviour, for example, it may be nonmeasurable.)

26. Suppose $0 \leq g(a) \leq M$ for all a. Show that $g + M$ is subadditive.

27. If f is subadditive, $f(0) \geq 0$.

28. The following are subadditive: (a) log x, $x \geq 2$; (b) the characteristic function of the irrationals; (c) f^{α}, where $0 \leq \alpha < 1$, f is subadditive, and $f(a) \geq 0$ for all a; (d) $f(x) = 0$ for $x \leq 0$, 1 for $x > 1$.

29. Let e be a set in a linear space. Show that the characteristic function of e is subadditive if and only if $\tilde{e} + \tilde{e} \subset \tilde{e}$.

30. Let f be a subadditive function defined on $(0, \infty)$. Define $p(x) = f(x)$ for $x > 0$, $f(-x)$ for $x < 0$, arbitrary but $\leq 2 \inf \{f(t): t > 0\}$ for $x = 0$. Show that p is subadditive if and only if $0 \leq f(x) \leq f(t) + f(x + t)$ for all $x > 0$, $t > 0$. In particular this is true if $f(x) \geq 0$ for all $x > 0$, and f is increasing.

31. Let g be a real, monotonely decreasing, nonnegative function on $(0, \infty)$, such that $f(x) = xg(x)$ is increasing. Show that p, defined as in problem 30, is subadditive.

32. Let u be a real sequence satisfying $u_{m+n} \leq u_m + u_n$ for m, $n \in \omega$, and let $v_n = u_n/n$. Show that v is a convergent sequence or tends to $-\infty$, and $\lim v_n = \inf \{v_n: n = 1, 2, \ldots\}$.

▲33. Show that no isomorphism from c onto c_0 can be given by a matrix. (See Problem 11.)

2.5 Arithmetic

We shall define an arithmetic of sets in a linear space, the space being fixed throughout this section. Sets in the space will be denoted by A, B, scalars by c, t, and D will be a set of scalars.

By $A + B$ is meant $\{a + b: a \in A, b \in B\}$; tA means $\{ta: a \in A\}$; DA means $\{ta: t \in D, a \in A\}$; $- A = \{- a: a \in A\}$, $A - B = \{a - b: a \in A, b \in B\}$. As usual, we adopt a convention about the empty set, namely $\emptyset + A = \emptyset A = D\emptyset = \emptyset$. Also $a + B$ is an abbreviation for $\{a\} + B$, called the *translation* of B by a.

The reader should familiarize himself with as much of the ordinary arithmetic as is legal in this setting. Specifically, $A + B = B + A$ is trivial, as is $0 + A = A$, and $(A + B) + C = A + (B + C)$. Three quarters of the distributive law holds, namely

$$(1) \qquad\qquad\qquad t(A + B) = tA + tB,$$

and

$$(2) \qquad\qquad\qquad (s + t)A \subset sA + tA.$$

〚Let $x \in t(A + B)$. Then $x = t(a + b) = ta + tb \in tA + tB$. The other half of (1), and (2) are proved similarly.〛

The inclusion in (2) may be strict. 〚In R^2, let $X = \{(x, 0): x \in R\}$, $Y = \{(0, x): x \in R\}$, and $A = X \cup Y$. Then $A + A = R^2$ while $2A = A$. Thus $A + A \neq 2A$.〛 A blinding light is thrown on this by Problem 9.

We now introduce four important properties of sets in a linear space.

The set A is called *symmetric* if $A = - A$. A more appropriate term would be symmetric with respect to 0 since $- A$ is the reflection of A in 0.

The set A is called *balanced* if $tA \subset A$ for all scalars t satisfying $|t| \leq 1$. Choosing $t = - 1$ shows that a balanced set is symmetric 〚since $- A \subset A$ leads immediately to $A \subset - A$, hence $A = -A$]. Another way of saying that A is balanced is to say that $DA \subset A$, where D is the unit disk in E; that is, $D = \{z \in E : |z| \leq 1\}$, or, if we are dealing with a real linear space, $D = [-1, 1]$.

Example 1. Let A be a nonsquare, plane rectangle (with interior) centered at 0. Then A is balanced as a subset of the real linear space R^2, but A is not balanced as a subset of the (complex) linear space E, since, for example, $iA \not\subset A$.

The set A is called *convex* if $sA + tA \subset A$ for all pairs of scalars s, t satisfying $s \geq 0$, $t \geq 0$, $s + t = 1$. We could just as well have written $sA + tA = A$ by (2). That "convex" is a suitable description of these sets will be evident if we rephrase the definition thus, $ta + (1 - t)b \in A$ for all scalars t satisfying $0 \leq t \leq 1$, and $a, b \in A$. For $\{ta + (1 - t)b : 0 \leq t \leq 1\}$ is, in R, R^2, R^3, the straight line segment joining the points a, b. [Consider, for example, R^2; let $a = (x_0, y_0)$, $b = (x_1, y_1)$. Then $z \in \{ta + (1 - t)b : 0 \leq t \leq 1\}$ if and only if $z = (tx_0 + (1 - t)x_1, ty_0 + (1 - t)y_1)$; that is, $z = (x, y)$ with $x = tx_0 + (1 - t)x_1$, $y = ty_0 + (1 - t)y_1$.] Because of this fact, we interrupt our presentation to define line and line segment.

The *line* through a, b is the set $\{ta + (1 - t)b : t \in R\}$, the *line segment* joining a, b is the set $\{ta + (1 - t)b : 0 \leq t \leq 1\}$.

Notice that the line lives in a kind of half-dimensional world. For example, E is one dimensional [[$\{1\}$ is a Hamel basis; so is $\{i\}$]], yet lines are proper subsets of E. In real linear space this anomaly disappears.

The definition of convexity can now be rephrased, a set is convex if and only if it includes the line segment joining any two of its points.

Our conventions yield that the empty set is balanced and convex.

The set A is called *absorbing* if for each vector x, there exists $\epsilon < 0$ such that $tx \in A$ whenever t is a scalar satisfying $|t| \leq \epsilon$.

Here we insist that t is allowed to be complex, unless, of course, we are considering a real linear space. Another way of saying that A is absorbing is to say that for each vector x, $Dx \subset A$ where D is a sufficiently small (depending on x) disk in E, (or interval in R, if we are in a real linear space) centered at 0.

Example 2. The following set is sometimes called *Schatz's apple*. It is the plane set A consisting of the union of two closed unit disks centered at $(1, 0)$, $(-1, 0)$, and the line segment joining $(0, -1)$ to $(0, 1)$. Let us consider the plane as R^2, a real linear space. Then A is absorbing since every line through the origin meets it in an interval of positive length. Next, consider the plane as E, a (complex) linear space. Now A is no longer absorbing, since A includes no disk of positive radius centered at the origin. This example shows (for real linear space, and may be modified to show for linear space in general) that an absorbing set need not include a convex absorbing set. Another example is furnished by the solution to Problem 27 below. Finally we observe that there exists no absorbing set $B \subset R^2$ such that $B + B \subset A$.

We say that A is *absorbing at a* if $A - a$ is absorbing. Clearly, A is absorbing at 0 if and only if it is absorbing; also, if A is absorbing at a, it follows that $a \in A$. We call A *somewhere absorbing* if it is absorbing at some point, *nowhere absorbing* if it is absorbing at no point.

The following characterization is the most convenient way to use these ideas.

THEOREM 1.   A *is absorbing at* a *if and only if to any vector* b, *there corresponds a* $\delta > 0$ *such that for each scalar* t *satisfying* $|t| \leq \delta$, $a + tb \in A$.

Notice that this is not the most obvious characterization since $a + tb$ does not lie on the line segment joining a and b (even if t is real).   The proof follows from the fact that A is absorbing at a if and only if $A - a$ is absorbing.   This in turn is true if and only if $tb \in A - a$ for all sufficiently small $|t|$.//

We now present a few results about the way linear maps affect the four properties.   In brief, the properties are preserved.

THEOREM 2.   *Let* X, Y *be linear spaces and* f: X $\to$ Y *a linear map.   If a subset* A *of* X *has any one of the properties, symmetric, balanced, convex,* f[A] *has the same property.   If* f *is onto, and* A *is absorbing at* a, f[A] *is absorbing at* f(a).

If A is symmetric, $-f[A] = f[-A] = f[A]$.   If A is balanced, let $D = \{z \in E: |z| \leq 1\}$.   Then $Df[A] = f[DA] \subset f[A]$.   If A is convex and $0 \leq t \leq 1$, $tf[A] + (1 - t)f[A] = f[tA + (1 - t)A] \subset f[A]$.   Finally, let f be onto, and A absorbing at a.   Let $y \in Y$.   Then $y = f(x)$ for some $x \in X$.   By Theorem 1, there exists $\delta > 0$ such that $|t| \leq \delta$ implies $a + tx \in A$.   This in turn implies that $f(a) + ty = f(a + tx) \in f[A]$.//

THEOREM 3.   *Let* X, Y *be linear spaces and* f: X $\to$ Y *a linear map.   If a subset* A *of* Y *has any one of the properties, symmetric, balanced, convex,* f^{-1}[A] *has the same property.   If* A *is absorbing at* a *and* a $\in$ f[X], f^{-1}[A] *is absorbing at each member of* f^{-1}[{a}].

By our conventions on the empty set we may assume $f^{-1}[A]$ to be nonempty.   The first three parts of Theorem 3 follow from an argument exactly like that used to prove Theorem 2, taking account of Problem 15 below.   Next, assume that A is absorbing at $a \in f[X]$, and that $a = f(x)$, $x \in X$.   Let $y \in X$.   By Theorem 1, $a + tf(y) \in A$ for all sufficiently small $|t|$.   But $a + tf(y) = f(x + ty)$ and so $f(x + ty) \in A$; that is, $x + ty \in f^{-1}[A]$ for all sufficiently small $|t|$.//

COROLLARY 1.   *Let* f *be a linear functional, not identically zero.   Let* A *be a set which is absorbing at* a.   *Then* f(a) *is interior to* f[A].

Of course, interior refers to the space of scalars; $f(a)$ lies inside a circle (or interval, for real linear space) of points of $f[A]$.   The Corollary follows from Theorem 2 since the hypotheses imply that f is a linear map of the space onto the scalars.   Thus $f[A]$ is a subset of E which is absorbing at $f(a)$.   It is now easy to see that $f[A]$ includes a small circle centered at $f(a)$, [Problem 17].//

COROLLARY 2.   *Let* f *be a linear functional, not identically zero.   Let* A *be a set which is absorbing at all its points.   Then* f[A] *is an open subset of the scalars.*

The following two results will find their main application in the study of separation, Chapter 3.   The first one deals with a linear map from the scalars into the linear space.

There is essentially only one such map which is not identically zero, namely, let a be a nonzero vector and define $f(t) = ta$ for each scalar t. The range of f is the one-dimensional subspace spanned by a, Corollary 3 states how this subspace meets an absorbing set; it is in this form that the next two results should be remembered and intuitively understood, for example, Corollary 4 says that a straight line meets a set which is absorbing at all its points in an open set.

COROLLARY 3. *Let* f *be a linear map, not identically zero, from the scalars into a linear space. Let* A *be a set in the space which is absorbing at all its points. Then* f^{-1}[A] *is an open subset of the scalars.*

This follows from Theorem 3, taking account of Problem 17. Observe that $f^{-1}[A]$ may be empty.//

COROLLARY 4. *Let* A *be absorbing at all its points. Let* a, b *be vectors. Then* {t $\in$ R: ta $+$ (1 $-$ t)b $\in$ A} *is open subset of* R.

Consider the space to be a real linear space. 〖Ignore the complex scalars.〗 For $t \in R$, define $f(t) = t(a - b)$. Then f is linear, and the set mentioned is $f^{-1}[A - b]$. The result follows from Corollary 3.//

Problems 2.5

In this list, unless otherwise specified, A, B, D are sets in a linear space; a, b, c, x, y, z are vectors (members of the linear space); X, Y are linear spaces.

1. $\{x \in s: |x_n| \leq n$ for all $n\}$ is not absorbing in s, but its intersection with m is absorbing in m.

2. $\{x \in s: |x_n| < 1/n$ for all $n\}$ is not absorbing in c_0, but its intersection with E^∞ is absorbing in E^∞.

3. Two distinct points in a real linear space are linearly dependent if and only if the line passing through them also passes through 0.

★4. $A \cap (-A)$ is symmetric. It is absorbing if A is.

★5. A is absorbing if and only if, given any vector x, there exists a real number k such that $x \in tA$ for each scalar t satisfying $|t| > k$.

★6. Let A be symmetric. Then $x \in y + A$ if and only if $y \in x + A$; $x \in B + A$ if and only if $x + B$ meets A; D meets $B + A$ if and only if $D + A$ meets B.

★7. If B is absorbing at x, $B + A$ is absorbing at each point of $x + A$.

★8. If A is balanced and s, t are scalars with $|s| \geq |t|$, then $sA \supset tA$.

★9. A is convex if and only if $sA + tA \subset (s + t)A$ for all positive scalars, s, t.

10. Find a nonconvex subset A of R^2 satisfying $A + A = 2A$.

11. Let A be convex. Then A is absorbing if and only if, given any vector x, there exists $\epsilon > 0$ such that $tx \in A$ for $0 < t < \epsilon$. More generally, A is absorbing at a if and only if $a + tx \in A$ for $0 < t < \epsilon$. The assumption that A is convex may not be omitted.

★12. In Problem 11, the assumption that A is convex may be omitted in a real linear space.

★13. If A is absorbing, $\bigcup_{n=1}^\infty nA$ is the whole space.

14. The converse of Problem 13 is false in E and in R^2.

★15. Let $f: X \to Y$ be a linear map, let A, B be sets in Y, and let S be a set of scalars. Show that $Sf^{-1}[A] = f^{-1}[SA]$, and $f^{-1}[A] + f^{-1}[B] \subset f^{-1}[A + B]$.

16. The inclusion in Problem 15 cannot be replaced by equality.

★17. An absorbing set in E and a convex absorbing set in R^2 must include some cell centered at 0. (A cell is the interior of a circle.)

★18. If f is a linear map, $f[\bigcup_{n=1}^{\infty} nA] = \bigcup nf[A]$.

19. A linear subspace is balanced and convex, but not somewhere absorbing unless it is the whole space.

20. If a linear map is constant on some somewhere absorbing set, it is identically zero.

21. Let f be a linear functional on a real linear space, and t a scalar. Show that all but one of $(f < t)$, $(|f| < t)$, $(f \leq t)$, $(|f| \leq t)$, $(f = t)$, $(|f| = t)$ are convex. Which are absorbing? symmetric? balanced?

22. Every absorbing set includes a balanced absorbing set.

23. If A is somewhere absorbing, $A - A$ includes a convex absorbing set.

24. Let D be a disk in R^2. Show that $D - D$ includes a disk centered at 0.

25. Every absorbing set includes a Hamel basis.

26. Find all points at which the subset of E^∞ given in Problem 2 is absorbing.

27. Construct a set in R^2 which is absorbing at exactly one point.

28. The dense cone is nowhere absorbing.

29. Does there exist $b \in c_0$ such that $\{x \in c_0 \colon |x_n| \leq |b_n| \text{ for all } n\}$ is absorbing in c_0? Same question for c.

30. Give an example in a complex linear space of a nonconvex balanced set.

31. Give an example in R^2 of two convex, nowhere absorbing sets A, B such that $A + B$ is absorbing at all its points, (and is not empty). [The dense cone, together with its negative, is an example in R^∞.]

32. Prove the Euclidean parallel postulate. (Playfair's axiom.)

2.6   Convex and affine sets

Many of the concepts of functional analysis center about the idea of convexity. The geometric results in Chapter 3 on separation of convex sets by means of hyperplanes passed between them have far-reaching analytic consequences which will be explored later in this book.

In this section, A, B are subsets of a linear space.

DEFINITION 1.   *A weighted mean of a set A is a linear combination of A with nonnegative real coefficients adding up to 1.*

Thus a weighted mean is $\sum_{k=1}^{n} t_k a_k$ with $a_k \in A$, $t_k \geq 0$, $\sum_{k=1}^{n} t_k = 1$. As remarked in connection with linear combinations in Section 3, each weighted mean can be considered to be $\sum ta$, in which all the elements a of A are mentioned, but at most a finite number of the t are different from 0. A weighted mean of weighted means of a set A is again a weighted mean of A [for

$$\sum_{k=1}^{m} t_k \sum_{r=1}^{n} t_{kr} a_r = \sum_{r=1}^{n} a_r \sum_{k=1}^{m} t_k t_{kr},$$

and

$$\sum_{r=1}^{n} \sum_{k=1}^{m} t_k t_{kr} = \sum_{k=1}^{m} t_k \sum_{r=1}^{n} t_{kr} = \sum_{k=1}^{m} t_k = 1].$$

LEMMA 1.   *A convex set contains all of its weighted means.*

Let A be convex, and w a weighted mean of A. Then $w = \Sigma_{k=1}^{n} t_k a_k$, $t_k \geq 0$, $\Sigma t_k = 1$. If $n = 1$ or 2, the result is obvious. We proceed by induction. Assuming, as we may, that $t_{n+1} \neq 1$, we have

$$\sum_{k=1}^{n+1} t_k a_k = t_{n+1} a_{n+1} + (1 - t_{n+1}) \sum_{k=1}^{n} [t_k/(1 - t_{n+1})] a_k.$$

This is a weighted mean (with 2 terms!) of a_{n+1} and $\Sigma_{k=1}^{n} [t_k/(1 - t_{n+1})] a_k$. But these are members of A, the latter by the induction hypothesis because its coefficients are nonnegative, it has n terms, and

$$\sum_{k=1}^{n} t_k/(1 - t_{n+1}) = [1/(1 - t_{n+1})] \cdot \sum_{k=1}^{n} t_k = [1/(1 - t_{n+1})](1 - t_{n+1}) = 1.//$$

DEFINITION 2. *The set of all weighted means of a set is called its convex hull.*

The following result should be compared with Section 2, Theorem 2.

THEOREM 1. *The convex hull* H *of a set* A *is the smallest convex set which includes* A.

First, H is convex [for if t is a positive scalar, and $h_1, h_2 \in H$, $th_1 + (1 - t)h_2$ is a weighted mean of H, hence, as pointed out above, a weighted mean of A; thus, by definition, it belongs to H].
Next, assume that B is a convex set including A. We shall prove that B includes H. This will complete the proof. [Let $h \in H$. This means that h is a weighted mean of A, thus automatically it is a weighted mean of B. By Lemma 1, $h \in B$.]//

Facts

Those readers intending to postpone Chapter 3 (see Section 3.1) may, similarly, postpone Facts (iii), (iv), and (vii) in the list that follows.

(i) If A, B are convex, and s, t are scalars, $sA + tB$ is convex.

(ii) Translation and *magnification* (multiplication by a scalar) preserve convexity.

(iii) Let A be convex, and absorbing at a, let $b \in A$. Then A is absorbing at each point of the line segment joining a, b, except possibly at b. (Thus Saturn is not convex.)

(iv) Let A, B be convex. Assume that B is somewhere absorbing but is not absorbing at any point of A (for example $B \cap A$). Then $B - A$ is not absorbing at 0. (See Section 5, Problem 31 which shows, paradoxically, that the assumption that B is somewhere absorbing cannot be omitted.)

(v) Let A be a subset of a real linear space, and f a linear functional satisfying $f(x) \leq 1$ for $x \in A$, then $f(x) \leq 1$ for $x \in H$, the convex hull of A.

(vi) Let A be a convex subset of a real linear space, f a linear functional and t a scalar such that $f(a) \neq t$ for all $a \in A$. Then either $f(a) < t$ for all $a \in A$ or $f(a) > t$ for all $a \in A$.

(vii) Let A be a convex set which is absorbing at a, and let b be an arbitrary vector. Then A is absorbing at $a + tb$ for all sufficiently small $t \geq 0$.

Proofs

(i) Using formula (1) of Section 5, we have, for $0 < r < 1$, that $r(sA + tB) + (1 - r)(sA + tB) = rsA + rtB + (1 - r)sA + (1 - r)tB = s[rA + (1 - r)A] + t[rB + (1 - r)B] \subset sA + tB$, since A, B are convex.

(ii) A translation of a set A is $A + b$, but $\{b\}$ is convex, so the result follows from (i). The proof for magnification follows by taking $s = 0$ in (i).

(iii) Let c be a point other than b on the line segment joining a, b. We shall show that A is absorbing at c. To this end, let x be an arbitrary vector. (The student may now mark the four points a, b, c, x on a piece of paper, he will observe that we are doing a simple exercise in plane geometry. The point is that x sees a surrounded by A, say by a circle of points of A. It sees c surrounded by a smaller circle lying within an angle with vertex at b.) The proof proceeds thus, $c = ta + (1 - t)b$ for some t, $0 < t \leq 1$. There exists $\delta > 0$ such that $a + sx \in A$ for $|s| \leq \delta$. Then for $|s| \leq t\delta$, $c + sx = t[a + (s/t)x] + (1 - t)b \in A$ since A is convex and $a + (s/t)x \in A$, $b \in A$.

(iv) Assume $B - A$ is absorbing at 0, and that B is absorbing at b. We obtain a contradiction as follows. Choose any $a \in A$. Then $t(a - b) \in B - A$ for some $t > 0$ since $B - A$ is absorbing. Thus for some $a' \in A$, $b' \in B$ we have $t(a - b) = b' - a'$. This implies that $a' + ta = b' + tb$. Consider $c = (a' + ta)/(1 + t) = (b' + tb)/(1 + t)$. Then $c \in A$ since A is convex. But c lies on the line segment joining b', b and $c \neq b'$. Thus, by (iii), B is absorbing at c; that is, B is absorbing at a point of A, contradicting the hypothesis.

(v) This is true because $\{x: f(x) \leq 1\}$ is a convex set including A, thus it includes H. (The set mentioned is convex because it is $f^{-1}(-\infty, 1]$, see Section 5, Theorem 3.)

(vi) By Section 5, Theorem 2, $f[A]$ is convex, hence it is an interval. Thus it lies entirely above or entirely below t, which it does not contain.

(vii) Choose $\delta > 0$ such that $x \equiv a + \delta b \in A$ [Section 5, Theorem 1]. For $0 \leq t < \delta$, $a + tb$ lies on the line segment joining a to x, $[a + tb = (1 - t/\delta)a + (t/\delta)x]$ and is not equal to x (unless $b = 0$, in which case the result is trivial). The result follows by Fact (iii).//

DEFINITION 3. *A nonempty set* A *is called affine if* tA $+ (1 - t)$A $\subset$ A *for all scalar* t.

Thus an affine set is convex; a linear subspace is affine.

THEOREM 2. A *is affine if and only if it is a translate of a linear subspace. The linear subspace is* A $-$ A, *and* A $=$ A $+ ($A $-$ A$)$.

Suppose that A is affine. Let $S = A - A$. To show that S is a linear subspace, let t be a scalar. Then $tS + S = t(A - A) + (A - A) = tA - tA + A - A \subset tA + (1 - t)A - A$ $[(A - tA)/(1 - t) \subset A] \subset A - A$ [since A is affine] $= S$. Thus S is a linear subspace. Moreover $A + S = A + A - A = 2A - A$ [since A is convex; see Section 5, Problem 9⟧ $= A$ ⟦since A is affine, (take $t = 2$).⟧ Now let $a \in A$ (A is still being assumed affine). Then $A = a + S$. ⟦$a + S \subset A + S = A$. Conversely, $A - a \subset A - A = S$ and so $A \subset a + S$.⟧ Thus A is a translate of S. The proof is completed by showing that a translate of a linear subspace is affine. ⟦Let S be a linear subspace, a a vector, and t a scalar. Then $t(a + S) + (1 - t)(a + S) = ta + tS + (1 - t)a + (1 - t)S = a + S$. (Notice that $tS = (1 - t)S = S + S = S$). Thus $a + S$ is affine.⟧//

Remark. An affine set is the translate of a unique subspace, for if S, T are subspaces and $a + S = b + T$ we have $S = b - a + T = u + T$, say. Thus $S = S - S = u + T - (u + T) = T - T = T$.

THEOREM 3. *Let* A *be an affine set. Then the following conditions are equivalent:*

    (i) $0 \in A$,

    (ii) A *is a linear subspace,*

    (iii) $A = A - A$.

Clearly, condition (iii) implies condition (ii) ⟦Theorem 2⟧ and condition (ii) implies condition (i). Finally, if $0 \in A$, we have, by Theorem 2, $A = 0 + A - A$.//

Problems on linear space 2.6

1. The convex hull of a set with two points is the line segment joining them.

★2. The intersection of any family of convex sets is convex.

★3. The convex hull of a set is the intersection of the family of all convex sets which include it.

★4. Let H be the convex hull of a set A. If $0 \in A$, or indeed, if $0 \in H$, then $H = \{\Sigma t_k a_k : t_k \geq 0, \Sigma t_k \leq 1, a_k \in A\}$.

5. The convex hull of a balanced set is balanced.

6. Let the *convex balanced hull* of a set be the intersection of the family of all convex balanced sets which include it. Show that this hull is always convex and balanced.

7. The convex balanced hull of a set includes the convex hull of the set and they may be unequal.

8. Extend Fact (v) as follows. Let f be a linear functional satisfying $|f(x)| \leq 1$ for all $x \in A$. Then $|f(x)| \leq 1$ for all x in the convex balanced hull of A.

9. The set of points at which a convex set is absorbing is convex.

10. Let A, B be convex sets. The convex hull of $A \cup B$ is

$$\{sa + tb : a \in A, b \in B, s \geq 0, t \geq 0, s + t = 1\}.$$

11. An affine set is nowhere absorbing unless it is the whole space.

12. An *affine mean* of a set A is defined to be a linear combination of A with coefficients adding up to 1. Prove the analogues of Lemma 1, Theorem 1, and Problem 3, changing Definition 2 to a definition of *affine hull*.

13. Use Problem 12 to shorten the proof of Theorem 2; namely, $A + A - A = A$ since any member of $A + A - A$ is an affine mean of A.

14. Let $a \in A$. Show that the affine hull of A is $a + [\text{span of } (A - a)]$, and that the span of A is the affine hull of $A \cup \{0\}$. (Hence the span and affine hull coincide for a set containing 0.)

15. Invent a theory of affine independence and basis to parallel the theory of linear independence and Hamel basis.

16. The *rank* of an affine set A is defined to be the dimension of $A - A$. The *rank* of a set is defined to be the rank of its affine hull. Show that rank is invariant under translation but (Hamel) dimension is not.

17. Let r, d be, respectively, the rank and dimension of a set.   Show that either $d = r$ or $d = r + 1$. Give criteria for the two cases.

18. "Convex" cannot be dropped in Fact (vii).

19. Let A_1 be a set and for $n = 1, 2, \ldots$ define $A_{n+1} = \bigcup \{[tA_n + (1 - t)A_n]: 0 \le t \le 1\}$. Show that $\bigcup_{n=1}^{\infty} A_n$ is the convex hull of A_1.

2.7   Balloons and cones

DEFINITION 1.   *A balloon is a convex, balanced, absorbing set.*

In the familiar Euclidean spaces of low dimension, a balloon might be a sphere centered at 0 with or without part or all of its boundary.   At any rate, it would include such a sphere.   In most typical situations involving infinite dimensional spaces, however, (suitably topologized, Chapter 9) there are balloons which are not neighborhoods of zero [Section 7.5, Example 4], albeit, their closures are neighborhoods of 0 in many interesting cases. These remarks are presented here for the benefit of the student who, impatient of linearity, and eager to begin analysis, will ask why we do not now investigate the topology generated by the balloons.   The answer is that the resulting theory would be so special as to exclude spaces of great interest.

The whole space is, of course, a balloon, so also are spheres centered at 0 in R^2, R^3, E, *et cetera*.   Further examples of balloons are furnished by Problems 1, 3, and 4.   A valuable characterization of balloons in terms of seminorms is given in Section 4.2, Theorem 1.

DEFINITION 2.   *A cone is a nonempty set* K *which has the property that* tK $\subset$ K *for every scalar* t *which is positive or 0.*

Any linear subspace is a cone.   An example of a cone in E is the region between two rays issuing from the origin, including neither, one, or both rays; a special case of this is the upper half plane, including the positive real axis.

Facts

The remarks on postponement given before the list of Facts in Section 6 apply also to Fact (v) below.

(i)   A cone K is convex if and only if $K + K \subset K$.

(ii)   Let K be a convex cone, then $K \cap - K$ is a real linear subspace.

(iii)   Let K be a convex cone, then the real span of K is $K - K$.

(iv)   Let K be a convex set, then $\bigcup \{tK: t \ge 0\}$ is a convex cone.

(v)   Suppose that a convex cone K is absorbing at some point a in $- K$.   Then K is the whole space.

(vi)   Every convex absorbing set includes a balloon.

Proofs

(i) By Section 5, Problem 9, K is convex if and only if $sK + tK \subset K$ for all $s > 0, t > 0$. Since $sK = tK = K$ 〚Problem 7〛 the result follows.

(ii) Clearly $K \cap - K$ is a cone, further, being the intersection of convex sets it is convex. It is also symmetric.

Thus, for any real scalar s, $s(K \cap - K) + (K \cap - K) = |s|(K \cap - K) + (K \cap - K)$ 〚since $K \cap - K$ is symmetric〛 $= (K \cap - K) + (K \cap - K) = K \cap - K$. 〚Fact (i).〛

(iii) Since any element of $K - K$ is a real linear combination of K, it follows that $K - K$ is included in the real span of K. Conversely, any real linear combination u of K is $\Sigma s_k a_k - \Sigma t_k b_k$ with $s_k > 0$, $t_k > 0$, a_k, $b_k \in K$. Thus $u \in \Sigma s_k K - \Sigma t_k K = K + K + \cdots + K - (K + K + \cdots + K) = K - K$.

(iv) Let the given set be called B. Clearly, B is a cone, and if x, $y \in B$ then $x \in sK$, $y \in tK$ for some $s \geq 0, t \geq 0$, thus $x + y \in sK + tK = (s + t)K$ 〚since K is convex〛 $\subset B$.

(v) Since $a \in - K$ we have $- a \in K$. But also K is absorbing at a. Thus K is absorbing at each point of the segment joining $- a$ to a 〚Section 6, Fact (iii)〛, in particular at 0. (This is trivial if $a = 0$.) But then $K = \cup_{n=1}^{\infty} nK$ 〚since K is a cone〛 $=$ whole space 〚since K is absorbing, Section 5, Problem 13〛.

(vi) Let $B = \cap \{tK: |t| = 1\}$, K being convex and absorbing; B is convex. 〚It is an intersection of convex sets.〛 Also B is absorbing. 〚Let a be an arbitrary vector, t a scalar with $|t| = 1$. Then $sa \in K$ for $|s| \leq \delta$, say, and this implies that $(s/t)a \in K$ since $|s/t| = |s|$, and this, in turn, implies that $sa \in tK$. Thus $sa \in B$ for $|s| \leq \delta$.〛 Finally, B is balanced. 〚Let $b \in B$, $|s| \leq 1$. If $s = 0$, $sb \in B$. If $s \neq 0$, we must show $sb \in tK$ for all t with $|t| = 1$. Now, by definition of B,

$$b \in \frac{|s|t}{s} K \qquad \text{since} \qquad \left| \frac{|s|t}{s} \right| = 1, \qquad \text{thus} \quad \frac{s}{|s|t} b \in K.$$

Since K is convex and $0 \in K$, $(s/t)b \in K$; that is, $sb \in tK$.〛//

Problems on linear space 2.7

1. Let H be a Hamel basis. Show that the following are balloons,

$$\{x: x = \Sigma th, \Sigma |t| \leq 1\}, \qquad \{x: x = \Sigma th, \Sigma |t|^2 < 1\}, \qquad \{x: x = \Sigma th, |t_1| \leq 1,$$

t_1 being the coefficient of a certain fixed $h_1 \in H\}$.

2. Select a Hamel basis for R^2 and draw the balloons of Problem 1.

★3. Let f be a linear functional. Show that $\{x: |f(x)| \leq 1\}$ is a balloon.

4. Any finite intersection of balloons is a balloon.

5. "Finite" cannot be omitted in Problem 4. (Give an example in E.)

6. Must the union of two balloons be a balloon?

★7. If K is a cone, $tK = K$ for all $t > 0$.

8. If K is a convex cone, $K + K = K$.

9. If K is a convex cone, $K \cap - K$ and $K - K$ are, respectively, the largest real linear subspace included in, and the smallest real linear subspace which includes K.

10. What is the relationship between $K - K$ and $K \cup - K$ if K is a convex cone?

11. The intersection of any family of cones is a cone.

12. Define analytically, as was done with span and convex hull, the *conical hull* of a set, and show that it is the intersection of all cones which include the set.

★13. Let K be a convex cone, b a vector not in K. Show that $\{a + tb: a \in K, t \geq 0\}$ is a convex cone properly including K, and is the smallest convex cone which includes K, b. It is called the cone *generated by K, b.*

14. Let $I = [0, 1]$. Let $S = \{x \in R^{(I)}: \Sigma |x(t)| \leq 1\}$. Show that S is a balloon in $R^{(I)}$, but not in R^I.

15. Let K be a convex cone. Given vectors a, b, define $b \geq a$ to mean $b - a \in K$. Show that this makes the linear space into a poset, and in addition, that $b \geq a$ implies $b + x \geq a + x$ for any x, and $b \geq a$ implies $tb \geq ta$ for any positive scalar t. These conditions define what is called an *ordered linear space.* The order is said to be *generated by K.*

16. The order in Problem 15 is antisymmetric if and only if $K \cap - K = \{0\}$.

17. The order in Problem 15 is total if and only if $K \cap - K = \{0\}$ and $K \cup - K$ is the whole space.

18. What cone generates the trivial order?

19. Given an ordered linear space, let $K = \{a: a \geq 0\}$. Show that K is a convex cone and that K generates the order; K is called the *positive cone.*

20. In R^2, define $(x, y) \geq (u, v)$ to mean $x \geq u$ and $y \geq v$. Verify that R^2 is an ordered linear space and find the positive cone. Do Problems 16, 17 apply?

21. Find the positive cone for the lexicographic order in R^2.

22. Show that the dense cone (is convex and) totally orders R^∞. (See problem 17.)

23. A vector e in an ordered linear space A is called an *order identity* if to each $a \in A$, there corresponds a positive scalar t with $- te \leq a \leq te$. Show that e is an order identity if and only if the positive cone is absorbing at e. (Assume that A is a real linear space.)

24. Real c_0, real s, real l^p, $p > 0$, have no order identity. Real m and real c have 1 as order identity. (In all these spaces, the order is the natural one in which $a \geq 0$ means $a_n \geq 0$ for all n.) Prove this and show the connection with Section 5, Problem 29.

25. An *order ideal* in an ordered linear space A is a linear subspace I such that $0 \leq a \in I$ implies $[0, a] \subset I$. (Here $[0, a] = \{x: 0 \leq x \leq a\}$.) A *proper* order is ideal I is one which satisfies $I \neq A$. In particular a linear subspace without positive elements is an order ideal. Show that a proper order ideal contains no order identity.

26. Find the order ideals in R^2 with the order of Problem 20.

27. A linear functional f on an ordered linear space A is called *positive* if $f(a) \geq 0$ for all $a \geq 0$. Suppose that A has an order identity e, f is positive, and $f(e) = 0$. Show that $f = 0$.

28. Let K be a convex cone. Show that $K \setminus - K$ is convex.

29. Classify as true or false: A cone is convex if and only if the characteristic function of its complement is a convex function.

2.8 Quotient Space

DEFINITION 1. *Two subspaces* S, T *of a linear space* A *are called complementary if* $S \cap T = \{0\}$, $S + T = A$

For example, the X axis and Y axis are complementary subspaces of R^2; $\{0\}$ and A are complementary subspaces of any linear space A.

Of course many different subspaces might be complementary to one subspace, for example any nonhorizontal line through 0 is complementary to the X axis in R^2, similarly any plane through 0 not including the X axis is complementary to the X axis in R^3.

What is more significant is the fact that *every subspace has a complementary subspace.* ⟦Given a subspace S, let B be a Hamel basis for S. Extend B to a Hamel basis H for the whole space and let T be the span of $H \setminus B$. If $a \in S \cap T$, a is a linear combination of B and $H \setminus B$, that is, a linear combination of H in two different ways. This can happen only if $a = 0$ and the trivial linear combination is involved in each case. If a is an arbitrary vector, it is a linear combination of H, hence the sum of two linear combinations, one of B and one of $H \setminus B$.⟧

We now define the important concept of *quotient space.* Let S be a subspace of a linear space A. The quotient space A/S is defined as follows. Its elements are subsets of A, namely translations of S. Specifically $A/S = \{a + S : a \in A\}$. These are of course, affine sets in A. Since $a + S = b + S$ whenever $a - b \in S$ ⟦$a - b \in S$ implies $a + S = b + (a - b) + S = b + S$⟧, we are being prejudiced whenever we denote an element of A/S by $a + S$, somebody else might call it $b + S$ with $b \neq a$. With this warning we proceed.

We make A/S into a linear space by defining $(a + S) + (b + S) = a + b + S$, $t(a + S) = ta + S$ for $a, b \in A$, scalar t. For $t \neq 0$, and all a, b, this agrees with the definition Section 5. The zero element of A/S is $0 + S$, that is, S.

The *natural homomorphism* $\phi: A \to A/S$ is defined by $\phi(a) = a + S$. This is clearly a linear map and satisfies $\phi^{-1}[\{0\}] = S$. ⟦Here 0 refers to $S \in A/S$, while S on the right-hand side is a subset of A. If $\phi(a) = 0$, this means $a + S = S$, hence $a \in S - S = S$. Conversely, if $a \in S$, $\phi(a) = a + S = S$.⟧

We now make the important observation that *the neutral homomorphism* $\phi: A \to A/S$ *is one to one on any subspace* T *complementary to* S ⟦for, suppose that $a \in T$ and $\phi(a) = 0$; then $a \in S$; but $S \cap T = \{0\}$, thus $a = 0$⟧, *and* $\phi|T$ *is onto* A/S. ⟦Let $a + S$ be an arbitrary member of A/S. Since $S + T = A$, we have $a \in S + T$; thus $a = s + t$, $s \in S$, $t \in T$. Then $\phi(t) = \phi(a - s) = \phi(a) - \phi(s) = \phi(a) = a + S$.⟧

We have now proved that A/S *and* T *are isomorphic*, S, T, *being any pair of complementary subspaces.* This has the additional nontrivial bonus result that all complements of a subspace are isomorphic with each other. This allows us to make the following definition, confident that it yields a number depending only on S (and A, of course) but not on the particular complement chosen.

DEFINITION 2. *The Hamel codimension, or, simply, codimension of a subspace* S *is the Hamel dimension of any subspace complementary to* S; *it is also the Hamel dimension of* A/S.

An instructive example is R^3/X, X being the X axis, $\{(x, 0, 0): x \in R\}$. This is the collection of all lines parallel to the X axis and is obviously in one-to-one correspondence with the YZ plane.

In many applications it is sufficient to quote Theorem 1 without any reference to the concept of quotient space (as, for example, in Theorem 1, Section 3.1).

THEOREM 1. *Let* A *be a linear space and* S *a subspace. Then there exists a linear space* A_1 *and a linear map* $f: A \to A_1$ *such that* $S = f^{-1}[\{0\}]$.

Of course, we take $A_1 = A/S$, and f the natural homomorphism.//

Another important aspect of quotient space is that it formalizes the idea of negligible difference. If $a + S = b + S$, then a, b are equivalent as far as A/S is concerned. They are sometimes said to be equivalent (mod S).

Example 1. Consider M, the linear space of Lebesgue measurable real functions on $[0, 1]$, and S the subspace of those which vanish almost everywhere. In doing integration and measure theory, it is M/S in which we operate, rather than M, because we identify two functions which are equal almost everywhere.

Remark. Suppose that $f: A/S \to A_1$ is a linear map, A, A_1 being linear spaces, and S a subspace of A. It is natural to define $F: A \to A_1$ by $F = f \circ \phi$. This means simply that $F(a) = f(a + s)$. Which linear maps F can be gotten in this way? A necessary condition is that $F(a) = 0$ for $a \in S$. This turns out to be sufficient as well. [If F vanishes on S, we define f by $f(a + S) = F(a)$; a priori, f might not be well defined because we insist that $f(a + S) = f(b + S)$ if $a + S = b + S$. However, this turns out to be true, for if $a + S = b + S$ it follows that $a - b \in S - S = S$ and so $F(a - b) = 0$, that is, $F(a) = F(b)$.]

It is very common and useful to identify f and F and say, *a linear map on* A *is also defined on* A/S *provided it vanishes on* S.

Thus, in Example 1, $I(f) = \int_0^1 f$ defines I on M and M/S. But $J(f) = f(1/2)$ defines J on M, but not on M/S, since functions agreeing almost everywhere need not agree at $1/2$. Hence the expression $f(1/2)$ never arises in Lebesgue measure theory.

Problems 2.8

In this list, S, T are subspaces of a linear space A.

1. Check carefully that A/S is a linear space.

2. Denoting Hamel dimension by d, $d(S) + d(A/S) = d(A)$.

3. $A/\{0\} = A$, $A/A = \{0\}$. (Notice that, strictly speaking, each member of $A/\{0\}$ is a subset, rather than a member, of A.)

4. Let S, T be complementary subspaces, and $S_1 \in A/S$. Show that $S_1 \cap T$ contains exactly one point.

★5. Find the codimension of c_0 in c.

6. A *projection* is a linear map p from A to itself which satisfies $p^2 = p$; that is, $p(px) = px$ for all x. Let $S = \{x: px = x\}$, $T = \{x: px = 0\}$. Show that S, T are complementary, and that $p[A] = p[S] = S$, $p[T] = \{0\}$. (Here p is called the projection *on* S, *along* T.)

7. Let p be a projection and $q = 1 - p$ (here $1: A \to A$ is the identity, $1(x) = x$). Show that q is a projection, that $pq = qp = 0$, and that q leads (by the procedure of Problem 6) to the same pair (in the opposite order) of complementary subspaces.

8. Let, S, T be complementary subspaces. Then for each $x \in A$, $x = s + t$ for a unique $s \in S$, $t \in T$. Define $p: A \to A$, $q: A \to A$ by $px = s$, $qx = t$. Show that p, q are projections on S along T, and on T along S, respectively. (See Problem 7.)

9. Suppose that $S \subset T$. Let p, q be projections on S, T, respectively. Show that $qp = p$ but that pq may not be p. What additional assumption would insure $pq = p$? (Here and in Problem 10, qp is being used to stand for $q \circ p$.)

10. Investigate (say, for R^3, and try to generalize) for what projections p, q, it would be true that

(a) $p + q$ is a projection,   (d) $pq = qp$,

(b) $p - q$ is a projection,   (e) $pq = 0$.

(c) pq is a projection,

11. Give reasonable definitions which will make $A \times B$ a linear space, A, B being linear spaces. Then show that if S, T are complementary subspaces of A, A is isomorphic with $S \times T$.

12. Prove the converse of Theorem 1; that is, any space A_1 with the given property is isomorphic with A/S, and an isomorphism $g: A_1 \to A/S$ can be so chosen that $f \circ g$ is the natural homomorphism.

13. Interpret the last remark in this section as $(A/S)^{\#} = S^{\perp}$.

14. Let B be a set and Z a class of subsets of B which is closed under finite unions. Let $N = \{f \in R^B: (\text{there exists } W \in Z: f(x) = 0 \text{ for all } x \notin W)\}$. Show that N is a linear subspace of R^B. Show that Example 1 is a special case.

15. The codimension of c in m is infinite.

16. Let A, B be arbitrary sets, and $f: A \to B$. A subset S of A is called *saturated* if $S = f^{-1}[f[S]]$. Prove that $f^{-1}[T]$ is saturated for any $T \subset B$. Now suppose that A, B are groups, and $f: A \to B$ a homomorphism. Show that a subgroup S of A is saturated if and only if $S \supset f^{-1}[\{e\}]$. (Here, e is the identity in B.)

2.9 Finite-dimensional space

Although the finite dimensional case is regarded as the trivial one in functional analysis, finite codimension is of the first importance. Since codimension is defined in terms of dimension (of a quotient space), some of the theory of finite-dimensional spaces must be developed. This will be kept to the minimum which is sufficient for further developments. Although not the main purpose of this section, some of the settings used illustrate and illuminate techniques which will reappear in a topological setting.

THEOREM 1. *Let* A *be finite dimensional, then* A$^{\#}$ *has the same Hamel dimension as* A.

Since A is isomorphic with E^n, [Section 4, Theorem 4] it suffices to prove the result for E^n, or R^n if the space is real linear. This simplifies only the notation.

We shall show that $H \equiv (P_1, P_2, \ldots, P_n)$ is a Hamel basis for $(E^n)^{\#}$, P_k meaning, as usual, the kth coordinate. H spans $(E^n)^{\#}$. ⟦Let f be an arbitrary linear functional on E^n. Then for any $a \in E^n$ we have $a = \Sigma P_k(a)\delta^k$, thus $f(a) = \Sigma P_k(a)f(\delta^k) = [\Sigma f(\delta^k)P_k](a)$, and so $f = \Sigma f(\delta^k)P_k$.⟧ H is linearly independent. ⟦Let $\Sigma t_k P_k = 0$. Let r be one of the integers $1, 2, \ldots, n$. Then

$$0 = (\sum_{k=1}^{n} t_k P_k)(\delta^r) = \sum_{k=1}^{n} t_k P_k(\delta^r) = t_r.⟧//$$

COROLLARY 1. *Let* A *be finite dimensional and* $(b_1, b_2, \ldots, b_n)$ *a basis for* A. *Then there exists a basis* $(l_1, l_2, \ldots, l_n)$ *for* A$^{\#}$ *with* $l_i(b_j) = 0$ *for* i $\neq$ j, 1 *for* i = j.

The set $(\{b_i\}, \{l_j\})$ is called a *biorthogonal pair*. For each j, $1 \leq j \leq n$, let l_j be a linear functional on A with $l_j(b_j) = 1$, $l_j(b_i) = 0$ for $i \neq j$. ⟦Since $(b_1, b_2, \ldots, b_n)$ is linearly independent, l_j exists.⟧

Now $(l_1, l_2, \ldots, l_n)$ is linearly independent. ⟦If $\Sigma_{k=1}^{n} t_k l_k = 0$, then for each j, $1 \leq j \leq n$, $0 = \Sigma_{k=1}^{n} t_k l_k(b_j) = t_j$.⟧ The Hamel dimension of $A^{\#}$ is n ⟦Theorem 1⟧; hence $(l_1, l_2, \ldots l_n)$ is a basis. ⟦Otherwise, it could be extended to a basis which would then have more than n points.⟧//

We know from Theorem 1 that $A^{\#}$ is isomorphic with A (if A is finite dimensional). However, no particular isomorphism is of interest. On the other hand, there is a very natural and useful isomorphism between $A^{\#\#}$ (that is, $(A^\#)^\#$) and A. This is given in Theorem 2 which is a representation theorem for $A^{\#\#}$.

Given $a \in A$, $f \in A^\#$, $f(a)$ is a scalar. We are accustomed to thinking of this as a function of a for fixed f. Obeying the famous dictum, "*man muss immer umkehren,*" we now consider $f(a)$ as a function of f for fixed a.

DEFINITION 1.   *For each $a \in$ A, define $\hat{a} \in$ A$^{\#\#}$ by $\hat{a}(f) = f(a)$ for all $f \in$ A$^\#$.*

The symbol $\hat{a}$ is pronounced, "*a hat.*"

The map $a \rightarrow \hat{a}$ is called the *natural embedding* of A into $A^{\#\#}$. Since $\hat{a}(tf + g) = (tf + g)(a) = tf(a) + g(a) = t\hat{a}(f) + \hat{a}(g)$, $\hat{a}$ is linear. The natural embedding is an isomorphism into. $[(ta + b)^\wedge(f) = f(ta + b) = tf(a) + f(b) = t\hat{a}(f) + \hat{b}(f)$ and so $(ta + b)^\wedge = t\hat{a} + \hat{b}$. Further, if $\hat{a} = 0$, then for all $f \in A^\#$, $0 = \hat{a}(f) = f(a)$ and so $a = 0$ since $A^\#$ is total over A by Section 4, Corollary 1. Thus the embedding is one to one.$]$ Let $\hat{A}$ be the image of A; that is, $\hat{A} = \{\hat{a}: a \in A\}$. Clearly $\hat{A}$ is a linear subspace of $A^{\#\#}$. We now have the important result that for a finite-dimensional space A, the natural embedding is onto $A^{\#\#}$; that is, $\hat{A} = A^{\#\#}$.

THEOREM 2.   *Let* A *be finite dimensional, and* F *a linear functional on* A$^\#$*; then* F $= \hat{a}$ *for some $a \in$ A.*

Let $(d_1, d_2, \ldots, d_n)$ be a basis for A. Then $(\hat{d}_1, \hat{d}_2, \ldots, \hat{d}_n)$ is linearly independent $[$since the map $a \rightarrow \hat{a}$ is an isomorphism$]$, hence spans $A^{\#\#}$ $[$since, by Theorem 1, $A^{\#\#}$ has dimension $n]$. Thus $\hat{A}$ spans $A^{\#\#}$, hence $\hat{A} = A^{\#\#}$ $[$Section 3, Problem 7$]$ since $\hat{A}$ is a linear subspace.//

Another proof, which gives a construction for a in terms of F is spelled out in Problem 2.

THEOREM 3.   *Let* A *be finite dimensional and* S *a proper subspace of* A$^\#$. *Then* S *is not total over* A.

Let $F \in A^{\#\#}$, $F \neq 0$ but $F(f) = 0$ for $f \in S$ $[$Section 4, Theorem 2$]$. By Theorem 2, $F = \hat{a}$ for some $a \in A$. This a has the property that $a \neq 0$ $[$since $\hat{a} \neq 0$, the natural embedding being an isomorphism$]$, but for all $f \in S$, $f(a) = \hat{a}(f) = 0$. Thus S is not total.//

An abbreviated proof runs, S is not total over $A^{\#\#}$ by Section 4, Theorem 2; but $A^{\#\#} = A$ by Theorem 2.

Problems on linear space 2.9

★1. Let A have basis $(b_1, b_2, \ldots, b_n)$ with biorthogonal linear functionals $(l_1, l_2, \ldots, l_n)$. Show that for each $a \in A$, $a = \sum_{k=1}^{n} l_k(a)b_k$, and for each $f \in A^\#$, $f = \sum f(b_k)l_k$.

2. Write out this proof of Theorem 2. For $F \in A^{\#\#}$, let $a = \sum F(l_k)b_k$ (see Problem 1). Then $F = \hat{a}$.

3. A finite product of finite dimensional spaces is, with natural definitions, a finite dimensional linear space; of what dimension?

4. Show that Theorems 1 and 2 are false for every infinite dimensional space. $[$A cardinality argument is sufficient, use Section 3, Problem 10, and Section 4, Problem 13.$]$

5. Theorem 3 is false for every infinite dimensional space. ⟦Choose $F \in A^{\#\#} \setminus \hat{A}$, by Problem 4. Then $\{f \in A^{\#}: F(f) = 0\}$ is total over A.⟧

6. Let S be the span in $c^{\#}$ of $\{P_n: n = 1, 2, \ldots\}$. Show that S is total over c, but $S \neq c^{\#}$. [lim $\notin S$.]

7. Let A be a finite-dimensional space, and S a subspace of $A^{\#}$. Given $f \in A^{\#} \setminus S$, there exists $a \in A$ such that $f(a) = 1$ but $g(a) = 0$ for all $g \in S$.

▲8. Let m be a positive integer. Let $\{f_n\}$ be a sequence of linear functionals defined on R^m. Suppose further that for each $a \in R^m$, $\{f_n(a)\}$ is a bounded sequence. Prove that there exists a number M such that if $a = (a_1, a_2, \ldots, a_m)$ satisfies $a_1^2 + a_2^2 + \cdots + a_m^2 < 1$, it follows that $|f_n(a)| < M$ for each n.

2.10 Maximal subspaces and hyperplanes

DEFINITION 1. *A maximal subspace is a subspace of codimension 1. A hyperplane is a translation of a maximal subspace.*

For example, the maximal subspaces of R^3 are the planes containing 0; those of R^2, the lines containing 0. R has only one maximal subspace, $\{0\}$; c_0 is a maximal subspace of c ⟦Section 8, Problem 5⟧. The hyperplanes of R^3 are the planes, of R^2 the lines, of R the points; $\{a: \lim a_n = t\}$ is a hyperplane in c for each scalar t.

Facts

(i) A proper subspace is maximal if and only if it is not properly included in any proper subspace.

(ii) A proper subspace S is maximal if and only if, for each vector $a \notin S$, $a \oplus S$ is the whole space.

(iii) In Fact (ii), replace "each" by "some."

(iv) Let f be a non-identically-zero linear functional, then $f^{\perp} \equiv \{x: f(x) = 0\}$ is a maximal subspace.

(v) Let S be a maximal subspace. Then there exists a linear functional f such that $S = f^{\perp}$. (See Corollary 2 for extent of uniqueness.) Moreover we can choose any $a \notin S$ and make $f(a) = 1$.

(vi) A hyperplane is a maximal affine set; that is, an affine set H in A is a hyperplane if and only if it is not properly included in any affine proper subset of A.

Proofs

(i) Suppose first that S, T are distinct proper subspaces of A with $S \subset T$. Then A/S has dimension at least 2. ⟦We shall exhibit two linearly independent elements. Let $a \in A \setminus T$, $b \in T \setminus S$. Then $a + S$ and $b + S$ are linearly independent in A/S, for suppose t, u are scalars and $t(a + S) + u(b + S) = S$ the zero element of A/S. Then $ta + ub \in S$, thus $ta \in S - ub \subset T - T = T$ and so, since $a \notin T$ we have $t = 0$. From this $ub \in S$ and so $u = 0$ since $b \notin S$.⟧ Thus S is not maximal.

Next assume that S is not maximal, but is a proper subspace of A. Then A/S has dimension at least 2. Let $x + S$, $y + S$ be linearly independent elements of A/S. S is properly included in $x \oplus S$ [for $x \in (x \oplus S) \setminus S$] and $x \oplus S$ is a proper subspace of A. [As we shall now show, $y \notin x \oplus S$. Assume, on the contrary, that $y \in x \oplus S$. Then there exists a scalar t, and $a \in S$ such that $y = tx + a$. Thus $(y + S) - t(x + S) = (y - tx) + S = S$, contradicting the linear independence of $x + S$, $y + S$ in A/S.]

(ii) If S is maximal and $a \notin S$, $a \oplus S$ is a subspace properly including S. By Fact (i), it must be the whole space.

If S is not maximal, the construction used in the second half of the proof of Fact (i) yields a vector a such that $a \oplus S$ is a proper subspace properly including S. (We could also prove this by observing that the codimension of S in $a \oplus S$ is 1 if $a \notin S$.)

(iii) Suppose that for some a, $a \oplus S$ is the whole space. Let x be an arbitrary vector $\notin A$. Since $x \in a \oplus S$ we have $x = ta + b$ for some scalar t, $b \in S$. Clearly $t \neq 0$. Since $a = (1/t)x - b$ we have $a \in x \oplus S$ thus $a \oplus S \subset x \oplus S$ and so $x \oplus S$ is also the whole space.

(iv) There exists a vector a such that $f(a) \neq 0$. The proof is concluded by showing that $a \oplus f^{\perp}$ is the whole space. [Let b be an arbitrary vector, and set $x = b - [f(b)/f(a)]a$. Then $f(x) = 0$, that is, $x \in f^{\perp}$. Thus $b = x + [f(b)/f(a)]a \in a \oplus f^{\perp}$.]

(v) Let S be a maximal subspace and let a be a vector $\notin S$. For each vector x, there exists a scalar t and $b \in S$ such that $x = ta + b$ [by Fact (ii)]; t is uniquely determined by x [for if $x = ta + b = t'a + b'$, then $(t - t')a = b' - b \in S$, thus $t - t' = 0$ since $a \notin S$]. Let $f(x) = t$. This defines a functional on the whole space. The functional f is linear [for, if $x = ta + b$, $y = ua + c$, b, $c \in S$, and s is a scalar, $sx + y = (st + u)a + sb + c$, and $sb + c \in S$, thus $f(sx + y) = st + u = sf(x) + f(y)$]. Finally $f^{\perp} = S$ [for $x \in S$ if and only if the representation of x as $ta + b$ is $0a + x$, and this is true if and only if $f(x) = 0$].

(vi) Let H be a hyperplane, S an affine proper subset of A with $S \supset H$. Then $S - S \supset H - H$. But $H - H$ is a maximal subspace since H is its translate [Section 6, Theorem 2 and Remark]. This $S - S = H - H$ [otherwise $S - S = A$, and again by Section 6, Theorem 2, $S = A$]. Now S is a translate of $S - S$, that is, of $H - H$ and so $S = H$. [They are both translates of the same subspace, and $S \supset H$.]

Conversely, suppose that H is affine but not a hyperplane. Then $H - H$ is not a maximal subspace. Let S be a proper subspace properly including $H - H$. Then $H + S$ is affine [$t(H + S) + (1 - t)(H + S) = tH + (1 - t)H + tS + (1 - t)S \subset H + S$], properly includes H[$H + S \supset H + 0 = H$, and if $a \in S \setminus (H - H)$ and $h \in H$ then $h + a \in (H + S)$ but $h + a \notin H$ since $a \notin H - H$] and is a proper subset of A. [If $0 \notin H + S$ then surely $H + S$ is proper. If $0 \in H + S$, say $0 = h + a$, $h \in H$, $a \in S$, then $h = -a \in S$. Thus, using Section 6, Theorem 2, $H = h + (H - H) \subset S + S = S$ and so $H + S \subset S + S = S$ which is proper.]//

It is clear from Facts (iv) and (v) that maximal subspaces and linear functionals are intimately related; we shall study one of them and draw conclusions about the other. This is the situation in analytic geometry where we speak of planes, or, equivalently, of the equations of planes, the latter being $ax + by + cz = 0$; that is, $f(x, y, z) = 0$, where f is a linear functional. The plane, then, if $f^{\perp}$.

We are now going to obtain relations among linear functionals from inclusion relations among their nullspaces. The main result is Corollary 1.

The following lemma contains the fundamental algebraic result from which much of the dual and quotient theory will follow without further computation. (By dual theory is meant the study of linear maps.)

LEMMA 1. *Let* A *be a linear space and* $(f_1, f_2, \ldots, f_n)$ *a finite set of linear functionals on* A. *Let* S *be a subset of* A *with more than* n *points. Then there exists a nontrivial linear combination of* S *at which each* f_k *is zero.*

Let $a_1, a_2, \ldots, a_{n+1}$ be distinct members of S. Then there exist scalars $t_1, t_2, \ldots, t_{n+1}$ not all zero, such that $\Sigma_{k=1}^{n+1} t_k f_m(a_k) = 0$ for $m = 1, 2, \ldots, n$, since a system of n equations in $n + 1$ unknowns always has a nontrivial solution. But these equations say that $f_m(\Sigma t_k a_k) = 0$ for $m = 1, 2, \ldots, n.//$

LEMMA 2. *Let* Φ *be a family of linear functionals on* A. *Let* $S = \cap \{f^\perp : f \in \Phi\}$; *that is,* S *is the set of points at which each* $f \in \Phi$ *vanishes. Then* Φ *is total over* A/S.

Here each $f \in \Phi$ is defined on A/S by $f(a + S) = f(a)$ according to the last remark of Section 8. Suppose that $f(a + S) = 0$ for each $f \in \Phi$. This means that for each $f \in \Phi$, $f(a) = 0$, that is, $a \in f^\perp$. Thus $a \in S$, so $a + S = S$, the zero element of $A/S.//$

THEOREM 1. *Suppose that a linear space* A *has defined on it a finite total family* Φ *of linear functionals. Then* A *is finite dimensional, the dimension of* A *being not more than the number of elements of* Φ. *Moreover* Φ *spans* $A^\#$.

The first part is a trivial consequence of Lemma 1. The second part follows from Section 9, Theorem 3 [for, if Φ does not span $A^\#$, its span is not total, hence, a fortiori, Φ is itself not total].//

THEOREM 2. *Let* $S_1, S_2, \ldots, S_n$ *be maximal subspaces of* A. *Then the codimension of* $S \equiv \cap_{k=1}^n S_k$ *is not more than* n.

For each $k = 1, 2, \ldots, n$, let f_k be a linear functional with $f_k^\perp = S_k$. By Lemma 2, $(f_1, f_2, \ldots, f_n)$ is total over A/S. The result now follows by Theorem 1.//

THEOREM 3. *Let* g, $f_1, f_2, \ldots, f_n$ *be linear functionals on* A. *Suppose that* g(a) = 0 *for each* a *such that* $f_1(a) = f_2(a) = \cdots = f_n(a) = 0$, *that is,* $g^\perp \supset \cap_{k=1}^n f_k^\perp$. *Then* g *is a linear combination of* $(f_1, f_2, \ldots, f_n)$.

Let $S = \cap_{k=1}^n f_k^\perp$. Then A/S is finite dimensional, by Theorem 2. $(f_1, f_2, \ldots, f_n)$ is total over A/S by Lemma 2, thus it spans $(A/S)^\#$ by Theorem 1. Now the hypothesis is that g vanishes on S, thus, as usual, we may consider g to be defined on A/S by $g(a + S) = g(a)$; that is, $g \in (A/S)^\#$. Hence g is a linear combination of $(f_1, f_2, \ldots, f_n)$ on A/S, say $g(a + S) = \Sigma_{k=1}^n t_k f_k(a + S)$ for all a. But this means that $g(a) = \Sigma_{k=1}^n t_k f_k(a)$ for all $a.//$

COROLLARY 1. *Let* g, $f_1, f_2, \ldots, f_n$ *be linear functionals such that* $|g(a)| < 1$ *for each* a *such that* $f_1(a) = f_2(a) = \cdots = f_n(a) = 0$. *Then* g *is a linear combination of* $(f_1, f_2, \ldots, f_n)$.

Since g is bounded on the linear subspace $\cap_{k=1}^{n} f_k^{\perp}$, it follows that g is zero on this subspace 〚Section 4, Problem 17〛.   The result follows by Theorem 3.//

COROLLARY 2.   *Let* f, g *be linear functionals such that* $f^{\perp} \subset g^{\perp}$.   *Then there exists a constant (scalar)* t *such that* g $=$ tf.   *If* g *is not identically* 0, t $\neq$ 0, *and* $f^{\perp} = g^{\perp}$.

This is a special case of Theorem 3.   A direct proof runs as follows.   Let a be a vector such that $f(a) \neq 0$.   Given any vector b, let $x = b - [f(b)/f(a)]a$.   Then $f(x) = 0$.   Hence $g(x) = 0$, that is, $g(b) = [g(a)/f(a)]f(b)$.   With $t = g(a)/f(a)$ this is the required result.//

THEOREM 4.   *If* f *is a linear functional not identically zero and* t *is a scalar,* $\{a: f(a) = t\}$ *is a hyperplane.   Conversely, every hyperplane has this form.*

Let f, t be given.   We first note that $H \equiv \{a: f(a) = t\}$ is not empty.   〚Let $f(a) \neq 0$, then $f[ta/f(a)] = t$.〛   Next let a be an arbitrary member of H.   Then $H - a = f^{\perp}$.   〚Let $x \in H - a$ then $x = h - a$ for some h with $f(h) = t$, and so $f(x) = t - t = 0$.   Conversely if $f(x) = 0$, let $h = x + a$, then $f(h) = t$, so $h \in H$, and $x = h - a \in H - a$.〛

Conversely, let H be a hyperplane.   Then, by definition, there exists a maximal subspace S, and vector h such that $H = h + S$.   Let f be a linear functional with $f^{\perp} = S$.   Now let $t = f(h)$, then $H = \{x: f(x) = t\}$.   〚If $x \in H$, $x = h + a$ for some $a \in S$, so $f(x) = t$; conversely, if $f(x) = t$, $f(x - h) = 0$, thus $x - h \in f^{\perp} = S$ and so $x \in h + S = H$.〛//

Corollary 2 shows that a linear functional is almost determined by its set of zeros.   It is, in fact, determined up to a multiplicative constant.   We now see that it is entirely determined by the set where is assumes the value 1.   This set is nonempty if $f \neq 0$.

THEOREM 5.   *Let* f, g *be linear functionals which are equal on a hyperplane* H *not containing* 0.   *Then* f $=$ g.

Let $u = f - g$.   Then $u^{\perp} \supset H$ properly.   〚$0 \in u^{\perp} \setminus H$.〛   By Fact (vi), $u^{\perp}$ is the whole space.//

LEMMA 3.   *Let* A, B *be linear spaces, and* f: A $\rightarrow$ B *a linear map.   Suppose that* H *is a set in* A *satisfying* f[H] $=$ B.   *Then* A $=$ H $+$ f^{-1}[{0}].

(Note that H need not be a subspace.   For example, consider $P_1: R_3 \rightarrow R$.)

Let $a \in A$.   By hypothesis, $f(a) \in f[H]$, that is, $f(a) = f(h)$ for some $h \in H$.   Then $a = (a - h) + h \in f^{-1}[\{0\}] + H$.//

THEOREM 6.   *Let* A, B *be linear spaces, and* f: A $\rightarrow$ B *a linear map onto.   Let* T *be a maximal subspace of* B.   *Then* f^{-1}[T] *is a maximal subspace of* A.

Let $S = f^{-1}[T]$.   Then $S \neq A$, since f is onto.   Let H be a subspace of A which properly includes S.   Then $f[H]$ properly includes T and so $f[H] = B$.   By Lemma 3, $A = H + f^{-1}[\{0\}] \subset H + S \subset H + H = H$.   Thus $H = A$, and so S is maximal.//

We remark, finally, that maximal subspaces are sometimes not easy to find explicitly. For example, the reader will find it difficult to name explicitly a maximal subspace of m

which includes c or a linear functional on m, not identically zero, which vanishes on c. We know, of course, that such exist.

Problems 2.10

Each problem whose data are unspecified refers to a linear space A.

1. Prove Fact (ii) by means of the observation given at the end of its proof.

2. Deduce Theorem 1 from Theorem 2.

3. Show that Theorems 2 and 3 are false if $n = \infty$, and that, in Theorem 1, the dimension of A may be greater than the cardinality of Φ if the latter is allowed to be infinite. $[\![\{P_n\}$ is total over $s.]\!]$

★4. Every proper subspace is included in a maximal subspace.

★5. Let S be a maximal subspace and x a vector not in S. There exists a unique linear functional f with $f^{\perp} = S$, $f(x) = 1$.

6. In R^2, let S be the line through 0 and $(1, 2)$. Find a linear functional f such that $f^{\perp} = S$, $f(2, 3) = 4$.

★7. In Theorem 4, every hyperplane can be expressed in the given form with $t = 1$ or 0.

8. Show that $\{f \in C : f(1) = 2\}$ is a hyperplane in C.

9. Express the hyperplane of Problem 8 in the form mentioned in Theorem 4.

10. Every pair of linear functionals on a given space are equal on some maximal subspace.

11. A matrix A is called almost regular if $\lim_A x = \lim x$ for all x in some maximal subspace of c. Show that every conservative matrix is almost regular $[\![$Problem 10$]\!]$.

12. The complement of any hyperplane not containing 0 includes a balloon. $[\![$The hyperplane is $(f = 1)$, the balloon is $(|f| \leq \frac{1}{2})$.$]\!]$

13. Extend Theorem 2 by allowing each S_k to have finite codimension.

14. Given any nonzero vector a, there exists a maximal subspace not containing a.

15. Let f, g be linear functionals on a real linear space such that $f(a) \leq g(a)$ for all a. Show that $f = g$.

16. Let f, g be linear functionals such that $|f(a)| = |g(a)|$ for all a. Show that $f = tg$ for some scalar t.

17. Deduce Theorem 6 from Section 8, Problem 16. $[\![$Any subspace of A properly including S is saturated.$]\!]$

18. If, in Theorem 6, f is not onto, then $f^{-1}[T]$ is either a maximal subspace or all of A.

19. Is $\{f : f'(\frac{1}{2})$ exists$\}$ a maximal subspace of real C?

20. A subspace S is maximal if and only if the dimension of $S \cap B$ is positive for every two dimensional subspace B.

21. Let S be a subspace of finite codimension. Then there exists a finite set of linear functionals $\{f_1, f_2, \ldots, f_n\}$ such that $S = \bigcap f_k^{\perp}$. $[\![$Choose a basis for $(A/S)^{\#}.]\!]$

22. Let S be an affine set of finite codimension with $0 \notin S$. Then there exists a finite set $(f_1, f_2, \ldots, f_n)$ of linear functionals such that $S = \{x : f_k(x) = 1$ for $k = 1, 2, \ldots, n\}$. $[\![$If $S = a + T$, choose a basis in $(A/T)^{\#}$ from the hyperplane $\{f : f(a) = 1\}.]\!]$

23. Let K be a linear subspace of real F, not consisting entirely of continuous functions. Suppose that K has the property that every $f \in K$ satisfying $f(0) = 0$ is continuous. Prove that, conversely, every continuous member f of K satisfies $f(0) = 0$.

24. Let H be a hyperplane in a (complex) linear space. Let a, b be vectors not in H. Show that a, b can be connected by a path made of line segments not meeting H. [Specifically, there exists c such that the line segments joining a to c and c to b do not meet H.]

25. Let f be a linear functional on an ordered linear space with order identity e. Suppose that $f(e) = 1$. Show that f is positive if and only if $f^{\perp}$ is an order ideal. (See Section 7, Problems 15 to 27.)

26. Let A be a row-finite matrix whose rows are linearly independent. Show that $r_A = s$. (Problem 29 generalizes this result.) ⟦Given $y \in s$, let f be a linear functional on E^∞ with $f(a_n) = y_n$, a_n being the nth row of A. This is possible by Section 4, Problem 22. Then, with $x_n = f(\delta^n)$ for $n = 1, 2, \ldots$ we have $y = Ax$.⟧

27. Show that "row-finite" cannot be omitted in Problem 26. ⟦Section 1.2, Problem 23.⟧

28. Show that "rows" cannot be replaced by "columns" in Problem 26.

29. Let A be a row-finite matrix. Show that $y \in r_A$ if and only if, for each finite set $(t_1, t_2, \ldots t_n)$ of scalars satisfying $\sum_{r=1}^{n} t_r a_{rk} = 0$ for $k = 1, 2, \ldots$, it follows that $\sum_{r=1}^{n} t_r y_r = 0$. ⟦The condition is clearly necessary. The proof given for Problem 26 shows it sufficient.⟧ This result is due to O. Toeplitz.

30. Express the result of Problem 29 in the form $r_A = \bigcap \{ f^\perp : f \in K \}$, where K is the class of linear functionals on s taking the form $f(x) = \sum_{r=1}^{m} t_r x_r$ and vanishing on the rows of A, (that is, $r_A = K^{\perp\perp}$).

2.11   Real versus complex

Let A be a linear space. The *associated real linear* space A_R is what A becomes if we ignore all but real scalars. Thus the vectors of A_R are the same as those of A, and for any real number t and $a \in A_R$ (that is, $a \in A$) we define ta to be what it is in A. For example, the real linear space associated with E is, essentially, R^2.

The dimension of A_R is twice that of A, thus of course if A is infinite dimensional their dimensions are equal. ⟦Let H be a Hamel basis for A. Let $H_1 = H \cup iH$. Clearly H_1 spans A_R (with real scalars of course) and H_1 is linearly independent in A_R since a (real) linear combination of H_1 is a complex linear combination of H.⟧

We next observe (Theorem 1) that a linear functional is uniquely determined by its real part. Specifically, let f be a linear functional on a (complex) linear space. Define g, h by $g(a) =$ real part of $f(a)$, $h(a) =$ imaginary part of $f(a)$, for each a. Thus $f(a) = g(a) + ih(a)$ for each a; g, h are real-valued, *real linear* functions; that is, $g(ta + b) = tg(a) + g(b)$ for real t, and vectors a, b; a similar result holds for h.

THEOREM 1. *Let* g *be a real-valued real linear function defined on a (complex) linear space* A. *There exists a unique real valued function* h *defined on* A *such that* g $+$ ih *is a linear functional on* A.

The function h turns out to be real linear. First let us prove that if there is one such h, there is only one. ⟦Suppose $f \equiv g + ih$ is linear. Then for any vector a, $g(ia) + ih(ia) = f(ia) = if(a) = ig(a) - h(a)$. Equating real parts yields $h(a) = -g(ia)$. This shows that h is uniquely determined and is real linear.⟧ Next we show that such an h exists by constructing it. The proof of uniqueness shows the way! ⟦Define h by setting $h(a) = -g(ia)$ for all a. Let $f = g + ih$, that is,

(1) $$f(a) = g(a) - ig(ia).$$

Clearly f is additive and real linear. Thus we have only to show $f(ia) = if(a)$. But $f(ia) = g(ia) + ih(ia) = g(ia) - ig(iia) = g(ia) + ig(a) = -h(a) + ig(a) = if(a)$.⟧//

Not only is a linear functional f determined by its real part Rf, but it often imitates Rf in its behaviour (Theorem 2). This will sometimes allow the reduction of a problem to a special case involving real numbers.

THEOREM 2.   *Let* f *be a linear functional and assume that* $Rf(a) \leq 1$ *for all* $a \in S$, S *being a certain balanced set.   Then* $|f(a)| \leq 1$ *for all* $a \in S$.

Let $a \in S$, and $f(a) = re^{i\theta}$, $r \geq 0$, θ real.   Then $|f(a)| = r = f(ae^{-i\theta}) = Rf(ae^{-i\theta}) \leq 1$. [The last two steps are justified by the facts that $f(ae^{-i\theta}) = r$ is real, and $ae^{-i\theta} \in S$, since S is balanced.]//

THEOREM 3.   *Every maximal real linear subspace of a linear space includes a maximal subspace.*

Of course a maximal real linear subspace of A is, by definition a maximal subspace of A_R. Letting S be such a subspace, we have $S = g^\perp$ for some real valued real linear functional g on A.   Let $f = g + ih$ be linear.   Then $f^\perp \subset g^\perp$ [for if $f(a) = 0$, then $g(a) = Rf(a) = 0$].//

Problems on linear space 2.11

★1. The following are real linear subspaces of a linear space, the set of points where (a) a real linear functional is zero, (b) a linear functional is zero, (c) a linear functional is real.

★2. Let f_1, f_2 be linear functionals and assume that $Rf_1(a) \leq |f_2(a)|$ for all a.   Prove that $|f_1(a)| \leq |f_2(a)|$ for all a.

3. Let f_1, f_2 be linear functionals such that $Rf_1(a) \leq Rf_2(a)$ for all a.   Show that $f_1 = f_2$.

4. Let f_1, f_2 be linear functionals such that $|Rf_1(a)| \leq |Rf_2(a)|$ for all a.   Show that f_1 is a real multiple of f_2.

5. Let A be a (complex) linear space, and S a maximal subspace of A.   Show that A has a maximal real linear subspace which includes S.   Find all of them.

6. Give an example of a real linear space that is not the associated real linear space of any (complex) linear space.

7. Suppose that a real linear space A has defined a linear function $f: A \to A$ satisfying $f[f(a)] = -a$ for all $a \in A$.   Show that A is the real linear space associated with some complex linear space. [Define $ia = f(a)$.]

8. The existence of f in Problem 7 is necessary as well as sufficient.   [Define $f(a) = ia$.]

9. Let H be a set and A a linear subspace of $B_1[H]$ with $1 \in A$.   For $x \in A$, $f \in A^\#$, define $\|x\| = \sup \{|x(h)|: h \in H\}$, $\|f\| = \sup \{|f(x)|: \|x\| \leq 1\}$.   Suppose that $\|f\| = f(1) = 1$.   Show that $f(x)$ is real if $x(h)$ is real for all $h \in H$, and that $f(x) \geq 0$ if $x(h) \geq 0$ for all $h \in H$.

▲2.12   Distributions, linear theory

This section is devoted to an incomplete (but self-contained) sketch of the theory of distributions.   It illustrates admirably an elegant interplay of the concept of maximal subspace with operations of elementary calculus.   See Appendix N for further details.

Let A be the real linear space of real functions defined on R each of which is differentiable infinitely often and each of which has the property known as *compact support;* namely, given any $f \in A$, there exists an interval $[a, b]$ such that $f(x) = 0$ for all $x \notin [a, b]$.   The interval will depend on f.   A member of $A^\#$ will be called a *distribution.*   Thus, for our purposes, a distribution is a linear functional on A.   The reader is warned that this does not agree with general usage which restricts the use of the word distribution to members of a certain subset of $A^\#$.   However, nothing that is said here will have to be unlearned by one who goes further; all theorems are true and all examples and definitions are applicable in the general theory.

Example 1.   For $f \in A$, let $I(f) = \int_{-\infty}^{\infty} f$, $\delta(f) = f(0)$, $H(f) = \int_{0}^{\infty} f$.

Then I, δ, H are distributions; δ is called the Dirac distribution, H the Heaviside distribution.

Let $DA = \{f' : f \in A\}$.   (Here f' is the derivative of f.)

LEMMA 1. $DA = \left\{f : \int_{-\infty}^{\infty} f = 0\right\} = I^{\perp}$.

Suppose first that $f \in DA$; that is, $f = g'$ for some $g \in A$.   Then $\int_{-\infty}^{\infty} f = \lim \int_{-m}^{n} g' = \lim g(n) - g(m) = 0$.   Conversely, if $\int_{-\infty}^{\infty} f = 0$, let $g(x) = \int_{-\infty}^{x} f$.   For sufficiently small x, $g(x) = 0$; for sufficiently large x, $g(x) = \int_{-\infty}^{\infty} f = 0$.   Thus $g \in A$; moreover $f = g'$.//

DEFINITION 1.   *The derivative* F' *of a distribution* F *is defined by* $F'(f) = -F(f')$ *for* $f \in A$.

Example 2.   Let $F(f) = \int_{-\infty}^{\infty} x^3 f(x)\,dx$.   Then $F'(f) = -\int_{-\infty}^{\infty} x^3 f'(x)\,dx = \int_{-\infty}^{\infty} 3x^2 f(x)\,dx$. ⟦Integrate by parts and use the fact that f has compact support.⟧

Example 3. $I' = 0$, $H' = \delta$.   ⟦$H'(f) = -H(f') = -\int_{0}^{\infty} f' = -\lim_{n \to \infty} \int_{0}^{n} f' = \lim f(0) - f(n) = f(0) = \delta(f)$.⟧

We now turn to the problem of integration.   If $G' = F$, we call G a *primitive* of F, and the problem is, given F, to find G.   Now we know how G must be defined on DA, namely, $G(f') = -F(f)$.   Having defined G on DA, a linear subspace of A, we extend it to all of A in any way.   Then $G'(f) = -G(f') = F(f)$ since $f' \in DA$ and so $G' = F$.

It is interesting to ask how many primitives a given distribution has.   Let G_1, G_2 be two primitives of F (that is, $G_1' = G_2' = F$) and let $G = G_1 - G_2$.   Then $G' = 0$, and so for any $f \in A$, $0 = G'(f) = -G(f')$.   Thus G vanishes on DA.   But Lemma 1 says that $DA = I^{\perp}$ and so $G = KI$ for some constant K ⟦Section 10, Corollary 2⟧.   Thus any two primitives of a distribution differ by KI and it is reasonable to write $\int F = G + KI$, where $G' = F$, K is a constant.

Example 4.   Let us evaluate $\int H$.   Calling it G, for $f \in DA$, say $f = g'$, we have $G(f) = -H(g) = -\int_{0}^{\infty} g = -\int_{0}^{\infty} dx \int_{-\infty}^{x} f(t)\,dt = -\int_{0}^{\infty} dx \int_{-\infty}^{\infty} f(t)\,dt + \int_{0}^{\infty} dx \int_{x}^{\infty} f(t)\,dt$. The first integral is 0.   (Keep in mind that because of compact support many of the infinities do not enter.)   The second integral is $\int_{0}^{\infty} f(t)\,dt \int_{0}^{t} dx = \int_{0}^{\infty} tf(t)\,dt$.

We now come to the main idea and motivation, the concept of distribution as generalized function.   In the following discussion $C[R]$ denotes real $C[R]$.   For each continuous real function F of a real variable we define a distribution, calling it F also, by the formula $F(f) = \int_{-\infty}^{\infty} F(x) f(x)\, dx$. (In reality we are defining an isomorphism of $C[R]$ into $A^{\#}$ [Problem 6], but speaking of it as an embedding of $C[R]$ in $A^{\#}$.) Those distributions obtained in this way will be called *functions*.

Example 5: The Dirac delta δ is not a function. [Suppose $F \in C[R]$ satisfies $\int_{-\infty}^{\infty} F(x) f(x)\, dx = f(0)$ for all $f \in A$. For $0 < \epsilon < 1$, define $f_{\epsilon} \in A$ by $f_{\epsilon}(x) = \exp[x^2/(x^2 - \epsilon^2)]$ for $|x| < \epsilon$, 0 for $|x| \geq \epsilon$. Let $M = \max\{|F(x)|: -1 \leq x \leq 1\}$. Then $1 = f_{\epsilon}(0) = \int_{-\epsilon}^{\epsilon} F(x) f_{\epsilon}(x)\, dx \leq M \int_{-\epsilon}^{\epsilon} f_{\epsilon} \leq 2M\epsilon$. This is a contradiction for small ϵ.]

The important observation now is that *if a function is differentiable in the ordinary sense, then it is also differentiable as a distribution, and the results agree.* [For $\int_{-\infty}^{\infty} F'(x) f(x)\, dx = -\int_{-\infty}^{\infty} F(x) f'(x)\, dx = -F(f')$, by integration by parts.]

This simplifies analysis because every function has a derivative. (Its derivative may, however, not be a function.) For example, certain computations with the Dirac distribution may be carried forward rigorously, yielding results that can be formally obtained with the fictitious Dirac delta function.

Example 6: The derivative of $|x|$. Let $F(x) = |x|$. Then $F'(f) = -F(f') =$

$$-\int_{-\infty}^{\infty} |x| f'(x)\, dx = -\int_{-\infty}^{0} x f'(x)\, dx + \int_{0}^{\infty} x f'(x)\, dx = -\int_{-\infty}^{0} f + \int_{0}^{\infty} f =$$

$2H(f) - I(f)$. If we call this distribution sgn, we have the formula $d|x|/dx = \operatorname{sgn} x$.

Finally we notice that the function 1 leads to the distribution I. Thus our earlier result $\int F = G + KI$ may be written $\int F = G + K$, and we have the intuitively appealing statement, two primitives differ by a constant.

Problems on distributions 2.12

1. The Heaviside distribution H is not a function.
2. Show that $H' = \delta$.
3. If F is a function, so is any primitive of F.
4. Check that $f_{\epsilon} \in A$ (see Example 5).
5. The primitives of H are functions.
6. The map from real $C[R]$ to $A^{\#}$ described in the text is an isomorphism into, and is not onto.
7. Show that A'' has codimension 2 in A (see Lemma 1).
8. A distribution F is called *positive* if $F(f) \geq 0$ for all $f \in A$ satisfying $f(t) \geq 0$ for all t. Suppose that F is a function and F'' is positive. Show that F is convex; that is, F satisfies formula (1) of Section 1.4.
9. Show that the derivative of $x^{-1/3}$ is the distribution

$$-\frac{1}{3} \int_{-\infty}^{\infty} x^{-4/3}[f(x) - f(0)]\, dx.$$

3

SEPARATION

3.1 Support

The results of this chapter are used for the first time, in an essential way, in Chapter 12. They are also used to give a brief proof of the Hahn-Banach theorem in Chapter 4; however, another, self-contained, proof of the Hahn-Banach theorem is given for the sake of those who wish to postpone the reading of Chapter 3.

In R^3, a plane tangent to a sphere is said to *support* the sphere. A plane not meeting a given sphere may be found by translating a supporting plane. In this section we generalize and prove results of this nature. The argument begins in a real space, and is later extended to the complex case.

LEMMA 1. *In a real linear space, let* K *be a convex cone which is absorbing at each point of* $K_0 \equiv K \setminus -K$. *Then* K_0 *is absorbing at each of its points.*

It may be that $K = -K$ in which case K_0 is empty. The lemma is then vacuously true.

If one considers $K \cap -K$ a kind of boundary of K, the hypothesis says that K is absorbing at each of its nonboundary points. For example, in R^2 let $K = \{(x, y): y \geq 0\}$.

To prove the result, suppose that K_0 is not absorbing at $a \in K_0$. This means that there exists a vector x such that for all $\epsilon > 0$

$$(1) \qquad \qquad a + tx \notin K_0$$

for some t, $0 < t < \epsilon$. [Section 2.5, Problem 12]. Thus we can choose $t > 0$ so that, simultaneously, relation (1) holds and K is absorbing at $a + tx$ [since K is absorbing at a; see Section 2.6, Fact (vii)]. In particular, $a + tx \in K$ and so from formula (1), $a + tx \in -K$. Since K is absorbing at a point of $-K$, K is the whole space [Section 2.7, Fact (v)]. Thus K_0 is empty.//

LEMMA 2. *Let* A *be a real linear space and* K *a convex cone in* A *such that*

(i) $K \cup -K - A$,
(ii) K *is absorbing at each point of* $K \setminus -K$.

Then $K \cap -K$ *is a maximal subspace of* A, *or is all of* A.

The student should follow the proof with some diagram such as $K =$ the upper half-plane in R^2.

Let $S = K \cap - K$. S is a subspace [Section 2.7, Fact (ii)]. If S is not all of A, we may find $b \in K \setminus - K$ [since, otherwise $K \subset - K$ and so $S = A$ by assumption (i)]. The proof will be concluded by showing that $b \oplus S$ is all of A. Now A can be separated into three parts, S, $K \setminus S$, and $(- K) \setminus S$ by assumption (i). Obviously $S \subset b \oplus S$, and each of the remaining two sets is the negative of the other. Since $b \oplus S$ is a subspace, it will be sufficient to prove $(- K) \setminus S \subset b \oplus S$. To this end, let $x \in (- K) \setminus S = (- K) \setminus K$.

We apply Section 2.5, Corollary 4 to the line B passing through b and x, and conclude by Lemma 1 that it meets each of $K \setminus - K$, $- K \setminus K$ in an open subset of B (in the sense explained in Section 2.5). These two sets include b, x respectively, so they are not empty. Hence their union does not exhaust the connected set B. This means that there is a point $z \in B \cap S$. Such z is $tb + (1 - t)x$ for some real t which is not 1 since $b \notin S$. Hence $x = [1/(1 - t)]z - [t/(1 - t)]b \in b \oplus S.//$

Example 1. It is instructive to observe the role played by assumption (ii). Let K be the right half plane $(x > 0)$ in R^2 together with the positive Y axis and the origin. Then K is not absorbing at points of the positive Y axis; assumption (ii) is false, as is the conclusion of the lemma. (A casual remark: K is the positive cone for the lexicographic order in R^2; see Section 1.5, Example 2, and Section 2.7, Problem 21). Another example of this nature is the dense cone, which does not satisfy the conclusion of Lemma 2.

DEFINITION 1. *A set* K *is said to lie on one side of a maximal subspace* S *of a real linear space if there exists a linear functional* f *such that* $f^\perp = $ S *and* f(a) ≥ 0 *for all* a $\in$ K. *It is said to lie strictly on one side if there exists* $\epsilon > 0$ *such that* f(a) $\geq \epsilon$ *for all* a $\in$ K.

Thus S lies on one side of S (but not strictly), as does any subset of S. In R^2, the circle of center $(0, - 5)$ and radius 2 lies strictly on one side of the X axis since we may choose $f(x, y) = - y$, $\epsilon = 1$.

LEMMA 3. *Let* B *be a convex subset of a real linear space. Suppose that* B *is not absorbing at 0 but is absorbing at some point* a. *Then there exists a maximal subspace* S *such that* B *lies on one side of it.*

In brief, we take the largest convex cone including B but not containing $- a$. Lemma 2 will then yield S as the intersection of this cone with its negative. The details follow:

(i) For all $t > 0$, $- a \notin tB$. [If $- a \in tB$ for some $t > 0$, 0 lies on the line segment[t] joining $(- a)/t$ to a and so B is absorbing at 0 by Section 2.6, Fact (iii). This contradicts the hypothesis.]

(ii) Let Q be the class of all convex cones each of which includes B and does not contain $- a$. Q is not empty since $\cup \{tB: t \geq 0\} \in Q$ [see Section 2.7, Fact (iv)]. Order Q by containment; it contains a maximal chain. Let the union of this maximal chain be K. K is a cone. [If $t > 0$, we can prove that $tK \subset K$ by the following argument: let $k \in K$; then k belongs to one of the cones in the chain and so tk belongs to that cone; hence $tk \in K$.] K is convex. [We can prove that $K + K \subset K$ by the following argument: let $k_1, k_2 \in K$; then there exist cones K_1, K_2 in the chain with $k_1 \in K_1$, $k_2 \in K_2$; since Q is a chain, one of these two cones includes the other; hence one of then contains both k_1 and k_2, hence, since it is a convex cone, it contains $k_1 + k_2$. Thus $k_1 + k_2 \in K$.⟧ Since we wish to apply Lemma 2, we now turn to its hypotheses.

(iii) $K \cup - K$ is the whole space. ⟦Let b be a vector which is not in K. The cone generated by K, b (Section 2.7, Problem 13) is a convex cone properly including K, hence it includes $- a$ since otherwise we could adjoin it to Q, contradicting the maximality of Q. This shows that for some $t > 0$, $k \in K$, we have $- a = k + tb$. But then $- b = (1/t)(a + k) \subset (1/t)(K + K) \subset (1/t)K \subset K$. Hence $b \in - K$.⟧

(iv) K is absorbing at each point which is not in $- K$. ⟦Let $b \in K \setminus - K$. Thus $b \notin - K$, and so $- b \notin K$. Since $- b \notin K$, we run through the proof of (iii) replacing b by $- b$, and obtain $- a = k + t(- b)$ for some $t > 0$, $k \in K$. Thus $tb = a + k$ and so $\frac{1}{2}tb = \frac{1}{2}(a + k)$ lies on the line segment joining a and k. Since B is absorbing at a, K is too. Moreover $k \in K$ and so K is absorbing at $\frac{1}{2}tb$, by Section 2.6, Fact (iii). Thus $(2/t)K$ is absorbing at b. But $(2/t)K \subset K$, hence K is absorbing at b.⟧

(v) Lemma 2 now shows that $K \cap - K$ is a maximal subspace. ⟦It is not the whole space since $- a \notin K$.⟧ Thus there exists a linear functional f with $f^\perp = K \cap - K$ and $f(a) = 1$. It follows that $f(b) \geq 0$ for all $b \in B$. ⟦Suppose, on the contrary, that $f(b) < 0$ for some $b \in B$. Observe that $- a = [b/f(b) - a] + b/[- f(b)]$. The first term on the right belongs to $f^\perp$, hence to K. The second term on the right belongs to K since it is a positive multiple of b, and $b \in K$. Thus $- a \in K + K \subset K$, a false conclusion.⟧//

In a finite-dimensional space it would be unnecessary, in Lemma 3, to assume that B is somewhere absorbing ⟦Problems 4 and 6⟧. In general this assumption cannot be dropped ⟦Problem 7⟧.

LEMMA 4. *Let* a, B, S *be as in Lemma 3. Let* f *be the (unique) linear functional such that* $f^\perp = S$, $f(a) = 1$. *Then* $f(b) > 0$ *for each* b *at which* B *is absorbing.*

Here, $f(b)$ is interior to $f[B]$ ⟦Section 2.5, Corollary 1⟧ which, in turn, is a subset of the nonnegative reals ⟦Part (v) in the proof of Lemma 3⟧.//

We now extend these results to a general (complex) linear space.

LEMMA 5. *Let* K *be a convex subset of a linear space such that* K *is absorbing at all its points and* $0 \notin K$. *Then there exists a maximal subspace not meeting* K.

Lemmas 3 and 4 provide that there exists a maximal real linear subspace S which does not meet K. The subspace S includes a maximal subspace ⟦Section 2.11, Theorem 3⟧.//

THEOREM 1. *Let* K *be a convex subset of a linear space* A *such that* K *is absorbing at all its points. Let* S *be an affine set not meeting* K. *Then* S *can be extended to (that is,* S *is a subset of) a hyperplane not meeting* K.

Suppose first that S is a subspace. (We shall now make use of the quotient space A/S. If the student wishes, he may avoid this by referring to Section 2.8, Theorem 1 and taking A_1 instead of A/S.) Recall the canonical homomorphism $\phi: A \to A/S$, and the Facts (Section 2.5) connecting linear maps and the properties, convex and absorbing. First, $\phi[K]$ is convex and absorbing at all its points since ϕ is linear and onto. Moreover $0 \notin \phi[K]$ since $\phi^{-1}[\{0\}] = S$ does not meet K. Thus, by Lemma 5, there exists a maximal subspace T of A/S which does not meet $\phi[K]$. $\phi^{-1}[T]$ is a maximal subspace ⟦Section 2.10, Theorem

6], includes S [since $\phi[S] = \{0\} \subset T$], and does not meet K [since $\phi\phi^{-1}[T] = T$ does not meet $\phi[K]$]. This completes the proof in the case, S is a subspace. For an arbitrary affine set S we have $S = a + S_0$ for some subspace S_0 and $a \in S$. Using the first part of the proof, we extend S_0 to a maximal subspace S_1 not meeting $K - a$. Then $a + S_1$, is a hyperplane including S and not meeting K.//

Problems 3.1

1. Let K be the open sphere in R^3 given by $\{(x, y, z): x^2 + y^2 + (z - 3)^2 < 1\}$. Carry out the construction of Lemma 3, proceeding through the various steps. From your construction obtain at least two maximal subspaces not meeting K.

2. Extend the line $(y = x + 1, z = 0)$ to a hyperplane not meeting the set K in Problem 1.

3. Where does the proof of Lemma 2 break down in an attempt to apply it to K in Example 1.

4. A set is called *relatively absorbing* if it is absorbing in its span. Let K be a convex subset of a real linear space which is relatively absorbing at all its points and with $0 \notin K$. Show that K lies strictly on one side of some maximal subspace.

5. Extend Theorem 1 by inserting "relatively" before "absorbing" as in Problem 4.

6. A convex set in a finite dimensional space is relatively somewhere absorbing.

7. The dense cone does not lie on one side of any hyperplane; that is, every linear functional not identically zero must, for any real number t, have values on it both greater than and less than t. [If $f(\delta^n) \neq 0$, $f(u\delta^n + \delta^{n+1})$ may have any value by suitable choice of u.]

8. Prove Lemma 2 in the complex case. [Section 2.7, Problem 28 may be useful.]

9. In part (v) of the proof of Lemma 3, show that $f(b) \geq 0$ for all $b \in B$ by noting that $f[K \setminus - K]$ is convex [Section 2.7, Problem 28; Section 2.5, Theorem 2] and not absorbing at 0.

3.2 Separation

A generalization of the problem of finding a supporting hyperplane for a set is that of passing a hyperplane between two sets.

DEFINITION 1. *Two sets, S, T are said to be separated by a linear functional* f *if* f $\neq 0$ *and there exists a real number* t *such that* Rf(a) $\leq$ t $\leq$ Rf(b) *for all* a $\in$ S, b $\in$ T *or such that* Rf(a) $\geq$ t $\geq$ Rf(b) *for all* a $\in$ S, b $\in$ T. *They are said to be strictly separated if there exists* ϵ > 0 *such that* Rf(a) $\leq$ t $- \epsilon <$ t $+ \epsilon \leq$ Rf(b) *for all* a $\in$ S, b $\in$ T, *or a similar modification of the alternative condition.*

Of course, in a real linear space, the designation R, for real part, may be dropped. If S, T are separated by f, we say that they *lie on opposite sides of* the real hyperplane $H = (Rf = t)$; *strictly on opposite sides of* H if the separation is strict. The language used in these definitions is modified for convenience. We use: S, T are separated by H; S is separated from T by f; H separates S, T; and other, similar variants of obvious meaning.

Warning. We speak of separation by a real hyperplane, but not by a hyperplane, since the extension of a hyperplane to a real hyperplane is not unique. For example, in E, a hyperplane, being a point, can be extended to an arbitrary line through the point. Although one could define separation by a hyperplane, it is not worth the trouble.

Observe that S is separated from 0 if and only if there exists a maximal real linear subspace such that S lies on one side of it. Observe also that nondisjoint sets may possibly be separated; for example, the intervals $[0, 1]$, $[1, 2]$ of R are separated by the hyperplane $\{1\}$, and by f given by $f(x) = x$ for $x \in R$.

Example 1. Let S be the subset of R^2 (or E) consisting of $\{(x, y): xy \geq 1, x \geq 0\}$, and let X be the X axis, $\{(x, y): y = 0\}$. These are disjoint closed convex sets. Then X is a real hyperplane which separates S, X. [Defining f on R^2 by $f(x, y) = y$ we have $X = f^\perp$ and $f(a) \geq 0 \geq f(b)$ for all $a \in S$, $b \in X$.] The sets cannot be strictly separated. [If g is any linear functional on R^2, $g(x, y) = ux + vy$ for some fixed scalars u, v. If $u \neq 0$, $g[X] = R$ which meets $g[S]$, while if $u = 0$, $v \neq 0$, then g vanishes on X and, for strict separation we would need $0 \leq t - \epsilon < t + \epsilon \leq vy$ for all $y \in S$, (or the same with the inequalities reversed). This is clearly impossible.]

Facts

(i) Let S, T be subsets of a real linear space, and suppose that there exists a linear functional f such that $u \equiv \inf \{f(b): b \in T\} > v \equiv \sup \{f(a): a \in S\}$. Then S, T are strictly separated by f.

(ii) With S, T as in Fact (i), suppose that a linear functional f exists such that for some $t > 0$, $f(b) - f(a) \geq t$ for all $b \in T$, $a \in S$. Then S, T are strictly separated by f.

(iii) In Facts (i) and (ii), "real" may be omitted, and "f" replaced by "Rf."

(iv) Two sets in a linear space can be separated if and only if they can be separated in the associated real linear space. The same is true for strict separation.

(v) Let S, T be subsets of a linear space, then S, T can be separated (or separated strictly) if and only if $T - S$, $\{0\}$ can be separated (separated strictly).

Proofs

(i) Let $t = \frac{1}{2}(u + v)$, $\epsilon = \frac{1}{2}(u - v)$. Then for all $a \in S$, $b \in T$, $f(a) \leq v = t - \epsilon < t + \epsilon = u \leq f(b)$.

(ii) Inf $\{f(b): b \in T\} - \sup \{f(a): a \in S\} = \inf \{f(b) - f(a): b \in T, a \in S\}$ [Section 1.1, Problems 2, 3] $\geq t$. The result now follows from Fact (i).

(iii) This is obvious.

(iv) If the sets are separated by f in A, Rf separates them in A_R, the associated real linear space. Conversely, if g separates them in A_R, let $f = g + ih$ be linear [Section 2.11, Theorem 1]; then f separates them in A [since $g = Rf$].

(v) By Fact (iv), we may assume that the space is a real linear space. Suppose first that S, T are strictly separated. Then there exist a linear functional f and real numbers t, ϵ with $\epsilon > 0$ such that $f(a) \leq t - \epsilon < t + \epsilon \leq f(b)$ for all $a \in S$, $b \in T$. For $x \in T - S$, we have $f(x) \geq 2\epsilon$ [since $f(b - a) = f(b) - f(a) \geq (t + \epsilon) - (t - \epsilon) = 2\epsilon$]. Thus $f(x) \geq \epsilon + \epsilon > \epsilon - \epsilon = f(0)$. This shows that $T - S$ is strictly separated from $\{0\}$.

Conversely, if $T - S$ is strictly separated from $\{0\}$, there exist a linear functional f, and scalars t, ϵ with $\epsilon > 0$ such that $f(x) \geq t + \epsilon > t - \epsilon \geq f(0)$ for all $x \in T - S$. Then for $a \in S$, $b \in T$ we have $f(b) - f(a) = f(b - a) \geq t + \epsilon > t - \epsilon \geq f(0) = 0$, thus $t \geq \epsilon > 0$ and $f(b) - f(a) > t$. By Fact (ii), S, T are strictly separated.

The proof for (not necessarily strict) separations is similar but easier [take $\epsilon = 0$].//

THEOREM 1. *Let* S, T *be convex sets and assume that* T *is somewhere absorbing but that* T *is not absorbing at any point of* S *(for example, if* S, T *are disjoint). Then* S, T *can be separated.*

The set $T - S$ is convex [Section 2.6, Fact (i)], somewhere absorbing [Section 2.5, Problem 7], but not absorbing at 0 [Section 2.6, Fact (iv)]. Thus, by Section 1, Lemma 3, there exists a maximal subspace not meeting $T - S$; that is, $T - S$ can be separated from $\{0\}$. The result follows from Fact (v).//

The hypothesis that T is somewhere absorbing cannot be dropped [$S = \{0\}$, $T =$ the dense cone; see Section 1, Problem 7].

THEOREM 2. *Let* S, T, *be convex sets and* G *a convex set which is absorbing at* 0, *such that* S + G *does not meet* T. *Then* S, T *can be strictly separated.*

Fact (iv) allows us to assume that the space is a real linear space. $(T - S) - G$ is somewhere absorbing [Section 2.5, Problem 7], is convex [Section 2.6, Fact (i)], and does not contain 0 [by hypothesis, $T - S$ does not meet G]; hence there is a maximal subspace not meeting $(T - S) - G$ [Section 1, Lemma 3]. In other words, there exists a linear functional f, $f \neq 0$, with $f(x) \geq 0$ for all $x \in (T - S) - G$. There exists $g \in G$ such that $f(g) > 0$ [since $f[G]$ is, by Section 2.5, Theorem 2, an absorbing subset of R]; thus, for all $a \in S$, $b \in T$, $f(b) - f(a) = f(b - a - g) + f(g) \geq f(g)$. Fact (ii) provides that S, T are strictly separated.//

The hypothesis that G is somewhere absorbing cannot be dropped. [Take $G = \{0\}$ and S, T disjoint convex sets which cannot be separated, as given above, following Theorem 1.]

Problems 3.2

In this list, S, T are sets in a linear space, and f is a linear functional defined on the space.

1. Suppose that S, T lie on opposite sides of each of two parallel hyperplanes [that is, $(f = u)$, $(f = v)$, with $u \neq v$]. Show that S, T can be strictly separated.

2. In R^2, the sets $\{(x, t): xy > 1, x \geq 0\}$ and $\{(x, y): xy < -1, x \geq 0\}$ can be separated, but not strictly.

3. Suppose that for all $a \in S$, $b \in T$, $Rf(a) \leq Rf(b)$. Show that S, T can be separated.

4. If, in Problem 3, "$\leq$" is replaced by "$<$," can we conclude that the separation can be made strict?

5. Suppose that for all $a \in S$, $b \in T$, $Rf(a) \leq u < Rf(b)$. Show that $Rf(x) < u$ if S is absorbing at x.

6. Prove a converse of Theorem 2; that is, if S, T are strictly separated, a set G with the given properties can be found.

7. Suppose that S, T are disjoint convex sets, each of which is the convex hull of a finite set. Show that S, T can be separated.

8. Give a reasonable definition of "separation by a hyperplane" in the complex case.

4

PARANORMS AND SEMINORMS

4.1 Paranorms

The concept of paranorm is a generalization of that of absolute value.   The paranorm of x may be thought of as the distance from x to 0.

DEFINITION 1.   *A paranorm is a real function* p *defined on a linear space, and satisfying Conditions* (i) *through* (v) *for all vectors* a, b,

(i) $p(0) = 0$

(ii) $p(a) \geq 0$

(iii) $p(-a) = p(a)$

(iv) $p(a + b) \leq p(a) + p(b)$ *(the triangular inequality)*

(v) *if* $\{t_n\}$ *is a sequence of scalars with* $t_n \to t$ *and* $\{a_n\}$ *is a sequence of vectors with* 0, *then* $p(t_n a_n - ta) \to 0$ *(continuity of multiplication).*

★*Example 1.*   For $a \in E$, define $p(a) = |a|$.

★*Example 2.*   For $a \in E$, define $p(a) = |a|/(1 + |a|)$
    To prove Condition (iv), for any complex numbers a, b, we have

$$\frac{|a + b|}{1 + |a + b|} = (|a + b|^{-1} + 1)^{-1} \leq [(|a| + |b|)^{-1} + 1]^{-1}$$

$$= \frac{|a|}{1 + |a| + |b|} + \frac{|b|}{1 + |a| + |b|} \leq \frac{|a|}{1 + |a|} + \frac{|b|}{1 + |b|}$$

Notice that $p(a) < 1$ for all $a \in E$.

A paranorm p for which $p(a) = 0$ implies $a = 0$ will be called *total*.   This agrees with the use of total in Section 2.4.

★*Example 3.*   For $a \in l^p$, $0 < p < 1$, define $q(a) = \Sigma_{k=1}^{\infty} |a_k|^p$.   Then q is a paranorm. The triangular inequality is Minkowski's inequality for $0 < p < 1$ 〚Section 1.4〛.   Next, for any sequence $\{a_n\}$ of points in l^p with $q(a_n - a) \to 0$ and $\{t_n\}$ of scalars with $t_n \to t$, we have $q(t_n a_n - ta) = q[(t_n - t)a_n + t(a_n - a)] \leq q[(t_n - t)a_n] + q[t(a_n - a)] = |t_n - t|^p q(a_n) + |t|^p q(a_n - a) \to 0$. (We used the fact that $\{q(a_n)\}$ is bounded $[\![q(a_n) \leq q(a) + q(a_n - a)]\!]$.)

DEFINITION 2. *For any two paranorms* p, q, p *is stronger than* q *and* q *is weaker than* p *if, whenever* $\{a_n\}$ *is a sequence such that* $p(a_n) \to 0$, *then also* $q(a_n) \to 0$. *If each is stronger than the other* p *and* q *are said to be equivalent; otherwise one is strictly stronger and one is strictly weaker.*

Remark. If p is stronger than q, then $p^\perp \subset q^\perp$ $[\![$for if $p(a) = 0$, application of the definition to the sequence $\{a, a, \ldots\}$ yields $q(a) = 0]\!]$.

★*Example 4.* Define p, q, r on R^2 by $p(x, y) = |x| + |y|$, $q(x, y) = |x|/(1 + |x|) + |y|$, $r(x, y) = |x|$. Here p is strictly stronger than r $[\![$since $p(a) \geq r(a)$ for all a, and since $r(0, 1) = 0 \neq p(0, 1)]\!]$; q is strictly stronger than r $[\![$for if $q(x_n, y_n) \to 0$, it follows that $|x_n|/(1 + |x_n|) \to 0$, hence that $|x_n| \to 0$; but, $r(0, 1) = 0 \neq q(0, 1)]\!]$. Also p, q are equivalent.

If we set $h(x, y) = |y|$, r, h are *noncomparable;* that is, h is not stronger than r and r is not stronger than h $[\![h^\perp$ x is not included in $r^\perp$ and $r^\perp$ is not included in $h^\perp]\!]$.

Facts

In this list A is a linear space; a, b, a_n are vectors; t, t_n are scalars; p, q, are paranorms.

(i) $p(a - b) \geq |p(a) - p(b)|$

(ii) For any positive integer n, $p(na) \leq np(a)$, $p(a/n) \geq p(a)/n$.

(iii) If $\{t_n\}$ is bounded, and $p(a_n) \to 0$, then $p(t_n a_n) \to 0$.

(iv) $p^\perp$ is a linear subspace of A; however $(p = t)$ need not be an affine set.

(v) For any a, p is constant on the affine set $a + p^\perp$.

(vi) If there exists a number M such that $q(a) \leq Mp(a)$, then p is stronger than q. The converse is false.

(vii) Suppose that p is zero on a linear subspace S and that $p(a + S)$ is defined to be $p(a)$ as in Section 2.8. Then p is a paranorm on A/S; p is total on $A/p^\perp$.

(viii) Suppose that p, q are both zero on a linear subspace S and that p is stronger than q on A/S. Then p is stronger than q.

(ix) The set $(p < \epsilon)$ is absorbing for each $\epsilon > 0$.

Proofs

(i) $p(a) \leq p(a + b) + p(-b) = p(a + b) + p(b)$, thus $p(a) - p(b) \leq p(a + b)$. By symmetry, $p(b) - p(a) \leq p(a + b)$.

(ii) $p(na) = p(a + a + \cdots + a) \leq p(a) + \cdots + p(a) = np(a)$. From this, $np(a/n) \geq p(n \cdot a/n) = p(a)$.

(iii) If the result is false, there exists $\epsilon > 0$ such that $p(t_n a_n) \geq \epsilon$ for infinitely many n. From these values of n, extract a subsequence $\{n(k)\}$ such that $t_{n(k)} \to$ some limit t. Then $p(a_{k(n)}) \to 0$, $p(t_{k(n)} a_{k(n)}) \to 0$, but $p(t_{k(n)} a_{k(n)}) \geq \epsilon$.

(iv) Suppose that $a \in p^\perp$. For any scalar t, $p(ta) = 0$. [Let $t_n = t$, and let $a_n = a$ for $n = 1, 2, \ldots$. Then $p(a_n) \to 0$ [indeed $p(a_n) = 0$] thus $p(t_n a_n - t \cdot 0) \to 0$; that is, $p(ta) = 0$.] Moreover, if a, $b \in p^\perp$, $p(a + b) \leq p(a) + p(b) = 0$. Thus $a + b \in p^\perp$. An example in which $(p = 1)$ is not affine is given by $p(a) = |a|$, for $a \in E$.

(v) Let $b \in a + p^\perp$. Then $|p(b) - p(a)| \leq p(b - a)$ [Fact (i)] $= 0$, since $b - a \in p^\perp$.

(vi) If $p(a_n) \to 0$, then $q(a_n) \to 0$. That the converse is false is shown by Example 2 in which q is stronger than r, but for any constant M, $r(x, 0) = |x| > M > M |x|/(1 + |x|) = Mq(x, 0)$ if $|x| > M$.

(vii) Checking the five parts of the definition of paranorm, we have $p(0 + S) = p(0) = 0$, $p(a + S) = p(a) \geq 0$, $p(-a + S) = p(-a) = p(a) = p(a + S)$, $p(a + S + b + S) = p(a + b + S) = p(a + b) \leq p(a) + p(b) = p(a + S) + p(b + S)$, $p[t_n(a_n + S) - t(a + S)] = p(t_n a_n - ta) \to 0$. Finally, with $S = p^\perp$, if $p(a + S) = 0$, then $p(a) = 0$ so that $a \in S$ and $a + S = S$. Thus p is total.

(viii) Suppose that $p(a_n) \to 0$. Then $p(a_n + S) \to 0$, hence $q(a_n + S) \to 0$; that is, $q(a_n) \to 0$.

(ix) Let a be an arbitrary vector. If a is not absorbed by $(p < \epsilon)$, there exists a sequence $\{t_n\}$ of scalars with $|t_n| \to \infty$, $a \notin t_n(p < \epsilon)$; that is, $a/t_n \notin (p < \epsilon)$. But this means that $p(a/t_n) \geq \epsilon$, contradicting part of the definition of paranorm.//

A valuable method of forming a paranorm from a sequence of paranorms will now be given. Its importance lies, not in its form, which could be altered [Problems 19 and 20], but in Property (2) given in Theorem 1. Usually one need only remember that a paranorm with this property exists.

THEOREM 1.   *Let $\{p_n\}$ be a sequence of paranorms on a linear space.   Let*

$$(1) \qquad p(a) = \sum_{k=1}^{\infty} \frac{1}{2^k} \cdot \frac{p_k(a)}{1 + p_k(a)} \qquad (\text{Fréchet combination of } \{p_n\}).$$

Then

(a) *p is a paranorm and satisfies*

$$(2) \qquad p(a_n) \to 0 \text{ if and only if } p_k(a_n) \to 0 \text{ for each k.}$$

(b) *p is the weakest paranorm which is stronger than every p_k.*
(c) *p is total if and only if $\{p_k\}$ is a total set.*

The result also applies to a finite collection of paranorms, since we may take all but a finite number of the p_k to be identically zero. The factors 2^{-k} ensure convergence of the series; they could be replaced by $1/k!$, for example. The first three parts of the definition of paranorm are trivially true of p. Next, as in Example 2, we have

$$\frac{p_k(a + b)}{1 + p_k(a + b)} \leq \frac{p_k(a)}{1 + p_k(a)} + \frac{p_k(b)}{1 + p_k(b)}.$$

Multiplying by 2^{-k} and summing yields the triangular inequality.

The last part of the definition of paranorm will follow from statement (2) since each p_k is a paranorm.

To prove statement (2), assume first that $p(a_n) \to 0$. For each k, n,

$$p(a_n) \geq \frac{1}{2^k} \frac{p_k(a_n)}{1 + p_k(a_n)}.$$

Multiplying by the denominator on the right and transposing, we obtain $2^k p(a_n) \geq p_k(a_n)[1 - 2^k p(a_n)]$. From this, $p_k(a_n) \to 0$ as $n \to \infty$.

Conversely, assume that $p_k(a_n) \to 0$ for each k. For any m,

$$p(a_n) \leq \sum_{k=1}^{m} \frac{1}{2^k} \cdot \frac{p_k(a_n)}{1 + p_k(a_n)} + \sum_{k=m+1}^{\infty} \frac{1}{2^k} \to 2^{-m} \text{ as } n \to \infty.$$

Since m is arbitrary, it follows that $p(a_n) \to 0$.

Part (*b*) is proved by the observation that p is stronger than every p_k [statement (2)] and that if q is a paranorm stronger than every p_k, then $q(a_n) \to 0$ implies $p_k(a_n) \to 0$ for every k and so, by (2), $p(a_n) \to 0$. Thus q is stronger than p.

Part (c) is trivial.//

★*Example 5.* For $a \in s$, define $p_k(a) = |a_k|$ for $k = 1, 2, \ldots$. This gives s a total paranorm by means of equation (1).

★*Example 6.* For $a \in E_c$, $k = 1, 2, \ldots$, define $p_k(a) = \max \{|a(z)|: |z| \leq k\}$. This gives E_c a total paranorm by means of equation (1). In fact, each p_k is total.

Problems 4.1

In this list, p, q are paranorms on a linear space, unless otherwise specified.

1. Show that $|x|^p + |y|^p$, $0 < p < 1$, defines a paranorm on R^2.

★2. If $p(a - b) = 0$, then $p(a) = p(b)$, but not conversely.

★3. If $p(a) = 0$, then $p(a + b) = p(b)$ for all b.

4. Does $h(x + iy) = |x|$ define a paranorm on E? [No].

★5. Let A be a linear space. For $a \in A$, define $q(a) = 1$ if $a \neq 0$, $q(0) = 0$. Show that q is not a paranorm.

6. Let q be a real function on a linear space satisfying Definition 1, Parts (i), (ii), (iii), (iv), and the condition $q(a_n) \to 0$ implies $q(t_n a_n) \to 0$ for every $\{t_n\}$. Show that q need not be a paranorm. [Problem 5].

7. In Definition 1, Part (v) may be replaced by the pair of assumptions $p(a_n - a) \to 0$, $t_n \to 0$ imply $p(t_n a_n) \to 0$, and $p(a_n) \to 0$ implies $p(ta_n) \to 0$ for each t. (A further weakening of the assumptions is given in Section 11.2, Problem 24.)

8. In Definition 1, Part (v) may be replaced by the pair of assumptions $p(a_n) \to 0$, $t_n \to t$ imply $p(t_n a_n) \to 0$ and $t_n \to 0$ implies $p(t_n a) \to 0$ for each a.

9. If $p(a) \neq 0$ and $p(ta) = 0$, then $t = 0$.

10. Prove the converse of Fact (viii)

★11. Show that $(p < \epsilon)$ is absorbing at all its points.

12. A paranorm on E is either total or identically zero. [Fact iv.]

13. If p is a total paranorm, and q is stronger than p, then q is also total.

14. If p is a total paranorm, so is $p + q$, and $p + q$ is stronger than p.

15. Let p, q be paranorms. Show that $p + q$ is equivalent to q if and only if q is stronger than p.

16. Let p be a paranorm.   Then, p, $p/(1 + p)$, p^r $(0 < r \leq 1)$, tp (t a positive scalar), $p \wedge 1$ are all paranorms and are all equivalent.   ($f \wedge g$ is defined by $(f \wedge g)(a) = \min \{f(a), g(a)\}$.)

17. Show that the following do not define paranorms on R^2: $(x^2 - y^2)^{1/2}$, $(x^3 - y^3)^{1/3}$.

18. For $a \in E^{\infty}$, $a \neq 0$, let $g(a) = |a_m|$ where a_m is the last nonzero term of a, and $g(0) = 0$. Show that g is not a paranorm.

19. Show that in Theorem 1, $p = \Sigma\ (p_k \wedge 2^{-k})$ also satisfies the conclusions of the theorem.

20. Show that in Theorem 1, $p(a) = \inf\ \{\Sigma_{k=1}^n p_k(a) + 1/n\colon n = 1, 2, \ldots\}$ also satisfies the conclusions of the theorem.

21. Define p as in Section 2.4, Problem 31, and assume $p(x) > 0$ for all $x \neq 0$.   Show that p is a total paranorm on R.

22. Give an example of a paranorm for R which is not monotone on $[0, \infty)$.   [Problem 21]

4.2   Seminorms

A seminorm is a paranorm which has an additional homogeneity property.

DEFINITION 1.   *A seminorm is a real function*, p, *defined on a linear space and satisfying, for all vectors* a, b, *scalar* t,

(i)   p(a) $\geq$ 0,
(ii)   p(a + b) $\leq$ p(a) + p(b) (*the triangular inequality*),
(iii)   p(ta) = |t|p(a) (*homogeneity*).

A norm is a total seminorm.

A norm p satisfies $p(a) > 0$ if $a \neq 0$.

A seminorm is a paranorm.   [The first four parts of the definition of paranorm are trivial. The last part follows from $p(t_n a_n - ta) = p[t_n(a_n - a) + (t_n - t)a] \leq |t_n| p(a_n - a) + |t_n - t| p(a) \to 0$ if $t_n \to t$, $p(a_n - a) \to 0$.]

★*Example 1.*   For any linear functional f, define $p(a) = |f(a)|$.   Then p is a seminorm which is never a norm (except when the space is one- or zero-dimensional).

★*Example 2.*   Define the norm p on $B_1[X]$ by $p(a) = \sup\ \{|a(x)\colon x \in X\}$.   Then, for example, $p(a + b) \leq \sup\ (|a(x)| + |b(x)|) \leq \sup |a(x)| + \sup |b(x)| = p(a) + p(b)$.

★*Example 3.*   Define the norm q on l^p, $p \geq 1$, by $q(a) = \{\Sigma |a_n|^p\}^{1/p}$.   The triangular inequality is Minkowski's inequality, Section 1.4.

The differences in behavior caused by the homogeneity of seminorms are outlined in the following list of facts, all of which fail for paranorms in general [except for sufficiency in Fact (v)].

Facts

In this list, p, q are seminorms and f is a linear functional on a linear space A.

(i) Suppose that p is bounded on an affine set S.   Then p is constant on S, and zero on the linear subspace, $S - S$, of which S is a translate.   In particular, if p is bounded on a linear subspace, it vanishes there.   A norm cannot be bounded on any affine set with more than one point.

(ii) Suppose that $R[f(a)] \leq p(a)$ for all a.   Then $|f(a)| \leq p(a)$ for all a.

(iii) Suppose that $(p < 1) \cap (f = 1)$.   Then $|f(a)| \leq p(a)$ for all a.   The converse is also true.

(iv) If $p(a) < 1$ implies $q(a) \leq 1$ for all a, then $p(a) \geq q(a)$ for all a.   In other words, $(p < 1) \subset (q \leq 1)$ implies $p \geq q$.

(v) p is stronger than q if and only if there exists a constant M such that $q(a) \leq Mp(a)$ for all a.

(vi) If q is bounded on $(p < 1)$, then p is stronger than q.

Proofs

(i) Suppose first that S is a linear subspace.   If there exists $a \in S$ with $p(a) \neq 0$, p is unbounded on S, since for any scalar t, $ta \in S$ and $p(ta) = |t|p(a)$.

Next, let S be an affine set.   If p is bounded on S, it is surely bounded on $S - S$ [since $p(a - b) \leq p(a) + p(b)$].   Hence p is zero on $S - S$, as just proved, since $S - S$ is a linear subspace [Section 2.6, Theorem 2].   By Section 1, Fact (v), p is constant on S, since S is a translate of $S - S \subset p^{\perp}$.   (That this result fails for paranorms is shown by Section 1, Example 2.)

(ii) Let a be a vector, then $f(a) = re^{i\Theta}$ with r, Θ real.   Then $f(ae^{-i\Theta}) = r$ is real and so is less than or equal to $p(ae^{-i\Theta}) = p(a)$; that is, $r \leq p(a)$.   But $r = |f(a)|$.   (The same proof was used in Section 2.11, Theorem 2.)   [For paranorms, take $p(z) = |x| + |y|/(1 + |y|)$ for $z = x + iy \in E$, and $f(z) = z$.]

(iii) If for some a, $|f(a)| > p(a)$, then $a/f(a) \in (p < 1) \cap (f = 1)$.   [For paranorms, let $p(x) = (|x|)^{1/2}$, $f(x) = \frac{1}{2}x$ for $x \in R$.]

(iv) If there exists a such that $p(a) < q(a)$, choose a number t satisfying $p(a) < t < q(a)$. Then $p(a/t) < 1$, but $q(a/t) > 1$, contradicting the hypotheses.

(v) If M exists, this was proved in Section 1, Fact (vi).   Now suppose that p is stronger than q.   If no such M exists, for each positive integer n there exists a_n such that $q(a_n) > n^2 p(a_n)$.   Now $p(a_n) \neq 0$ for each n [for if $p(a_n) = 0$ then $q(a_n) = 0$ by Section 1, Remark on Definition 2].   Then with $b_n = a_n/np(a_n)$ we have $p(b_n) = 1/n \to 0$, $q(b_n) > n \to \infty$. Thus p is not stronger than q.   [For paranorms, see Section 1, Fact (vi).]

(vi) Suppose that $q \leq M$ on $(p < 1)$.   If $M \neq 0$, apply Fact (iv) to q/M yielding $q(a) \leq Mp(a)$ for all a.   Thus by Fact (v), p is stronger than q.   If $M = 0$, we have $q^{\perp} \supset (p < 1)$.   But $(p < 1)$ is absorbing [Section 1, Fact (ix)] and $q^{\perp}$ is a linear subspace [Section 1, Fact (iv)].   Hence $q^{\perp}$ is the whole space; that is, $q = 0$.//

As might be expected from examination of $(x^2 + y^2)^{1/2}$ in R^2, there is a strong connection between seminorms and spheres centered at 0.   In a linear space in general, the concept of sphere has no obvious meaning, but certainly a balloon, being convex, balanced, and absorbing, resembles our intuitive idea of a sphere.   It is rather easy to see that $(p < 1)$ $(p \leq 1)$ are balloons [Theorem 1], but it is not trivial that every balloon can be obtained from a seminorm in a similar way.   To describe how this is done, we give a procedure for constructing a seminorm from a given balloon B.   The seminorm is called the *Minkowski gauge*, or, simply, the *gauge* of B.

The gauge p is defined by

(1) $$p(a) = \inf \{t > 0 \colon a \in tB\}$$

for each vector a.

Facts

In this list, B is a balloon, p is its gauge, u is a scalar, and a is a vector.

(vii) $u > p(a)$ implies $a \in uB$.

(viii) $u < p(a)$ implies $a \notin uB$.

(ix) $a \in uB$ implies $p(a) \leq u$.

(x) $(p < 1) \subset B \subset (p \leq 1)$.

(xi) p is a seminorm.

(xii) p is a norm if and only if B includes no linear subspace of positive dimension.

Proofs

(vii) It is possible to choose t with $a \in tB$, $u > t > p(a)$, by definition of inf; but $tB = u \cdot (t/u) \cdot B \subset uB$ since B is balanced.

(viii) u is less than every member of $\{t > 0; a \in tB\}$.

(ix) This is the same as Fact (viii).

(x) The first inclusion is Fact (vii), the second is Fact (ix).

(xi) $p(ua) = |u| p(a)$ [for $sa \in tB$ if and only if $|s|a \in tB$ since B, and hence tB, is balanced]].   Only the triangular inequality remains to be proved.   Let a, b be vectors and $\epsilon > 0$.   Then, by Fact (vii), $a \in [p(a) + \epsilon]B$, $b \in [p(b) + \epsilon]B$ and so $a + b \in [p(a) + \epsilon]B + [p(b) + \epsilon]B = [p(a) + p(b) + 2\epsilon]B$ since B is convex [Section 2.5, Problem 9]. Thus, by Fact (ix), $p(a + b) \leq p(a) + p(b) + 2\epsilon$.   Since ϵ is arbitrary, the result follows.

(xii) If the gauge p is not a norm, $p^{\perp}$ is a subspace of positive dimension and is included in B since $p^{\perp} \subset (p < 1)$.   Conversely, suppose that B includes a subspace S of positive dimension.   Then $S \subset B \subset (p \leq 1)$.   Thus p is bounded on S; hence [Fact (i)]] it is zero on S.   Consequently, p is not a norm.//

THEOREM 1.   *Given any balloon* B, *there exists a unique seminorm* p *such that* $(p < 1) \subset B \subset (p \leq 1)$.   *Conversely, given a seminorm* p, *the sets* $(p < 1)$, $(p \leq 1)$ *are balloons.*

The gauge of B satisfies the inclusion relations given and is a seminorm [Facts (x), (xi)]]. To show uniqueness, suppose that p, q satisfy $(p < 1) \subset B \subset (q \leq 1)$ and $(q < 1) \subset B \subset (p \leq 1)$.   By Fact (iv), $p = q$.

To show the converse, if $p(a) < 1$, then $p(ta) < 1$ if $|t| \leq 1$. Hence $(p < 1)$ is balanced. It is also convex [for if $p(a) < 1$, $p(b) < 1$, $0 < t < 1$, then $p[ta + (1 - t)b] \leq |t|p(a) + |1 - t|p(b) < 1$], and it is absorbing [Section 1, Fact (ix)]. A similar proof works for $(p \leq 1)$.//

Example 4. Consider, in R^2, the set $\{(x, y): x^2 + y^2 < 1\} \cup \{(1, 0)\} \cup \{(- 1, 0)\}$, that is, an open circle together with two boundary points. This set is a balloon but is neither $(p < 1)$ nor $(p \leq 1)$; it lies between [here $p(x, y) = (x^2 + y^2)^{1/2}$]. This illustrates the fact that in Theorem 1, B may be strictly between the two sets shown.

COROLLARY 1. *Given a balloon* B, *there exists a balloon* B_1 *such that* $B_1 + B_1 \subset B$.

If p is the gauge of B, let $B_1 = (p < \frac{1}{2})$. Then B_1 is a balloon by Theorem 1 [applied to the seminorm $2p$]. Moreover, if $a, b \in B_1$ we have $p(a + b) \leq p(a) + p(b) < 1$, thus $a + b \in B$.//

Sometimes the geometric aspect (balloon) is easier to use than the analytic aspect (gauge), sometimes not. For example, it is obvious that the intersection of two balloons B_1, B_2 is a balloon. It is not quite so obvious that max (p_1, p_2) is a seminorm if p_1, p_2 are seminorms. The two facts are the same, since max (p_1, p_2) is the gauge of $B_1 \cap B_2$ (if p_1, p_2 are the gauges of B_1, B_2). It is also clear that $B_1 \cup B_2$ need not be a balloon, but not quite so clear that min(p_1, p_2) need not be a seminorm. Again these two facts are the same. A similar remark is that the hypothesis of Fact (iii) can be stated, "If a hyperplane and a balloon are disjoint . . . ."

We conclude this section with an analogue of Section 2.10, Corollary 1.

THEOREM 2. *Let* q, p_1, p_2, . . . , p_n *be seminorms,* M, $\epsilon > 0$ *numbers such that if* $p_k(a) < \epsilon$ *for* k = 1, 2, . . . , n, *it follows that* q(a) $\leq$ M. *Then* q(a) $\leq (M/\epsilon) \sum_{k=1}^{n} p_k(a)$ *for all a.*

If the conclusion is false, there exist a vector a and a scalar t such that $q(a) > t > (M/\epsilon)\sum_{k=1}^{n} p_k(a)$. Let $b = (M/t)a$. Then for each r, $1 \leq r \leq n$, $p_r(b) = (M/t)p_r(a) \leq (M/t)\sum p_k(a) < \epsilon$ while $q(b) > M$.//

Problems 4.2

In this list p, q are seminorms unless otherwise indicated.

1. Prove that $(x^2 + y^2)^{1/2}$, $|x| + |y|$, max $(|x|, |y|)$, $(|x|^p + |y|^p)^{1/p}$ with $p \geq 1$, define norms on R^2.
2. Prove that sup $\{|a_n|: n = 1, 2, . . .\}$ defines a norm on l^p, $p > 0$.
3. For $a \in E^\infty$, let $g(a) = \sum_{k=1}^{5}|a_k|$ and $h(a) = \sum_{k=1}^{\infty}|a_k|$. Show that h is a norm and g is a seminorm, but not a norm. What is $g^\perp$?
4. Where was the fact that B is absorbing used in the proof of Theorem 1?
5. In Theorem 1, it is sufficient to assume that B is balanced, is absorbing, and satisfies $B + B \subset 2B$.
6. In Theorem 1, it is not necessarily true that $a \in p(a)B$.
7. Theorem 2 is not valid for paranorms. (Give an example in R with $n = 1$.)
8. In E^∞, let $B = \{a: |a_n| \leq n$ for $n = 1, 2, . . .\}$. Evaluate the gauge of B.
9. Let $q \neq 0$, then p is stronger than q if and only if inf $\{p(a): q(a) = 1\} > 0$.
10. p is stronger than q if and only if for each $\epsilon < 0$, there exists $\delta > 0$ such that $(p < \delta) \subset (q < \epsilon)$.

11. Let $p \neq 0$, then p is stronger than q if and only if $(p = 1)$ is q-bounded [that is, $q(a) \leq M$ for $p(a) = 1$].

12. p is stronger than q if and only if for each sequence of vectors $\{a_n\}$ such that $p(a_n) \to 0$, the sequence $\{q(a_n)\}$ is bounded.

13. The norm $\sum_{k=1}^{n} |a_k|$ is stronger than every seminorm on E^n. (Thus "the" strongest seminorm is a norm. See also Problem 21.) $[\![p(a) = p(\sum a_k \delta^k) \leq \sum |a_k| p(\delta^k) \leq M \sum |a_k|.]\!]$

14. On m, $\sum |a_n|/2^n$ defines a norm strictly weaker than that defined by $\sup |a_n|$.

15. On l, $\sum |a_n|/2^n$ defines a norm strictly weaker than that defined by $\sum |a_n|$.

16. For $a \in l$, let $g(a) = \sum |a_n|$, $h(a) = \sup |a_n|$. Show that g is strictly stronger than h.

17. For $f \in C$, define $p(f) = \left\{ \int_0^1 |f|^2 \right\}^{\frac{1}{2}}$, $q(f) = \max \{ |f(x)| : 0 \leq x \leq 1. \}$ Show that q is strictly stronger than p.

18. Let p be a paranorm satisfying $p(ta) \leq |t| p(a)$ for all scalar t, vector a. Show that p is a seminorm.

19. Given any linear space, there is a norm defined on it. $[\![$Use a Hamel basis, and $p(a) = \max |t|$, where $a = \sum th.]\!]$

20. Given a seminorm g, there is a stronger norm h; however $p \geq q$ does not imply that $p - q$ is a seminorm.

▲21. All norms on E^n are equivalent.

▲22. Show that an infinite-dimensional linear space cannot have a finite separating family of seminorms (compare with Section 2.10, Theorem 1). (Here we must modify our definition of separating. In this problem only, a separating family of seminorms separates any pair a, b of points unless $a = tb$ for some scalar t with $|t| = 1$.)

▲23. In $l^{\frac{1}{2}}$, show that the gauge of the convex hull of the unit disk $D(0, 1)$ is a norm. (Use q, Section 1, Example 3, to define D.)

▲24. How does $\sum |a_n|$ compare with the norm in Problem 23?

4.3 Semimetric space

DEFINITION 1. *A semimetric for a set is a function* d *of two variables satisfying, for all* a, b, c *in the set,*

      (i) $d(a, b) = d(b, a) \geq 0$,

      (ii) $d(a, a) = 0$,

      (iii) $d(a, c) \leq d(a, b) + d(b, c)$ *(the triangular inequality)*.

The set together with the semimetric is called a semimetric space.

The number $d(a, b)$ is also called the *distance between* a, b. Of course, denoting the semimetric space by A, we have $d \colon A \times A \to R$. A *metric* is a semimetric satisfying $d(a, b) > 0$ if $a \neq b$, and a space with it is called a *metric* space. If a subset of a semimetric space A is mentioned, it is automatically assumed to be given the semimetric of A, and it is called a *subspace of* A. The most familiar of all metric spaces are E, R, with $d(a, b) = |a - b|$, and R^2 with $d(a, b) = [(a_1 - b_1)^2 + (a_2 - b_2)^2]^{\frac{1}{2}}$.

We define the *cell* $N(a, r)$, *disk* $D(a, r)$, and *circumference* $C(a, r)$, of center a and radius r as, respectively $\{b \colon d(a, b) < r\}$, $\{b \colon d(a, b) \leq r\}$, $\{b \colon d(a, b) = r\}$. (The letter N is used for cell to remind the reader of the word "neighborhood.")

A point a is said to be *interior* to a set S if for some $r > 0$, $N(a, r) \subset S$. A set S is said to be a *neighborhood* of a if a is interior to S. A set is called *open* if it is a neighborhood of each of its elements, or if it is empty. Finally a set is called *closed* if its complement is open. Clearly $[\![$Problem 12$]\!]$, $N(a, r)$ is open and $D(a, r)$, $C(a, r)$ are closed for all a, r.

The *diameter* of a set S is sup $\{d(x, y): x \in S, y \in S\}$. The *distance $d(S, T)$ between two nonempty sets S, T* is defined to be inf $\{d(a, b): a \in S, b \in T\}$. The distance $d(a, S)$ from a point a to a set S is defined to be $d(\{a\}, S)$.

DEFINITION 2. *A sequence $\{x_n\}$ is said to be convergent with limit* a, *or converge to* a, *in symbols*, $x_n \to a$, *if given any neighborhood* G *of* a, $x_n \in G$ *for almost all* n.

In a semimetric space, $x_n \to a$ if and only if $d(x_n, a) \to 0$ [Problem 5].

It is possible for a sequence to converge to two different limits [if $d(x, y) = 0$ then the sequence $\{x, x, x, \ldots\}$ converges to both x and y] but if $x_n \to a$ and $x_n \to b$ we have $d(a, b) = 0$ [since $d(a, b) \leq d(a, x_n) + d(x_n, b) \to 0$]. Thus, *in a metric space, limits are unique.* If a sequence $\{x_n\}$ has a unique limit a (as every convergent sequence does in a metric space) we shall write lim $x_n = a$.

DEFINITION 3. *A function* f: A $\to$ B *is said to be continuous at* a $\in$ A *if for every neighborhood* G$(\subset$B$)$ *of* f(a), $f^{-1}[G]$ *is a neighborhood of* a; f *is said to be continuous on* A *if it is continuous at each point of* A.

THEOREM 1. *Let* A, B *be semimetric spaces.* f: A $\to$ B *is continuous at* a $\in$ A *if and only if whenever* $\{x_n\}$ *is a sequence converging to* a, f(x_n) $\to$ f(a).

Let f be continuous at a, $x_n \to a$, and let G be a neighborhood of $f(a)$. Then $f^{-1}[G]$ is a neighborhood of a, thus $x_n \in f^{-1}[G]$ for almost all n, $f(x_n) \in G$ for almost all n. Thus $f(x_n) \to f(a)$. Conversely, if f is not continuous at $a \in A$, there exists a neighborhood G of $f(a)$ such that $f^{-1}[G]$ is not a neighborhood of a. For $n = 1, 2, 3, \ldots$, $N(a, 1/n) \not\subset f^{-1}[G]$, since the latter is not a neighborhood of a, and we can choose $x_n \in N(a, 1/n) \setminus f^{-1}[G]$. Then $x_n \to a$ since $d(x_n, a) < 1/n$, but $f(x_n) \not\to f(a)$ since $f(x_n) \not\in G$.//

Given a paranorm p, if we define $d(a, b) = p(a - b)$, d is a semimetric [for example, $d(a, c) = p(a - c) = p(a - b + b - c) \leq p(a - b) + p(b - c) = d(a, b) + d(b, c)$]. It is a metric if and only if p is total.

DEFINITION 4. *A semimetric* d *for a linear space is said to be invariant if there exists a paranorm* p *such that* d(a, b) = p(a − b).

We shall say that the paranorm *yields* the semimetric and the semimetric *comes from* the paranorm. Since $p(a) = d(a, 0)$, a given semimetric comes from at most one paranorm. Clearly an invariant semimetric d satisfies the equation,

(1) $$d(a + x, b + x) = d(a, b);$$

hence its name. However the discrete metric (Problem 8) satisfies equation (1) but is not an invariant metric [Section 1, Problem 5].

We can now rephrase part (v) of the definition of paranorm in Section 1 thus: if $t_n \to t$, $a_n \to a$, then $t_n a_n \to ta$.

DEFINITION 5. *A semimetric space which is also a linear space is called a linear semimetric space, a linear metric space, a seminormed space, or a normed space, if the semimetric comes from a paranorm, a total paranorm, a seminorm, or a norm, respectively.*

A discussion of this definition is given at the beginning of Chapter 6. As an example, define p, q on R^2 by $p(x, y) = |x| + |y|$, $q(x, y) = (x^2 + y^2)^{1/2}$. Then (R^2, p), (R^2, q) are both normed spaces, and are different.

Given a linear semimetric space, we must distinguish by some very special notation the particular paranorm which has been chosen. We denote its value at a by $!a!$ If it is a seminorm, this will be written $\|a\|$. Thus, for example, a seminormed space $(A, \|\cdot\|)$ is a linear space A, together with a seminorm $\|\cdot\|$ defined on it. We always denote the space, simply, by A, leaving it to be understood from the context which paranorm has been honored by the designation $!\cdot!$ or $\|\cdot\|$.

It happens that many of the linear spaces which occur in classical situations (c_0, l^p, etc.) have one norm or total paranorm defined on each of them which, in some sense, is more natural than all others. For example, the space l^p, $p \geq 1$, certainly reminds us forcibly of the norm, $|\Sigma|a_n|^p|^{1/p}$. Apart from the naturalness of these various paranorms, they have a much stronger claim to our attention than can now be apparent. To anticipate, in the language of Chapters 5 and 9, each linear space of the type mentioned (with a few exceptions) has a unique invariant metric which is complete and such that coordinates or points (Section 1.3) are continuous. This will be proved in Section 11.3. See particularly Corollary 3 and the Remark following it.

The spaces and natural paranorms are those listed in the Table of Spaces. For some of these, the given functions have been proved to be paranorms and seminorms, as follows: $B_1[X]$, and so, also, $C_1[X]$, A_C, m, c_0, c in Section 2, Example 2; l^p, $p \geq 1$, and so, also, R^n, E^n in Section 2, Example 3; l^p, $0 < p < 1$, in Section 1, Example 3; s in Section 1, Example 5; E_C in Section 1, Example 6; $C^{(n)}$, $C^{(\infty)}$ are handled similarly. The index may be consulted for discussions of c_A. For the remaining three spaces, standard Lebesgue integration techniques yield the results. Whenever any one of these spaces is mentioned it will always be assumed to have its *natural* invariant metric, the one given in the Table of Spaces.

For some of the spaces, convergence of sequences is described thus; $a_n \to 0$ has the following meanings: In A_C, $a_n(z) \to 0$ uniformly on $|z| \leq 1$; in E_C, $a_n(z) \to 0$ uniformly on each bounded subset of E; in M, $a_n \to 0$ in measure; in s, with $a_n = \{a_k^n\}$, $a_k^n \to 0$ as $n \to \infty$ for each fixed k [for E_C, s, the result quoted follows from Section 1, Theorem 1].

Example 1. The spaces M, L^p, may be considered to be semimetric spaces in which case the function J defined by $J(f) = f(\frac{1}{2})$ would be meaningful (compare Section 2.8, Example 1, and the remarks at the end of the section). However, J would not be continuous since it is possible to have $d(f, g) = 0$, $J(f) \neq J(g)$.

It is more customary to identify functions whose distance apart is 0, and thus make M, L^p into metric spaces. As pointed out in Section 2.8, J is then not defined.

DEFINITION 6. *The set of all continuous linear functionals on a space* A *will be denoted by* A′ *and called the dual space of* A.

Thus, $A' \subset A^\#$. Indeed, A' is a linear subspace of $A^\#$ [for example, if f, $g \in A'$, $f + g$ is continuous, since if $a_n \to a$, $(f + g)(a_n) = f(a_n) + g(a_n) \to f(a) + g(a) = (f + g)(a)$]. Thus A' is a linear space.

DEFINITION 7. *The unit disk in a linear semimetric space is the disk of center* 0 *and radius* 1. *The unit cell and circumference are defined similarly.*

The study of semimetric space will be continued in Chapter 5, that of linear semimetric space in Chapter 6.

Problems 4.3

In this list d is a semimetric; A, B and semimetric spaces, unless otherwise indicated. Sections 5.1 and 6.1 contain more problems in the same area.

★1. For every a, b, c, we have $|d(a, b) - d(a, c)| \leq d(b, c)$.

2. If $d(a, b) = 0$, then $d(a, c) = d(b, c)$ for all c; compare Section 1, Problem 3.

3. Let d be an arbitrary real function of two variables on a set. Show that the following assumptions imply that d is a metric: $d(a, b) = 0$ if and only if $a = b$, and for all a, b, c, $d(a, b) \leq d(a, c) + d(b, c)$.

4. $N(a, t) = \bigcup[N(a, r): r < t] = \bigcup[D(a, r): r < t] = \bigcup[C(a, r): r < t]$.

★5. In a semimetric space, $x_n \to a$ if and only if $d(x_n, a) \to 0$.

6. If $d(a, b) = 0$, and $x_n \to a$, then $x_n \to b$.

★7. For a sequence $\{a^n\}$ of points in E^r, $a^n \to 0$ if and only if $a_k^n \to 0$ for each k.

★8. (a) Let A be a set. For a, $b \in A$, let $d(a, b) = 1$ if $a \neq b$, while $d(a, a) = 0$. Verify that d is a metric. It is called the *discrete metric*. Identify $N(a, r)$, $D(a, r)$, $C(a, r)$ for $r = 2, 1, \frac{1}{2}, 0, -1$. (b) Let A be a set. For a, $b \in A$, let $d(a, b) = 0$. Verify that d is a semimetric. It is called the *indiscrete* semimetric. Continue as in (a).

★9. Suppose given a sequence $\{d_n\}$ of semimetrics on a set. State and prove the analogue of Section 1, Theorem 1, in which a semimetric is formed by taking the Fréchet combination of the sequence.

10. Let $z = (x, y)$, $w = (u, v)$ be points of R^2, and define $d(z, w) = 1$ if $x \neq u$, $|y - v| \wedge 1$ if $x = u$. Verify that d is a metric. Identify $N(0, r)$, $D(0, r)$ for $r = 2, 1, \frac{1}{2}$. Find out what convergence of a sequence means.

11. The diameter of $N(a, r)$, $D(a, r)$, $C(a, r)$ is less than or equal to $2r$. Given an example in which each is less.

★12. Show that $N(a, r)$ is open, and that $D(a, r)$, $C(a, r)$ are closed.

13. Give an example of a metric space in which $N(a, r)$ is closed for all r, and one in which it is not closed for some r.

★14. Show that the union of any collection and the intersection of any finite collection of open sets are open; that the intersection of any collection and the union of any finite collection of closed sets are closed. Show, by an example in R, that the words "finite" cannot be omitted.

★15. A finite subset of a metric space is closed. A finite true subset of a semimetric space is closed (a subset S is *true* if $x \in S$ whenever $d(x, y) = 0$ and $y \in S$).

16. Fix a and define $f(b) = d(a, b)$. Show that f is continuous.

17. In Problem 16, replace b by a set S.

★18. $A \to B$ is continuous on A if and only if $f^{-1}[G]$ is open whenever G is an open set in B.

19. $f: A \to B$ is continuous if and only if $f^{-1}[S]$ is closed whenever S is a closed set in B.

★20. Let f be a continuous real function. Show that

$$\{a: f(a) < x\} \text{ is open, } \{a: f(a) \leq x\} \text{ and } \{a: f(a) = x\}$$

are closed for each fixed real number x. (This, with Problem 16, yields Problem 12.)

21. Let a linear space of nonzero dimension be given the discrete metric. Show that this metric does not come from a paranorm; that is, it is not a linear metric [see Section 1, Problem 5].

22. A semimetric d comes from a seminorm if and only if $d(ta, tb) = |t|d(a, b)$, $d(a + c, b + c) = d(a, b)$ for all a, b, c and scalar t.

23. Suppose that $a_n \to a$ and $b_n \to b$ in a linear semimetric space. Show that $a_n + tb_n \to a + tb$ for any scalar t.

★24. Show that a linear map between linear semimetric spaces is continuous everywhere if it is continuous at one point [if $x_n \to x$, then $x_n + a - x \to a$]. A seminorm defined on a linear semimetric space is continuous everywhere if it is continuous at 0 [$|p(x) - p(y)| \le p(x - y)$]. (Problem 25 gives a better result.)

25. A seminorm defined on a linear semimetric space is continuous everywhere if it is continuous somewhere.

★26. For each n, P_n is continuous on s and l^p, $0 < p < 1$.

27. Let P be the set of polynomials in A_c. Show that D, the differentiation operator is not continuous.

28. Replace A_c by E_c in Problem 27. Now D is continuous.

29. In Problem 27, replace A_c by C. Now, is D continuous?

30. The natural paranorms for s, m, c, c_0, $l^p(p > 0)$, E^n, $n = 1, 2, \dots$, have the same order as the spaces; that is, if A, B are any two of these spaces with $A \subset B$, then, on A, the paranorm of A is stronger than that of B. It is strictly stronger if and only if A is not a closed subset of B. [It is expected that this problem will be done by simple enumeration of cases. It is a special case of Section 11.3, Corollary 1 and Lemma 1.]

31. Show that the unit disk of m is closed in s.

4.4   Seminormed space

As we saw in Section 2, seminorms are somewhat better behaved than paranorms in general. Their important place in functional analysis rests ultimately on the convexity of the set $(p < 1)$, p being a seminorm. This is because convexity is a basic assumption (see Chapter 3). Some of the properties of seminorms can be carried over to those paranorms which are formed from a sequence of seminorms as in Section 1, Theorem 1. These are characterized in Section 12.1 as those paranorms leading to locally convex topologies. By that time, attention will have shifted away from the paranorm to the sequence of seminorms, and then to arbitrarily large sets of seminorms.

DEFINITION 1. *Let* p *be a seminorm defined on a seminormed space. Then* $\|p\|$ *(pronounced norm of* p*) is defined to be* sup $\{p(a): \|a\| \le 1\}$. *Similarly, if* f *is a linear functional,* $\|f\| =$ sup $\{|f(a)|: \|a\| \le 1\}$; *more generally, if* f *is a linear map from a seminormed to a seminormed space,* $\|f\| =$ sup $\{\|f(a)\|: \|a\| \le 1.\}$

The first definition actually includes the others; for example, if f is a linear functional and $p(a) = |f(a)|$ for all a, then $\|p\| = \|f\|$. $\|p\|$ measures the size of p on the unit disk. Clearly, if $\|p\| = 0$ it follows that $p = 0$ [for given a with $p(a) \ne 0$, let $b = a/(1 + \|a\|)$, then $\|b\| < 1$ and so $\|p\| \ge p(b) > 0$]. In case p is defined on a seminormed space A, and S is a subset of A, we shall use the notation $\|p\|_S$ to denote sup $\{p(a): \|a\| \le 1, a \in S.\}$

If $\|p\| < \infty$ we say that p is a *bounded seminorm*. (Actually it is bounded on the unit disk, not on the whole space.) Similarly, a *bounded linear map* is one whose norm is finite.

★*Example 1.* Let $h(x, y) = 3x + 4y$ for $(x, y) \in R^2$. Since $h(\frac{3}{5}, \frac{4}{5}) = 5$ and $\|(\frac{3}{5}, \frac{4}{5})\| = 1$ (remember that R^2 has its natural norm) we have $\|h\| \ge 5$.

Next, let $a = (x, y)$ have $\|a\| \leq 1$. By Hölder's inequality (with $p = q = 2$), $|3x + 4y|$ $\leq (3^2 + 4^2)^{1/2} \cdot (x^2 + y^2)^{1/2} \leq 5$. Thus $\|h\| \leq 5$ and finally $\|h\| = 5$.

★*Example 2.* Define h on c_0 by $h(a) = \Sigma_{n=1}^{\infty} a_n/n!$. Then for all $\|a\| \leq 1$ we have, for each k, $|a_k| \leq \|a\| \leq 1$ and so $|h(a)| \leq \Sigma 1/n!$. On the other hand, let m be a fixed positive integer and define $a = \Sigma_{k=1}^{m} \delta^k = (1, 1, \ldots, 1, 0, 0, 0, \ldots)$. Then $\|a\| = 1$ and $h(a) = \Sigma_{k=1}^{m} 1/n!$. Thus $\|h\| \geq \Sigma_{k=1}^{m} 1/n!$ for all m. This, coupled with the earlier inequality, yields $\|h\| = \Sigma_{k=1}^{\infty} 1/n!$.

★*Example 3.* Make E^{∞} into a normed space by defining $\|a\| = \sup \{|a_n|: n = 1, 2, \ldots\}$; that is, E^{∞} is a *normed subspace* of c_0. Let $h(a) = \Sigma_{n=1}^{\infty} |a_n|$. This defines a norm on E^{∞} and it satisfies $\|h\| = \infty$ [for $\|\Sigma_{n=1}^{m} \delta^n\| = 1$ while $h(\Sigma_{n=1}^{m} \delta^n) = m$, thus $\|h\| \geq m$ for any m].

LEMMA 1. *Let* p *be a bounded seminorm defined on a seminormed space. Then* $p(a) \leq \|p\| \cdot \|a\|$ *for all* a.

By definition, $\|a\| < 1$ implies $p(a) \leq \|p\|$. By Section 2, Theorem 2 [take $M = \|p\|$, $n = \epsilon = 1$] $p(a) \leq \|p\| \cdot \|a\|$.//

THEOREM 1. *Let* p *be a seminorm and* f *a linear map from a seminormed space to a seminormed space, in particular,* f *may be a functional. Then* p, f *are continuous if and only if they are bounded; that is,* $\|p\| < \infty$, $\|f\| < \infty$, *respectively.*

If $\|p\| < \infty$, p is continuous at 0 [Lemma 1], hence everywhere [Section 3, Problem 24]. If $\|p\| = \infty$, for $n = 1, 2, \ldots$, there exist a_n with $\|a_n\| \leq 1$, $p(a_n) > n^2$. Then $a_n/n \to 0$ [$\|a_n/n\| \leq 1/n$], while $p(a_n/n) > n$, so that p is not continuous at 0. The proof for f is the same.//

Theorem 1 is not valid for linear metric spaces in general; for example, in s the unit disk is the whole space, so it is unreasonable to discuss $\|p\|$. ($\|p\|$ would be infinite unless $p = 0$.) The result can be extended if we extend the idea of disk in a seminormed space in a more appropriate way. The result is given in Section 10.5, Theorem 4.

We are now prepared for the first of the three fundamental theorems of functional analysis. The Hahn-Banach extension theorem occurs repeatedly in embedding theory, representation theory, and existence theory, as well as in applications to classical analysis. The essence of the result lies in Theorem 2. However, in referring to it we will usually be thinking of one of the various corollaries listed below. We shall give two proofs of Theorem 2. The first is short and easy, following from the separation theory of Chapter 3. The second is less instructive, longer and more computational, but has the advantage of being more nearly self-contained. In particular, it is independent of Chapter 3, and, indeed, the results of Chapter 3 can be deduced from Theorem 2. The second proof is based on ideas of L. Nachbin. Reference to a third proof is given in Appendix K.

THEOREM 2. *(The Hahn-Banach theorem). Let* S *be a subspace of a linear space. Let* p *be a seminorm defined on the whole space and* f *a linear functional defined on* S *such that* $|f(a)| \leq p(a)$ *for all* $a \in S$. *Then there is an extension* F *of* f *which is a linear functional on the whole space and which satisfies* $|F(a)| \leq p(a)$ *for all* a.

Proof I (using Chapter 3). If $f \equiv 0$, the result is trivial; we shall assume that $f \not\equiv 0$. The set $(f = 1)$ is an affine subspace (a translate of $f^{\perp}$) which does not meet the balloon $(p < 1)$.

By the support theorem (Section 3.1, Theorem 1; see also Section 1, Problem 11), we can extend it to a hyperplane H not meeting $(p < 1)$. Since $p(0) = 0$, H does not pass through the origin and so it is not a (linear) subspace, hence it is $(F = 1)$ for some linear functional F. $F(a) = f(a)$ for $a \in S$ [for in S, the sets $(F = 1)$ and $(f = 1)$ are the same; hence $F = f$ by Section 2.10, Theorem 5] and $|F(a)| \leq p(a)$ for all a [Section 2, Fact (iii)].//

Before giving the promised second proof we restate Theorem 2 in a way that simplifies the details of the proof. We list this restatement as Corollary 1.

COROLLARY 1. *Let* S *be a linear subspace of a seminormed space* A. *Let* f *be a linear functional defined on* S. *Then there exists an extension* F *of* f *which is a linear functional defined on all of* A *and which satisfies* $\|F\|_A = \|f\|_S$.

If $\|f\|_S = \infty$, any extension of f will have infinite norm. If $\|f\|_S < \infty$, take, in Theorem 1, $p(a) = \|f\|_S \cdot \|a\|$.//

Those who are satisfied with this proof may turn to Corollary 2. We give here the promised second proof of Theorem 2, proving the obviously equivalent Corollary 1. We begin with a criterion for ensuring that an extension by one dimension will not increase the norm.

LEMMA 2. *Let* A, B *be seminormed spaces and* F: A $\rightarrow$ B *a continuous linear map.* *Let* W *be a linear subspace of* A *and suppose that* $\|F\|_W = 1$. *Let* x $\in$ A $\setminus$ W. *Then* $\|F\|_{x \oplus W} = 1$ *if and only if* F(x) *belongs to every disk in* B *of the form* D[b, r(b)] *where* r(b) = inf $\{\|x - w\| : w \in W,$ F(w) = b)}.

If $\|F\|_{x \oplus W} = 1$, let $b \in F[W]$. Then for each $w \in W$ with $F(w) = b$, we have $\|F(x) - b\| = \|F(x - w)\| \leq \|x - w\|$. Taking the inf over all such w yields $\|F(x) - b\| \leq r(b)$.

If, conversely, $F(x)$ belongs to every disk of the given form, let $a = \alpha x + w$, $w \in W$, α a scalar. In view of what we are trying to prove, we may assume that $\alpha \neq 0$. Then $\|F(a)\| = |\alpha| \cdot \|F(x + w/\alpha)\|$. With $w' = -w/\alpha$, $b = F(w')$, we have $\|F(a)\| = |\alpha| \cdot \|F(x) - b\| \leq |\alpha| \cdot r(b) \leq |\alpha| \cdot \|x - w'\| = \|\alpha x + w\| = \|a\|$. Thus $\|F\|_{x \oplus W} \leq 1$.//

LEMMA 3. *Let* A, B *be seminormed spaces,* W *a linear subspace of* A, *and* F: W $\rightarrow$ B *a linear map with* $\|F\|_W = 1$. *Let* x $\in$ A $\setminus$ W. *Then every pair of disks* D[b, r(b)] *has nonempty intersection, where* b $\in$ F[W], *and* r(b) *is as given in Lemma 2.*

For $b_1 = F(w_1)$, $b_2 = F(w_2)$, we have $\|b_1 - b_2\| = \|F(w_1 - w_2)\| \leq \|w_1 - w_2\| \leq \|w_1 - x\| + \|x - w_2\|$. Taking the inf over all such w_1, w_2 yields $\|b_1 - b_2\| \leq r(b_1) + r(b_2)$. Then $tb_1 + (1 - t)b_2$ belongs to both disks if $t = r(b_2)/[r(b_1) + r(b_2)]$.//

We can now prove Corollary 1. We may assume $\|f\|_S = 1$ [for we can extend $f/\|f\|_S$ instead of f; and the cases $\|f\|_S = 0$, ∞ are trivial].

Assume first that A is a real linear space. Let $P = \{g: g$ is a linear functional of norm one defined on some subspace of A which includes S and $g = f$ on $S\}$. For $g_1, g_2 \in P$, define $g_2 \geq g_1$ to mean that g_2 is an extension of g_1. This makes P a poset. It is not empty, since $f \in P$. Let C be a maximal chain and W the linear subspace of all vectors a such that $g(a)$ is defined for some $g \in C$. There is an extension F of f defined on W and satisfying $\|F\|_W = 1$. [Simply define $F(a) = g(a)$ for any $g \in C$ such that $g(a)$ is defined. This defines F uniquely since C is a chain. F is linear. For example, given a, $b \in W$ let g_1, $g_2 \in C$ with $g_1(a)$, $g_2(b)$ defined. Say $g_2 \geq g_1$. Then $g_2(a)$ is defined, thus, so is $g_2(a + b)$ and so $F(a + b) = g_2(a + b) = g_2(a) + g_2(b) = F(a) + F(b)$. Also $|F(b)| =$

$|g_2(b)| \le \|b\|.]$ Thus the proof is concluded by showing that $W = A$. If $W \ne A$, let $x \in A \setminus W$.

In Lemma 3, take $B = R$. The disks $D[b, r(b)]$ are now closed intervals. Since any two then intersect, they all intersect; that is, there exists a real number t such that $b - r(b) \le t \le b' + r(b')$ for all $b, b' \in R$. Extend F linearly to $x \oplus W$, taking $f(x) = t$. By Lemma 2, $\|F\|_{x \oplus w} = 1$. The existence of this extension of F to one more dimension contradicts the maximality of C.

We now turn to the complex case.

Let g be the real part of f. In the associated real linear space, g is a linear functional. We extend it to a real linear functional G defined on the whole space, and define F to be the linear functional whose real part is G [Section 2.11, Theorem 1]. Since $|G(a)| \le \|a\|$ for all a, it follows that $|F(a)| \le \|a\|$ for all a [Section 2, Fact (ii)]. Applying Section 2.11, Theorem 1, we see that F is an extension of f.//

COROLLARY 2. *Let* A *be a seminormed space,* S *a subspace, and* a *a vector, not in* S. *Then there exists a linear functional* f, *defined on* A *with* f(a) = 1, f(x) = 0 *for* x $\in$ S, *and* $\|f\|$ = 1/d(a, S). *(Here we intend* $\|f\|$ = ∞ *if* d(a, S) = 0.)

We define f on $a \oplus S$ by $f(a) = 1$, $f(x) = 0$ for $x \in S$. Then, by Corollary 1, extend f to the whole space without increase of norm. Now if $\|f\| < \infty$ we have, for any $x \in S$, using Lemma 1, $\|f\| \cdot \|a - x\| \ge |f(a - x)| = 1$. Thus $\|a - x\| \ge 1/\|f\|$ and so $d(a, S) \ge 1/\|f\|$. (This shows in particular that $d(a, S) = 0$ implies $\|f\| = \infty$.) On the other hand, let $y \in a \oplus S$. Then $f(y) = 0$ if $y \in S$, while if $y \notin S$, $y = x + ta$ for some $x \in S$, scalar $t \ne 0$, from which it follows that $f(y) = t$, hence $y = x + f(y)a$ for some $x \in S$. Thus $\|y\|/|f(y)| = \|a - (-x)/f(y)\| \ge d(a, S)$ [since $-x/f(y) \in S$]. Thus $|f(y)| \le \|v\|/d(a, S)$ and so $\|f\| \le 1/d(a, S)$ [Problem 3].//

COROLLARY 3. *Given any element* a, *with* $\|a\| \ne 0$, *of a seminormed space, there exists a linear functional* f *with* f(a) = $\|a\|$, $\|f\|$ = 1. *In particular, if* A *is a normed space,* A' *is total over* A.

Choose a function as in Corollary 2, with $S = \{0\}$ and then multiply it by $\|a\|$.//

The dual result is not valid. Given a linear functional $f \ne 0$ (equivalent to $\|f\| \ne 0$) there may not exist a vector a with $f(a) = \|f\|$, $\|a\| = 1$ [Example 4, below]. If such a vector a exists, we shall say that *f assumes a maximum on the unit disk at* a. Strictly speaking, it is $|f|$ which assumes a maximum.

If there exists a *with* $|f(a)| = \|f\|$, $\|a\| = 1$, *then* f *assumes a maximum on the unit disk* [for with $f(a) = \|f\|e^{i\theta}$, let $b = ae^{-i\theta}$; then $\|b\| = 1$, $f(b) = \|f\|$].

Example 4: The function h *of Example 2 does not assume a maximum on the unit disk.* [Let $a \in c_0$, $\|a\| \le 1$. Since $a_n \to 0$, we must have $|a_k| < 1$ for some k, and $|h(a)| \le \Sigma\{1/n!: n = 1, 2, \ldots ; n \ne k\} + |a_k|/k! < \Sigma_{n=1}^{\infty} 1/n! = \|h\|$.]

A hyperplane H satisfying $d(a, H) = r > 0$ is said to be *tangent* to the disk $D(a, r)$. This does not imply that H meets $D(a, r)$.

Example 5. Let f be a linear functional with $\|f\| = 1$ such that f does not assume a maximum on the unit disk [for example, let $f = h/\|h\|$ in Example 4]. Let $H = (f = 1)$, and let $0 < \epsilon < 1$. There exists x with $\|x\| = 1$, $|f(x)| > 1 - \epsilon$. Let $b = x/f(x)$. Then

$b \in H$, $\|b\| < 1/(1 - \epsilon)$.   Thus $d(0, H) \leq 1$.   Conversely,

(1) $\|y\| \leq 1$ implies $|f(y)| < 1$

since f does not assume a maximum on the unit disk, and so $y \notin H$.   Thus $d(0, H) \geq 1$. We have now proved that H is tangent to the unit disk.   That it does not meet it follows from statement (1).

COROLLARY 4.   *Let S be a set in a seminormed space and* f *a functional defined on* S.   *Suppose that there exists a number* M *such that for every pair of finite sets* $\{t_1, t_2, \ldots, t_n\}$ *of scalars, and* $\{a_1, a_2, \ldots, a_n\}$ *of members of* S, *we have*

(2) $|\sum_{k=1}^{n} t_k f(a_k)| \leq M\|\sum_{k=1}^{n} t_k a_k\|,$

then f *can be extended to a linear functional* F *on the whole space with* $\|F\| \leq M$.   *Conversely, if such an extension* F *exists,* (2) *must hold with* M *replaced by* $\|F\|$.
(Compare with Section 2.4, Problem 22).

The converse is trivial [for, $\Sigma t_k f(a_k) = F(\Sigma t_k a_k)$].   Now assume that inequality (2) holds. We first extend f to the span of S by defining $F(b) = \Sigma_{k=1}^n t_k f(a_k)$ if $b = \Sigma_{k=1}^n t_k a$.   If, perchance, $b = \Sigma_{k=1}^m s_k a'_k$ as well, we have by inequality (2), $|\Sigma t_k f(a_k) - \Sigma s_k f(a'_k)| \leq M\|\Sigma t_k a_k - \Sigma s_k a'_k\| = M\|b - b\| = 0$, so that $F(b)$ has the same value no matter how b is expressed as a linear combination of S.   Then, again, $|F(b)| = |\Sigma t_k f(a_k)| \leq M\|\Sigma t_k a_k\| = M\|b\|$ and so $\|F\| \leq M$ [problem 3].   Finally we extend F to the whole space without increasing its norm [by Corollary 1].//
The next example shows that the Hahn-Banach theorem cannot be extended in exactly its given form to linear maps in general.

Example 6.   Let f be defined on the subspace c_0 of c by $f(a) = a$.   Then f is defined on a subspace of c and has its values in c_0.   Moreover $\|f\| = 1$.   But any extension of f to all of c is a projection of c onto c_0 and hence has norm greater than 1 [Problem 34].

A finite-dimensional example is given in Problem 33.   An application (due to P. D. Lax) of the Hahn-Banach theorem will now be given.

Example 7: The Riemann mapping theorem.   Let Γ be a simple closed curve in the complex plane with a unique tangent at each point, enclosing a bounded open region G.
For each complex z let z_1 be the reflection of z in the tangent to Γ at the point nearest to z [z_1 will be well defined for z near Γ; for z not near Γ, there may be many closest points].   Assume that Γ is so smooth that $|(t - z)/(t - z_1)| \to 1$ uniformly for $t \in \Gamma$ as $z \to \Gamma$; that is, $d(z, \Gamma) < \delta(\epsilon)$ implies $||(t - z)/(t - z_1)| - 1| < \epsilon$ for all $t \in \Gamma$.
The *Dirichlet problem* for a function $g \in$ real $C[\Gamma]$ is that of finding a real function u, harmonic in G, continuous in $\bar{G}$ with $u = g$ on Γ.   There will be at most one such function. Henceforth, in this example, real $C[\Gamma]$ will be denoted, simply, by $C[\Gamma]$.
Let S be the subset of $C[\Gamma]$ for which the Dirichlet problem can be solved. S is at least one dimensional since all constant functions are harmonic, and it is obviously a linear subspace of $C[\Gamma]$.
Fix $z_0 \in G$.   Define a linear functional f on S by the formula, $f(g) = u(z_0)$ where u is the solution of the Dirichlet problem for g. f is continuous [$|f(g)| = |u(z_0)| \leq \sup \{|u(t)|$:

$t \in \bar{G}\} = \sup \{|u(t)|: t \in \Gamma\} = \|g\|$ since $u = g$ on Γ. Here we have used the fact that harmonic functions must assume their maximum on the boundary]. In fact $\|f\| = 1$ [since for $g = 1$, $f(g) = \|g\| = 1$]. By means of the Hahn-Banach theorem we imagine f to be extended to all of $C[\Gamma]$ with $\|f\| = 1$.

Now for any $z \notin \Gamma$, we may define $g_z \in C[\Gamma]$ by $g_z(t) = \log |t - z|$, and $v(z) = f(g_z)$ defines a real function v on all the complex plane except Γ.

We are going to show that v is harmonic in G. This will follow from $\triangle v(z) = f(\triangle g_z) = 0$, where $\triangle$ is the Laplacian operator, if we can justify the differentiation. Consider first $[g_{z+h}(t) - g_z(t)]/h$, where h is a nonzero real number. As $h \to 0$, this expression tends to $(\partial/\partial x)g_z(t)$. Furthermore, for each fixed z, it tends uniformly to this limit for $t \in \Gamma$. [If h is small, $z = x + iy$, $t = \sigma + i\tau$,

$$\left| \frac{\log |z + h - t| - \log |z - t|}{h} - \frac{x - \sigma}{|z - t|^2} \right| = \left| \frac{x + \theta h - \sigma}{|z + \theta h - t|^2} - \frac{x - \sigma}{|z - t|^2} \right|, 0 < \theta < 1,$$

using the fact that

$$\frac{\partial}{\partial x} \log |z - t| = \frac{x - \sigma}{|z - t|^2}.$$

Set $m = z - t$, $r = $ real part of m, in the above difference. It then becomes

$$\left| \frac{r + \theta h}{|m + \theta h|^2} - \frac{r}{|m|^2} \right|.$$

Now $|m|$ takes a positive minimum, and r is bounded, since Γ is compact. Thus this difference tends to 0 uniformly as $h \to 0$.] Thus, $(g_{z+h} - g_z)/h$ tends to a limit in $C[\Gamma]$ as $h \to 0$ through real values. Similarly one proves that the difference quotient defining the Laplacian of g_z tends to 0 in $C[\Gamma]$. Since f is continuous, the result follows. Thus v is harmonic.

Next, for $t \in \Gamma$ and $w \in G$, $v(w) \to \log |z_0 - t|$ as $w \to t$ [$g_w - g_{w_1} \to 0$ in $C[\Gamma]$, by the smoothness hypothesis on Γ. Thus $v(w) - v(w_1) \to 0$. But $v(w_1) \to \log |z_0 - t|$ since $w_1 \to t$ and $v(w_1) = \log |z_0 - w_1|$, the solution of the Dirichlet problem for g_{w_1} being $\log |z - w_1|$, since $w_1 \notin \bar{G}$.] (The function $v(z) - \log |z - z_0|$ for all z, $z_0 \in G$, $z \neq z_0$, is called the *Green's function* for Γ. It vanishes for $z \in \Gamma$ and is harmonic in z except at $z = z_0$, where it has a $+\infty$ of logarithmic type.) Finally, let ϕ be an analytic function whose real part is v, and $\psi(z) = (z - z_0)e^{-\phi(z)}$. Then $\psi(z_0) = 0$; ψ is analytic in G; and for $z \in \Gamma$, $|\psi(z)| = |z - z_0|e^{-\log|z-z_0|} = 1$. Thus ψ maps Γ conformally onto the unit circle. This is the Riemann mapping theorem for Γ.

Problems 4.4

In this list it is assumed that all problems, except the first, refer to a nontrivial seminormed space A; that is, one in which there is a vector x with $\|x\| > 0$. Unless otherwise specified, p, q are seminorms and f is a linear functional on A.

★1. Let A, B be seminormed spaces with either A or B trivial; that is, the seminorm vanishes identically. Then if $f: A \to B$ is continuous, $\|f\| = 0$.

★2. $\|p\| = \sup \{p(a): \|a\| = 1\} = \sup \{p(a): \|a\| < 1\} = \sup \{p(a)/\|a\|: \|a\| \neq 0\}$.

★3. Let g be a seminorm or a linear functional defined on a seminormed space. Show that if $|g(a)| \leq M\|a\|$ for all a, then $\|g\| \leq M$. Obtain the same result if the range of g is in a seminormed space, replacing $|g(a)|$ by $\|g(a)\|$.

4. Let g be a seminorm or a linear map defined on a seminormed space A with values in a normed space. Suppose that g is bounded (that is, $\|g\| < \infty$). Show that $g(a) = 0$ if $\|a\| = 0$. Thus g is defined on A/S, where $S = \{a\colon \|a\| = 0\}$.

★5. $\|p + q\| \leq \|p\| + \|q\|$.

6. Let $f\colon X \to Y$, $g\colon Y \to Z$. Show that $\|g \circ f\| \leq \|g\|\,\|f\|$. (Here, $g \circ f\colon X \to Z$.)

★7. Show that for every k, $\|P_k\| = 1$. Here P_k is defined on any one of E^n, R^n, c_0, c, m, l^p, $p \geq 1$.

8. Show that for every t, $\|P_t\| = 1$. Here P_t is defined on C.

9. Define f on R^2 by $f(x, y) = sx + ty$. Suppose that R^2 is given the norms, respectively, $|x| + |y|$, $(|x|^p + |y|^p)^{1/p}, p > 1$, and max $(|x|, |y|)$. Show that $\|f\|$ is, respectively, max $(|s|, |t|)$, $(|s|^q + |t|^q)^{1/q}$, $1/p + 1/q = 1$, and $|s| + |t|$. (Notice what happens as $p \to +\infty$.)

10. Let R^2 be given the seminorm $\|(x, y)\| = |x|$ and let $f(x, y) = sx + ty$. Show that $\|f\| = \infty$ if $t \neq 0$, and $\|f\| = |s|$ if $t = 0$.

11. Find $\|\lim\|$ where lim is the usual limit functional defined on c.

12. Let f be a linear functional not identically zero and $\epsilon > 0$. Show that there exists a with $f(a) = 1$, $\|a\| \leq (1 + \epsilon)/\|f\|$.

13. In R^3, let $S = \{(x, y, z)\colon x + 2y + 3z = 0\}$. Define a linear functional f on S by $f(z, y, z) = x - y$. Find an extension of f to all of R^3 with the same norm as f.

14. With S as in Problem 13, find a linear functional f with $f(a) = 0$ for $a \in S, f(2, 1, 0) = 1$, and verify that $\|f\| = 1/d[(2, 1, 0), S]$.

15. Let R^3 be given the norm, $\|(x, y, z)\| = |x| + |y| + |z|$. Let $S = \{(x, y, z)\colon x + 2y = z = 0\}$. Define a linear functional f on S by $f(x, y, z) = x$. Give two different extensions of f with the same norm as f.

16. (This problem has nothing to do with the Hahn-Banach theorem.) Let S be a subspace of A, and f a bounded linear map from S to a seminormed space. Show that there exists an extension F of f to $\{x\colon d(x, S) = 0\}$, with $\|F\| = \|f\|$.

17. Assuming that $f(a) = 1$, show that $\|f\| = 1/d(a, f^{\perp})$.

18. $d[f^{\perp}, (f = 1)] = 1/\|f\|$.

19. For $b \in n$, define f on l by $f(x) = \sum_{n=1}^{\infty} b_n x_n$. Show that $\|f\| = \sup |b_n|$.

20. For $b \in l$, define f on m by $f(x) = \sum_{n=1}^{\infty} b_n x_n$. Show that $\|f\| = \sum |b_n|$.

21. For $b \in l^q$, define f on $l^p (1/p + 1/q = 1)$ by $f(x) = \sum b_n x_n$. Show that $\|f\| = [\sum |b_n|^q]^{1/q}$.

22. Let P be the space of all polynomials on R with $\|f\| = \max \{|f(t)|\colon 0 \leq t \leq 1\}$. Let g, h be linear functionals on P given by $g(f) = \int_0^1 f(t) \sin t\, dt$, $h(f) = \int_0^{\pi} f(t) \sin t\, dt$. Show that $\|g\| < \infty$, $\|h\| = \infty$.

23. For each complex number z, define $\hat{z} \in E_C^{\#}$ by $\hat{z}(a) = a(z)$. Fix an integer $n > 0$, and give E_C the norm $\|a\| = \max \{|a(z)|\colon |z| \leq n\}$. Show that $\hat{z}$ is continuous if and only if $|z| \leq n$.

24. Define g on c by $g(a) = \sum_{n=1}^{\infty} (-1)^n a_n/n!$. Show that g does not assume a maximum on the unit disk.

25. Define h on c by $h(a) = -\lim a + \sum_{n=1}^{\infty} a_n/n!$. Show that h does not assume a maximum on the unit disk.

26. Let f be discontinuous. Show that $f^{\perp}$ is dense; that is, $f^{\perp}$ meets every open set.

27. Give an example of a continuous functional on c_0 which is not bounded on the unit disk (it will not be linear, of course). $[\![\sum |a_n|^n.]\!]$

28. Following the ideas of the second proof of Theorem 2, show that if a seminormed space A_1 has a certain intersection property (if every pair of disks in a certain family intersect, the whole family has nonempty intersection), then every linear map $f\colon S \to A_1$ can be extended to any seminormed space of which S is a subspace without increase of norm (see Appendix K).

29. Let H be a discrete metric space. Show that real $B_1[H]$ has the intersection property given in Problem 28.

★30. (This problem is used only in the proof of Section 12.4, Theorem 5, and the succeeding part of Section 12.4.) Let $p_1, p_2, \ldots, p_n$ be seminorms and f a linear functional such that $|f| \leq \sum_{k=1}^{n} p_k$.

(The inequality is to be construed as pointwise, that is, holding for each $a \in A$.) Show that there exist linear functionals $f_1, f_2, \ldots, f_n$ such that $f = \Sigma f_k$ and $|f_k| \leq p_k$ for each k. 〚For $n = 2$, define a seminorm q on $A \times A$ by $q(a, b) = p_1(a) + p_2(b)$. Let $g(a, a) = f(a)$. Extend g to all of $A \times A$ with $|g| \leq q$. Take $f_1(a) = g(a, 0)$, $f_2(a) = g(0, a)$. Proceed by induction.〛

31. Suppose that $\{a_n\}$ is a sequence of vectors satisfying $\|a_n\| \to 0$, and $\{s_n\}$ is a sequence of scalars with $s_n \nrightarrow 0$. Show that, given any real number M, there exists a finite set $\{t_1, t_2, \ldots, t_n\}$ of scalars such that $|\Sigma_{k=1}^n t_k s_k| > M \|\Sigma_{k=1}^n t_k a_k\|$. 〚Corollary 4.〛

32. Let A be said to have property (e) if, for any subspace S of A, any seminormed space A_1, and any linear map $f: S \to A_1$, f can be extended to all of A without increase of norm. Let A be said to have property (p) if there exists a projection of norm 1 from A onto any subspace of A which contains a vector a with $\|a\| \neq 0$. Show that a space has property (e) if and only if it has property (p).

33. Show that R^3 with the norm $\|(x, y, z)\| = \max(|x|, |y|, |z|)$ does not have property (p) of Problem 32. 〚Consider the subspace $x + y + z = 0$.〛

34. Show that c does not have property (p) of Problem 32. 〚Any projection onto c_0 has norm greater than 1.〛

35. The Hahn-Banach theorem holds for maps from a seminormed space into R^2 with the norm $\|(x, y)\| = \max(|x|, |y|)$. Prove this (a) directly, (b) by means of problem 28.

36. Let S be a subspace of A, f a bounded linear functional defined on S, z a vector with $d(z, S) > 0$, and r a scalar. Show that there exists an extension of f to a bounded linear function F with $F(z) = r$. (However we cannot enforce $\|F\| = \|f\|$. See Problem 37.)

37. If, in Problem 36, $\|a + tz\| \geq \|a\|$ for every scalar t and $a \in S$ (one might describe this by saying that z is perpendicular to S, as it would be in R^2 or R^3), then we can choose F so that $\|F\| = \|f\|$.

▲38. Take $\|f\| = 1$ in Corollary 1. Show that the extension is unique if and only if g is linear, where $g(b) = \inf\{\|b + a\| - f(a): a \in S\}$ for every vector b.

39. Let $A: m \to m$ be a matrix. Show that $\|A\| = \sup_n \Sigma_{k=1}^\infty |a_{nk}|$.

40. Let c have the norm, $\|x\| = \sup(|x_1|, |2x_1 + x_2|, |2x_2 + x_3|, \ldots, |2x_n + x_{n+1}|, \ldots)$. Show that $\|\lim\| = \frac{1}{3}$, and $\|P_n\| = 1$ for $n = 1, 2, \ldots$

41. Let A be a conservative triangle, $B = A^{-1}$. Suppose that B has convergent columns. Let c have the norm $\|x\| = \sup|(Ax)_n|$. Find $\|\lim\|$. Show that $\|P_n\| = \Sigma_{k=1}^n |b_{nk}|$. (Problem 40 shows that the hypothesis that B has convergent columns cannot be dropped.)

42. Let Q be an $n \times n$ real, positive definite, symmetric matrix. For $a \in R^n$, define $\|a\| = (\Sigma\Sigma a_n q_{nk} a_k)^{1/2}$. Define f on R^n by $f(a) = \Sigma t_k a_k$. Show that $\|f\| = (\Sigma\Sigma t_n q'_{nk} t_k)^{1/2}$ where $Q^{-1} = (q'_{nk})$.

43. We say that $a_n \to a$ *weakly* if $f(a_n) \to f(a)$ for every $f \in A'$. Show that this implies that $\liminf \|a_n\| \geq \|a\|$. 〚Choose f with $f(a) = \|a\|$, $\|f\| = 1$. Then $\|a_n\| \geq |f(a_n)| \to \|a\|$.〛

44. Suppose that for every $f \in A'$, $Rf(a_n) \to Rf(a)$. Show that $a_n \to a$ weakly.

45. A point x in a set S is called an *extreme point* of S if x does not belong to any line segment joining two points of S which are distinct from each other and from x. Show that the unit disk of l has extreme points, while that of c_0 has none. (Compare the situation in R^2 with the norms, respectively, of c_0, l. The two resulting spaces are congruent, (see Section 6.1, Definition 2,) while c_0, l are not, because of the extreme point property just mentioned.)

46. A positive linear functional on real $B_1[H]$ is continuous (H is an arbitrary set). 〚For $a \in B_1[H]$, $\|a\| \pm a \geq 0$, thus $\|a\| f(1) \pm f(a) \geq 0$. Hence $\|f\| = f(1)$.〛 Problem 48 extends this result.

47. Let A be an ordered real linear space with order identity e. Define $\|a\| = \inf\{t > 0: -te \leq a \leq te\}$. Show that this is a norm, that $\|e\| = 1$, and that, with $e = 1$, this yields the natural norm for real $B_1[H]$, real c, *et cetera*.

48. In the situation described in problem 47, every positive linear functional is continuous, indeed $\|f\| = f(e)$.

49. Let P_2 be the space of real polynomials of degree 2 or less with norm as in Problem 22. Let $g(f) = f'(0)$ for $f \in P_2$. Evaluate $\|g\|$.

▲50. What is the extension, without increase of norm, of g, Problem 49, to P_3?

5

SEMIMETRIC SPACE

5.1 Semimetric space

This section continues the discussion begun in Section 4.3. We assume, in the following definitions, that a semimetric space is given and the sets mentioned are in it. The numbered definitions in this section are so worded that they may be taken bodily into Chapter 9.

DEFINITION 1. *The closure of a set* S, *written* S̄, *is the intersection of all closed sets which include* S.

Notice that there is always a closed set which includes S [the whole space] and so the class mentioned is not empty. $\bar{S}$ is closed [Section 4.3, Problem 14] and is the smallest closed set which includes S. For semimetric spaces we have an instructive equivalence.

THEOREM 1. *Let* S *be a set, and* a *a point in a semimetric space. Then* a $\in$ S̄ *if and only if there exists a sequence* $\{x_n\}$ *of points of* S *with* $x_n \to$ a.

Suppose first that $a \notin \bar{S}$. Then $\tilde{\bar{S}}$ is an (open) neighborhood of a not meeting S. Thus any sequence of points of S must lie entirely outside this neighborhood, and so cannot converge to x. Conversely, suppose that $a \in \bar{S}$. For each positive integer n, $N(a, 1/n)$ meets S [since, otherwise its complement would be a closed set including S but not a, contradicting $a \in \bar{S}$.] For $n = 1, 2, \ldots$ let $x_n \in N(a, 1/n) \cap S$. Then $x_n \to a$, since $d(a, x_n) < 1/n.//$

COROLLARY 1. *A set* S *in a semimetric space is closed if and only if whenever* $x_n \in$ S *for* n $= 1, 2,$ $\ldots$, *and* $x_n \to$ a *it follows that* a $\in$ S.

DEFINITION 2. *A function* f: A $\to$ B *is called a homeomorphism from* A *into* B *if it is one to one and continuous and* f^{-1}: f[A] $\to$ A *is also continuous; a homeomorphism onto if, in addition,* f *is onto. In this case we say that* A, B *are homeomorphic.*

Our next definition (isometry) will have no counterpart in Chapter 9. A function $f: A \to B$, A, B being semimetric spaces, is called an *isometry* if it is one to one and $d[f(a), f(b)] = d(a, b)$ for all $a, b \in A$. (The assumption "one to one" is redundant if A is a metric space.) Two spaces are called *isometric* if there is an isometry from each onto the other. An isometry is clearly a homeomorphism.

DEFINITION 3. *A function* f: A → B *is called open, or interior, if* f[G] *is open whenever* G *is open.*

This generalizes the property of having a continuous inverse, for a function is open if it has a continuous inverse (defined on the whole range space; in particular, f is onto) ⟦Section 4.3, Problem 18⟧, while some functions are open which have no inverse at all, for example $P_1: R^2 \to R$. Clearly f is open if and only if $f[N]$ is a neighborhood of $f(a)$ whenever N is a neighborhood of a.

DEFINITION 4. *A set* S *is called dense in a set* T *if* $\bar{S} \supset T$; *it is called dense if it is dense in the whole space. If a set is dense in some open (nonempty) set, it is called somewhere dense; if not, it is called nowhere dense.*

Thus S is somewhere dense if and only if $\bar{S}$ includes a cell of positive radius. For example, the set of rational numbers is dense in R, while R is not dense in R^2; indeed, it is nowhere dense in R^2. The famous Weierstrass approximation theorem says that the set of polynomials is dense in real C.

DEFINITION 5. *A set is said to be of first category if it is the union of a countable family of nowhere dense sets; if not, it is said to be of second category.*

In this definition, nowhere dense means nowhere dense in the semimetric space. For example, the set of rationals is of first category in R ⟦for it is a countable union of points; each point is nowhere dense, its closure, namely itself, having no interior point, since it includes no cell of positive radius⟧, and also in R^2 ⟦since it is nowhere dense in R^2⟧. It is also of first category in itself. The set ω of integers is of first category in R ⟦since it is nowhere dense in R⟧ but is of second category in itself. ⟦Each of its points is a cell of radius $\frac{1}{2}$ (or any other number between 0 and 1); thus each of its points is somewhere dense and so ω has no subsets, except the empty set, which are nowhere dense. Our conclusion also follows from the Baire category theorem, which is given in Section 3.⟧

If a set is given two semimetrics d_1, d_2, we say that d_1 is *stronger than* d_2, and d_2 is *weaker than* d_1 if, whenever $\{x_n\}$ is a sequence satisfying $x_n \to x(d_1)$ [that is, $d_1(x_n, x) \to 0$], it follows that $x_n \to x(d_2)$. If each is stronger than the other, we call the semimetrics *equivalent;* otherwise one is *strictly* stronger, and one is strictly weaker. This agrees with the definition of strength given in Section 4.1, Definition 2, in which the semimetric comes from a paranorm.

THEOREM 2. *A stronger semimetric is one with more open sets; that is,* d_1 *is stronger than* d_2 *if and only if every* d_2-*open set is* d_1-*open.*

Suppose first that every d_2-open set is d_1-open. Let $x_n \to x(d_1)$, and let G be a d_2-neighborhood of x. Clearly G is a d_1-neighborhood of x ⟦for x is d_2-interior to G, hence d_1-interior⟧, thus $x_n \in G$ for almost all n. Hence $x_n \to x(d_2)$.

Conversely, suppose that not every d_2-open set is d_1-open. Then there exists a set G which is d_2-open, but not d_1-open. Let x be a point of G which is not d_1-interior to G.

Since x is not d_1-interior to G, G does not include any d_1 cell centered at x and so for each $n = 1, 2, 3, \ldots$, it follows that $N_1(x, 1/n) \not\subset G$. (The notation N_1 denotes a d_1-cell.) Thus there exists $x_n \in N_1(x, 1/n) \setminus G$. Since, for all n, $x_n \notin G$, it follows that $x_n \not\to x(d_2)$. However $x_n \to x(d_1)$ [since $d_1(x_n, x) < 1/n \to 0$; Section 4.3, Problem 5]. By definition of strength, it follows that d_1 is not stronger than d_2.//

Problems 5.1

In this list, (A, d) is a semimetric space; S, T are sets in A.

1. $d(x, S) = 0$ if and only if $x \in \bar{S}$.

★2. Give an example of a function from one metric space to another which is continuous, one to one, and onto, but is not a homeomorphism. [The identity map with the discrete metric on its domain.]

★3. Give an example of a function from $[0, 1]$ to itself which is continuous and onto, but not open (it may also be monotone). (Such a function cannot be one to one; see Section 9.5, Theorem 4.)

4. Let f be an analytic function in the sense of the theory of functions of a complex variable. Then f is open (if it is not constant), and the maximum modulus theorem is a corollary.

5. Consider R^+, and $R^+ \cup \{-1\}$ as subspaces of R. Show that they are not isometric, but that each is isometric into the other. (Thus metric spaces do not obey the crisscross condition for isometry.)

★6. A set is dense if and only if every open set (except $\emptyset$) contains a point of it.

★7. S is dense in T if and only if, for every point of T, there is a sequence of points of S which converges to it.

8. Show that the set of step functions (each with a finite number of steps) is dense in real C.

9. The union of a finite collection of nowhere dense sets is nowhere dense.

10. The complement of a dense open set is nowhere dense and the complement of a dense G_δ is of first category. (A G_δ is a set which is the intersection of a sequence of open sets.)

11. l is dense, but of the first category, in c_0.

12. m is dense, but of the first category, in s.

★13. The discrete metric is stronger than every semimetric.

14. Let d_1, d_2 be semimetrics for a set A. Show that d_1 is stronger than d_2 if and only if $i: (A, d_1) \to (A, d_2)$ is continuous. Also d_2 is stronger than d_1 if and only if this map is open.

★15. State and prove the analogue for semimetrics of Section 4.1, Problem 13.

★16. Let d_1, d_2 be semimetrics for a set A, with d_1 stronger than d_2. Show that if $f: (A, d_2) \to B$ is continuous, so is $f: (A, d_1) \to B$. What is the situation for maps from B to A? [$f_1 = f_2 \circ i$; see Problem 14.]

17. A real function f is called *lower semicontinuous* if $\{a: f(a) \leq t\}$ is closed for each real t. We shall extend the definition to allow $f(a) = +\infty$ for certain a, the convention being that if $f(x) = +\infty$, $x \notin \{a: f(a) \leq t\}$ for all t. Prove that if the domain of f is a semimetric space, f is lower semicontinuous if and only if for each sequence $\{a_n\}$ with $a_n \to a$, $\liminf f(a_n) \geq f(a)$, with the usual convention if $f(a) = +\infty$, *et cetera* (compare with Section 4.4, Problem 43). If $-f$ is lower semicontinuous, we call f *upper semicontinuous*.

18. Let Φ be a family of real continuous functions, $f(a) = \sup \{g(a): g \in \Phi\}$ for each a. Show that f is lower semicontinuous.

19. Σa_n is not lower semicontinuous on the normed space E^∞ with $\|a\| = \sup |a_n|$.

20. Deduce Section 4.3, Problem 31 from Problem 18, above.

21. Find a metric space which is a bounded subset of the Euclidean plane with the Euclidean distance, and which is isometric with a proper subset of itself.

22. Show that a compact (Chapter 9) metric space cannot be isometric with a proper subset of itself.

23. A space is called *separable* if it has a countable dense set in it. Show that every separable metric space is isometric with a subset of m. 〖Let $\{a_n\}$ be dense, fix b. Let $u(x) = \{d(x, a_n) - d(a_n, b)\}$.〗

24. Show that A is isometric with a subset of $C_1[A]$. 〖Fix b. Define $u(a) \in C_1[A]$ by $u(a)(\alpha) = d(a, \alpha) - d(\alpha, b)$.〗

25. Let D be a dense subset of A. Show as in Problem 24 that A is isometric with a subset of $C_1[D]$. This has the advantage that Problem 23 is a special case.

26. In the map given in proof brackets in Problem 24 show that any two distinct points of A, neither of which is b, map into linearly independent elements of $C_1[A]$. For three points this may be no longer true. 〖Let $A = (b, x, y, z)$, $d(b, y) = d(b, z) = d(x, y) = d(x, z) = 1$, $d(b, x) = d(y, z) = 2$. Then $u(x) = u(y) + u(z)$.〗

27. c_0 is separable but m is not. 〖In c_0 the set of finite sequences with rational terms is dense. In m the set of sequences of zeros and ones has $\|a - b\| = 1$ for any two members. There are an uncountable number of them because there are uncountably many numbers in the interval $[0, 1]$, each of which can be written in binary notation as a sequence of zeros and ones.〗

5.2 Cardinality and structure

The remarks in this section are classified as trivial by mathematicians. There is one central idea: let A be a set, let B be a space of some kind, and assume that A and B are in one-to-one correspondence; then A can be given structure to make it identical (that is, isomorphic, homeomorphic, isometric, . . .) with B. For example, let B be a metric space and let $u: A \to B$ be a one-to-one correspondence from A onto B. For x, $y \in A$ define $d(x, y) = d[u(x), u(y)]$. This makes A a metric space isometric with B, indeed u is the isometry. We say that the metric has been *transferred* from B to A.

The question is often raised, can a space be given a different structure? This is equivalent to asking, is the space of the same cardinality as some space with a different structure?

Example 1. Make the interval $(0, 1)$ of R into a metric space of infinite diameter. This is done by observing that the cardinality of $(0, 1)$ is the same as that of R.

Example 2. Make the interval $(0, 1)$ of R into a linear space. Again we choose a function $u: (0, 1) \to R$ which is one to-one and onto and we set $ta + b = u^{-1}[tu(a) + u(b)]$.

These examples are trivial and could hardly be expected to have any application. A slightly deeper remark is the following: if A, B are semimetric spaces and $u: A \to B$ is a homeomorphism onto, then the semimetric of B, when transferred to A, is equivalent to that of A. For example, if $\{x_n\}$ is a convergent sequence in A, then $\{u(x_n)\}$ is convergent in B and so $\{x_n\}$ is, by definition, convergent in A under the transferred semimetric D defined by $D(a, b) = d[u(a), u(b)]$ for $a, b \in A$.

Example 3. Make the interval $(0, 1)$ of R into a metric space of infinite diameter with an equivalent metric. Here we take $u: (0, 1) \to R$ to be $u(x) = \log(-\log x)$ or any other homeomorphism onto, and use it to remetrize $(0, 1)$ as in Example 1.

Of course, the problem raised in Example 3 is identical with the problem: find a homeomorphism of $(0, 1)$ with a space of infinite diameter.

Suppose, again, that A is a set, B a space of some kind, and that A, B are in one-to-one correspondence by $u: A \to B$. Let f be any function defined on B. Then $f \circ u$ is an exactly similar function on A with the transferred structure.   We call $f \circ u$ the result of *transferring* f to A.   As expected, we have, in the case of seminormed spaces, entirely without calculation, the fact that $\|f\|$ is unchanged by the transfer [A, B, and f, $f \circ u$, are being identified].

★*Example 4*.   Let A be the set of all sequences a such that $na_n \to 0$.   Define $u: A \to c_0$ by $u(a) = \{na_n\}$.   This is a one-to-one correspondence onto.   Now consider the continuous linear functional f on c_0 given by $f(a) = \Sigma a_n/n!$.
    The following remark should be regarded as a triviality.   Transferring f to A yields the function $f(a) = \Sigma na_n/n!$, and $\|f\| = \Sigma 1/n!$.

Problems 5.2

  1. Make $(0, 1)$ into a 3-dimensional linear space.
  2. Make the integers into a metric space with the property that each integer is the limit of a convergent sequence of other integers.
  3. Show that use of a continuous function $f: A \to B$ will transfer to A from B a semimetric weaker than that of A.   What f would yield a strictly weaker one?
  4. Make the set of positive integers into a totally ordered poset such that between any two integers there is another integer.
  5. Show that the interval $[0, 1]$ of R cannot be given an equivalent metric in which it has infinite diameter.
  6. What is the largest dimension of any linear space into which $(0, 1)$ could be made?
  7. Let A be a triangle.   Then $A: c_A \to c$ is a one-to-one correspondence onto.   Show that the natural norm for c_A is the result of transferring to it the natural norm of c.
  8. (Continuing Problem 7.)   Define $f \in c'$ by $f(x) = \chi \lim x + \Sigma t_n x_n$, $\Sigma |t_n| < \infty$.   Transfer f to c_A.   What functional results?   [$\chi \lim_A x + \Sigma t_n (Ax)_n$.]
  9. A matrix A is called *reversible* if the equation $y = Ax$ has a unique solution x for each $y \in c$. For a reversible matrix A, show how to make c_A a normed space congruent with c.   Continue as in Problem 8.
▲10. Give an example of a row-infinite reversible matrix.

5.3   Completeness

In the parts of functional analysis dealing with semimetric spaces, completeness is a crucial assumption.   On the one hand, the historically important examples, R, E, l^2, to name a few, are complete.   On the other hand, the powerful theorems such as the closed graph theorem (Chapter 11), cease to be true if the assumption of completeness is dropped and counterexamples to many nice assertions abound among incomplete spaces.

    DEFINITION 1.   *A Cauchy sequence in a semimetric space is a sequence* $\{a_n\}$ *such that to each* $\epsilon > 0$, *there corresponds a number* N *such that* $d(a_p, a_q) < \epsilon$ *whenever* p $>$ N *and* q $>$ N.
    A semimetric space is called complete if every Cauchy sequence in it is convergent.

As two examples of incomplete spaces we cite the space of rational numbers and the interval $(0, 1)$, each as a subspace of R.   In the first of these two spaces a nonconvergent Cauchy sequence is given by a sequence of rationals converging to an irrational number, in the second by the sequence $\{1/n\}$. Two other incomplete spaces are the space of polynomials as a normed subspace of C [that is, $\|f\| = \max\{|f(t)|: 0 \leq t \leq 1\}$] and E^∞ as a normed subspace of m. In the first space we choose a sequence of polynomials converging uniformly on $[0, 1]$ to a nonpolynomial function, for example, $\{\Sigma_{k=0}^n x^k/k!\}$, and in the second, $\{a_n\}$, where $a_n = \Sigma_{k=1}^n \delta^k/k = \{1, \frac{1}{2}, \frac{1}{3}, \ldots, 1/n, 0, 0, \ldots\}$. In all four examples, the chosen sequence is convergent in a space including the given one, hence is a Cauchy sequence. [*Every convergent sequence is a Cauchy sequence* since $d(a_p, a_q) \leq d(a_p, a) + d(a_q, a)$, so, if $a_n \to a$, $d(a_p, a_q)$ can be made small by taking p, q sufficiently large.] Every Cauchy sequence is of this form because every metric space is a dense subset of some complete space, [Problems 23, 24] called its *completion*.

The spaces E and R are complete. This is the *fundamental principle of convergence*. We shall give two other examples of complete spaces.

Example 1: C is complete. Let $\{f_n\}$ be a Cauchy sequence in C. For each $x \in [0, 1]$, we have $|f_p(x) - f_q(x)| \leq \|f_p - f_q\|$ and so $\{f_n(x)\}$ is a Cauchy sequence of complex numbers; hence it is convergent. Let $f: [0, 1] \to E$ be defined by $f(x) = \lim f_n(x)$ for each x. Then $f_n \to f$ uniformly on $[0, 1]$ [since, given $\epsilon > 0$, $|f_p(x) - f_q(x)| < \epsilon$ for sufficiently large p, q (independent of x), and all x; letting $p \to \infty$ we obtain $|f(x) - f_q(x)| \leq \epsilon$ for sufficiently large q]. Finally $f \in C$, since the limit of a uniformly convergent sequence of continuous functions is continuous; and $\|f - f_n\| \to 0$, that is, $f_n \to f$.//

Before turning to the other example, we interpolate a definition and a lemma. A sequence $\{x_n\}$ is said to be *metrically bounded* if it is included in some disk, that is, if there exists a point a and a real number r such that $d(a, x_n) \leq r$ for all n.

LEMMA 1. *A Cauchy sequence is metrically bounded.*

Let $\{x_n\}$ be a Cauchy sequence. Choose a number M such that $d(x_p, x_q) < 1$ for $p > M$, $q > M$. Let $r_1 = \max\{d(x_k, x_{M+1}): k = 1, 2, \ldots, M\}$, $r = \max(1, r_1)$. Then for $k = 1, 2, \ldots, M$, $d(x_k, x_{M+1}) \leq r_1 \leq r$, while for $k > M$, $d(x_k, x_{M+1}) < 1 \leq r$. Thus $x_k \in D(x_{M+1}, r)$ for all k.//

LEMMA 2. *Every Cauchy sequence is included in a disk and the disk may be chosen to have any desired point as center.*

Let a be any point. Let $t = d(a, x_{M+1}) + r$, using the notation of the proof of Lemma 1. Clearly $x_k \in D(a, t)$ for all k.//

In the case of a seminormed space, we usually take $a = 0$, and announce that if $\{x_n\}$ is a Cauchy sequence, $\{\|x_n\|\}$ is bounded.

Example 2: l^p, $p \geq 1$, is complete. Let $\{a^n\}$ be a Cauchy sequence. We are using superscripts, that is, $\{a^n\} = \{a^1, a^2, \ldots\}$, and $a^n = \{a_1^n, a_2^n, \ldots\}$, thus each a_k^n is a complex number. For each k, $|a_k^m - a_k^n| = [|a_k^m - a_k^n|^p]^{1/p} \leq \|a^m - a^n\|$, and so, for each fixed k, $\{a_k^n\}$ is a Cauchy sequence of complex numbers, hence convergent. Let $a_k = \lim_{n\to\infty} a_k^n$. This defines a sequence $a = \{a_k\}$ of complex numbers, $a \in l^p$. [For each m, n, $\Sigma_{k=1}^m |a_k^n|^p \leq \Sigma_{k=1}^\infty |a_k^n|^p = (\|a^n\|)^p < M$ for some number M (independent of m, n) by Lemma 2. Taking the limit as $n \to \infty$, we obtain $\Sigma_{k=1}^m |a_k|^p \leq M$, hence $\Sigma_{k=1}^\infty |a_k|^p \leq M$ since m is arbitrary.]

Then $a^n \to a$ [Given $\epsilon > 0$, there exists a number N such that $\|a^m - a^n\| < \epsilon$ for $m > N$ $n > N$. Thus, for each q, $[\Sigma_{k=1}^q |a_k^m - a_k^n|^p]^{1/p} \leq \|a^m - a^n\| < \epsilon$. Taking the limit as $m \to \infty$, we obtain $[\Sigma_{k=1}^q |a_k - a_k^n|^p]^{1/p} \leq \epsilon$. Since q is arbitrary we have, finally, $\|a - a^n\| \leq \epsilon$ if $n > N$].//

Finally we remark that L^p, $p > 0$, is complete. This is a standard fact of Lebesgue measure theory.

In describing completeness it is customary to say that the semimetric, or the seminorm, is complete. Thus for the set of rationals, the ordinary metric is incomplete, while the discrete metric is complete [Problem 9]. This means that the set of rationals with the ordinary metric is incomplete, while, with the discrete metric, it is complete.

DEFINITION 2.   *A complete normed space is called a Banach space.   A complete linear metric space is called a Fréchet space.*

We now turn to the Baire category theorem, a fundamental result. It is the tool by means of which completeness is used in most phases of functional analysis. We shall give its statement and proof after a preliminary lemma.

LEMMA 3.   *Let $\{G_n\}$ be a sequence of dense open sets in a complete semimetric space.   Then the intersection $\cap G_n$ is also dense.*

Let N be a cell. G_1, being dense and open, meets N in an open set, hence their intersection includes a disk, say $D(a_1, r_1) \subset N \cap G_1$. For the same reason, $G_2 \cap N(a_1, r_1)$ includes a disk, say $D(a_2, r_2)$ and we may take $r_2 < \frac{1}{2}r_1$. Continuing in this way, we obtain a decreasing sequence $\{D(a_n, r_n)\}$ with $D(a_n, r_n) \subset N \cap G_n$ for each n, and $r_n \to 0$. Since for $m > n$, $a_m \in D(a_n, r_n)$, we have $d(a_m, a_n) \leq r_n$. It follows that $\{a_n\}$ is a Cauchy sequence, hence convergent. Let $a_n \to a$. Then $a \in D(a_n, r_n)$ for each n [since $a_m \in D(a_n, r_n)$ for $m > n$, $a_m \to a$, and $D(a_n, r_n)$ is closed]. Clearly $a \in N$ and $a \in G_n$ for each n. Since N is arbitrary, $\cap G_n$ is seen to be dense [Section 1, Problem 6].//

THEOREM 1.   THE BAIRE CATEGORY THEOREM.   *A complete semimetric space is of second category in itself.*

Let $\{A_n\}$ be a sequence of nowhere dense sets. Then $\{\tilde{\bar{A}}_n\}$ is a sequence of dense [since $\bar{A}_n$ has no interior points] open sets, hence, by Lemma 3, has nonempty intersection. This shows that $\cup A_n$ is not the whole space, and completes the proof.//

We did not use the full force of Lemma 3. It was merely the nonemptiness, rather than the density, of $\cap G_n$ that was used. Had we used the density, we would have gotten the result that any cell of positive radius in a complete semimetric space is of second category in the space.

Problems on semimetric space 5.3

★1. $\{a_n\}$ is a Cauchy sequence if and only if, for any $\epsilon > 0$, there exists N such that $p > q > N$ implies $d(x_p, x_q) < \epsilon$.

★2. If a Cauchy sequence has a convergent subsequence, it is convergent.

3. If $\{x_n\}$, and $\{y_n\}$ are Cauchy sequences, $\{d(x_n, y_n)\}$ is convergent.

4. If $\Sigma d(x_n, x_{n+1}) < \infty$, then $\{x_n\}$ is a Cauchy sequence.

5. A real Cauchy sequence $\{x_n\}$ converges to inf $\{\sup \{x_k: k \geq n\}: n = 1, 2, 3, \ldots\}$.

★6. A closed set in a complete semimetric space is itself complete, and a complete subspace of any metric space is closed. (Here, metric cannot be replaced by semimetric). A complete true subspace of a semimetric space is closed.

★7. Give an example of two homeomorphic metric spaces, one of which is complete, and one not. $[f: R \to (-1, 1)$, given by $f(x) = x/(1 + |x|).]$ As in Section 2, we see that this is also an example of two equivalent metrics, only one of which is complete.

8. A homeomorphism need not preserve Cauchy sequences [Problem 7], but a homeomorphism between complete semimetric spaces preserves Cauchy sequences.

9. Prove the completeness of (a) every discrete metric space, (b) every indiscrete semimetric space, (c) every finite semimetric space.

10. Prove the completeness of (a) R^2, (b) E^n.

11. Prove the completeness of some of the spaces listed in the Table of Spaces. [In the case of E_C, A_C, the Weierstrass double series theorem may be used.]

12. Show that E^∞ is not complete with $\|x\| = \Sigma |x_n|$.

13. Show that c is complete with the norm given in Section 4.4, Problem 40, and not complete with $\|x\| = \sup(|x_1|, |x_1 + x_2|, |x_2 + x_3|, \ldots)$

14. Show that C is not complete with the (unnatural) norm, $\|f\| = \int_0^1 |f|$.

★15. If a semimetric d is the Fréchet combination of a sequence $\{d_n\}$ of semimetrics on a set A as in Section 4.3, Problem 9, show that a sequence of points is a Cauchy sequence in (A, d) if and only if it is a Cauchy sequence in each (A, d_n).

16. Continuing Problem 15. If each d_n is complete, so is d.

17. Continuing Problem 16, d may be complete while each d_n is not. $[E_C$. That $\|\cdot\|_n$ is not complete follows from consideration of a power series with finite radius of convergence larger than n.]

18. Let A be a semimetric space and let B be the metric space obtained by identifying points whose distance apart is 0. (B may be taken to be the subset obtained by selecting one point from each true subset of A of diameter 0, or we may take B to be the set of all true subsets of A of diameter 0; compare with Section 2.8.) Show that B is complete if and only if A is.

19. Let A, B be semimetric spaces and $f: A \to B$. If f maps each convergent sequence into a Cauchy sequence, f is continuous.

20. A function $f: A \to B$, A, B semimetric spaces, is called *closed* if whenever $x_n \to x$ and $f(x_n) \to y$, it follows that $y = f(x)$. Let A, B be semimetric spaces, and $f: A \to B$. For a, $b \in A$, define $D(a, b) = d(a, b) + d[f(a), f(b)]$. (a) Show that D, d are equivalent if and only if $f: (A, d) \to B$ is continuous. (b) Show that $f: (A, D) \to B$ is continuous. (c) Assume that $f: (A, d) \to B$ is continuous, and (A, d) is complete. Show that (A, D) is complete (see Problem 7). (d) Assume that $f: (A, d) \to B$ is closed and that (A, d) and B are complete; show that (A, D) is complete. (e) Assume that (A, D) and (A, d) are complete and that B is a metric space; show that $f: (A, d) \to B$ is closed.

21. A closed additive map between linear semimetric spaces is real linear.

22. A perfect set in a complete metric space is noncountable. (A is called *perfect* if it is closed, nonempty, and each point of A is a limit of a sequence of other points of A; that is, $A \setminus \{x\}$ is dense in A for each x.) [If countable, it would be of first category in itself.]

23. A *completion* of a metric space A is a complete metric space in which A is dense. Show that $u[A]$ in Section 1, Problem 24, is a completion of A.

24. Let A_1 be the set of Cauchy sequences in a semimetric space A. For $x, y \in A_1$, define $d(x, y) = \lim_{n\to\infty} d(x_n, y_n)$. Show that this makes A_1 into a complete semimetric space in which A is dense. [Define $f: A \to A_1$ by $f(a) = \{a, a, a, \ldots\}$. Then f is an isometry onto a dense set in A_1.] If A is a metric space, and A_1 is made into a metric space as in Problem 18, it will be a completion of A.

25. Any two completions of a metric space are isometric.

26. Let $\{D_n\}$ be a sequence of disks in a complete metric space satisfying $D_{n+1} \subset D_n$ for each n, and radius $D_n \to 0$. Show that $\cap D_n$ is not empty. Show also that neither of the hypotheses, "completeness," and "radius $D_n \to 0$," can be dropped.

27. Give an example of a complete metric space which is the union of two disjoint subsets which are homeomorphic with each other and such that one of the two subsets is nowhere dense. (There is a subspace of R^2 with this property.)

28. Give an example of a noncomplete metric space which is homeomorphic with its completion. (There is a subspace of R^2 with this property.)

29. The set of rationals is not a G_δ in R [Section 1, Problem 10].

30. Show that a metric space A is open in its completion if and only if it is *locally complete;* that is, each point is included in some complete disk of positive radius.

31. A locally complete metric space may be given an equivalent complete metric. [Let A_1 be its completion, D as in Problem 20 with $f(a) = 1/d(a, A_1 \setminus A)$, $B = R$. Part (a) applies by Problem 30.] A partial converse is given in the next problem, and an exact result in Problem 33.

32. Let A be a metric space and B a subset of A which is homeomorphic with some complete metric space, or equivalently, which can be given an equivalent complete metric. Show that B is a G_δ in A. [Let $G_n = \{x \in \bar{B}$: there exists r such that the diameter of $f[N(x, r)] < 1/n\}$; here f is the postulated homeomorphism. Then $B = \cap G_n$.]

33. Prove the converse of Problem 32, assuming that A is complete; that is, if B is a G_δ in A, B can be given an equivalent complete metric.

6

LINEAR SEMIMETRIC SPACE

6.1 Linear semimetric space

We continue the discussion begun in Section 4.3. This chapter bears the same relationship to Chapter 10, that the preceding chapter bears to Chapter 9.

In attempting to combine the studies of linear spaces and semimetric spaces, one might be inclined to begin with a set that is simultaneously a semimetric space and a linear space. Such an assumption would be too broad, since no connection is assumed between the semimetric and the linear operations. As a single example, we would be unable to prove that if $a_n \rightarrow a$, then $a_n - a \rightarrow 0$. Under these circumstances each result would be either a semimetric or a linear result, and the theories would best be carried out separately.

It is natural to restrict our attention to those spaces, each of which is a linear and a semimetric space and which has the additional property that the linear operations are continuous functions; that is, that ta and $a + b$ are continuous functions of the scalar t and the vectors a, b.

It turns out, however, that such a space must have the property that its semimetric is equivalent to a semimetric which comes from a paranorm. This will be proved in Section 10.4, Theorem 2. It is for this reason that in Section 4.3, Definition 5, a linear semimetric space is defined to be one whose semimetric comes from a paranorm. The theorem of Chapter 10 which was just mentioned assures us that this definition is as general as the one suggested above. Recall, of course, that, as proved in Section 4.3 just before Definition 5, the functions ta and $a + b$ are continuous in case the semimetric comes from a paranorm.

DEFINITION 1. *A linear function which is also a homeomorphism is called a linear homeomorphism. If it is an isometry, it is called a congruence.*

DEFINITION 2. *Two spaces are called linearly homeomorphic if there is a linear homeomorphism from one onto the other. They are called congruent if there is a congruence from one onto the other.*

Thus for example, if A is a triangle, c_A and c are congruent [Section 5.2, Problem 7].

THEOREM 1. *Let A be a linear semimetric space, B a linear metric space, and* f: A → B *a continuous additive function. Then* f *is real linear.*

By Section 2.4, Theorem 1, f is rational homogeneous. Now, given any real number t, let $\{r_n\}$ be a sequence of rationals converging to t. Then for any vector a, $r_n a \to ta$ ⟦by Part (v) of the definition of paranorm⟧, hence $f(r_n a) \to f(ta)$. But $f(r_n a) = r_n f(a)$ and so $f(r_n a) \to tf(a)$. Thus $f(ta) = tf(a)$, since in B, a metric space, limits are unique.//

For the next result recall the notation $!a!$ for paranorm given in Section 4.3.

LEMMA 1. *Let $\{a_n\}$ be a Cauchy sequence. Then $\{a_n\}$ has a subsequence $\{b_n\}$ satisfying* $\Sigma\, !b_{n+1} - b_n! < \infty$.

Choose N_1 so that $m > n \geq N_1$ implies $!a_m - a_n! < \frac{1}{2}$. Choose $N_2 > N_1$ so that $m > n \geq N_2$ implies $!a_m - a_n! < \frac{1}{4}$, and in general $N_k > N_{k-1}$ so that $m \geq n > N_k$ implies $!a_m - a_n! < 2^{-k}$. Let $b_n = a_{N_n}$.//

Problems 6.1

Each problem in this list deals with a linear semimetric space, unless otherwise stated.

1. For $z = (x, y) \in R^2$, let $!z! = |x| + |y|/(1 + |y|)$. Show that this is a paranorm. Draw $C(0, 1)$, $C(0, \frac{1}{2})$.

2. Show that the paranorm given in Problem 1 is equivalent to the Euclidean norm, $(x^2 + y^2)^{1/2}$.

★3. For any positive integer n, $nN(0, 1) \subset N(0, n)$.

★4. In a seminormed space $rN(0, s) = sN(0, r) = N(0, rs)$ if $r > 0$, $s > 0$, and similar results for C and D in place of N.

5. In l^p, $0 < p < 1$, $N(0, r) = r^{1/p}N(0, 1)$ for $r > 0$.

6. $N(a, r) - N(a, r) \subset N(0, 2r)$.

★7. In a seminormed space, $N(a, r) - N(a, r) = N(0, 2r)$. ⟦For $\|x\| < 2r$, let $u = a + \frac{1}{2}x$, $v = a - \frac{1}{2}x$. Then $x = u - v$.⟧

8. $!x!$ is a continuous function of x. ⟦$|\,!a! - !b!\,| \leq !a - b!$.⟧

★9. A continuous linear map between linear semimetric spaces is uniformly continuous; that is, given $\epsilon > 0$, there exists $\delta > 0$ such that $d(x, y) < \delta$ implies $d[f(x), f(y)] < \epsilon$. ⟦First take $x = 0$.⟧

★10. A continuous linear map between linear semimetric spaces preserves Cauchy sequences. ⟦Use Problem 9.⟧ Hence any linear semimetric space linearly homeomorphic with a complete linear semimetric space is complete. In particular, equivalent invariant semimetrics have the same Cauchy sequences and hence are both complete or both not complete. (Problem 43 gives a better result.)

11. If $na \to 0$ as $n \to \infty$, show that $!a! = 0$.

12. $\overline{\{0\}} = \{a \colon !a! = 0\}$. [This is a linear subspace by Section 4.1, Fact (iv).]

13. A neighborhood of 0 is absorbing.

14. Suppose that $\{t_n\}$ is a sequence of scalars and a a vector with $!a! \neq 0$ such that $\{t_n a\}$ is convergent. Show that $\{t_n\}$ is convergent.

15. In a seminormed space, show that $\overline{N(0, r)} = D(0, r)$ for $r \neq 0$.

16. Give an example of a linear metric space such that $\overline{N(0, 1)} \neq D(0,1)$. ⟦A one-dimensional example can be based on Section 4.1, Problem 21.⟧

17. Suppose that $\{a_n\}$ is a Cauchy sequence of vectors, and $\{t_n\}$ a convergent sequence of scalars. Show that $\{t_n a_n\}$ is a Cauchy sequence.

18. Suppose that $\{a_n\}$ is a sequence of vectors with $a_n \to 0$. Show that there exists a sequence $\{t_n\}$ of scalars with $t_n \to \infty$, $t_n a_n \to 0$.

19. An open set G is convex if and only if $G + G = 2G$.

20. If G is open, so are $a + G$, tG, for any vector a, and scalar $t \neq 0$.

21. The convex hull of an open set is open.

22. If A, B are subsets of a linear semimetric space such that $A - B$ is closed, and $d(A, B) = 0$, then A, B have a point in common.

23. In Theorem 1, f need not be homogeneous.

★24. Let f, g be continuous functions from a semimetric space to a linear semimetric space. Show that $f + g$ is continuous.

25. Given a continuous linear functional on a linear metric space (even a one-dimensional one), there need not exist a constant M such that $|f(a)| \leq M$!a! for all a. 〚!a! $= |a|/(1 + |a|)$ for $a \in R$.〛

26. Given a continuous linear function from a linear metric space to itself (even a two-dimensional one), there need not exist a constant M such that !$f(a)$! $\leq M$!a! for all a. 〚!(x, y)! $= |x| + |y|/(1 + |y|)$, $f(x, y) = (x + y, 0)$.〛

★27. Let S be a dense set in a seminormed space, and f a continuous linear functional. Show that $\|f\|_S = \|f\|$. 〚If $b \in S$, $\|b\| = \|a\| = 1$, then $|f(a)| \leq |f(a - b)| + |f(b)| \leq \|f\| \cdot \|a - b\| + \|f\|_S$.〛

28. All total paranorms on E are equivalent. (Hence each one-dimensional subspace of a linear metric space is linearly homeomorphic with E. The same is true for real spaces and R.)

29. Let !a! $\neq 0$. Show that $C(0, \frac{1}{2}$!a!$)$ is not empty, and give an example in which $C(0, 2$!a!$)$ is.

★30. Suppose that in a seminormed space, $C(a, r)$ contains three collinear points x, y, z. Then it includes the whole line segment joining x, y.

31. Show that Problem 30 is false in general for linear metric space. 〚$(|z|)^{1/2}$ on E.〛

32. In a normed space, given vectors a, b with $\|a\| = \|b\| = 1$, show that there exists a vector x with $\|x\| = 1$, $\|a - x\| = \|b - x\|$.

33. Show that Problem 32 is false in general for linear metric space. 〚R^2, !(x, y)! $= |x|/(1 + |x|) + |y|/(1 + |y|)$.〛

34. In a normed space, let x, y, z, be points on a line in that order (that is, $y = tx + (1 - t)z$, $0 < t < 1$). Show that

$$\frac{\|z\| - \|y\|}{\|z - y\|} \geq \frac{\|z\| - \|x\|}{\|z - x\|} \geq \frac{\|y\| - \|x\|}{\|y - x\|}.$$

35. On a linear semimetric space in which the semimetric is not a metric, there can exist no continuous total paranorm.

36. A lower-semicontinuous linear functional is continuous.

37. An upper-semicontinuous seminorm is continuous.

38. Give an example of a lower-semicontinuous noncontinuous norm. 〚$\Sigma|a_n|$ on $E^\infty \subset c_0$; Section 5.1, Problem 18.〛

39. If every separable closed linear subspace of a linear semimetric space is complete, the space is complete.

40. If some disk of positive radius in a normed space is complete, the normed space is complete. (Hence a complete subset of an incomplete normed space is nowhere dense.)

41. (a) The completion of a linear metric space is a linear metric space. (b) However it is possible to have a linear metric space which has a noninvariant metric equivalent to its invariant metric and whose completion is not a linear space. 〚Give R the metric which makes it isometric with $(0, 1)$, (see Section 5.2.) Its completion is $[0, 1]$. One way to see that this is not a linear metric space is to note that $\{n^2\}$ is a Cauchy sequence but $(1/n) \cdot n^2$ does not tend to 0. Another is from the fact that it is compact.〛 Read through your proof of (a) and find where it breaks down in applying it to the example in (b). *Note.* R with

$$d(a, b) = \frac{|a - b|}{1 + |a - b|}$$

falls into case (a), while with

$$d(a,\, b) = \left| \frac{|a|}{1 + |a|} - \frac{|b|}{1 + |b|} \right|$$

falls into case (b).

42. If a linear subspace of a complete linear semimetric space is a G_δ set, it is closed.   〖We may assume it is dense.   It is isometric (by translation) with a subset of its complement, hence of first category by Section 5.1, Problem 10.   This contradicts the Baire category theorem.〗

43. Suppose that a linear semimetric space B has an equivalent complete semimetric.   Show that B is complete.   〖If the second semimetric is invariant, use Problem 10.   Otherwise, make B into a metric space as in Section 5.3, Problem 18; then by Section 5.3, Problem 32, B is closed in its completion, taking account of Problem 42 of this section.〗   (This result is due to Victor Klee.)

▲44. Let A, B be real normed spaces, and $f: A \to B$ an isometry satisfying $f(0) = 0$.   Show that f is linear.   〖Show first that it preserves mid-points.〗

▲45. Suppose that p is a continuous paranorm on s.   Show that there exists an integer n such that $(p < 1) + E^n = s$.   (Hence s has no continuous norm defined on it.)

▲46. Suppose that p is a paranorm on s.   Show that there exists an integer n such that $(p < 1) + E^n$ is dense.

6.2   Series in linear metric space

As usual, given a sequence $\{a_n\}$, we may form the sequence $\{\Sigma_{k=1}^n a_k\}$, calling it the *series* Σa_n.   If $\Sigma_{k=1}^n a_k \to a$ as $n \to \infty$, we say that the series *converges to* a or has *sum* a.   In a linear metric space, a series could have at most one sum and we may write $\Sigma a_n = a$.   This is the usual identification, customary in elementary calculus, between a series and its sum.   *For the remainder of this section we shall operate in a linear metric space, except when the contrary is stated.*

If a series Σa_n satisfies $\Sigma \,!a_n! < \infty$, it is said to be *absolutely convergent*.   A convergent series need not be absolutely convergent 〖$\Sigma (-1)^n/n$ in R〗 and an absolutely convergent series need not be convergent 〖Problem 3〗.

THEOREM 1.   *An absolutely convergent series in a Fréchet space is convergent.*

If Σa_n is absolutely convergent, then for $m > n$,

$$! \sum_{k=1}^m a_k - \sum_{k=1}^n a_k ! = ! \sum_{k=n+1}^m a_k ! \leq \sum_{k=n+1}^m !a_k!$$

hence $\{\Sigma_{k=1}^n a_k\}$ is a Cauchy sequence.//

The following examples illustrate the computations involved in discussions of convergence.

★*Example 1:* c_0.   For what sequences $\{a_n\}$ of scalars is $\Sigma a_n \delta^n$ convergent to c_0?   The answer is, precisely those sequences which tend to 0.   In other words, $\Sigma a_n \delta^n$ *is convergent in* c_0 *if and only if* $a = \{a_n\} \in c_0$.   Moreover, *it converges to* a; *that is*, $a = \Sigma a_n \delta^n$.   〖Suppose first that $a \in c_0$, then $\|a - \Sigma_{k=1}^n a_k \delta^k\| = \|(0, 0, \ldots, 0, a_{n+1}, a_{n+2}, \ldots)\| = \max\,\{|a_k|: k > n\} \to 0$.   Conversely, if $a \notin c_0$, $\|\Sigma_{k=p}^q a_k \delta^k\| = \max\,\{|a_k|: p \leq k \leq q\}$ so that $\Sigma a_k \delta^k$ is not even a Cauchy sequence.〗

★*Example 2: c.* Suppose that $a \in c$. Let $L = \lim a$. From Example 1, $\Sigma(a_n - L)\delta^n = \{a_n - L\} = a - L1$ and so $a = L1 + \Sigma(a_n - L)\delta^n$ for $a \in c$. Keep in mind that in c, as in c_0, $\Sigma a_n \delta^n$ converges if and only if $a \in c_0$.

★*Example 3: s.* It is much easier for a sequence to converge in s than in c, since, in s, $a^n \to a$ if and only if $a_k^n \to a_k$ for each k. Thus, for example, if $a^n = (a_1, a_2, \ldots, a_n, 0, 0, 0, \ldots) = \Sigma_{k=1}^n a_k \delta^k$, then $a^n \to a$ since $a_k^n = a_k$ as soon as $n \geq k$. What we have proved is that for each $a \in s$, the series $\Sigma a_n \delta^n$ is convergent; in fact, $\Sigma a_n \delta^n = a$. This actually proves more, namely a uniqueness result: if $a = \Sigma b_n \delta^n$ then $b_n = a_n$ for each n. ⟦By what has just been proved, $\Sigma b_n \delta^n = b$, thus $a = b$. We are using strongly the fact that since s is a metric space; limits are unique.⟧

DEFINITION 1. *Let* S *be a set in a linear semimetric space* A. *The linear closure of* S *is the smallest closed linear subspace of* A *which includes* S. S *is called fundamental if its linear closure is all of* A.

The linear closure of S is the intersection of all closed linear subspaces of A which include S. S is fundamental if and only if the linear span of S is dense, that is, if and only if every member of A can be approximated by a finite linear combination of S. This last condition means that, for any vector a, and any $\epsilon > 0$, there exists a finite linear combination b of S such that $!a - b! < \epsilon$.

In Section 2.2, the span of a set was defined to be the set of its (finite) linear combinations and it was proved that the span of S is the smallest linear subspace which includes S. If we let S_1 be the linear closure of S and S_2, the set of infinite linear combinations of S (that is, $\{\Sigma t_n b_n : t_1, t_2, \ldots, \text{ scalars; and } b_1, b_2, \ldots \in S\}$), then $S_2 \subset S_1$. ⟦Suppose $a \in S_2$ and let T be a closed linear subspace including S. Then there exist scalars $t_1, t_2, \ldots$, and $b_1, b_2 \ldots \in S$ with $u_n \equiv \Sigma_{k=1}^n t_k b_k \to a$ as $n \to \infty$. Now each u_n belongs to any linear subspace which includes S, in particular, to T. Thus $a \in T$ since T is closed.⟧ It is possible that $S_2 \neq S_1$ ⟦Example 4⟧; that is, S_2 may not be closed ⟦since it lies between S_1 and the span of S, which is dense in S_1⟧. In Section 3, we shall study in detail cases in which $S_1 = S_2$.

Example 4. Let S be the subset of real C consisting of the powers, x^n, $n = 0, 1, 2, \ldots$. The Weierstrass approximation theorem states that S is fundamental. However, C has members which are not infinite linear combinations of S (power series converging uniformly on $[0, 1]$), for example, $|x - \frac{1}{2}|$.

Problems on linear metric space 6.2

★1. If Σa_n is convergent, then $a_n \to 0$, but not conversely.

2. In c_0, $\Sigma(1/n)\delta^n$ is convergent, but not absolutely convergent.

3. Give E^∞ the norm of c_0. Show that $\Sigma(1/n^2)\delta^n$ is absolutely convergent, but not convergent.

4. Prove that if Σa_n is convergent, then $!\Sigma a_n! \leq \Sigma !a_n!$ (the latter possibly infinite.)

5. For $x \in l^p, p > 0, x = \Sigma x_n \delta^n$ in l^p, and for $x \notin l^p, \Sigma x_n \delta^n$ is a divergent series in l^p. Prove this (a) for $p \geq 1$, (b) for $0 < p < 1$.

6. If Σa_n is convergent, so is $\Sigma_{n=m}^\infty a_n$ for each m, and it tends to 0 as $m \to \infty$.

7. Let $\{b_n\}$ be a sequence such that $\Sigma(b_{n+1} - b_n)$ is absolutely convergent.   Show that $\{b_n\}$ is a Cauchy sequence.   (A partial converse is Section 1, Lemma 1.)

★8. If f is a continuous linear map between linear metric spaces and Σa_n is convergent, then $f(\Sigma a_n) = \Sigma f(a_n)$.

9. If f is a closed linear map between linear semimetric spaces, and Σa_n and $\Sigma f(a_n)$ are both convergent, then $f(\Sigma a_n) = \Sigma f(a_n)$.   (In particular $\Sigma f(a_n)$ converges to a unique limit.)

10. Define $g_n \in E_C$ by $g_n(z) = z^n$.   Show that in E_C, $f = \Sigma[f^{(n)}(0)/n!]g_n$.   (The convergence in E_C is *not* pointwise.)

11. Define $g_n \in A_c$ by $g_n(z) = z^n$.   Show that in A_C, the formula of problem 10 holds if and only if f is a power series which is uniformly convergent in $|z| \leq 1$, and give an example of $f \in A_C$ not satisfying this condition.

★12. $\{\delta^n\}$ is fundamental in c_0 but not in c.

13. A linear semimetric space has a fundamental sequence if and only if it is separable.

14. Let S be a subset of a seminormed space.   Then S is fundamental if and only if every continuous linear functional vanishing on S is identically zero.   (The result is false for linear metric space in general, see Section 7.5, Example 9.)

15. Let $S = \{\delta^n : n = 1, 2, \ldots\} \subset c$.   Show that S is closed, but its span is E^∞, hence is not closed.   Show that the linear closure of S is not the span of the closure of S.

16. For any set S, the linear closure of S is equal to the closure of the span of S.   (Compare with Section 1.5, Problem 15. $P = $ class of all sets in the space, $A = $ set of linear subspaces, $B = $ set of closed sets.)

6.3   Basis

We have already encountered the Hamel basis, a purely linear concept in which, perforce, only finite sums occur.   The Schauder basis allows infinite sums.

DEFINITION 1.   *A Schauder basis for a linear metric space is a sequence* $\{b_n\}$ *such that for any vector* a *there exists a unique sequence* $\{t_n\}$ *of scalars such that* $\Sigma_{n=1}^\infty t_n b_n = $ a.   *The series* $\Sigma t_n b_n$ *which converges to* a *is called the expansion of* a.

For a finite-dimensional space the concepts of Schauder and Hamel basis coincide.   Also, in E^∞, if we give it, say, the metric of c_0, $\{\delta^n\}$ is both a Schauder and a Hamel basis.   In all other cases of interest, however, the concepts differ.   For example, in c_0, $\{\delta^n\}$ is a Schauder basis, ⟦it was proved in Section 2, Example 1 that each $a \in c_0$ is $\Sigma a_n \delta^n$; the expansion is unique, for $\Sigma b_n \delta^n$ diverges if $b \notin c_0$, and converges, if $b \in c_0$, to b, not a, if $\{b_n\} \neq \{a_n\}$⟧ but not a Hamel basis, since its span is E^∞, a proper subset of c_0.   On the other hand, any Hamel basis of c_0 is uncountable ⟦Section 2.3, Example 1⟧ and so is automatically not a Schauder basis.   Even if we allowed uncountable Schauder bases, the two concepts of basis differ fundamentally.   For example, it is possible for $(\Sigma_{n=1}^\infty b_n, b_1, b_2, \ldots)$ to be a linearly independent set ⟦Section 2.2, Problem 10⟧.

We shall use the word "basis" to mean "Schauder basis."

★*Example 1.* c_0, l^p, $p > 0$, *and* s *have* $\{\delta^n\}$ *as basis.*   In Section 2, it was shown that for each vector a in one of these spaces, $a = \Sigma a_n \delta^n$.   Moreover $\Sigma b_n \delta^n$ either diverges or converges to b, not a, if $\{b_n\} \neq \{a_n\}$.

★*Example 2.* c has $\{1, \delta^1, \delta^2, \delta^3, \ldots\}$ *as basis.* The reasoning of Example 1 may be applied to Section 2, Example 2.

It is not known whether A_C has a basis. It is also not known whether there exists a separable Banach space with no basis (see Problem 23). An example of a separable Fréchet space with no basis is given in Section 11.4, Example 1. The spaces C and L^p, $p \geq 1$, have bases (see Appendix E).

Consider now a linear metric space A which has a basis $\{b_n\}$. By definition, for each $a \in A$, there exists a unique sequence $\{t_n\}$ of scalars with $\Sigma t_n b_n = a$. Thus if, for $n = 1, 2, \ldots$, we define l_n by $l_n(a) = t_n$, we will have linear functionals l_n defined on A. [For example, since $l_n(x)b_n + l_n(y)b_n = [l_n(x) + l_n(y)]b_n$, we have $\Sigma[l_n(x) + l_n(y)]b_n = x + y$. But also $\Sigma l_n(x + y)b_n = x + y$. Thus $l_n(x + y) = l_n(x) + l_n(y)$ since the expansion of $x + y$ is unique.]

Notice that $l_n(b_n) = 1$ while $l_n(b_k) = 0$ if $n \neq k$; that is, $(\{b_n\}, \{l_n\})$ is a biorthogonal pair. The functions l_n are called the *coordinate functionals relative to the basis* $\{b_n\}$, or simply *coordinate functionals*, if the basis is clear from the context.

The functions l_n are not to be confused with P_n given by $P_n(a) = a_n$ (Section 1.3). The P_n are also called coordinates. In the case of a sequence space with $\{\delta^n\}$ as basis (for example, c_0, s), $l_n = P_n$ for each n.

★*Example 3.* In c, let $b_1 = 1$, $b_2 = \delta^1$, $b_3 = \delta^2, \ldots$; then $l_1(a) = \lim a$, $l_2(a) = a_1 - \lim a$, $l_3(a) = a_2 - \lim a, \ldots$ [this is true because of the formula in Section 2, Example 2.] Thus $l_1 = \lim$, $l_n = P_{n-1} - \lim$, for $n = 2, 3, 4, \ldots$.

The designations l_n, P_n are of course unambiguous, it is the word "coordinate" whose meaning must be judged from context. A very natural question is whether or not these functionals are continuous. This turns out to be a useful question to answer. In Example 4 it is shown that, in general, the answer is negative. Our first indication of the importance of completeness (except for the Baire category theorem, of which we have had no application thus far) lies in the assertion that the coordinates are continuous if the space is complete. This will be proved in Section 11.4, Theorem 1 (by arguments resting ultimately on the Baire theorem). We shall give here an elementary proof of a more special result, Theorem 1. Theorem 1 does not contain, nor is it contained in, the ultimately more useful theorem of Chapter 11. (Our proof of the latter theorem is arranged so that it depends on the result given here.)

★*Example 4: A normed space with basis* $\{b_n\}$, *in which* l_1 *is not continuous.* (See also problems 4 and 5.) If l_1 is continuous we cannot have $b_n \to b_1$ [since $l_1(b_n) = 0$ for $n = 2, 3, \ldots$, while $l_1(b_1) \to 1$]. Thus it suffices to construct a basis $\{b_n\}$ with $b_n \to b_1$. Let our space be E^∞ as a subspace of c_0 (that is, E^∞ is a normed space with $\|x\| = \max\{|x_n|: n = 1, 2, \ldots\}$). Let $b_1 = \delta^1$, $b_n = \delta^1 + (1/n)\delta^n$ for $n = 2, 3, \ldots$. Clearly $b_n \to b_1$ and so it remains to prove that $\{b_n\}$ is a basis. Let $a \in E^\infty$ and suppose that $a_n = 0$ for $n > r$. Let $t_1 = a_1 - \Sigma_{k=2}^r k a_k$, $t_2 = 2a_2$, $t_3 = 3a_3, \ldots$, $t_n = na_n, \ldots$, then $\Sigma_{k=1}^r t_k b_k = a$. [$\Sigma_{k=1}^r t_k b_k = \{t_1, 0, 0, 0, \ldots\} + \{t_2, (\frac{1}{2})t_2, 0, 0, \ldots\} + \{t_3, 0, (\frac{1}{3})t_3, 0, 0, \ldots\} + \ldots + \{t_r, 0, 0, \ldots, 0, (1/r)t_r, 0, \ldots\} = \{\Sigma_{k=1}^r t_k, (\frac{1}{2})t_2, (\frac{1}{3})t_3, \ldots, (1/r)t_r, 0, 0, \ldots\} = \{a_1, a_2, \ldots, a_r, 0, 0, \ldots\} = a$.]

Moreover, the t_k are uniquely determined by a.   ⟦If $a = \Sigma_{k=1}^{\infty} u_k b_k$, we must have $u_n = 0$ for $n < r$ since the nth term of the sequence $\Sigma u_k b_k$ is $(1/n)u_n$, as in the above calculation, and this must be a_n.   Repeating the above calculation gives $\Sigma u_k = a_1$, $(\frac{1}{2})u_2 = a_2$, . . . , and so

$$u_1 = a_1 - \sum_{k=2}^{r} u_k = a_1 - \sum_{k=2}^{r} k a_k, \; u_2 = 2a_2, \; . \; . \; . \; .$$

Thus the coefficients are uniquely determined.⟧//

LEMMA 1.   *Let* A *be a linear semimetric space and* a $\in$ A, !a! $\neq$ 0.   *Let* f *be a linear functional on* A *and* g: A $\rightarrow$ A *be defined by* g(x) = f(x)a.   *Then if* g *is continuous, so is* f.

If f is not continuous, it is not continuous at 0, ⟦Section 4.3, Problem 24⟧ hence there exists a sequence $\{x_n\}$ with $x_n \rightarrow 0$, and $\{1/f(x_n)\}$ bounded ⟦make $|f(x_n)| \geq \epsilon > 0$⟧.   Now $g(x_n) \rightarrow 0$, since g is continuous; hence $g(x_n)/f(x_n) \rightarrow 0$ by Section 4.1, Fact (iii).   But $g(x_n)/f(x_n) = a$, hence !a! = 0.//

In case A is a linear metric space, we may replace the hypothesis !a! $\neq$ 0 by $a \neq 0$.   The converse of Lemma 1 is a special case of Part (v) of the definition of paranorm.

DEFINITION 2.   *A basis* $\{b_n\}$ *is called monotone if it has the following property: for each vector* a = $\Sigma t_k b_k$, *the sequence* $\{ !\Sigma_{k=1}^{n} t_k b_k! \}$ *is monotonely increasing.*   See the remark on the word "increasing" in Section 1.1.

THEOREM 1.   *Suppose that* $\{b_n\}$ *is a monotone basis for a linear metric space* A.   *Then the coordinate functionals relative to the basis are continuous.*

Let n be a positive integer.   Define g: $A \rightarrow A$ by $g(a) = l_n(a)b_n$.   Then

$$!g(a)! = \; ! \sum_{k=1}^{n} l_k(a)b_k - \sum_{k=1}^{n-1} l_k(a)b_k! \leq \; ! \sum_{k=1}^{n} ! + \; ! \sum_{k=1}^{n-1} ! \leq 2 !a!$$

by the monotoneness assumption.   Thus g is continuous at 0, hence everywhere.   ⟦Section 4.3, Problem 24.⟧   The result follows from Lemma 1.//

★*Example 5.*   The various classical spaces c_0, l^p, $p > 0$, s, all have the monotone basis $\{\delta^n\}$. The space c has $\{1, \delta^1, \delta^2, . . .\}$ as monotone basis ⟦for if, given x, we set $t = \lim x$, and $u_n = t1 + \Sigma_{k=1}^{n}(x_k - t)\delta^k = \{x_1, x_2, . . . , x_n, t, t, t, . . .\}$, we have $\|u_n\| = \max(|t|, |x_1|, |x_2|, . . . , |x_n|)$ which is monotone⟧.   Thus in each case the coordinate functionals are continuous, either by Theorem 1 or by a trivial check in each case ⟦for example in c_0, $\|l_n\| = 1$ for each n⟧.

Example 6.   In R^2, let D be the inside of a symmetric parallelogram with $(1, 0)$ outside and $(1, 1)$ inside, neither one being on the boundary ⟦for example, the parallelogram with vertices at $(0, -2)$, $(\frac{8}{5}, 2)$, $(0, 2)$, $(-\frac{8}{5}, -2)$⟧.   Let R^2 be normed by the gauge function of D.   Then $\|\delta^1\| > 1$, $\|\delta^1 + \delta^2\| < 1$ ⟦$\delta^1 + \delta^2 = (1, 1)$⟧.   Thus (δ^1, δ^2) is a nonmonotone basis.   Of course R^2 has an equivalent norm (its natural one) with which the basis is monotone.

The study of the basis will be continued in Section 11.4.

Problems on linear metric space 6.3

In this list $\{b_n\}$ is a basis, l_n, $n = 1, 2, \ldots$, the coordinate functionals. (Problems on basis occur also in Section 11.4.)

★1. $b_n \neq 0$ for each n.

2. In a normed space, $\|l_n\| \geq 1/\|b_n\|$.

3. In a normed space, let $S_n = \mathrm{span}\{b_k : k \neq n\}$. Then $\|l_n\| \geq 1/d(b_n, S_n)$.

4. Let p be the subspace of real C consisting of polynomials. Let $b_n(x) = x^n$ for $n = 0, 1, 2, \ldots$. Show that $\{b_n\}$ is a basis for P and that $l_n(a) = a^{(n)}(0)/n!$.

5. In Problem 4, l_0 is continuous but l_1 is not. ⟦Let $a(x) = (1 - x)^n$. Then $l_1(a) = -n$, $\|a\| = 1$.⟧

6. Let A have basis $\{b_n\}$. For $a \in A$, define $f(a) = \{l_n(a)\}$. Show that f is an isomorphism between A and a certain sequence space B with basis $\{\delta^n\}$, and with $l_n = P_n$. (We may then use f to transfer the metric from A to B, so that finally, A is congruent with B.)

7. The space B in Problem 6 always includes E^∞, or R^∞. It cannot be either c or m.

8. Apply the procedure of Problem 6 to c, using the basis given in Example 2. Show that this yields the isomorphism between c and c_0 given in Section 2.4, Problem 11. Show also that it is a linear homeomorphism.

9. In Problem 8, find the transferred norm on c_0 that makes it congruent with c.

10. A basis for a dense subspace need not be a basis for the whole space, even if the latter is a Banach space. ⟦The basis in Example 4 is not a basis for c_0. The basis in Problem 4 is not a basis for C.⟧

11. A sequence is called *basic* if it is a basis for its linear closure. Show that any subsequence of $\{\delta^n\}$ is basic in c_0, c, m, l^p, $p > 0$.

12. A subsequence of a basis need not be basic, even in a normed space. ⟦In Example 4, $\{b_2, b_3, b_4, \ldots\}$ is not basic, since its linear closure includes b_1. In Problem 4, $\{b_2, b_4, b_6, \ldots\}$ is not basic, since its linear closure includes b_1.⟧

13. In Example 4, evaluate l_n and show that it is continuous, for $n = 2, 3, \ldots$

14. For Example 4, and Problem 4, find the space B of Problem 6. In the case of Example 4, find also the transferred norm.

15. For each n, l_n is continuous if and only if $d(b_n, S_n) > 0$. (Use the notation of Problem 3.)

16. In Lemma 1 the assumption $!a! \neq 0$ cannot be dropped or replaced by $a \neq 0$. ⟦In R^2, define $\|(x, y)\| = |y|$, $f(x, y) = x$, $g(x, y) = (x, 0)$, $a = (1, 0)$. Note that $g^\perp$ is not closed even though g is continuous.⟧

17. If $\{b_n\}$ is a monotone basis, then $\{!\sum_{k=1}^n t_k b_k!\}$ is an increasing sequence for any sequence $\{t_n\}$ of scalars.

18. If $\{\delta^1, a\}$ is a monotone basis for R^2, a is a multiple of δ^2.

19. Show directly that the bases given in Example 4 and Problem 4 are not monotone.

20. Suppose that $\{b_n\}$ is a monotone basis for a normed space. Show that $\|l_n\| \leq 2/\|b_n\|$ and that the space c shows that this is inequality is best possible.

21. In a normed space, define, for each $n = 1, 2, \ldots$, $u_n(a) = \sum_{k=1}^n l_k(a) b_k$. Show that $\{b_n\}$ is a monotone basis if and only if $\|u_n\| \leq 1$ for each n.

22. In the proof of Theorem 1, g is a projection.

★23. A space with a basis is separable. ⟦The set of all finite rational linear combinations is dense.⟧

24. Let A be a triangle. Continuing Section 5.2, Problem 7, c_A has transferred to it a basis from the basis $\{1, \delta^1, \delta^2, \ldots\}$ of c. Show that this basis is $\{b^n\}$, where $b_1^n = \sum_{k=1}^n q_{nk}$, $b_2^n = q_{1n}$, $b_3^n = q_{2n}$; $\ldots$, $Q = A^{-1}$. Find the biorthogonal functionals.

6.4   Representation of functionals

For certain spaces it is possible, and usually useful, to find a simple form for every continuous linear functional.   In R^2 and R^3, for example, there is a natural correspondence (not one-to-one) between the functionals and, respectively, the lines and planes.   Another representation for a function f on R^3 would be $f(x, y, z) = ax + by + cz$, with $a = f(1, 0, 0)$, $b = f(0, 1, 0)$, $c = f(0, 0, 1)$, and

$$(1) \qquad\qquad \|f\| = \sqrt{a^2 + b^2 + c^2}.$$

Identifying f with the point (a, b, c) yields a natural correspondence between $(R^3)'$ and R^3 which is, indeed, a congruence, if $(R^3)'$ is given the norm (1).

We shall refer to the *most general* continuous linear functional as being of a certain form. This is to be interpreted as a theorem and its converse; every continuous linear functional is of the given form and every function of the given form is continuous and linear.

★*Example 1: The most general continuous linear functional* f *on* s *is given by*

$$(2) \qquad\qquad f(a) = \sum_{k=1}^{n} t_k a_k,$$

where t_1, t_2, . . . , t_n *depend only on* f.

This means that, for any f, there exists a finite set of scalars t_1, t_2, . . . , t_n such that for all a, equation (2) holds; and conversely, given a finite set of scalars t_1, t_2, . . . , t_n, if we define f by equation (2), it will be linear and continuous.

To prove this we suppose first that f is given.   Now s has $\{\delta^n\}$ as a basis; every $a \in s$ satisfies $x = \Sigma a_k \delta^k$ [Section 3, Example 1]. Thus $f(a) = \Sigma a_k f(\delta^k)$.   Let $t_k = f(\delta^k)$.   Then $f(a) = \Sigma t_k a_k$.   In particular, the series $\Sigma t_k a_k$ converges for all sequences a.   This implies that $t_k = 0$ for all sufficiently large k.   Now, conversely, since each P_k is continuous [Section 4.3, Problem 26], $\Sigma_{k=1}^{n} t_k P_k$ is continuous.   We thus have a natural isomorphism between s' and E^∞: to $f \in s'$ corresponds $\{f(\delta^n)\} \in E^\infty$, to $b \in E^\infty$, corresponds $f \in s'$ given by $f(a) = \Sigma b_n a_n$.   It is not unreasonable to write $s' = E^\infty$.

We have encountered (Section 4.3, Definition 6) the dual space A' of a linear semimetric space A, that is, the set of continuous linear functionals on A.   In case A is a seminormed space, there is a natural norm defined on A', namely $\|f\|$ is, as usual, defined by

$$(3) \qquad\qquad \|f\| = \sup \{|f(a)|: \|a\| \leq 1\}.$$

This has all the properties of a norm, and makes A' a normed space.   It is convenient to use the notation A^* for this normed space, reserving A' for the purely linear space.

DEFINITION 1.   *Let* A *be a seminormed space.   Then* A*, *the conjugate space of* A, *is the space* A' *together with the usual norm, given by equation* (3).

THEOREM 1.   *Let* A *be a seminormed space.   Then* A* *is a Banach space.*

Only the completeness of A^* is nontrivial.   Let $\{f_n\}$ be a Cauchy sequence in A^*.   For each $a \in A$, and integers m, n, $|f_m(a) - f_n(a)| = |(f_m - f_n)(a)| \leq \|f_m - f_n\| \cdot \|a\|$ and so $\{f_n(a)\}$ is a Cauchy sequence of scalars.   Define a functional f on A by $f(a) = \lim f_n(a)$ for each a; f is linear [for example $f(a + b) = \lim f_n(a + b) = \lim (f_n(a) + f_n(b)) = f(a) +$

$f(b)$]. Moreover, f is continuous. [Section 5.3, Lemma 2 provides that the sequence $\{f_n\}$ is norm bounded; that is, there exists a number M such that $\|f_n\| < M$ for all n. Thus $|f_n(a)| \leq M\|a\|$ for all n, a and so $|f(a)| \leq M\|a\|$ for all a.] Finally, $f_n \to f$. [Given $\epsilon > 0$, and any a with $\|a\| \leq 1$, we may find N such that $p > N$, $q > N$ imply $|f_p(a) - f_q(a)| < \epsilon$. Letting $p \to \infty$, we obtain $|f(a) - f_q(a)| \leq \epsilon$ and so $\|f - f_q\| \leq \epsilon$ for $q > N$.]//

★*Example 2: The most general continuous linear functional on l is given by*

$$f(a) = \Sigma t_n a_n,$$

where the sequence $\{t_n\}$ is bounded and, indeed, $\|f\| = \sup |t_n|$. We express this by $l^* = m$.

For any $a \in l$, we have $a = \Sigma a_n \delta^n$; hence $f(a) = \Sigma t_n a_n$ where $t_n = f(\delta^n)$. Now $|t_n| = |f(\delta^n)| \leq \|f\| \cdot \|\delta^n\| = \|f\|$; hence $\{t_n\}$ is a bounded sequence, indeed $\sup |t_n| \leq \|f\|$. On the other hand, if $\|a\| \leq 1$ we have $|f(a)| = |\Sigma t_n a_n| \leq \sup |t_n| \cdot \Sigma |a_n| = \sup |t_n| \cdot \|a\| \leq \sup |t_n|$. Consequently, $\|f\| = \sup |t_n|$. Conversely, for any bounded sequence $\{t_n\}$ of scalars, let $f(a) = \Sigma t_n a_n$ for $a \in l$. Then f is continuous since $|f(a)| \leq \sup |t_n| \cdot \Sigma |a_n| = \sup |t_n| \cdot \|a\|$. Thus l^* is congruent with m under the correspondence, to $f \in l^*$ corresponds $\{f(\delta^n)\} \in m$, to $b \in m$ corresponds $f \in l^*$ given by $f(a) = \Sigma b_n a_n$.

Example 3: The most general continuous linear functional on l^p, $p > 1$, is given by

$$f(a) = \Sigma t_n a_n,$$

where $t \in l^q$, q being defined by

(4) $$1/p + 1/q = 1$$

and $\|f\| = \|t\|_q \equiv \{\Sigma |t_n|^q\}^{1/q}$. We express this by writing $(l^p)^* = l^q$, $1/p + 1/q = 1$, $p > 1$.

As in the earlier examples, with $t_n = f(\delta^n)$ we have $f(a) = \Sigma t_n a_n$; moreover, Hölder's inequality provides that $|f(a)| \leq \|t\|_q \cdot \|a\|_p$ (perhaps $\|t\|_q = \infty$) hence $\|f\| \leq \|t\|_q$. Next, let n be a positive integer. Define $a \in l^p$ (in fact, $a \in E^\infty$) by $a_k = 0$ for $k > n$, and for each k such that $t_k = 0$, where, as usual, $t_k = f(\delta^k)$. For other values of k, let $a_k = |t_k|^q/t_k$. The guiding idea is that $|a_k|^p = |t_k|^q$. (Compare Section 1.4, Problem 3.) We shall use this identity repeatedly. Then

$$f(a) = \sum_{k=1}^{n} |t_k|^q = \sum_{k=1}^{n} |a_k|^p = \|a\|_p \left(\sum_{k=1}^{n} |a_k|^p \right)^{1-1/p} = \|a\|_p \left(\sum_{k=1}^{n} |t_k|^q \right)^{1/q}.$$

Thus $\|f\| \geq \{\Sigma_{k=1}^n |t_k|^q\}^{1/q}$, this shows that $t \in l^q$ and, together with the earlier inequality, that $\|f\| = \|t\|_q$. Conversely if $t \in l^q$, Hölder's inequality yields the facts that $f(a) \equiv \Sigma t_k a_k$ is defined for all $a \in l^p$, and $|f(a)| \leq \|t\|_q \cdot \|a\|_p$ so that f is continuous.

Notice, from Examples 2 and 3, that $l^{p*} = l^q$ if $p > 1$, where q is given by equation (4) and $l^{p*} = m$ if $p = 1$. If we allow $p \to 1 +$ in equation (4), we obtain $q \to + \infty$, and so there is a certain sense in which it would be reasonable to use the name l^∞ for m. This is supported by the fact that the m norm, $\sup |a_n|$, is actually $\lim_{p \to \infty} (\Sigma |a_n|^p)^{1/p}$ [Section 1.4, formula (12)].

★*Example 4: The most general continuous linear functional on c_0 is given by* $f(a) = \Sigma t_k a_k$ *with $t \in l$ and $\|f\| = \|t\|_l \equiv \Sigma |t_k|$, $t_k = f(\delta^k)$. In particular, $\Sigma |t_k| < \infty$. Thus $c_0^* = l$.*

The proof is similar to, but easier than, those of the earlier examples ⟦Problem 10⟧.

★*Example 5.*   The space c is different from the others because of the special nature of its basis.   We have for each $a \in c$, $a = L1 + \Sigma(a_n - L)\delta^n$ with $L = \lim a$.   Thus, if f is a continuous linear functional we have $f(a) = Lf(1) + \Sigma(a_n - L)t_n$ with $t_n = f(\delta^n)$.   Now $\Sigma|t_n| < \infty$ by Example 4 ⟦since f is a continuous linear functional on c_0⟧ thus $f(a) = [f(1) - \Sigma t_n] \cdot L + \Sigma t_n a_n = \chi L + \Sigma t_n a_n$ where $\chi = \chi(f) = f(1) - \Sigma f(\delta^n)$, $t_n = f(\delta^n)$.   To determine the norm of f, observe first that for each a, obviously

(5) $$|f(a)| \leq \|a\|(|\chi| + \Sigma|t_n|).$$

On the other hand, let n be a positive integer and define $a_k = \operatorname{sgn} t_k$ for $k = 1, 2, \ldots, n$, and $a_k = \operatorname{sgn} \chi$ for $k = n + 1, n + 2, \ldots$.   Then $a \in c$ and $\|a\| = \sup |a_k| \leq 1$ while $f(a) = |\chi| + \Sigma_{k=1}^{n}|t_k| + R_n$, where

$$|R_n| = |\operatorname{sgn} \chi \sum_{k=n+1}^{\infty} t_k| \leq \sum_{k=n+1}^{\infty} |t_k| \to 0 \qquad \text{as} \qquad n \to \infty.$$

Thus $\|f\| \geq |\chi| + \Sigma|t_k|$.   Thus, finally $\|f\| = |\chi| + \Sigma|t_k|$.   Conversely, if $|\chi| + \Sigma|t_k| < \infty$, $f(a) \equiv \chi L + \Sigma t_k a_k$ is defined for all $a \in c$ and is continuous since inequality (5) obviously holds.

Our final result is that c^* is congruent with l, with $f \in c^*$ corresponding to $\{\chi, f(\delta^1), f(\delta^2), \ldots\}$, while to $b \in l$ corresponds $f \in c^*$ given by $f(a) = b_1 \lim a + \Sigma_{n=1}^{\infty} b_{n+1} a_n$.

We see from Examples 4 and 5 that c_0^* and c^* are congruent. c_0 and c are not themselves congruent ⟦c has an extreme point on its unit disk, namely $x = 1$; c_0 has no such extreme point, Section 4.4, Problem 45⟧.   However c_0, c are linearly homeomorphic ⟦Section 3, Problem 8⟧.

Example 6: Summability.   Let A be a triangle.   We have seen that c_A is congruent with c under the map $A: c_A \to c$.   [This and the following remarks concern Section 5.2 and Problems 7, 8 of that section.]   Let $B = A^{-1}$.   If f is a continuous linear functional on c_A we may define g on c by $g(x) = f(Bx)$, (transferring f to c).   From Example 5, for $x \in c_A$, we obtain the relation,

(6) $$f(x) = g(Ax) = \alpha \lim Ax + \Sigma t_k(Ax)_k,$$

where $t_k = g(\delta^k) = f(B\delta^k) = f(b^k)$, say (that is, b^k is the kth column of B), $\alpha = \alpha_A(f) = \chi(g) = g(1) - \Sigma g(\delta^k) = f(B1) - \Sigma f(b^k)$, and $B1$ is the sequence of row sums of B; that is, $(B1)_n = \Sigma_{k=1}^{n} b_{nk}$.   Also $\|f\| = \|g\| = |\alpha| + \Sigma|t|_k$.   It is important to observe that each P_n is continuous on c_A (recall that $P_n(x) = x_n$).   ⟦$P_n(x) = |x_n| = |\Sigma_{k=1}^{n} b_{nk}(Ax)_k| \leq \|x\| \Sigma_{k=1}^{n}|b_{nk}|$.   (Of course, $\|x\| = \sup \{|(Ax)_r|: r = 1, 2, \ldots\}$.)⟧

The congruence of c_A with c was extended to the case in which A is reversible, in Section 5.2, Problem 9.   Formula (6) holds in this case also.   We are unable, at present, to investigate further the functionals on c_A, since, unlike the case in which A is a triangle, we do not known the form of the inverse map.   For this reason, it is far from obvious that the P_n are continuous.   Proofs will be given in Section 12.4.

Example 7: Summability.   Let us consider a special case of Example 5.   Let A be a conservative matrix.   Then $\lim_A$ is defined and linear on c.   It is also continuous. ⟦$|(Ax)_n| \leq \|A\| \cdot \|x\|$.   For $\|A\| < \infty$, see Section 1.2, Problem 17.   For an interpretation of $\|A\|$, see Section 4.4, Problem 39.   Thus $|\lim_A x| \leq \|A\| \cdot \|x\|$.]   By Example 5 we have, for $x \in c$,

(7) $$\lim_A x = \chi \lim x + \Sigma a_k x_k,$$

where

(8) $$\chi = \chi(A) = \lim_A 1 - \Sigma \lim_A \delta^k = \lim_{n \to \infty} \sum_{k=1}^{\infty} a_{nk} - \sum_{k=1}^{\infty} a_k.$$

Here a_k stands for $\lim_{n \to \infty} a_{nk} = \lim a^k$, a^k being the kth column of A.   Of course $\Sigma |a_k| < \infty$ since a_k is the t_k of Example 5.   The number $\chi(A)$ is of great importance in summability. If $\chi(A) \neq 0$, A is called *coregular;* if $\chi(A) = 0$, A is called *conull.*   A regular matrix is coregular.   See also Problems 14, 15 and 16.

Example 8: $B_1[H]$.   Here H is an arbitrary set, and we shall take $B_1[H]$ to be the set of all bounded real functions on H.   We omit the extension to the complex case.   The space m is obtained by taking $H = \omega$.   The pleasant type of representation used in all the preceding examples, namely, the use of a basis, is no longer available (for example, m is not separable, hence has no basis).   Another, more general, representation is available in terms of characteristic functions of subsets of H (compare this with the fact that $\delta^1 \in m$ is the characteristic function of $\{1\} \subset \omega$).

For any subset e of H, let χ_e be its characteristic function; that is, $\chi_e(h) = 1$ if $h \in e$, 0 if $h \notin e$.   We now form a Riemann sum.   Let a partition π of H be given; that is, π is a subdivision of H into a finite collection $e(1)$, $e(2)$, $\ldots$, $e(n)$ of disjoint subsets, some possibly empty (whose union is H), and with a designated point h_k in each nonempty $e(k)$, $k = 1, 2, \ldots, n$.   Occasionally it will be unnecessary to specify the h_k points; $e(1)$, $e(2)$, $\ldots$, $e(n)$ will be given, and the collection $\{e(1), e(2), \ldots, e(n)\}$ will be called π. Given two partitions π_1, π_2, we shall say that π_2 refines π_1, in symbols $\pi_2 \geq \pi_1$ if every set in π_2 is included in a set in π_1; that is, if, whenever $\pi_1 = \{e(1), \ldots e(t); h_1, \ldots, h_t\}$ and $\pi_2 = \{e'(1), \ldots, e'(r); h'_1, \ldots, h'_r\}$, then each $e'(k)$ is included in some $e(s)$.   (The numbers h'_k, h_k do not enter into this definition.)   Next, given $a \in B_1[H]$, and π, define

(9) $$\sigma(\pi, a) = \sum_{k=1}^{n} a(h_k)\chi_{e(k)}.$$

Then $\sigma(\pi, a) \in B_1[H]$; it is a "step function;" that is, it is constant on each of a finite collection of sets whose union is H, namely, it has the value $a(h_k)$ on $e(k)$, $k = 1, 2, \ldots, n$.

To each $\epsilon > 0$, $a \in B_1[H]$, there corresponds π_0 such that

(10) $$\|a - \sigma(\pi, a)\| < \epsilon \qquad \text{for} \qquad \pi \geq \pi_0.$$

[Let $u < -\|a\|$, $v > \|a\|$, $n > (v - u)/\epsilon$, n an integer.   Let $y_0 = u$, $y_1 = u + (v - u)/n$, $y_2 = u + 2(v - u)/n$, $\ldots, y_n = u + n(v - u)/n = v$.   Let $e(k) = \{h: y_{k-1} < a(h) \leq y_k\}$ for $k = 1, 2, \ldots, n$.   Let $\pi_0 = \{e(1), e(2), \ldots, e(n)\}$.   Now if $\pi \geq \pi_0$, $\pi = \{E(1), E(2), \ldots, E(m); h_1, h_2, \ldots, h_m\}$.   For any $h \in H$, $h \in E(k) \subset e(r)$ for some k, r. Then $\sigma(\pi, a)(h) = \sum_{i=1}^{m} a(h_i)\chi_{e(i)}(h) = a(h_k)$.   But h and h_k both lie in $e(r)$, and so $|a(h) - a(h_k)| \leq y_k - y_{k-1} = (v - u)/n < \epsilon$.]

We now consider a continuous linear functional f on $B_1[H]$.

For each $e \subset H$, let $\mu(e) = f(\chi_e)$, we shall call this the f *measure* of e.   It satisfies $\mu(\emptyset) = 0$, and $\mu(e_1 \cup e_2) = \mu(e_1) + \mu(e_2) - \mu(e_1 \cap e_2)$ for all e_1, e_2 [since $\chi_{e_1 \cup e_2} = \chi_{e_1} + \chi_{e_2} - \chi_{e_1 \cap e_2}$;

check this by evaluating both sides at h in case (i) $h \in e_1 \setminus e_2$, (ii) $h \in e_2 \setminus e_1$, (iii) $h \in e_1 \cap e_2$, (iv) $h \notin e_1 \cup e_2$]. Thus μ is a so-called *additive set function*.

For example, suppose that h is fixed and f is defined by $f(a) = a(h)$ for all $a \in B_1[H]$. Then $\mu(e) = 1$ if $h \in e$, $\mu(e) = 0$ if $h \notin e$. We might refer to this f measure as a *unit mass concentrated* at h.

As a second example, let $H = \omega$, so that $B_1[\omega] = m$, and suppose that $f(a) = \Sigma a_n/n^2$. Then $\mu(e) = \Sigma\{1/n^2: n \in e.\}$

Now for fixed f and fixed a, relation (10) yields the fact that for any $\epsilon > 0$, there exists a partition π_0 such that for every $\pi \geq \pi_0$ we have $|f(a) - \Sigma a(h_k)\mu(e_k)| < \epsilon$. This fact is usually expressed

$$(11) \qquad\qquad f(a) = \int_H a(h)d\mu.$$

Letting $\int_H |d\mu|$ stand for *sup* $\{\Sigma_{e \in \pi}|\mu(e)|: \pi$ a partition of $H\}$, which might *a priori* be infinite, we have for any π, a, $|\Sigma a(h_k)|\mu(e_k)|| \leq \|a\| \cdot \int|d\mu|$ and so $\|f\| \leq \int|d\mu|$. On the other hand, for any partition $\pi = \{e(1), e(2), \ldots, e(n); h_1, h_2, \ldots, h_n\}$, define $a \in B_1[H]$ by $a(h) =$ sgn $\mu[e(k)]$ for $h \in e(k)$. Then $\|a\| = 1$ and $\Sigma|\mu[e(k)]| = \Sigma a(h_k)\mu[e(k)] = f[\Sigma a(h_k)\chi_{e(k)}] \leq \|f\|$. Thus $\int|d\mu| \leq \|f\|$ and so, finally, $\|f\| = \int|d\mu|$.

The following example is due to S. Mazur. The treatment given here is due to T. H. Hildebrandt.

Example 9: A separable subspace of m. Once again we restrict our discussion to the real case so that, in this example, m, $B_1[H]$ stand for real m, real $B_1[H]$. Let A be any separable subspace of $m = B_1[\omega]$. Let $\{d^n\}$ be a dense sequence in A. There exists a sequence $\{\pi_n\}$ of partitions of ω such that $\pi_{n+1} \geq \pi_n$ for each n, and $\sigma(\pi_n, d^k) \to d^k$ as $n \to \infty$ for each k. [For each k, choose $\{\pi_n^k\}$ with $\sigma(\pi_n^k, d^k) \to d^k$ as $n \to \infty$. Let $\pi_1 = \pi_1^1$; π_2 be a refinement of π_1, π_2^1, π_1^2, π_2^2; π_3 a refinement of π_2, π_3^1, π_3^2, π_1^3, π_2^3, π_3^3; ....] Then $\sigma(\pi_n, a) \to a$ for all $a \in m$. [Given any partition π, and $d \in m$, $\|a - \sigma(\pi, a)\| \leq \|a - d\| + \|d - \sigma(\pi, d)\| + \|\sigma(\pi, d) - \sigma(\pi, a)\| \leq 2\|a - d\| + \|d - \sigma(\pi, d)\|$. Now choose $d = d^k$ near a, and $\pi = \pi_n$ so that $d - \sigma(\pi, d)$ has small norm.] This discussion is independent of where the various integers $n_k \in e(k)$ are chosen, so we may assume that for each n, and each $e \in \pi_n$, the smallest integer in e has been designated. (Any other designation would serve our purpose.)

We now define a matrix $B = (b_{nk})$ thus: for each n, k let $b_{nk} = 0$ if k is not the smallest integer in one of the sets in π_n, while if k is the smallest integer in, say $e \in \pi_n$, let $b_{nk} = \mu(e)$. Thus $\sigma(\pi_n, a) = \Sigma_{k=1}^\infty b_{nk}a_k$. We thus have arrived at the result, *given a continuous linear functional* f *on a separable subspace* A *of* m, *there exists a row-finite matrix* B *such that* f(a) = lim$_B$ a *for all* a $\in$ A. In addition we can easily check that

$$\|f\| = \lim_{n \to \infty} \sum_{k=1}^\infty |b_{nk}|.$$

Problems 6.4

1. Given a sequence $\{t_n\}$ of complex numbers, there exists a continuous linear functional defined on s and satisfying $f(\delta^n) = t_n$ for all n, if and only if $t_n = 0$ for almost all n.

2. Show that the representation of Examples 1 through 6 are unique, that is, that the numbers $t_1, t_2, \ldots$ are uniquely determined by f. (Also χ in Example 5.)

3. Let A be a seminormed space and B a linear subspace. Show that $(\bar{B})^*$ is congruent with B^*.

★4. Let $L(A, B)$ denote the set of all continuous linear functions from A to B. Suppose that A is a seminormed space, and that B is a Banach space. Show that $L(A, B)$ is a Banach space with the usual norm (this generalizes Theorem 1). (Do not neglect to show that $L(A, B)$ is a linear space.)

5. Find a representation for $(R^2)'$ if $\|(x, y)\| = (|x|^p + |y|^p)^{1/p}, p \geq 1$.

6. If in Problem 5, we take $p = 1, 2$, or ∞, and multiply the given norm by, respectively, $2^{-\frac{1}{4}}$, 1, $2^{\frac{1}{4}}$, shall we have $(R^2)^*$ congruent with R? (For $p = \infty$, take $\|(x, y)\| = 2^{\frac{1}{4}} \max (|x|, |y|)$.)

7. Show that no result like that of Problem 6 holds for any other value of p.

8. Find all two-dimensional normed spaces A such that A^* is congruent with A.

9. In R^4, define $\|(x, y, z, w)\| = \{[2^{-\frac{1}{4}}(|x| + |y|)]^2 + [2^{\frac{1}{4}} \max (|z|, |w|)]^2\}^{\frac{1}{2}}$. Show that R^{4*} has the same norm except that (x, y), (z, w) are interchanged. Thus R^{4*} is congruent with R^4 (Section 7.2, Problem 17 generalizes this).

★10. Obtain the result of Example 4.

11. For $0 < p < 1$, $l^{p'} = m$.

★12. If $f \in c_0', c', m', l', l^{p'}\ (p > 1), s'$, it follows that $\{f(\delta^n)\} \in l, l, l, m, l^q, E^\infty$, respectively [for example, in Example 2, $t_n = f(\delta^n)$, and $\{t_n\}$ is bounded].

13. In Example 6, show that $\|P_n\| = \Sigma|b_{nk}|$. (Compare Section 4.4, Problems 40 and 41.)

14. A matrix A is called *multiplicative t* if $\lim_A x = t \lim x$ for all $x \in c$. Show that such a matrix satisfies $\chi(A) = t$.

15. $\chi(A) = \lim_{m \to \infty} \lim_{n \to \infty} \Sigma_{k=m}^\infty a_{nk}$; hence $|\chi(A)| \leq \|A\|$.

16. If A, B are conservative matrices $\chi(AB) = \chi(A)\chi(B)$.

17. In Example 7, it was proved that $\|\lim_A\| \leq \|A\|$, show that possibly $\|\lim_A\| < \|A\|$. [$a_{nn} = 1/n$, $a_{nk} = 0$ for $k \neq n$.]

18. Let A, B be triangles with $c_B \supset c_A$. Show that $\lim_B$ is a continuous linear functional on c_A. [$B = BA^{-1}A$, thus, using Section 1.2, Problem 19, $|(Bx)_n| \leq \|BA^{-1}\| \cdot \|x\|$. Hence $|\lim_B x| \leq \|BA^{-1}\| \cdot \|x\|$.]

19. If A is a matrix with $\|A\| < \infty$ and such that $a_k = \lim_{n \to \infty} a_{nk}$ exists for each k, show directly that $\Sigma|a_k| < \infty$. (In Example 7 this was deduced by using c.)

20. Let A be a conservative triangle and f a continuous linear functional on c_A; then $\chi(f) = \alpha_A(f)\chi(A)$. [From relation (6), $\chi(f) = f(1) - \Sigma f(\delta^r) = \alpha \lim_A 1 + \Sigma_{k=1}^\infty t_k \Sigma_{m=1}^k a_{km} - \Sigma_{r=1}^\infty (\alpha a_r + \Sigma_{k=r}^\infty t_k a_{kr})$. The two double series are absolutely convergent since $\Sigma\Sigma|t_k a_{kr}| \leq \|A\| \cdot \Sigma|t_k|$, thus they are equal and can be canceled.]

21. Let A be a conull triangle. Then, in c_A, c_0 is dense in c. [Let f be a continuous linear functional vanishing on c_0. By Problem 20 $\chi(f) = 0$ and so $f(1) = 0$. By the Hahn-Banach theorem $1 \in \bar{c}_0$.]

22. Let A be a coregular triangle and f a continuous linear function on c_A. Then f vanishes on c if and only if f is given by $f(x) = \Sigma_{r=1}^\infty t_r(Ax)_r$, in which $\{t_r\}$ is a *left annihilator* of A; that is, $\Sigma_{k=r}^\infty t_k a_{kr} = 0$ for all r (this may be written $f(x) = t(Ax)$ where t is a row vector, x a column vector). [By Problem 20 $\alpha_A(f) = 0$. The other condition is given by $f(\delta^r) = 0$. Conversely, if f has the given form, $f(x) = 0$ for all $x \in c$ by absolute convergence of a double sum as in Problem 20.]

23. Let A be a coregular triangle. Then in c_A, $\bar{c} \supset c_A \cap m$. [If f vanishes on c, it vanishes on $c_A \cap m$ as in Problem 22. The result follows from the Hahn-Banach theorem.]

24. A matrix A is said to be of *type M* (in honor of S. Mazur) if it has no left annihilator in l. Show that a coregular triangle A is of type M if and only if c is dense in c_A. [Use Problem 22 and the Hahn-Banach theorem.]

25. Let A be a regular triangle. Let B be a regular matrix with $c_B \supset c_A$. Then B is *consistent with A* for bounded sequences; that is, $\lim_B x = \lim_A x$ for $\in c_A \cap m$. [Problems 18 and 23.]

26. If, in Problem 25, A is also of type M, B is consistent with A; that is, $\lim_B x = \lim_A x$ for $x \in c_A$. [Problems 18 and 24.]

27. Let $a_{nk} = n^k$ and let $A = (a_{nk})$. Show that A is onto s; that is, for each $y \in s$, there exists a sequence x such that $y = Ax$. [Let f be an entire function satisfying $f(n) = y_n$ for $n = 1, 2, \ldots$]

28. Let A be a row-finite matrix; show that As is closed in s. 〖Section 2.10, Problem 30.〗 Row finiteness cannot be omitted. 〖Section 1.2, Problem 23.〗

29. A continuous linear map from s to itself has closed range. 〖Problem 28.〗 The result is false for maps of c_0 to itself. 〖$f(x) = \{x_n/n\}$.〗

30. Show that a set function μ is additive if and only if $\mu(e_1 \cup e_2) = \mu(e_1) + \mu(e_2)$ whenever e_1, e_2 are disjoint.

31. In Example 8, $f(1) = \mu(H)$.

32. In Example 8, let $h_1, h_2 \in H$. Find μ if $f(a) = a(h_1) + a(h_2)$ for all a.

33. In Example 8, the f measure need not be *countably* additive; that is, $\mu(\cup e_n) \neq \Sigma \mu(e_n)$ is possible with the e_n disjoint. 〖Extend lim from c to m by the Hahn-Banach theorem. Let $e_n = \{n\}$ for $n = 1, 2, \ldots$.〗

34. Let $f \in m'$ be a member of l. (This means that there exists $b \in l$ such that $f(a) = \Sigma b_n a_n$.) Find μ in Example 8. Show that μ is a sum of point masses.

35. Let $H = [0, 1]$. For $e \subset H$ define $\mu(e) = \Sigma\{2^{-n}: 1/n \in e\}$. Let $a(x) = 2x - 1$ for $0 \leq x \leq 1$. Evaluate $\int_H a(x)\, d\mu$. 〖$\log 4 - 1$.〗

36. Every additive set function μ defined on all subsets of a set H and satisfying $\int_H |d\mu| < \infty$ defines a continuous linear functional on $B_1[H]$ as in Example 8.

37. Define f on C by $f(x) = \int_0^1 x(t)t^2\, dt$. Show that f is continuous and $\|f\| = \frac{1}{3}$.

38. Define f on C by $f(x) = \int_0^1 x(t)(1 - 2t)\, dt$. Show that f is continuous and $\|f\| = \frac{1}{2}$.

★39. (This result is used only in Section 7.6, Application 3.) Let $g \in C$. Define f on C by $f(x) = \int_0^1 x(t)g(t)\, dt$. Show that f is continuous and $\|f\| = \int_0^1 |g(t)|\, dt$.

40. Let g be a function of bounded variation on $[0, 1]$. Define f on C by $f(x) = \int_0^1 x(t)\, dg(t)$. Show that f is continuous and $\|f\| = $ variation of g.

6.5 Quotient space

In this section we shall deal exclusively with seminormed spaces. A more general treatment is outlined in Section 10.2, Problem 31. The norm given in the statement of the following theorem will be regarded as the *natural norm* for A/S.

THEOREM 1. *Let* A *be a seminormed space and* S *a closed linear subspace. Define* $\|a + S\|$ *to be* $d(0, a + S)$. *This makes* A/S *into a normed space which is complete if* A *is. The natural homomorphism is continuous and open.*

(This norm for A/S is really very natural. Observe that the distance between two points in A/S is the same as their distance as subsets of A.)

We check the norm postulates.

If $a + S \neq 0$ in A/S, that is, if $a + S \neq S$, then $a \notin S$ and so $0 \notin a + S$.

Since $a + S$ is closed, it follows that $\|a + S\| = d(0, a + S) > 0$; that $\|ta + S\| = |t| \cdot \|a + S\|$ for scalar t is obvious. To prove the triangular inequality, we have $\|a + b + S\| = \inf \{\|a + b + c\|: c \in S\} = \inf \{\|a + b + c + d\|: c \in S, d \in S\} \leq \inf \{\|a + c\| + \|b + d\|: c \in S, d \in S\} = \inf \{\|a + c\|: c \in S\} + \inf \{\|b + d\|: d \in S\}$ 〖since c, d are independent〗 $= \|a + S\| + \|b + S\|$.

Now we consider ϕ, the natural homomorphism, given by $\phi(a) = a + S$. Clearly $\|\phi(a)\| \leq \|a\|$ [since $|\phi(a)| = \|a + S\| = \inf\{\|a + b\| : b \in S\} \leq \|a + 0\| = \|a\|$], thus ϕ is continuous. The fact that ϕ is open will follow [since ϕ is linear] from the fact, now to be shown, that $\phi[N(0, 1)] \supset N(0, 1)$. Let $b + S \in N(0, 1) \subset A/S$; that is, $\|b + S\| < 1$. Then there exists $a \in b + S$ such that $\|a\| < 1$ [by definition of $\|b + S\|$]. Thus $\phi(a) = a + S = b + S$ and so $b + S \in \phi[N(0, 1)]$.

Finally we prove that A/S is complete if A is. Let $\{a_n + S\}$ be a Cauchy sequence. It has a subsequence $\{b_n + S\}$ satisfying $\Sigma\|b_{n+1} - b_n + S\| < \infty$ [Section 1, Lemma 1]. Now for $n = 1, 2, \ldots$, choose $d_n \in b_n + S$ with $\|d_{n+1} - d_n\| < \|b_{n+1} - b_n + S\| + 2^{-n}$.

[Namely, choose $x_0 \in b_1 + S$ with $\|x_0\| < \|b_1 + S\| + 1$ and, for $n = 1, 2, \ldots$, choose $x_n \in b_{n+1} - b_n + S$ with $\|x_n\| < \|b_{n+1} - b_n + S\| + 2^{-n}$. These choices are possible by definition of the norm on A/S. Let $d_n = \Sigma_{k=0}^{n-1}x_k$.]

Then $\Sigma(d_{n+1} - d_n)$ is absolutely convergent, hence convergent [Section 2, Theorem 1] and with $d = d_1 + \Sigma(d_{n+1} - d_n)$ we have $d_n \to d$ [$d_n = d_1 + \Sigma_{k=1}^{n-1}(d_k - d_{k-1})$]. Then also $d_n + S \to d + S$ since ϕ is continuous; that is, $b_n + S \to d + S$ [$b_n + S = d_n + S$, since $d_n \in b_n + S$]. Thus $\{a_n + S\}$, the original Cauchy sequence, has a convergent subsequence and so is itself convergent [Section 5.3, Problem 2].//

THEOREM 2. *Let* A, S *be as in Theorem 1. For a linear functional* f *on* A *which vanishes on* S, *define* F *on* A/S *by* F(a + S) = f(a) *or, for a linear function* F *on* A/S, *define* f *on* A *by* f(a) = F(a + S). *In each of these two cases,* $\|F\| = \|f\|$.

The two cases are actually the same. Given f, and defining F, we obtain the same f again. Similarly, given F, and defining f, we obtain F again. Thus we shall assume f, F given satisfying $f = F \circ \phi$, ϕ being the natural homomorphism. We allow infinite norms (in case f, F are discontinuous). Since $f = F \circ \phi$, if F is continuous, so is f and $\|f\| \leq \|F\| \cdot \|\phi\| \leq \|F\|$.

On the other hand, let $0 < r < \|F\|$. (For example, if $\|F\| = \infty$, any positive r would do.) Choose a such that $\|a + S\| < 1$, $|F(a + S)| > r$. Then choose $b \in a + S$ with $\|b\| < 1$. We now have $\|f\| \geq \|b\| \cdot \|f\| \geq |f(b)| = |F(b + S)| = |F(a + S)| > r$. Thus $\|f\| \geq \|F\|$.//

Problems 6.5

In this list, S is a closed linear subspace of a seminormed space A; ϕ is the natural homomorphism onto A/S.

1. Show that $\|\phi\| = 1$.
2. A/S may be complete even if A is not.
3. If, in Theorem 1, S is assumed to be not closed, the seminorm on A/S is not a norm.
4. Extend Theorem 2 to apply to functions whose range is a normed space.
★5. If $d(a, S) \geq 1$, show that $\|a + S\| \geq 1$.
6. From $\|a + S\| = \|a\|$, $\|b + S\| = \|b\|$, it does not follow that $\|a - b + S\| = \|a - b\|$. [For example, $a - b \in S$.]

7
BANACH SPACE

7.1 The adjoint operation

If A, B are linear semimetric spaces and $T: A \to B$ a continuous linear map, a very natural map from B' to A' suggests itself. We shall call it T^*, the *adjoint* of T, and its definition is $(T^*f)(a) = f(Ta)$. This means that for $f \in B'$, $T^*f \in A'$; that is, T^*f is a functional on A, its value at $a \in A$ is, by definition, $f(Ta)$. It remains to check that this operation is really defined, that is, that $T^*f \in A'$ as claimed. [T^*f is surely a functional on A, it is obviously linear, and, since $T^*f = f \circ T$, it is the composition of two continuous functions, hence is continuous.]

★*Example 1.* Define $T_0 c_0 \to c_0$ by $Ta = \{a_n/n\}$. Then $\|T\| = 1$ [$\|\delta^1\| = \|T\delta^1\| = 1$]. T is one to one, but not onto [$Ta \neq \{n^{-\frac{1}{2}}\}$]. However, the range of T is dense [it includes E^∞]. We may consider $T^*: l \to l$, since $c_0^* = l$. For $f = \{b_n\} \in c_0^*$, $a \in c_0$ we have $(T^*f)(a) = f(Ta) = \Sigma b_n a_n/n$. Thus $T^*f = \{b_n/n\}$.

Convention. For the remainder of this section A, B are seminormed spaces, and $T: A \to B$ is linear and continuous.

THEOREM 1. $T^*: B^* \to A^*$ *is continuous, indeed* $\|T^*\| = \|T\|$.

For any $a \in A$, $f \in B^*$, we have $|(T^*f)(a)| = |f(Ta)| \leq \|f\| \cdot \|Ta\| \leq \|f\| \cdot \|T\| \cdot \|a\|$. Thus $\|T^*f\| \leq \|f\| \cdot \|T\|$ and so $\|T^*\| \leq \|T\|$. To prove the opposite inequality, let $\epsilon > 0$. We may choose a with $\|a\| \leq 1$, $\|Ta\| > \|T\| - \epsilon$ [by definition of $\|T\|$] and $f \in B^*$ with $\|f\| = 1, f(Ta) = \|Ta\|$ [by the Hahn-Banach theorem, Section 4.4, Corollary 3]. Then $(T^*f)(a) = f(Ta) = \|Ta\| > \|T\| - \epsilon$, while $\|a\| \leq 1$, and so $\|T^*f\| \geq \|T\| - \epsilon$. But also $\|f\| = 1$, and so $\|T^*\| \geq \|T\| - \epsilon$. Since ϵ is arbitrary, this completes the proof.//

An interesting example of the adjoint is obtained by considering a seminormed space A and a subspace S. Let $i: S \to A$ be the inclusion map; that is, $i(a) = a$. Then, for any $\in A^*$, $(i^*f)(a) = f(ia) = f(a)$ for $a \in S$; in other words, $i^*f = f|S$; i^* is the operation which carries the function f defined on A to the function which is the restriction of f to S.

The relationship between T and T^* is this: one of them obeys a condition resembling "onto" if and only if the other obeys a condition resembling "one to one." We shall give some examples (Theorems 2, 3, and Problem 8) to clarify this vague statement; in a more general situation the statement can be made exact (Problem 1.)

THEOREM 2. T^* *is one to one if and only if the range of* T *is dense.*

(In Example 1, T^* is one to one and T is not onto.) Suppose first that T^* is one to one. It is sufficient to prove that $T[A]$ is fundamental, since it is obviously a linear subspace. For this it is sufficient to prove that any linear functional on B which vanishes on $T[A]$ is identically zero [by the Hahn-Banach theorem]. Let $f \in B^*$, $f(b) = 0$ for $b \in T[A]$. Then, for all $a \in A$, $(T^*f)(a) = f(Ta) = 0$, since $Ta \in T[A]$. Thus $T^*f = 0$ and, since T^* is one to one, $f = 0$. Next, assume that T has dense range. If $T^*f = 0$ we have, for all $a \in A$, $f(Ta) = (T^*f)(a) = 0$. Thus f vanishes on $T[A]$, hence $f = 0$ since $T[A]$ is dense.//

With some additional assumptions, Theorem 2 can be strengthened by making the second condition, T is onto [Theorem 3].

A map T between seminormed spaces is said to be *norm increasing* if $\|Ta\| \geq \|a\|$ for all a, *norm decreasing* if $\|Ta\| \leq \|a\|$ for all a. If $T: A \rightarrow B$ is norm increasing and B is a normed space, T is clearly one to one and $T^{-1}: T[A] \rightarrow A$ is continuous [since for $b \in Ta$, $\|T^{-1}b\| \leq \|TT^{-1}b\| = \|b\|$].

THEOREM 3. *Let* A *be a complete seminormed space,* B *a normed space, and* T *norm increasing. Then* T^* *is one to one if and only if* T *is onto.*

Clearly, if T is onto, it has a continuous inverse [since it is norm increasing]. Half the result follows trivially from Theorem 2. Next suppose that T^* is one to one. Let $b \in B$. The range of T is dense [Theorem 2]. Thus we can find a sequence $\{b_n\}$ of points in the range of T with $b_n \rightarrow b$. Each $b_n = Ta_n$ for some $a_n \in A$, and for positive integers p, q we have $\|a_p - a_q\| \leq \|T(a_p - a_q)\| = \|b_p - b_q\|$. Hence $\{a_n\}$ is a Cauchy sequence and converges, say $a_n \rightarrow a$. Then $Ta = b$ since T is continuous and B is a normed space [$b_n \rightarrow b$ and $b_n \rightarrow Ta$, thus $Ta = b$]. This proves that T is onto.//

Finally we prove the formula

$$(1) \qquad\qquad (T_2T_1)^* = T_1^*T_2^*.$$

Suppose $T_1: A \rightarrow B$, $T_2: B \rightarrow C$. Then $T_2T_1: A \rightarrow C$, and $(T_2T_1)^*: C^* \rightarrow A^*$ is given by the conditions, for $h \in C^*$, $a \in A$, $[(T_2T_1)^*h](a) = h(T_2T_1a) = (T_2^*h)(T_1a) = [T_1^*(T_2^*h)](a)$. Since this is true for all $a \in A$, $(T_2T_1)^*h = T_1^*(T_2^*h) = (T_1^*T_2^*)(h)$ [by definition of $T_1^*T_2^*$]. Since this is true for all h, equation (1) follows.//

Problems 7.1

Unless otherwise stated, T, T_1, T_2 are continuous linear maps from A to B, where A, B are seminormed spaces.

1. (This problem has nothing to do with linear spaces or linear maps). Let A, B, C be sets. Given $T: A \rightarrow B$, we define $T^*: C^B \rightarrow C^A$ by $(T^*f)(a) = f(Ta)$ for $a \in A, f \in C^B$. Show that T^* is onto if and only if T is one to one; while T^* is one to one if and only if T is onto. (These results fail if we are restricted to linear functions on linear spaces.)

2. What is f^* if f is a functional?

3. $(T_1 + uT_2)^* = T_1^* + uT_2^*$ for scalar u.

4. Let A be an $n \times n$ real matrix, then A is a function from R^n to itself in the usual way. Show that A^* is the transpose of A. (Take R^{n*} to be R^n; the identification is that to $y \in R^n$ corresponds the function in R^{n*} whose value is $\sum y_k x_k$ at x.)

5. Define $T: c \to c_0$ by $Ta = \{a_n/n\}$. Evaluate T^*.

6. Define $T: c \to c$ by $Ta = \{a_n/n\}$. Find f such that $T^*f = 0$.

7. Show that Theorem 1 is equivalent to a statement of the form: the map $T \to T^*$ is an isometry. [Section 6.4, Problem 4.]

8. Let B be a normed space. Then T is one to one if and only if the range of T^* is total over A.

9. In Problem 8, we can let B be a seminormed space if we replace "T is one to one" by "$\|Ta\| = 0$ implies $a = 0$".

10. If T is a linear homeomorphism onto, so is T^*. $[\![(T^{-1})^* = (T^*)^{-1}.]\!]$

11. If, in Problem 10, T is also an isometry, so is T^*.

12. In Problem 10 it is not sufficient to assume that T is linear, continuous, one to one and onto (in order to obtain the same for T^*). $[\![$Let $A = l$, $B = l$ with the c_0 norm, $Ta = a$. Section 6.4, Problem 3 may be useful.$]\!]$

13. In Theorem 3, instead of T norm increasing, it is sufficient to assume that for some $\epsilon > 0$, $\|Ta\| \geq \epsilon \|a\|$ for all a.

14. Extend Theorem 3 by proving the following result: Let A, B be seminormed spaces with A complete; let $T: A \to B$ be linear, closed and norm increasing, and assume that T^* is one to one ($T: B^* \to A^\#$ and $\|Tf\| = \infty$ if $Tf \in A^\# \setminus A^*$); then T is onto and has a continuous inverse. $[\![$The same proof works.$]\!]$

15. (Orthogonality) Let $T: A \to A$. Suppose that, for a certain $a \in A, f \in A^*$, we have $Ta = ua$, $T^*f = vf$, where u, v are scalars, $u \neq v$. Show that $f(a) = 0$. $[\![uf(a) = fTa = T^*fa = vf(a).]\!]$

7.2 The second conjugate

We recall the correspondence $a \to \hat{a}$ between A and $A^{\#\#}$ defined by $\hat{a}(f) = f(a)$ for $f \in A^\#$ (Section 2.9), called the natural embedding. Now A^* is a linear subspace of $A^\#$, consisting precisely of those linear functionals on A which are continuous. There will be no confusion if we consider $\hat{a}$ as a function on A^* (strictly speaking, this is $\hat{a}|A^*$) since if $\hat{a} = \hat{b}$ on A^*, then $a = b$ and so $\hat{a} = \hat{b}$ on $A^\#$. $[\![$If $a \neq b$, there exists $f \in A^*$ with $f(a - b) \neq 0$, by the Hahn-Banach theorem. Thus $\hat{a}(f) \neq \hat{b}(f).]\!]$ So $\hat{a}$ is a member of $A^{*\#}$. It is continuous $[\![$Theorem 1$]\!]$ and so $\hat{a} \in A^{**}$ and the natural embedding carries A into A^{**}; indeed, it is a congruence into.

THEOREM 1. *Let* A *be a seminormed space and* $a \in A$. *Then* $\hat{a}$ *is a continuous linear functional on* A^*, *indeed* $\|\hat{a}\| = \|a\|$.

For any $f \in A^*$, $|\hat{a}(f)| = |f(a)| \leq \|a\| \cdot \|f\|$. Thus $\hat{a}$ is bounded, indeed, $\|\hat{a}\| \leq \|a\|$. This shows, in particular, that if $\|a\| = 0$, then $\hat{a} = 0$ and so, in this case, $\|\hat{a}\| = \|a\|$. Next, assume $\|a\| \neq 0$ and choose $f \in A^*$ such that $\|f\| = 1$, $f(a) = \|a\|$ $[\![$The Hahn-Banach Theorem; Section 4.4, Corollary 3$]\!]$. Then, since $\|f\| = 1$, we have $\|\hat{a}\| \geq |\hat{a}(f)| = |f(a)| = \|a\|.//$

DEFINITION 1. A *is called reflexive if the range* $\hat{A}$ *of the natural embedding is all of* A^{**}.

Thus A is reflexive if and only if for each $F \in A^{**}$, there exists $a \in A$ such that $F = \hat{a}$. That a Banach space A be reflexive, it is necessary that it be congruent with A^{**} [Theorem 1] but not sufficient [see Appendix H]. It is, of course, necessary and sufficient that A, A^{**} be congruent under the natural embedding.

Facts

(i) The natural embedding of a normed space in its second conjugate is a congruence into.

(ii) A reflexive normed space is complete.

(iii) The conjugate space of an infinite-dimensional, normed space is infinite dimensional. (This is false for seminormed space [for example, let $\|a\| = 0$ for all a] and for linear metric space [see Section 5, Example 9].)

Proofs

(i) Theorem 1.

(ii) It is congruent with its second conjugate, which is complete [Section 6.4, Theorem 1].

(iii) Let A^* be finite dimensional; then A^{**} is also. [Indeed $A^{*\#}$ is, by Section 2.9, Theorem 1.] By Theorem 1, A is congruent into A^{**}, hence A is finite dimensional.

THEOREM 2. *A finite-dimensional normed space is reflexive.*

Assume that A is finite dimensional, and denote its dimension by $d(A)$. Recall [Section 2.9, Theorem 1] that if A is finite dimensional

$$(1) \qquad\qquad d(A^{\#}) = d(A).$$

Since $A^* \subset A^{\#}$ it follows that

$$(2) \qquad\qquad d(A^*) \leq d(A).$$

In particular, A^* is finite dimensional, so we may apply relation (2) to it, obtaining

$$(3) \qquad\qquad d(A^{**}) \leq d(A^*)$$

But A is congruent with $\hat{A} \subset A^{**}$ and so $d(\hat{A}) = d(A) \leq d(A^{**})$. This, with relations (2) and (3), yields $d(\hat{A}) = d(A^{**})$. Thus $\hat{A} = A^{**}$ [Section 2.3, Problem 7].//

Observe the bonus result which follows from this proof, namely, that $A^* = A^{\#}$. [It was proved that $d(A) = d(A^{**})$. Hence, by relation (3), $d(A) \leq d(A^*)$. This, with relation (2) yields $d(A) = d(A^*)$; hence, by relation (1), $d(A^*) = d(A^{\#})$. Thus, $A^* = A^{\#}$, by the result cited at the end of the proof.] This is the remarkable fact that every linear functional on a finite-dimensional normed space is continuous.

Example 1. For p $>$ 1, l^p *is reflexive.* We give three different approaches, all equivalent, but differing in the amount of identification used.

First, we know already that $l^{p**} = l^p$ in the sense of Section 6.4, Example 3. However, our present task is to prove that each $F \in l^{p**}$ is $\hat{a}$ for some $a \in l^p$. One of the computations which yielded reflexivity of finite-dimensional space [Section 2.9, Problem 2] will work here, namely, let $x = \{F(P_n)\}$. Then $x \in l^p$. [In the congruence between l^{p*} and l^q given in Section 6.4, Example 3, $P_n \in l^{p*}$ corresponds to $\delta^n \in l^q$, since $P_n(a) = a_n = \Sigma_{k=1}^{\infty}\delta_k^n a_k$. Thus, transferring F to l^{q*}, we have $F(P_n) = F(\delta^n)$ and $\{F(\delta^n)\} \in l^p$ by Section 6.4, Problem 12.] And $F = \hat{x}$. [Let $f \in l^{p*}$. Then $f(x) = \Sigma t_n x_n$ where $t_n = f(\delta^n)$; that is, $f(x) = \Sigma f(\delta^n)F(P_n)$. On the other hand, transferring F to l^{q*} and f to l^q (that is, $\{f(\delta^n)\} \in l^q$) yields $F(f) = \Sigma F(P_n)f(\delta^n)$ by Section 6.4, Example 3 with q instead of p, $t_n = F(P_n) = F(\delta_n)$, $a_n = f(\delta^n)$. Thus $F(f) = f(x)$.]

Second, a very brief exposition of this example would be as follows: every functional F on l^q is given by $F(y) = \Sigma x_n y_n$, $y \in l^q$, $x \in l^p$. Thus $F = \hat{x}$.

Third, a more precise, but less instructive exposition, not using identifications, would proceed thus. Let $A = l^p$, $B = l^q$, and let $T: B \to A^*$ be the congruence discussed above, that is, $Tb = f$ given by $f(a) = \Sigma b_n a_n$. We know also that there exists a similar congruence $S: B^* \to A$. Now given $F \in A^{**}$, let $x = ST^*F$ and we shall have $F = \hat{x}$. [Given $f \in A^*$, $\hat{x}(f) = f(x) = \Sigma f(\delta^n)x_n = \Sigma x_n f(\delta^n) = (S^{-1}x)(T^{-1}f) = (T^*F)(T^{-1}f) = F(TT^{-1}f) = F(f)$.]

Example 2: c_0 *and* c *are not reflexive.* This is clear since their second conjugate is m; and c_0, c are not congruent with m [they are separable and m is not]. To illustrate the ideas given in Example 1 we give an independent proof which will explicitly yield the range of the natural embedding. We shall do this for c (for c_0 the range is c_0 [Problem 6]). Strictly speaking, the range is a subset, not of m, but of c^{**}. We shall give two arguments. The results of Section 6.4, Example 5, will be used freely.

First, a point $a \in c$ maps into a point of m; thus, for $b \in l$, treating b as a point in c^* gives $b(x) = b_1 \lim a + \Sigma b_{k+1}a_k = \Sigma x_k b_k$ where $x \in m$ is given by $x = (\lim a, a_1, a_2, a_3, \ldots)$. Thus each point of c maps into a point of m which is a convergent sequence, converging to its first term. Conversely, let x be a bounded sequence with $x_n \to x_1$. Let $a \in c$ be defined by $a_1 = x_2$, $a_2 = x_3$, $\ldots$, $a_n = x_{n+1}$, $\ldots$. Then the image of a in m under the construction just given is $\{\lim a, a_1, a_2, \ldots\} = \{x_1, x_2, x_3, \ldots\} = x$. We have just proved that the image of c in m under the natural embedding is the set of sequences converging to their first term.

Second, without using identifications we proceed as follows. Let $Q: c \to c^{**}$ be the natural embedding, $Qa = \hat{a}$. Let $T: l \to c^*$ be the natural congruence given by $Tb = f$ where $f(a) = b_1 \lim a + \Sigma b_{k+1}a_k$. And let $S: l^* \to m$ be given by $Sf = \{f(\delta^n)\}$. Then ST^* is the natural congruence between c^{**} and m, and we shall be interested in ST^*Qc, a subset of m. For $a \in c$, $S(T^*Qa) = \{(T^*Qa)(\delta^n)\} = \{(Qa)T(\delta^n)\} = \{T(\delta^n)(a)\} = \{T(\delta^1)(a), T(\delta^2)(a), T(\delta^3)(a), \ldots\} = \{\lim a, a_1, a_2, \ldots\}$. This is the same result as before.

Example 3. A particular member of c^{**} is of great interest, namely χ. Recall that $\chi(f) = f(1) - \Sigma f(\delta^k)$ for $f \in c^*$. In Section 6.4, Example 5, we learned that each $f \in c^*$ is given by $f(a) = \chi(f) \lim a + \Sigma t_k(f)a_k$, where $t_k(f) = f(\delta^k)$. Clearly $t_k \in \hat{c}$, in fact $t_k = \hat{\delta}^k$ for each k. We know that for each $f \in c^*$, $\|f\| = |\chi(f)| + \Sigma|t_k(f)|$, thus $|\chi(f)| \leq \|f\|$ and so χ is continuous, in fact $\|\chi\| \leq 1$. Indeed $\|\chi\| = 1$ [$\|\lim\| = 1$ and $\chi(\lim) = 1$ either directly because $\lim 1 - \Sigma \lim \delta^k = 1$, or because the representation of $\lim$ as a member of c^* is clearly $1 \cdot \lim + \Sigma 0 \cdot x_k$, hence $\chi = 1$]. $\chi \notin \hat{c}$. [If $\chi = \hat{a}$, $a \in c$, we would have, for all $f \in c^*$, $f(1) - \Sigma f(\delta^k) = f(a)$. For any fixed n, take $f = P_n$; that is, $f(a) = a_n$

for all a. This yields $1 - 1 = a_n$, thus $a = 0$. But $\chi \neq 0$, since $\|\chi\| = 1$]. Problem 9 carries the discussion a little further.

THEOREM 3. *Let* A *be a reflexive Banach space, then every continuous linear functional on* A *assumes a maximum on the unit disk.*

Let $f \in A^*$. By the Hahn-Banach theorem, there exists $F \in A^{**}$ with $\|F\| = 1$, $F(f) = \|f\|$. Since A is reflexive, $F = \hat{a}$ for some $a \in A$. Then $\|a\| = \|f\| = 1$, and $f(a) = F(f) = \|f\|.//$

Example 4. Define h on c_0 by $h(a) = \Sigma a_n/n!$ Then h does not assume a maximum on the unit disk [Section 4.4, Example 4]. This gives an independent proof that c_0 is not reflexive. Choosing F as in the proof of Theorem 3 with $\|F\| = 1$, $F(h) = \|h\|$, it follows that $F \in c_0^{**} \setminus \hat{c}_0$. Such an $F \in m$ (indeed the only one) is $F = 1$ [$F(h) = \Sigma h(\delta^n) = \Sigma 1/n! = \|h\|$]. Clearly $1 \notin \hat{c}_0$ [since $\hat{c}_0 = c_0 \subset m$].

Example 5. On c, the function h of Example 4 does assume its maximum on the unit disk [$h(1) = \|h\|$]. Let $f = -\lim + h$. Choosing $G = \{-1, 1, 1, 1, \ldots\}$ in m, $G(f) = \|f\| = \|G\|$, yet $G \notin \hat{c}$ since G does not converge to its first term. Here again, f has no maximum on the unit disk.

THEOREM 4. *Let* A *be a Banach space.* *Then* A *is reflexive if and only if* A^* *is.*

Suppose first that A is reflexive. Let $F \in A^{***}$. Define $f \in A^*$ by $f(a) = F(\hat{a})$ for $a \in A$. Then $F = \hat{f}$ [for given any point of A^{**} we may call it $\hat{a}$ for some $a \in A$, since A is reflexive, and $F(\hat{a}) = f(a) = \hat{a}(f)$].

Next assume that A is not reflexive. Now $\hat{A}$ is closed, since, being isometric with A, it is complete. Thus by the Hahn-Banach theorem we can find F, a continuous linear functional on A^{**} which vanishes on $\hat{A}$ but is not identically 0. Then $F \in A^{***} \setminus (A^*)^{\wedge}$ [If $F \in (A^*)^{\wedge}$ we would have $F = \hat{f}$ for some $f \in A^*$. Then for every $a \in A$, $f(a) = \hat{a}(f) = F(\hat{a}) = 0$ and so $f = 0$, and $F = 0$].//

The next result shows that every normed space has a property reminiscent of reflexivity. Each point of A^{**} is related to a point in A by means of finite dimensional subspaces of A^*, using Theorem 2.

THEOREM 5. HELLY'S THEOREM. *Let* A *be a seminormed space and* $\phi \in A^{**}$. *Let* S *be any finite-dimensional subspace of* A^* *and* $\epsilon > 0$. *Then there exists* a $\in$ A *with* $\|a\| < \|\phi\| + \epsilon$ *such that* $\phi = \hat{a}$ *on* S; *that is,* $\phi(f) = f(a)$ *for* f $\in$ S.

We shall assume $S \neq \{0\}$, the result being trivial otherwise. Let $H_0 = \{a: f(a) = \phi(f)$ for all $f \in S\}$. The theorem asserts precisely that H_0 is not empty, and that $d(0, H_0) \leq \|\phi\|$. (The following proof is suggested by the observation that H_0 is affine, hence a member of A/Z for some Z.) Let $Z = S^{\perp} \equiv \bigcap \{f^{\perp}: f \in S\}$. Then A/Z is finite dimensional [Section 2.10, Theorem 2]. Define $\Phi \in (A/Z)^{**}$ by the following procedure: for $F \in (A/Z)^*$ define $f \in A^*$ by

(4) $$f(x) = F(x + Z) \text{ for } x \in A.$$

Then set $\Phi(F) = \phi(f)$. It follows that $\|\Phi\| \leq \|\phi\|$. 〚Let $\|F\| \leq 1$. Define f by relation (4). Then $\|f\| = \|F\|$, by Section 6.5, Theorem 2, and $|\Phi(F)| = |\phi(f)| \leq \|\phi\| \cdot \|f\| = \|\phi\| \cdot \|F\| \leq \|\phi\|$.〛 By Theorem 2, $\Phi = \hat{H}$ for some $H \in A/Z$; and $\|H\| = \|\Phi\|$ 〚Theorem 1〛. Thus $\|H\| \leq \|\phi\|$.

The proof is completed by showing that $H \subset H_0$, since then, $d(0, H_0) \leq d(0, H) = \|H\| \leq \|\phi\|$. (Actually $H = H_0$, but this is not needed.) 〚Let $b \in H$, $f \in S$. Define F by relation (4). This is legal since f vanishes on Z. Then $\phi(f) = \Phi(F) = F(H) = F(b + Z) = f(b)$. Thus $b \in H_0$.〛//

Remark 1. A brief version of the proof runs thus: identifying Φ with ϕ, F with f, we have $S \subset (A/Z)^*$, $\phi \in (A/Z)^{**} = A/Z$ with norm $\|\phi\|_{Z^\perp} \leq \|\phi\|$. With $\phi \in A/Z$, choose $a \in \phi$ with $\|a\| \leq \|\phi\| + \epsilon$.

Remark 2. $H = H_0$ 〚it is easy to check that $H_0 - H_0 \subset S$; hence $H_0 = H_0 + S = h + S = H$, where h is chosen in H〛.

Remark 3. We cannot improve this result by taking $\epsilon = 0$, even if S is one dimensional. To demonstrate this, let f be a continuous linear functional not assuming its maximum on the unit disk 〚Example 4〛 and let S be its span; choose ϕ such that $\|\phi\| = 1$, $\phi(f) = \|f\|$. Then if $\phi(f) = f(a)$ we must have $\|a\| > 1$.

COROLLARY 1. *Let* $f_1, f_2 \ldots , f_n$ *be continuous linear functionals on a seminormed space* A. *Let* $s_1, s_2, \ldots , s_n$, M *be scalars such that for all scalars* $t_1, t_2, \ldots , t_n$ *we have* $|\Sigma t_k s_k| \leq$ M$\|\Sigma t_k f_k\|$. *Let* $\epsilon > 0$. *Then there exists* a $\in$ A *with* $\|a\| <$ M $+ \epsilon$, *and* $f_k(a) = s_k$ *for* $k = 1, 2, \ldots , n$.

Let $\phi \in A^{**}$ with $\|\phi\| \leq M$, $\phi(f_k) = s_k$ for $k = 1, 2, \ldots , n$ 〚possible by Section 4.4, Corollary 4〛. The result now follows by Helly's theorem.//

Problems 7.2

In this list, A, B are normed spaces, Q is the natural embedding of A in A^{**}, Q_n is the natural embedding of the nth conjugate space of A in the $(n + 2)$th.

1. $\hat{A}$ is total over A^*.

2. If $F \in A^{**} \setminus A$, $F^\perp$ is total over A. 〚Apply Section 2.10, Corollary 2 to $\hat{a}$ and F if $f(a) = 0$ for all $f \in F^\perp$.〛

3. Extend Theorem 2 to seminormed space. 〚Extend $F \in A^{**}$ to $F_1 \in A^{\#\#}$ and apply Section 2.9, Theorem 2.〛

4. If A is reflexive, A^* has no proper closed linear subspaces which are total over A.

5. In Example 1, prove directly that $\{F(P_n)\} \in l^p$. 〚Let $f = \Sigma_{k=1}^{\infty}(|t_k|^p/t_k)P_k$ where $t_k = F(P_k)$, as in Section 6.4, Example 3.〛

6. Find $\hat{c}_0$ in m.

7. Express $1 \in m$ as a member of l^* and of c^{**}. Is it in $\hat{c}$?

8. c is congruent with some but not all of its closed maximal subspaces. 〚It is not congruent with c_0; it is congruent with $\hat{c}$.〛

9. Express χ of Example 3 as a member of m. This gives an independent proof that $\chi \notin \hat{c}$. 〚For $b \in l$, $\chi(b) = b_1$, thus $\chi = \delta^1 \in m$.〛

10. For $a \in A$, $\hat{a}$ assumes a maximum on the unit disk of A^*.

11. Every closed hyperplane in a reflexive space has an element of minimum norm.

12. Prove Theorem 4 by means of the adjoint of the natural embedding. 〚For example, $F \in A^{***}$ implies $F = (Q^*F)^{\wedge}$ if A is reflexive.〛

13. Write a proof of Helly's theorem for the case in which S is one dimensional. Do not use quotient space.

14. Show that if $f: A \to B$, then $f^{**}|\hat{A} = f$. (Strictly speaking, $(f^{**}|\hat{A})Q = f$.)

15. $(\hat{A})^*$ is congruent with $(A^*)^\wedge$.

16. Let D be the unit disk in A, D_2 the unit disk in A^{**}. Then $\hat{D} = D_2$ if and only if A is reflexive.

17. Let A be reflexive; let $B = A \times A^*$ with B given the norm $\|(a, f)\| = (\|a\|^2 + \|f\|^2)^{1/2}$ for $a \in A$, $f \in A^*$. Show that B^* is congruent with B. (Section 6.4, Problem 9 is a special case.)

18. Suppose that A is a Banach space with A^* congruent with A in such a way that if a, $b \in A$ correspond respectively with f, g, then $f(b) = g(a)$. Show that A is reflexive. (Note: It is possible for a nonreflexive space to be congruent with its conjugate space. Let A be nonreflexive and congruent with A^{**}. Let B be as given in Problem 17.)

19. Any closed subspace and any linear homeomorph of a reflexive space are reflexive. 〚Let $B \subset A$, A reflexive. For $F \in B^{**}$, $Q^{-1}i^{**}F \in B$ where $i: B \to A$.〛

20. Q^*Q_1 is the identity map on A^*, while Q_1Q^* is the identity map on $(A^*)^\wedge$. Thus there is a sense in which $Q^* = Q_1^{-1}$.

21. Show that Q_1Q^* is a projection of A^{***} onto $(A^*)^\wedge$. Compare Section 4.4, Problem 34 which implies that there is no projection of norm 1 of m onto c_0. This shows that c_0 is not congruent to any conjugate space.

22. Show that $Q_2 = Q^{**}$ if and only if A is reflexive. 〚Let $f \in A^{**} \setminus \hat{A}$. Then Q_2f, $Q^{**}f$ differ at $F \in A^{***}$ if F vanishes on $\hat{A}$ but $F(f) = 1$.〛

23. (J. Dixmier) For any $g \in A^{**}$, $\|g\| = 1$, the line segment joining Q_2g to $Q^{**}g$ is made up entirely of points of norm 1. 〚Let $y \in A^*$ have $\|y\| = 1$, $|g(y)|$ very near 1, and consider $\hat{y}$.〛

24. Let S be a linear subspace of A^*. For $a \in A$, define $\|a\|_S = \|\hat{a}|S\|$; that is, $\|a\|_S = \sup \{|f(a)| : \|f\| \le 1, f \in S\}$. Show that this defines a seminorm on A, weaker than the original norm, which is a norm if and only if S is total over A. S is said to be *norming* if these two norms are equivalent.

25. Let $F \in c_0^{**}$ correspond to $1 \in m$. For $\delta^1 \in l$, show that $\|\delta^1\|_{F\perp} < \|\delta^1\|$.

26. Let $F \in c_0^{**} \setminus c_0$. Show that for some k, $\|\delta^k\|_{F\perp} < 1$.

27. For $a \in c$, $\|a\|_{\chi\perp} = \|a\|$.

▲28. (J. Dixmier) Let I, I_1, I_2, . . . be a partition of ω into disjoint infinite sets. Let $S = \{y \in l :$ for each $k \in I$, $y_k = (1/k)\Sigma_{n \in I_k}y_n.\}$ Show that S is a total subspace of c_0^* which is not norming.

29. Let S be a total linear subspace of A^*, and $a \in A$. Show that $\|a\|_S = d(\hat{a}, S^\perp)$, $S^\perp \subset A^{**}$.

30. Let B be a reflexive space and $U: B^* \to A^*$ a continuous linear map. Show that $U = T^*$ for some $T: A \to B$. [Define Ta by $(Ta)^\wedge = U^*\hat{a}$.]

31. If A^* has a norming subspace S which is reflexive, A is reflexive. 〚$i: S \to A^*$ is T^* for some $T: A \to S^*$, by Problem 30. By Section 1, Theorem 3 and Problem 13, T is onto. Now use Problem 19 and Theorem 4.〛

▲32. If A^* has a total subspace which is reflexive, A is reflexive.

7.3 Finite-dimensional space

We shall see here and, in a more general situation, in Section 10.6, that finite-dimensional spaces are quite well-behaved. For example, all norms are equivalent and all linear functionals are continuous. (The treatment given here makes no use of compactness.)

THEOREM 1. *A finite-dimensional normed space is complete.*

It is reflexive 〚Section 2, Theorem 2 and Fact (ii)〛.//

COROLLARY 1. *Any finite-dimensional linear subspace of a normed space is closed.*

It is complete 〚Theorem 1〛.//
For emphasis, we repeat the bonus result obtained in the proof of Section 2, Theorem 2.

THEOREM 2. *Every linear functional on a finite dimensional normed space is continuous.*

COROLLARY 2. *For a finite-dimensional normed space the coordinate functionals relative to any basis are continuous.*

They are linear.//   This also follows from the very general result, Section 11.4, Theorem 1.

THEOREM 3. *Every* n-*dimensional normed space is linearly homeomorphic with* E^n *(or* R^n*).*

Let $\{b_1, b_2, \ldots, b_n\}$ be a basis for the normed space A. Define $f: E^n \to A$ by $f(x) = \sum_{k=1}^{n} x_k b_k$ for $x = (x_1, x_2, \ldots, x_n) \in E^n$. Clearly f is an isomorphism onto. Also f is continuous 〚$\|f(x)\| \leq \Sigma |x_k| \, \|b_k\| \leq (\Sigma \|b_k\|^2)^{1/2} (\Sigma |x_k|^2)^{1/2}$, by Hölder's inequality. Thus $\|f\| \leq (\Sigma \|b_k\|^2)^{1/2}$〛. Now $f^{-1}: A \to E^n$ is given by $f^{-1}(a) = \{l_1(a), l_2(a), \ldots, l_n(a)\}$. Each l_k is continuous 〚Corollary 2〛 thus f^{-1} is continuous. 〚Let $M = \max \{\|l_k\|: k = 1, 2, \ldots, n.\}$ Then $\|f^{-1}(a)\| = (\Sigma |l_k(a)|^2)^{1/2} \leq (\Sigma M^2 \|a\|^2)^{1/2} = \sqrt{n} \, M \|a\|$. Thus $\|f^{-1}\| \leq \sqrt{n} \, M.$〛//

COROLLARY 3. *All norms on a finite-dimensional linear space are equivalent.*

We may take the linear space to be E^n. Any norm on E^n makes it a normed space which, by Theorem 3, is linearly homeomorphic with the (Euclidean) normed space E^n. Hence the norm is equivalent to the Euclidean norm.//

COROLLARY 4. *Let* p, q *be seminorms on a finite dimensional linear space* A *such that* $p^\perp = q^\perp$. *Then* p, q *are equivalent.*

Since p, q are norms on $A/p^\perp$, they are equivalent on it. The result follows from Section 4.1, Fact (viii).//   Another proof is given in Problem 14, and a slight extension in Problem 15.

Problems 7.3

1. Prove Theorem 1 for seminormed space.   〚Section 5.3, Problem 18 may be useful.〛
2. Corollary 1 is false for seminormed space.
★3. A Banach space cannot have a countably infinite Hamel basis.   In particular, E^∞ cannot be given a complete norm.   〚It would be of first category in itself, by Corollary 1.〛
4. Extend Theorem 3 by replacing "normed" by "seminormed" and adding the phrase, "E^n being seminormed by the natural norm of E^k for some $k \leq n$."
5. Theorem 2 is false for seminormed space.
6. Which step in the proof of Theorem 2 breaks down for seminormed space?
7. Every linear map from a finite-dimensional normed space to a seminormed space is continuous. (In particular, D, the derivative is continuous on the space of polynomials of degree n or less, as a normed subspace of C.   Compare Section 4.3, Problems 27, 28, and 29.)

8. Corollary 2 is false for seminormed space.

9. Let A be R^2 with $\|(x, y)\| = |x| + |y|$. Compute $\|f\|$ and $\|f^{-1}\|$ in Theorem 3. (Use R^2 instead of E^2.)

10. In problem 9, use $\|(x, y)\| = \max(|x|, |y|)$ instead.

11. In problem 9, use $\|(x, y)\| = (|x|^p + |y|^p)^{1/p}$, $p > 1$. (Check your result for $p = 2$.)

12. Write out a detailed proof of Corollary 3.

13. Prove the converse of Corollary 4. (If p, q are equivalent, $p^\perp = q^\perp$.)

14. Prove Corollary 4 by using Theorem 3 to transfer our attention, without loss of generality, to E^n. Then write $p(a) = p(a_1, a_2, \ldots, a_k)$ for some $k < n$. Similarly $q(a) = q(a_1, a_2, \ldots, a_k)$. Then p, q may be considered as norms on E^k.

15. Prove Corollary 4 in case A is not necessarily finite dimensional, but $p^\perp$ has finite codimension.

16. In Corollary 4, "$p^\perp = q^\perp$" cannot be replaced by the statement, "$p^\perp$ and $q^\perp$ have the same dimension."

7.4 Rotundity

The shape of the unit sphere in a normed space is of great interest. Our first example of this was the observation in Section 4.4, Problem 45 that l and c_0 are not congruent because of the existence of an extreme point in the unit disk of l. We shall see other consequences of knowledge of the unit sphere in this section.

DEFINITION 1. *A normed space is called rotund if every point of* $C(0, 1)$ *is an extreme point; that is,* $C(0, 1)$ *meets no line in three points.*

Compare this with Section 6.1, Problem 30.

A space is rotund if and only if $\mathbf{a} \neq \mathbf{b}$, *and* $\|\mathbf{a}\| = \|\mathbf{b}\| \leq 1$ *implies* $\left\|\dfrac{\mathbf{a} + \mathbf{b}}{2}\right\| < 1$. [It is clear that the given implication follows from rotundity. Conversely, if the space is not rotund, $C(0, 1)$ will contain a line segment and thus a pair of points together with their midpoint.] Clearly the 1 in Definition 1 may be replaced by any positive number. As usual, we say that the norm of a rotund space is rotund; for example, for R^2, $(x^2 + y^2)^{1/2}$ is a rotund norm, while $|x| + |y|$ is not.

LEMMA 1. *A convex set in a rotund space has at most one point of minimum norm. In other words, let* H *be a convex subset of a rotund space and let* $\mathbf{d} = \mathrm{d}(0, \mathrm{H})$. *Then* H *meets* $\mathrm{D}(0, \mathbf{d})$ *at most once.*

If $d = 0$ the result is obvious. Let $d \neq 0$. If H contained two distinct points of norm d, it would also contain their mid-point which, by definition of rotundity, would be of norm less than $d.//$

LEMMA 2. *Suppose that in Lemma 1 a point* h *of minimum norm exists and that* H *is affine,* say H = h + S, S *a linear subspace. Then* h *satisfies the following "orthogonality" condition:* $\|\mathrm{h} + \mathrm{tx}\| \geq \|\mathrm{h}\|$ *for all* $\mathrm{x} \in \mathrm{S}$, *scalar* t.

Obviously, $h + tx \in H.//$

The condition of Lemma 2 is called orthogonality by analogy with the case of R^2 in which the given condition holds if and only if h is perpendicular to S. The analogy must not be pushed too far however; see Problems 14 and 17. The theory of orthogonality finds its proper place in inner product space, Section 8.1, Problem 6.

LEMMA 3. *Let* f *be a continuous linear functional on a rotund space,* f $\neq$ 0. *There is at most one* a *with*

$$(1) \qquad\qquad \|a\| = 1, \qquad f(a) = \|f\|;$$

that is, f *takes on its maximum on the unit disk at most once.*

We apply Lemma 1 with $d = 1$ to the hyperplane $(f = \|f\|)$. That $d = 1$ follows from the observation that if $f(b) = \|f\|$ we have $\|f\| \cdot \|b\| \geq f(b) = \|f\|$ and so $\|b\| \geq 1.//$

Remark. In Lemma 3 we may replace conditions (1) by $\|a\| = r$, $f(a) = r\|f\|$ for a pre-assigned r. [If $r = 0$, this is trivial. Otherwise apply Lemma 3 to a/r.]

We are now going to think in terms of reflexivity, obtaining as our final result a sufficient condition, Theorem 1. Consider $F \in A^{**}$. If there exists $a \in A$ with $F = \hat{a}$ we have $F(g) = g(a)$ for all $g \in A^*$. In particular, let g have $\|g\| = 1$, $g(a) = \|a\|$, then a satisfies the conditions

$$(2) \qquad\qquad F(g) = g(a) = \|F\|$$

and indeed is uniquely determined by these conditions [apply the Remark following Lemma 3 with $r = \|F\|$, $f = g$].

Thus the search for a with $F = \hat{a}$ would begin by finding g with $\|g\| = 1$, $F(g) = \|F\|$ (perhaps impossible) and continue by seeking a satisfying conditions (2) (perhaps impossible). For the first step we substitute a sequence $\{g_n\}$, (Lemma 4), this being possible by definition of $\|F\|$. The second step will be considered in the proof of Theorem 1.

LEMMA 4. *Let* A *be a rotund space. Let* $F \in A^{**}$, $g_n \in A^*$ *for* n = 1, 2, . . . , $\|g_n\| = 1$, $|F(g_n)| \to \|F\|$. *Then there exists at most one* a $\in$ A *with* $\|a\| = \|F\|$, $F(g_n) = g_n(a)$ *for all* n.

Let $H = \{b : F(g_n) = g_n(b)$ for all $n\}$. If H is empty there is nothing to prove. If H is not empty, $d(0, H) \geq \|F\|$. [If $b \in H$, $|F(g_n)| = |g_n(b)| \leq \|b\|$, also $|F(g_n)| \to \|F\|$, thus $\|b\| \geq \|F\|$.] Since H is obviously convex, Lemma 1 implies that H meets $D(0, \|F\|)$ at most once.//

DEFINITION 2. *A normed space is called uniformly convex if, for any* $\epsilon > 0$, *there exists* $\delta > 0$ *such that*

$$(3) \qquad \|a\| \leq 1, \ \|b\| \leq 1, \ \|a + b\| > 2 - \delta \ \textit{implies} \ \|a - b\| < \epsilon.$$

If we write the third inequality as $\|\frac{1}{2}(a + b)\| > 1 - \frac{1}{2}\delta$, we see that a uniformly convex space is one such that if a, b are far apart members of the unit disk, their mid-point must be deep within it [$\|a - b\| \geq \epsilon$ implies $\|\frac{1}{2}(a + b)\| \leq 1 - \frac{1}{2}\delta$]. The following two examples will show that uniform convexity has to do with roundness of the unit sphere.

★*Example 1.* Let R^2 have the norm $\|(x, y)\| = |x| + |y|$. Then $\|\delta^1 + \delta^2\| = 2 > 2 - \delta$ for all $\delta > 0$ while $\|\delta^1 - \delta^2\| = 2$. Thus this norm is not uniformly convex.

★*Example 2.* R^2 with its usual norm is uniformly convex. In the proof we shall use the *parallelogram law*, $\|a + b\|^2 + \|a - b\|^2 = 2\|a\|^2 + 2\|b\|^2$ [if $ABCD$ is a parallelogram in the ordinary sense of plane geometry, $AC^2 + BD^2 = 2AB^2 + 2AD^2$; a proof in vector analysis is $|u + v|^2 + |u - v|^2 = (u + v) \cdot (u + v) + (u - v) \cdot (u - v) = u \cdot u + 2u \cdot v + v \cdot v + u \cdot u - 2u \cdot v + v \cdot v = 2|u|^2 + 2|v|^2$]. Thus if $\|a\| \leq 1$, $\|b\| \leq 1$ we have $\|a - b\|^2 \leq 4 - \|a + b\|^2 < 4 - (2 - \delta)^2 = 4\delta - \delta^2 < 4\delta = \epsilon^2$ if $\|a + b\| > 2 - \delta$ and $\delta = \epsilon^2/4$.

We observe that a uniformly convex space is rotund [if A is not rotund, let $\|a\| = \|b\| = 1$, $\|\frac{1}{2}(a + b)\| = 1$, $a \neq b$. Then $\|a + b\| = 2 > 2 - \delta$ for all $\delta > 0$, while $\|a - b\|$ is a fixed positive number]. The converse is false [Problem 13].

Example 3. That l^2 and L^2 are uniformly convex will follow trivially from Section 8.1, Theorem 3. For l^p, L^p, $p > 1$, see Appendix D. Of course, l and L are not rotund at all [for example, in l, $\|\delta^1\| = \|\delta^2\| = \|\frac{1}{2}(\delta^1 + \delta^2)\|$].

Uniform convexity plays a role similar to that of compactness (Chapter 9) in that it implies that certain sequences are convergent (see Lemma 5 and Theorem 2, below). The analogy is strengthened in that reflexivity of a space is implied by uniform convexity [Theorem 1] and also by a certain compactness condition [Section 13.4, Theorem 1].

LEMMA 5. *In a uniformly convex space, let $\{a_n\}$ be a sequence satisfying $\|a_n\| \to 1$, $\|a_m + a_n\| \to 2$. Then $\{a_n\}$ is a Cauchy sequence.*

The condition $\|a_m + a_n\| \to 2$ means, given $\delta > 0$, there exists M such that if $m > M$ and $n > M$, then

(4)
$$\big| \|a_m + a_n\| - 2 \big| < \delta$$

The proof will be given in two cases.

Case 1. $\|a_n\| \leq 1$ for all n. Let $\epsilon > 0$ be given, and δ chosen to satisfy condition (3). There exists M such that relation (4) holds for $m > M$, $n > M$. But this, in turn, implies that $\|a_m - a_n\| < \epsilon$ by definition of δ.

Case 2. Since $\|a_n\| \to 1$, we may assume that $\|a_n\| \neq 0$ for all n. Let a stand for a_n, b for a_m. Then

$$2 \geq \left\| \frac{a}{\|a\|} + \frac{b}{\|b\|} \right\| = \left\| \frac{a + b}{\|a\|} + \frac{\|a\| - \|b\|}{\|a\| \cdot \|b\|} \cdot b \right\|$$
$$\geq \frac{\|a + b\| - \big|\|a\| - \|b\|\big|}{\|a\|} \to 2 \qquad \text{as} \qquad m, n \to \infty.$$

Thus by Case 1, $\{a_n/\|a_n\|\}$ is a Cauchy sequence. Hence also a_n is a Cauchy sequence. [Let $t_n = \|a_n\|$ so that $t_n \to 1$, and let $c_n = a_n/\|a_n\|$ so that $\|c_n\| = 1$ and $\{c_n\}$ is a Cauchy sequence. Then $\|a_m - a_n\| = \|t_m c_m - t_n c_n\| \leq |t_m - 1| \cdot \|c_m\| + \|c_m - c_n\| + |1 - t_n| \cdot \|c_n\| \to 0$ as $m, n \to \infty$. Compare Section 6.1, Problem 17, which is more general.]//

THEOREM 1. (D. MILMAN AND B. J. PETTIS) *A uniformly convex Banach space is reflexive.*

Let $F \in A^{**}$ where A is uniformly convex. We may assume $\|F\| = 1$. Choose a sequence $\{g_n\}$, $g_n \in A^*$, $\|g_n\| = 1$, $|F(g_n)| > 1 - 1/n$ for $n = 1, 2, \ldots$. [This is possible by definition of $\|F\|$.⟧ For each fixed n, apply Helly's theorem and obtain a_n with $\|a_n\| < 1 + 1/n$, $F(g_k) = g_k(a_n)$ for $k = 1, 2, \ldots, n$. Then $\|a_n\| \to 1$ ⟦for $1 + 1/n > \|a_n\| \geq |g_n(a_n)| = |F(g_n)| > 1 - 1/n$⟧; also $\|a_m + a_n\| \to 2$ ⟦we may assume $m > n$ so that $\|a_m + a_n\| \leq \|a_m\| + \|a_n\| < 2 + 1/m + 1/n$, but also $\|a_m + a_n\| \geq |g_n(a_m) + g_n(a_n)| = |2F(g_n)| > 2 - 2/n$⟧.

By Lemma 5, $\{a_n\}$ is a Cauchy sequence, hence convergent, say $a_n \to a$. Then $\|a\| = 1$, $F(g_k) = g_k(a)$ for $k = 1, 2, \ldots$ ⟦since $F(g_k) = g_k(a_n)$ for $n \geq k$⟧. Once F and the g_k have been selected, a is determined uniquely ⟦Lemma 4⟧. Now we shall increase the conditions on a. Let $g_0 \in A^*$ be arbitrary and apply Helly's theorem to F and the functions $g_0, g_1, g_2, \ldots, g_n$. The above argument yields a (the same a) with $\|a\| = 1$, $F(g_k) = g_k(a)$ for $k = 0, 1, 2, \ldots$; in particular, $F(g_0) = g_0(a)$. ⟦Admittedly g_0 does not satisfy the conditions that the other g satisfy; we simply ignore this since all conclusions were drawn for $n \to \infty$.⟧ Thus $F = \hat{a}$.//

Another proof of Theorem 1 is given in Section 13.4, Problem 23. A very elegant proof can be constructed along the following lines: a normed space is called uniformly even if it satisfies the condition (of which we make no further use), given $\epsilon > 0$, there exists $\delta > 0$ such that if $\|a\| = 1$ and $\|b\| \leq \delta$, then $\|a + b\| + \|a - b\| \leq 2 + \epsilon\|b\|$; one proves that the conjugate of a uniformly convex space is uniformly even and the conjugate of a uniformly even space is uniformly convex. In particular, A^{****} is rotund and the result follows from Section 2, Problems 22 and 23 which say that if A is not reflexive, A^{****} is not rotund ⟦see Appendix I⟧.

THEOREM 2. *In a uniformly convex Banach space, every closed convex set* H *has a unique element of smallest norm.*

(Completeness cannot be dropped; see Problem 11. In Section 13.4, Corollary 2, this result—without uniqueness, of course—is extended to every reflexive space.) If $0 \in H$, there is nothing to prove. If $0 \notin H$, $d \equiv d(0, H) > 0$, since H is closed. Let $\{a_n\}$ be a sequence of points of H with $\|a_n\| \to d$. Then for any m, n, $\|a_m + a_n\| = 2\|\frac{1}{2}(a_m + a_n)\| \geq 2d$ since $\frac{1}{2}(a_m + a_n) \in H$, and so (since also $\|a_n\| \to d$), we have $\|a_m + a_n\| \to 2d$. Applying Lemma 5 to $\{a_n/d\}$, we conclude that $\{a_n/d\}$ is a Cauchy sequence, and hence so is $\{a_n\}$. Suppose that $a_n \to a$ ⟦$\{a_n\}$ is convergent since the space is complete⟧. Then $a \in H$, since H is closed, and $\|a\| = d$. That the element of smallest norm is unique follows from Lemma 1.//

COROLLARY 1. *A nonzero continuous linear functional on a uniformly convex Banach space assumes its maximum exactly once on the unit disk.*

This follows from Theorem 2, if H is taken to be the hyperplane $(f = \|f\|)$. It also follows from Section 2, Theorem 3, together with Theorem 1 and Lemma 1 above.//

Something can be said about the conjugate space of a uniformly convex space. The following result is used only in Example 4, and Section 5, Example 11. For simplicity we restrict ourselves to the real case. The idea is due to E. J. McShane.

LEMMA 6. *Let* f *be a linear functional on a uniformly convex real normed space with* $\|f\| = 1$. *Let* a *be an arbitrary point. Define* g: $R \to R$ *by* g(t) = $\|b + ta\|$ *where* b *is the unique point satisfying* f(b) = 1 = $\|b\|$. *Then if* g'(0) *exists, it is equal to* f(a).

For any scalar t, $g(t) - g(0) = \|b + ta\| - 1 \geq f(b + ta) - 1 = tf(a)$, and so for $t > 0$, $[g(t) - g(0)]/t \geq f(a)$ and for $t < 0$, $[g(t) - g(0)]/t \leq f(a).//$

Example 4: Representation of functions on L^p, $p > 1$. Let f, g, b, a, be as in the statement of Lemma 6. Then $g(t) = \left(\int_0^1 |b(x) + ta(x)|^p \, dx \right)^{1/p}$. Differentiating with respect to t and then setting $t = 0$ yields

$$1/p \left(\int |b(x)|^p \, dx \right)^{1/p-1} \cdot \int p|b(x)|^{p-1} \frac{a(x)b(x)}{|(bx)|} \, dx$$

[for convenience in differentiating, write $|b + ta|$ as $[(b + ta)^2]^{1/2}$]

$$= \int |b(x)|^{p-2} b(x) a(x) \, dx$$

[since $\|b\| = 1$]

$$= \int F(x) a(x) \, dx, \qquad \text{where } F(x) = |b(x)|^{p-2} b(x).$$

Then $F \in L^q$, $1/p + 1/q = 1$ [since $|F(x)|^q = |b(x)|^p$] and $\|F\| = 1$ [since $\|F\| = (\int |F(x)|^q)^{1/q} = (\int |b(x)|^p)^{1/q} = \|b\|^{p/q}$]. Thus, by Lemma 6, we have represented f by $f(a) = \int_0^1 F(x) a(x) \, dx$, $F \in L^q$, $\|F\| = \|f\|$. Notice that F is determined by f and does not depend on a.

Problems 7.4

1. Let R^2 be given the norm, $\|(x, y)\| = |x| + |y|$. In how many places does f assume its maximum on the unit sphere if

$$\text{(a)} \quad f(x, y) = x + 2y, \qquad \text{(b)} \quad f(x, y) = x + y?$$

2. A rotund seminorm must be a norm. (In Definition 1, replace "normed" by "seminormed.")

3. In a rotund space, $\|a + b\| = \|a\| + \|b\|$ implies that a, b are linearly dependent. [$a/\|a\|$, $b/\|b\|$, and $(a + b)/(\|a\| + \|b\|)$ are all unit vectors and lie on a line.]

4. In a rotund space, $\|a\| = \|b\| = 1$, $a \neq b$, $0 < t < 1$ implies that $\|ta + (1 - t)b\| < 1$.

5. If a normed space satisfies either of the conditions given in Problems 3, 4, then the norm is rotund.

6. The assumption "rotund" cannot be omitted (a) in Lemma 1, (b) in Lemma 2.

7. m is not rotund.

8. L is not rotund.

9. Let $\{a_n\}$ be a sequence in a uniformly convex space A. Suppose that $a_n \to a$ weakly and that $\|a_n\| \to \|a\|$. Show that $a_n \to a$. [Assume $\|a\| = 1$; choose f with $f(a) = 1 = \|f\|$.]

10. In Problem 9 it is sufficient to assume that $f(a_n) \to f(a)$ for every f in a norming subspace of A^*, (instead of every $f \in A^*$).

11. Let E^∞ be given the norm of l^2. This makes it uniformly convex, yet (compare Corollary 1) there exists a continuous linear functional [$f(a) = \Sigma a_n/n$] which does not assume its maximum on the unit sphere.

12. A finite-dimensional rotund space is uniformly convex.

13. The assumption of finite dimensionality cannot be dropped in Problem 12. [In E^∞, define $\|\delta^1\| = 1$,

$$\| \sum_{k=1}^n a_k \delta^k \| = \{ \| \sum_{k=1}^{n-1} a_k \delta^k \|^n + |a_n|^n \}^{1/n} \text{ for } n = 2, 3, 4, \ldots \}.$$

14. Let us say that a is *orthogonal* to b if $\|a + tb\| \geq \|a\|$ for all scalar t. Give an example of a two-dimensional normed space in which this relation is not symmetric (that is, there exists a pair a, b of vectors with a orthogonal to b, but b not orthogonal to a).

15. In a normed space, a is orthogonal to b in the sense of Problem 14 if and only if there exists a linear functional f with $\|f\| = 1$, $f(a) = \|a\|$, $f(b) = 0$.

16. Given an element a of a normed space whose dimension is at least 2, there exists an element $b \neq 0$ which is orthogonal to a in the sense of Problem 14. [Use Problem 15.]

17. Continue Problem 14 by showing that if a and b are orthogonal to x, it does not follow that $a + b$ is orthogonal to x.

18. Let A be a uniformly convex Banach space. Define $J: A^* \to A$ by $Jf = a$, a being the unique point satisfying $\|a\| = \|f\|$, $f(a) = \|f\| \cdot \|a\|$. [Corollary 1.] Then J is norm preserving and onto, but need not be one to one (a 2-dimensional example may be given), hence need not be linear.

19. If in Problem 18, $A = l^2$, and $f(a) = \Sigma b_n a_n$ for all $a \in l^2$, b being fixed, then $Jf = b$.

20. If A and A^* are both uniformly convex, the map J of Problem 18 is one to one, onto, and norm preserving, but need not be linear or isometric. [Give R^2 the norm of l^p, $p > 1$. Let $f(x, y) = ax + by$, then $Jf = (|a|^q + |b|^q)^{1/q - 1/p}$. (sgn a $|a|^{q-1}$, sgn $b \cdot |b|^{q-1}$). If $p \neq 2$, this is not linear. What if $p = 2$?]

21. Apply the method of Example 4 to l^p, $p > 1$.

22. Let R^2 be given a norm such that the unit circumference includes a line segment. Then the unit circumference in R^{2*} has a point at which the tangent is not unique. The converse is also true. So also are the result obtained by interchanging R^2 and R^{2*}, and its converse.

7.5 Pathology

In this section we give a list of what one might subjectively dub unpleasant examples. They are presented in order to lend color to theorems which state sufficient conditions that such behaviour cannot take place, for example, Section 3, Theorem 2, which states that on a finite-dimensional normed space every linear functional is continuous. In the index, under the heading Pathology, the reader will find references to other examples.

Example 1: A discontinuous linear functional on a normed space. Let l be given the norm of c_0; that is, $\|a\| = \sup |a_n|$. Let $f(a) = \Sigma a_n$. This defines f on l and f is linear and discontinuous [for, given a positive integer n, let $a = \Sigma_{k=1}^{n} \delta^k$, then $\|a\| = 1$, and $f(a) = n$; thus $\|f\| \geq n$, and so $\|f\| = \infty$].

The normed space of Example 1 is not complete. To give an example for a complete space, as we now do, apparently requires transfinite methods; Section 6, Theorem 3 makes this seem inevitable.

Example 2: Every infinite dimensional linear semimetric space has a discontinuous linear functional defined on it. Let $\{a_n\}$ be a linearly independent sequence. For each $n = 1, 2, 3, \ldots$, we can choose a positive scalar ϵ_n such that $!\epsilon_n a_n! < 1/n$. [This follows from part (v) of the definition of paranorm.] The sequence $\{\epsilon_n a_n\}$ is still linearly independent and moreover tends to 0. There exists a linear functional f such that $f(\epsilon_n a_n) = 1$ for all n. [Section 2.4, Problem 22]. Since $\epsilon_n a_n \to 0$, f is not continuous. In more general topological situations we are unable to give a construction for a discontinuous linear functional [Section 9.3, Problem 1].

Example 3: A discontinuous automorphism (a one-to-one linear map of a space onto itself) of any infinite-dimensional linear semimetric space (other than the trivial spaces in which !a! = 0 for all a). Let f be a discontinuous linear functional [Example 2] and fix a with $f(a) = 0$, $!a! \neq 0$. For each vector x, let $g(x) = x - af(x)$. Then g is linear, one to one [$g(x) = 0$ implies $x = af(x)$, thus $f(x) = f(a)f(x) = 0$, hence, finally, $x = af(x) = 0$] and onto [since $g[x + af(x)] = x + af(x) - af[x + af(x)] = x$]. But g is not continuous [since, if it were, af would be continuous and so f would be, by Section 6.3, Lemma 1].

Example 4: A balloon without interior in any infinite-dimensional normed space. Let f be a discontinuous linear functional on a normed space, and let $B = \{x: |f(x)| \leq 1\}$. If B had an interior point, it would include some cell $N(b, r)$, $r > 0$. Then for any vector a with $\|a\| < 1$, we have $b + ra \in N(b, r)$ thus $|f(b + ra)| \leq 1$. From this follows $|f(a)| \leq (1 + |f(b)|)/r$ and so $\|f\| < \infty$.

Example 5. A nowhere dense closed balloon. (The balloon given in Example 4 is dense [Problem 8]. Let E^∞ be given the norm $\|a\| = \sup |a_n|$. Let $B = \{a: |\Sigma_{k=1}^n a_k| \leq 1$ for $n = 1, 2, \ldots\}$. B is obviously balanced and convex; it is also absorbing [given a, let $t = \Sigma_{n=1}^\infty |a_n|$; then for $0 < \epsilon < 1/t$, $\epsilon a \in B$]. B is closed [since it is $\cap_{n=1}^\infty \{a: |\Sigma_{k=1}^n a_k| \leq 1\}$]. B has no interior [$(2/n)\Sigma_{k=1}^n \delta^k$ tends to 0 but does not belong to B for any n. Thus 0 is not interior to B. Neither is any other point for if $N(a, r) \subset B$, then $B = \frac{1}{2}(B + B) = \frac{1}{2}(B - B) \supset \frac{1}{2}[N(a, r) - N(a, r)] = \frac{1}{2}N(0, 2r) = N(0, r)$. Here we used the fact that B is convex, and Section 6.1, Problem 7].

Example 6: Two nonequivalent complete norms on the same linear space. To give noncomparable complete seminorms is too trivial [since we may take $p(x, y) = |x|$ and $q(x, y) = |y|$ for $(x, y) \in R^2$]. The required example is given thus. Let A, B be two Banach spaces of the same Hamel dimension, which are, however, not linearly homeomorphic. For example, c_0 and l^2 are not linearly homeomorphic, since the latter is reflexive and the former is not [in Section 2, see Examples 1 and 2, and Problem 19.] There is an isomorphism between A and B [Section 2.4, Theorem 4] and we may use it to give A a second norm (see Section 5.2) with which it is isometric with B. It turns out that the two norms are actually noncomparable [Section 11.2, Corollary 2].

Example 7: Two comparable norms, only the stronger being complete. The space is l. The stronger norm is its natural one, the weaker norm is that of c_0 (see Example 1).

Example 8: Two comparable norms, only the weaker being complete. For the sake of continuity of the ideas we have placed this example here. We are able to present it, but the proof that the construction is correct is supplied in Section 11.2, Corollary 2. We first construct two nonequivalent complete norms [Example 6] and add them to obtain the incomplete norm. (Either of the two original norms will do for the weaker complete norm.) That the stronger norm is incomplete will follow by the contradiction obtainable if it is assumed complete: By the result in Chapter 11 which is quoted above, it would be equivalent with each of the weaker norms which would then be equivalent with each other.

The corollary cited in Example 8 also explains why we are unable to proceed with a natural sequel to Examples 6, 7, and 8, namely an example of two comparable complete norms, which are not equivalent.

To introduce the next example, we recall the Hahn-Banach theorem (Section 4.4, Corollary 3) which asserts, in particular, that every normed space (indeed, every seminormed space in which there exists a vector a with $\|a\| \neq 0$) has a continuous linear functional, not identically zero, defined on it. This result does not extend to linear metric space [Examples 9, 10, 11]. In Section 12.2, it will be pointed out that the existence of functions is connected with the existence of convex neighborhoods of 0. Certainly, half of such a result is obvious. This is part (i) of Lemma 1. (A more general setting is described in Section 10.3, Problems 21 through 26 and Section 13.3, Problem 7.)

LEMMA 1. *Let* A *be a linear semimetric space such that* $A' \neq \{0\}$; *that is, there is a continuous linear functional* f, *not identically zero, defined on* A. *Then*

(i) *There is a convex neighborhood* G *of* 0 *in* A *with* $G \neq A$, *and*

(ii) $G + G + \cdots + G \neq A$, *no matter how many terms are taken in the sum.*

Let $G = (|f| < 1)$. G is a neighborhood of 0 by definition [Section 4.3, Definition 3]; G is convex [Section 2.5, Theorem 3]; $G \neq A$ [Section 2.4, Problem 17]. If there are n terms in the sum, we have $G + G + \cdots + G = nG$, since G is convex [Section 2.5, Problem 9 and formula (2)]. But $G \neq A = (1/n)A$, hence $nG \neq A.//$

Example 9: A space with no continuous linear functional except 0. This will be a linear semimetric space. An example of a linear metric space is obtained, as usual, by identifying points whose distance apart is 0 (Section 2.8, Example 1; Section 5.3, Problem 18). Let A be the space of real functions defined on $[0, 1]$, each of which has only a finite number of discontinuities. Define

$$!a! = \int_0^1 \frac{|a(x)|}{1 + |a(x)|} \, dx$$

for $a \in A$. This is the ordinary Riemann integral.

We shall show that Condition (ii) of Lemma 1 is violated for every neighborhood G of 0. Such a neighborhood must include a cell $N(0, r)$ with $r > 0$. Let $n > 1/r$ be an integer. Let $a \in A$. Subdivide $[0, 1]$ into n equal intervals $I_1, I_2, \ldots, I_n$. For $k = 1, 2, \ldots, n$, let $a_k \in A$ be defined by $a_k(x) = a(x)$ for $x \in I_k$, $a_k(x) = 0$ otherwise. Then

$$!a_k! = \int_{I_k} \frac{|a(x)|}{1 + |a(x)|} \, dx \leq \int_{I_k} 1 \, dx = 1/n,$$

$1/n$ being the length of I_k. Thus $!a_k! < r$ and so $a_k \in G$. But clearly $a = \Sigma a_k$ and so $a \in G + G + \cdots + G$, with n terms. Since a is arbitrary, we have $A \subset G + G + \cdots + G$. By Lemma 1, the result follows.

Example 10: A Fréchet space with no continuous linear functional except 0. Take the completion of the metric space given in Example 9 (see Problem 13).

Example 11. We shall show that L^p, $0 < p < 1$, has no nonzero continuous linear functional defined on it (this example is due to M. M. Day). This space is of interest because its paranorm has a property, resembling homogeneity, which is not shared by that of the preceding example, namely $!ta! = |t|^p!a!$ for scalar t. This, in turn, gives cells a shape resembling convexity [Problem 16] and boundedness [Section 10.3, Problem 13].

We first remark that given a set $E \subset [0, 1]$ with $|E| > 0$ ($|E|$ refers to the Lebesgue measure of E) and a number r, $0 < r < 2$, there exists a function $h \in L^r \setminus L^2$ such that $h(x) = 0$ for $x \notin E$. [Decompose E into a sequence $\{E_n\}$ of disjoint sets, define h to be α_n (to be specified) on E_n, $n = 1, 2, \ldots$, and 0 outside E. Then $\int |h|^m = \Sigma |E_n| \alpha_n^m$ and we can arrange that this be finite for $m = r$, infinite for $m = 2$; for example, $|E_n| = 2^{-n}|E|$, $\alpha_n = 2^{n/2}$.] Our second remark is that $L^2 \subset L^p$, and on L^2 the L^2 norm is stronger than the L^p paranorm. This means that if $a_n \in L^2$ for $n = 1, 2, \ldots$, and $\int |a_n|^2 \to 0$, then also $\int |a_n|^p \to 0$. [We may accept this as a known fact in integration theory. It is also given in Section 11.3, Example 6.]

We are now ready to deduce a contradiction from the assumption of the existence of a continuous linear functional f, not identically zero, on L^p. By the second remark, above, f is a continuous linear functional on L^2 and so there exists $F \in L^2$ such that $f(a) = \int_0^1 a(x)F(x)\,dx$ for all $a \in L^2$ [Section 4, Example 4]. Since F is not almost everywhere zero, we can find a positive number k and a set E of positive measure such that $|F(x)| \geq k$ for $x \in E$. Let $h \in L^{2p} \setminus L^2$ and $h(x) = 0$ for $x \notin E$ [first remark above]. Let $g(x) = h(x)^2 \, \mathrm{sgn}\, \{F(x)h^2(x)\}$. Thus $g \in L^p$. For $n = 1, 2, \ldots$, let $E_n = \{x \colon |g(x)| \leq n\}$. Let $g_n(x) = g(x)$ for $x \in E_n$, $g_n(x) = 0$ otherwise. Then $g_n \to g$ in L^p but $f(g_n) \to \infty$ [$g_n \in L^2$ since it is bounded and so

$$f(g_n) = \int g_n(x)F(x)\,dx = \int_{E_n} g(x)F(x)\,dx = \int_{E_n} |F(x)h^2(x)|\,dx \geq k \int_{E_n} |h^2(x)|\,dx \to \infty,$$

since $h \notin L^2$]. This contradicts the continuity of f.

Problems 7.5

1. Any linear semimetric space which is not a metric space has a discontinuous linear functional defined on it.

2. Let c be given the norm $\|a\| = \sup \{|a_{n-1} - a_n| \colon n = 1, 2, 3, \ldots\}$. (Take $a_0 = 0$.) Show that lim is a discontinuous linear functional.

3. Resolve this contradiction: if f is a linear functional on a normed space, f is continuous on each finite-dimensional subspace [Section 3, Theorem 2], and hence f is continuous everywhere [Section 4.3, Problem 24]; but this contradicts Example 1.

4. Let $b \in l$ and suppose that c is given the norm $\|x\| = \sup \{|x_n + \Sigma_{k=1}^{n-1} b_k x_k| \colon n = 1, 2, \ldots\}$. Show that lim is continuous on c with this norm.

▲5. Find $b \in l$ such that lim is not continuous on c with the norm $\|x\| = \sup \{|x_{n-1} + x_n + \Sigma_{k=1}^{n-1} b_k x_k| \colon n = 1, 2, \ldots\}$. Note: $x_0 = 0$. [$b_n = (-1)^n/n^2$ will do. Pointed out by W. K. Hayman.]

6. The exceptional case in Example 3 is essential; that is, if $!a! = 0$ for all a, every linear automorphism is continuous.

7. In Example 3, give a formula for g^{-1}.

8. The ballon in Example 4 is dense. [Section 4.4, Problem 26.]

★9. A balloon in a Banach space must be somewhere dense. [If B is absorbing, $\bigcup_{n=1}^{\infty} nB$ is the whole space; hence, by the Baire category theorem, not all nB can be nowhere dense.]

10. Let g be as in Example 3, and give another example like Example 6 by defining the new norm of x to be $\|g(x)\|$.

11. The space A of Example 9 has no continuous seminorm defined on it except 0. 〔Either argue that the seminorm topology would be weaker and the Hahn-Banach theorem would supply a continuous linear functional, or use Section 4.4, Theorem 2 directly.〕

12. The space A of Example 9, has no convex open proper subset. 〔Apply Problem 11 to the gauge of such a set.〕

13. The space of Example 10 is M.

14. Let A_B be the subspace of A in Example 9 consisting of bounded functions. Show that $A_B' = \{0\}$.

15. Define f on A_B, Problem 14, by $f(a) = \int_0^1 a(x)\,dx$. Show directly that f is not continuous.

16. Let A be a linear semimetric space and assume that there exists a number $p > 0$ such that for all scalar t and vector a, $!a! = |t|^p!a!$. Show that every cell centered at 0 satisfies, for $0 < u < 1$, $u + v = 1$, the inclusion $uN + vN \subset \alpha N$, where $\alpha = \max(1, 2^{(1/p)-1})$. (Thus, for $p \geq 1$, N is convex.)

17. Show that every infinite-dimensional linear metric space has a nonclosed linear subspace.

18. Give an example of a proper linear subspace which is of second category. 〔Let H be a Hamel basis for a complete linear metric space, $\{h_n\}$ a sequence of members of H, and $K = H \setminus \{h_n\}$. Let L_n be the span of $K \cup (h_1, h_2, \ldots, h_n)$. At least one L_n is of second category.〕

▲19. Given an example of two closed linear subspaces A, B such that $A + B$ is not closed. (See Section 11.2, Problem 21.)

20. For Example 3, use instead a permutation of a Hamel basis.

7.6   Uniform boundedness

The second of the three fundamental principles of functional analysis is the principle of uniform boundedness. (The first is the Hahn-Banach theorem.) Although a more general presentation is given in Section 12.3, the Banach space setting presented here is sufficiently general to cover many interesting applications, some of which are given. The principle is embodied in Theorems 1 and 2. For the first time, completeness plays an essential role, through the Baire category theorem.

DEFINITION 1. *Let* A *be a set,* B *a seminormed space, and* Φ *a family of functions* f: A $\to$ B. *Then* Φ *is said to be pointwise bounded if for each* a $\in$ A, *{f(a): f $\in \Phi$} is a bounded set in* B.

Thus Φ is pointwise bounded if and only if, for each $a \in A$, there exists a number M such that $\|f(a)\| \leq M$ for all $f \in \Phi$.

DEFINITION 2. *Let* A, B *be seminormed spaces and* Φ *a family of linear functions* f: A $\to$ B, *or seminorms defined on* A. *Then* Φ *is said to be uniformly bounded, or norm bounded, if there exists a number* M *such that* $\|f\| \leq$ M *for all* f $\in \Phi$.

★*Example 1.* Give E^∞ the norm, $\|a\| = \sup |a_n|$. For $n = 1, 2, \ldots$, let $q_n = n|P_n|$; that is, $q_n(a) = n|a_n|$. Then $\{q_n\}$ is pointwise bounded, in fact, $q_n(a) \to 0$ as $n \to \infty$ for each a. However $\{q_n\}$ is not uniformly bounded, in fact, $\|q_n\| = n$ 〔$q_n(\delta^n) = n$〕. This example shows that completeness cannot be omitted from Theorem 1.

THEOREM 1. *Let* Φ *be a pointwise bounded family of continuous seminorms on a complete seminormed space. Then* Φ *is uniformly bounded.*

For $n = 1, 2, \ldots,$ let $B_n = \{a : p(a) \leq n \text{ for all } p \in \Phi\}$. Then $\bigcup_{n=1}^{\infty} B_n$ is the whole space [given any vector a, there exists an integer k such that $p(a) \leq k$ for all $p \in \Phi$, since $\{p(a) : p \in \Phi\}$ is bounded; thus $a \in B_k$]. By the Baire category theorem, not all the sets $B_1, B_2, \ldots$ can be nowhere dense. Suppose that it is B_k that is somewhere dense. Since each $p \in \Phi$ is continuous, B_k is closed [it is $\bigcap\{(p \leq k) : p \in \Phi\}$] and so B_k includes a cell, say $N(b, r)$, $r > 0$. Now given any vector a with $\|a\| < 1$, let $x = b + ra$. Then $x \in N(b, r)$ and so $p(x) \leq k$ for all $p \in \Phi$. Then, for all $p \in \Phi$, $p(a) = p[(x - b)/r] \leq (1/r)[p(x) + p(b)] \leq 2k/r$. Thus $\|p\| \leq 2k/r$ for all $p \in \Phi$.//

Theorem 1 is often described as a resonance theorem. This name is plausible when the theorem is read as saying that if $\{\|p\| : p \in \Phi\}$ is unbounded, then there exists a point at which the seminorms are unbounded. Theorem 1 applies, in particular, to families of continuous linear functionals since their absolute values are seminorms. The next theorem is the dual of this particular case. In this case completeness need not be stipulated. This is due to the fact that A^* is automatically complete [Section 6.4, Theorem 1].

THEOREM 2. *Let* S *be a set in a seminormed space* A *such that for each* f $\in$ A$'$, f *is bounded on* S; *that is,* $\{f(a) : a \in S\}$ *is a bounded set in* E. *Then* S *is norm bounded; that is,* S *lies in a cell.* (*There exists a number* M *such that* $\|a\| < M$ *for all* a $\in$ S.)

Apply Theorem 1 to the Banach space A^*, with $\Phi = \hat{S}$. The hypothesis is that $\hat{S}$ is pointwise bounded on A^*.//

DEFINITION 3. *Let* A *be a set,* B *a semimetric space, and* $\{f_n\}$ *a sequence of maps from* A *to* B. *Then* $\{f_n\}$ *is called pointwise convergent if for each* a $\in$ A, $\{f_n(a)\}$ *is a convergent sequence in* B.

THEOREM 3. THE BANACH-STEINHAUS CLOSURE THEOREM. *Let* $\{f_n\}$ *be a pointwise convergent sequence of continuous linear functions from a complete seminormed space to a normed space. Then* f(a) $= \lim_{n \to \infty} f_n(a)$ *defines a continuous linear function* f.

That f is linear is trivial. By Theorem 1 there exists M such that $\|f_n\| < M$ for all n. Thus, for every vector a, $\|f_n(a)\| \leq M\|a\|$ for all n, and so $\|f(a)\| \leq M\|a\|$. Thus $\|f\| \leq M$.//

Theorem 3 shows that it is difficult to construct a discontinuous linear functional on a complete space. Anything of the form $\Sigma t_n x_n$ or $\int_a^b u(t)x(t)\,dt$ would be continuous in x since it is a limit of finite sums, themselves, presumably continuous. One may safely say that on a complete space, any linear functional that can be explicitly constructed is continuous. Apparently, Section 5, Example 2 contradicts this. The point, however, is that the function given there is shown to exist (by means of an extension theorem which uses a Hamel basis), but not explicitly constructed.

Example 2. Let $p > 1$, and suppose that a sequence $\{a_n\}$ of complex numbers has the property that

(1) $$\Sigma a_n b_n \text{ is convergent for every } b \in l^p.$$

Defining f on l^p by $f(b) = \Sigma a_n b_n$, Theorem 3 implies that f is continuous. From Section 6.4, Example 3, it then follows that $a \in l^q$, $1/p + 1/q = 1$. Thus we have the nontrivial result that property (1) implies that $a \in l^q$. This result was not obtained in Section 6.4, Example 3.

THEOREM 4. *Let* $\{f_n\}$ *be a uniformly bounded sequence of linear functionals on a seminormed space* A. *Then* $\{a\colon \lim_{n \to \infty} f_n(a)$ *exists$\}$ is a closed linear subspace of* A.

We have for each $a \in A$, $\{f_n(a)\} \in m$. Define $g\colon A \to m$ by $g(a) = \{f_n(a)\}$. Then g is linear and continuous $[\|g(a)\| = \sup_n |f_n(a)| \leq M\|a\|]$. Thus, since c is a closed linear subspace of m, $g^{-1}[c]$ is a closed linear subspace of A.//

The first of the following applications is a result of the type given in Example 2, but is deduced more directly from the uniform boundedness principle.

Application 1. (Section 1.2, Problem 11).   Suppose that a sequence $\{a_n\}$ of complex numbers has the property that $\Sigma a_n b_n$ converges for every $b \in c_0$. Let $f_n(b) = \Sigma_{k=1}^{n} a_k b_k$ define a functional f_n on c_0, $n = 1, 2, \ldots$. Each f_n is continuous; in fact, $\|f_n\| = \Sigma_{k=1}^{n} |a_k|$ [Section 6.4, Example 4, the proof is quite trivial in this (finite) case]. Since $\lim_{n \to \infty} f_n(b)$ exists for every b, it follows from Theorem 1 that $\sup \|f_n\| < \infty$; that is, $\Sigma |a_k| < \infty$.

Application 2. (Section 1.2, Problem 17: The Silverman-Toeplitz conditions.)   Let A be a matrix and assume that for every $x \in c_0$, $Ax \in m$. Then $\|A\| < \infty$. [By Application 1, $\Sigma_{k=1}^{\infty} |a_{nk}| < \infty$ for $n = 1, 2, \ldots$. Let $g_n(x) = \Sigma_{k=1}^{\infty} a_{nk} x_k$ define a functional g_n on c_0, $n = 1, 2, \ldots$. Then $\|g_n\| = \Sigma_{k=1}^{\infty} |a_{nk}|$ by Section 6.4, Example 4. Finally, by Theorem 1, $\sup \|g_n\| < \infty$; that is, $\|A\| < \infty$.] This shows that a conservative matrix A satisfies $\|A\| < \infty$. That $\lim_{n \to \infty} a_{nk}$ exists for each k follows from the fact that $\delta^k \in c_A$. That $\lim_{n \to \infty} \Sigma_{k=1}^{\infty} a_{nk}$ exists follows from the fact that $1 \in c_A$.

The Silverman-Toeplitz conditions are thus proved necessary that a matrix be conservative. We now prove them sufficient. Let g_n be defined as above. Then $\sup \|g_n\| < \infty$, moreover $\lim_{n \to \infty} g_n(1)$ and $\lim_{n \to \infty} g_n(\delta)^k$ exist for $k = 1, 2, \ldots$. Since $\{1, \delta^1, \delta^2, \ldots \}$ is fundamental in c, it follows from Theorem 4 that $\lim_{n \to \infty} g_n(x)$ exists for all $x \in c$.//

Application 3 (Du Bois-Reymond).   *There exists a continuous real function defined on* $[-\pi, \pi]$ *whose Fourier series diverges at* 0. Let A be the space real $C[-\pi, \pi]$. For $n = 1, 2, \ldots$ define $u_n \in A'$ by $u_n(f) = a_0/2 + \Sigma_{k=1}^{n} a_k$, where $a_0, a_1, \ldots$ are the familiar Fourier coefficients of f. Thus $u_n(f)$ is the value at 0 of a segment of the Fourier series of f.

If there exists no function with the property mentioned, then $\lim_{n \to \infty} u_n(f)$ exists for all $f \in A$. By Theorem 1, $\sup \|u_n\| < \infty$. We shall show that this is false. The familiar manipulations yield $u_n(f) = \int_{-\pi}^{\pi} f(x) g_n(x) \, dx$, where $g_n(x) = \dfrac{\sin (n + \frac{1}{2})x}{2\pi \sin \frac{1}{2} x}$. We have $\|u_n\| = \int_{\pi}^{\pi} |g_n(x)| \, dx$ [Section 6.4, Problem 39], thus

$$\|u_n\| \geq \sum_{k=0}^{n-1} \int_{(4k+1)/(4n+2)}^{(4k+3)/(4n+2)} |g_n(x)| \, dx \geq \frac{1}{2\pi \sqrt{2}} \Sigma \int \frac{dx}{\sin \frac{1}{2} x}$$

$$\geq \frac{1}{2\pi \sqrt{2}} \Sigma \int \frac{2 \, dx}{x} = \frac{1}{\pi \sqrt{2}} \sum_{k=0}^{n-1} \log \frac{4k + 3}{4k + 1} \geq \frac{1}{\pi \sqrt{2}} \sum_{k=0}^{n-1} \frac{2}{4k + 3}$$

[using $\log (1 + t) \geq t/(1 + t)$] and so, finally, $\|u_n\| \to \infty$.

Problems 7.6

1. Instead of assuming Φ pointwise bounded in Theorem 1, it is sufficient to assume that $\{f(a): f \in \Phi\}$ is bounded for each a in a set of second category in the space. With this assumption, the space need not be assumed complete.

2. In Theorem 1, "continuous" may be replaced by "lower semicontinuous" [the same proof works]. But see Problem 3.

3. A lower semicontinuous seminorm on a complete linear semimetric space is continuous [Problem 2 and Theorem 1]. See Section 6.1, Problem 38.

4. Instead of assuming $\{f_n\}$ pointwise convergent in Theorem 3, it is sufficient to assume that $\{f_n(a)\}$ is convergent for each a in a set of second category in the space. With this assumption, the space need not be assumed complete.

5. Instead of assuming $\{f_n\}$ pointwise convergent in Theorem 3, it is sufficient to assume that $\{f_n(a)\}$ is convergent for each a in a somewhere dense set, and that $\{f_n\}$ is uniformly bounded. The space need not be assumed complete.

6. In Problem 5, replace "somewhere dense" by "fundamental."

7. Completeness cannot be dropped in Theorem 3. [Let $f(a) = \Sigma a_n$ for $a \in E^\infty$, $\|a\| = \sup |a_n|$.]

8. Prove Theorem 4 for a sequence of seminorms.

9. Prove Theorem 4 for a sequence $\{f_n\}$ of linear maps from one Banach space to another.

10. With the hypotheses of Problem 9, prove that $\{a: f_n(a) \to 0\}$ is a closed linear subspace of A.

11. Modify Theorem 4 by replacing "uniformly bounded" by "pointwise bounded" and assuming A complete.

12. Let $\{a_n\}$ be a sequence in a seminormed space A such that $f(a_n) \to 0$ for all f in a set of second category in A^*. Show that $a_n \to 0$ weakly.

13. In Problem 12, assume that $\{a_n\}$ is bounded and replace "set of second category" by "fundamental set."

14. Obtain the result of Application 1 by the method of Example 2.

15. Let $\{f_n\}$ be a sequence of functions on a normed space with $\|f_n\| = 1$ for all n. It is possible that $f_n \to 0$ pointwise [for example, P_n on c_0] but this must take place with arbitrary slowness; that is, no sequence $\{\epsilon_n\}$ with $0 < \epsilon_n \to 0$ may be found such that $f_n(a) = 0(\epsilon_n)$ for each a.

16. Let A be a Banach space and $\{f_n\}$ a sequence of continuous linear functionals $\{f_n\}$ such that $\|f_n\| = 1$ for each n and $\bigcup_{k=1}^\infty \bigcap_{n=k}^\infty f_n^\perp$ is dense in A. Show that $f_n \to 0$ pointwise. (As a special case, take $f_n = P_n$, in which case the given condition holds for $A = c_0$ [Section 1.3, Problem 10] but not for $A = m$. See also Problem 15.)

17. In Problem 16, omit the condition $\|f_n\| = 1$ and obtain the conclusion $f_n(a) = o(\|f_n\|)$ for each a.

18. Let A be a conservative triangle, $B = A^{-1}$. Suppose that B has convergent columns and that c is a closed subset of c_A (Section 5.2, Problem 7). Show that $\|B\| < \infty$. [Section 4.4, Problem 41, and uniform boundedness.] (It follows that B is conservative, and $c_A = c$, by Section 12.4, Problem 32.)

8

HILBERT SPACE

8.1 Inner products

Of all topics included in this book, that of Hilbert space is the one best covered by expository texts. Because of this excellent and long-standing coverage, there will be no need for us to develop the subject fully. (See the Reader's Guide mentioned in Appendix A.) We shall restrict ourselves to a study of Hilbert space as a special kind of normed space, and develop a little of its structure in the spirit of the earlier chapters. The reader should be constantly aware that, in this chapter, very few aspects are given more than introductory treatment and that many basic results are omitted.

DEFINITION 1. *An inner product on a linear space is a complex valued function of two variables selected from the space, written* (a, b), *and satisfying the conditions:*

> (i) (a, b) *is linear as a function of* a *for fixed* b,
> (ii) $(b, a) = \overline{(a, b)}$ (the complex conjugate),
> (iii) $(a, a) > 0$ *if* $a \neq 0$.

The meaning of Condition (i) is that $(ta + b, c) = t(a, c) + (b, c)$ for scalar t and vectors a, b, c. It follows immediately that $(0, a) = (a, 0) = 0$ for all a, and that (a, b) is *conjugate linear* in b; that is, $(a, tb + c) = \bar{t}(a, b) + (a, c)$ [Problem 1].

Example 1. As examples of inner products we have, in

> (a) the spaces E^n, $(a, b) = \sum_{k=1}^{n} a_k \bar{b}_k$,
>
> (b) the spaces l^p, $1 \leq p \leq 2$, $(a, b) = \sum_{k=1}^{\infty} a_k \bar{b}_k$.

This series always converges, for, by Hölder's inequality, $\sum |a_k \bar{b}_k| \leq (\sum |a_k|^2)^{\frac{1}{2}} (\sum |b_k|^2)^{\frac{1}{2}}$.

> (c) the spaces L^2, C, $(a, b) = \int_0^1 a(t) \overline{b(t)} \, dt$.

A *real inner* product is defined similarly except that it is real valued, real linear (in its first variable), and satisfies $(a, b) = (b, a)$. We shall usually prove theorems for the (complex) inner product. The real case is always similar and we shall assume that it is covered.

★*Example 2.* Any linear space can be given an inner product. [Let H be a Hamel basis. For $x = \Sigma ah$, $y = \Sigma bh$, set $(x, y) = \Sigma a\bar{b}$.]

For convenience, the following result will be referred to as Cauchy's inequality.

THEOREM 1. CAUCHY-SCHWARZ-BUNYAKOWSKI INEQUALITY. $|(a, b)|^2 \le (a, a)(b, b)$ *for all* a, b. *Equality holds if and only if* a, b *are linearly dependent.*

The result is trivial if $b = 0$. We shall assume $b \ne 0$. Let $u = (b, b)$, $v = (a, b)$. Then u is real, $u > 0$, $\bar{v} = (b, a)$ and, using these, $0 \le (ua - vb, ua - vb) = (ua, ua) - (ua, vb) - (vb, ua) + (vb, vb) = u^2(a, a) - u\bar{v}v - v\bar{v}u + v\bar{v}u = u^2(a, a) - u|v|^2$. Thus $|v|^2 \le u(a, a) = (a, a)(b, b)$. Now if $|(a, b)|^2 = (a, a)(b, b)$, both ends of the above string of inequalities are zero and so $(ua - vb, ua - vb) = 0$. Thus $ua - vb = 0$, $u \ne 0$. Thus a, b are linearly dependent.//

We now construct a norm from a given inner product. We shall prove that $\|a\| = (a, a)^{1/2}$ defines a norm. Clearly $\|a\| \ge 0$, and $\|a\| > 0$ if $a \ne 0$. Also $\|ta\|^2 = (ta, ta) = t\bar{t}(a, a) = |t|^2\|a\|^2$, so that $\|ta\| = |t| \cdot \|a\|$ for scalar t. Finally, $(a + b, a + b) = (a, a) + (a, b) + (b, a) + (b, b) = \|a\|^2 + 2R(a, b) + \|b\|^2 \le \|a\|^2 + 2\|a\| \cdot \|b\| + \|b\|^2$ [Theorem 1] $= (\|a\| + \|b\|)^2$. Thus the triangular inequality is proved.

DEFINITION 2. *An inner product space is a linear space together with an inner product defined on it. It is also a normed space with the norm constructed from the inner product. If the norm is complete, the inner product space is called a Hilbert space.*

For example, any finite dimensional inner product space is a Hilbert space [Section 7.3, Theorem 1].

Example 3: E^n *is a Hilbert space.* We have $\|a\| = (\Sigma_{k=1}^n |a_k|^2)^{1/2}$. We know that it is a Banach space; it remains to observe that the norm is derived from an inner product, namely $(a, b) = \Sigma a_k \bar{b}_k$.

Example 4. Referring to Example 1 (b), the norm on l^p derived from the given inner product is $\|a\| = (\Sigma |a_k|^2)^{1/2}$. For $p = 2$, this is the natural norm and so l^2 is a Hilbert space. For $1 \le p < 2$, the norm derived from the inner product is not complete [Problem 17] and, in any case, it is not the natural norm so it is best forgotten. We shall see [Example 5] that these spaces are not Hilbert spaces at all. The same applies to Example 1 (c); here L^2 is a Hilbert space, C is not; the inner product does not yield the natural norm for C.

A fundamental property of any inner product, real or complex, is the parallelogram law, $\|a + b\|^2 + \|a - b\|^2 = 2\|a\|^2 + 2\|b\|^2$, which has already been mentioned in Section 7.4, Example 2. The proof is given by observing, as before, that $\|a \pm b\|^2 = (a \pm b, a \pm b) = \|a\|^2 \pm 2R(a, b) + \|b\|^2$. (For real inner products the proof is similar.)

The parallelogram law is expressed in terms of the norm, the inner product not occurring explicitly. Any norm not obeying it is not derived from an inner product. For example one might check that for R^2, the norm $\|a\| = |x| + |y|$ for $a = (x, y) \in R^2$ does not obey the parallelogram law [Problem 4]. However, the fact that this norm is not derived from an inner product follows even more easily from the fact that it is not rotund, the unit circumference being a square. Any norm derived from an inner product must be rotund, indeed uniformly convex, as we now show.

THEOREM 2. *An inner-product space is uniformly convex.*

This follows from the parallelogram law exactly as in Section 7.4, Example 2.//
It follows that any Hilbert Space is reflexive [Section 7.4, Theorem 1].

Example 5: l^p, $p \geq 1$, $p \neq 2$. *These are not Hilbert spaces.* For $p = 1$, the space is not rotund. For $p \geq 1$ the parallelogram law fails. [For example, $\|\delta^1 \pm \delta^2\| = \|\{1, \pm 1, 0, 0, \ldots\}\| = (1^p + 1^p)^{1/p} = 2^{1/p}$, while $\|\delta^1\| = \|\delta^2\| = 1$. Thus, for $p \neq 2$, the parallelogram law fails.]

Example 6. The norm of c_0 is not rotund; hence c_0 is not a Hilbert space. We can say more. Since c_0 is not reflexive, its norm is not equivalent to any norm derived from an inner product [Section 7.2, Problem 19].

THEOREM 3. *In an inner-product space* A, *fix* b $\in$ A, *and define f by f*(a) = (a, b). *Then f is a continuous linear functional on* A, *and* $\|f\| = \|b\|$.

We mean, of course, that f is continuous as a function on the inner-product space considered as a normed space. This follows from Cauchy's inequality since $|f(a)| \leq \|a\| \cdot \|b\|$, and so $\|f\| \leq \|b\|$. Since $f(b) = \|b\|^2$ we have also $\|f\| \geq \|b\|$.//
Since $(a, b) = \overline{(b, a)}$, it follows that for fixed a, (a, b) is a continuous function of b.

COROLLARY 1. *The set* a$^\perp \equiv$ {b: (a, b) = 0} *is a closed linear subspace.*

That $a^\perp$ is a linear subspace is obvious. That it is closed follows from the continuity of f in Theorem 3 [Section 4.3, Problem 20].//

COROLLARY 2. *If* Σb$_n$ *is a convergent series of vectors, then* $(\Sigma$b$_n$, a) = Σ(b$_n$, a) *for each vector* a, *the latter series being convergent.*

Application. We apply these ideas to elementary analytic geometry. Let e be the ellipse $x^2/a^2 + y^2/b^2 = 1$. We shall find the tangent to e at a point $(x_1; y_1) \in e$. (We are using a semicolon instead of a comma to avoid confusion with the inner-product notation.) For $z = (x; y) \in R^2$, $w = (u; v) \in R^2$, define $(z, w) = xu/a^2 + yv/b^2$. This makes R^2 an inner-product space in which e is the unit circumference. Define f on R^2 by $f(z) = (z, z_1)$, the inner product of z, z_1 where $z_1 = (x_1; y_1)$. Then $\|f\| = \|z_1\| = 1$ [since $z_1 \in e$].
The set $(f = 1)$ is tangent to the unit disk [proved as in Section 4.4, Example 5]. Thus the tangent to e is given by the set $(f = 1)$, this being $(z, z_1) = 1$, that is, $xx_1/a^2 + yy_1/b^2 = 1$.

Problems on inner-product space 8.1

★1. Show that $(0, a) = 0$ for all a, and that $(a, tb + c) = \bar{t}(a, b) + (a, c)$ for scalar t.

2. Show that $R(a, b)$ is a (real) inner product for the real linear space associated with a given inner-product space.

3. Show that, for a norm derived from an inner product, and nonzero vectors a, b, $\|a + b\| = \|a\| + \|b\|$ if and only if b is a positive multiple of a.

4. In R^2, the norm $\|a\| = |x| + |y|$ for $a = (x, y) \in R^2$ does not satisfy the parallelogram law.

5. Find, by use of inner products, the tangent to the ellipse $x^2 + xy + 3y^2 = 5$ at the point $(2, -1)$.

★6. Let a, b be called *orthogonal*, or *perpendicular to each other* if $(a, b) = 0$, equivalently, $(b, a) = 0$. We write $a \perp b$. Show that $0 \perp a$ for all a, and that $a \perp a$ if and only if $a = 0$.

7. For a set S in an inner-product space, let $S^\perp = \{b: b \perp a \text{ for all } a \in S\}$. (We say that any point in $S^\perp$ is *orthogonal* to S.) Show that $S \subset S^{\perp\perp} (\equiv (S^\perp)^\perp)$, and $S^\perp = S^{\perp\perp\perp}$ (see Section 2, Problem 3).

★8. Show that an orthogonal set of nonzero vectors is linearly independent. (An *orthogonal set* is a set of vectors, any two of which are orthogonal.)

★9. If $(a, b) = (a, c)$ for all a, then $b = c$. $[\![(a, b - c) = 0$ for all a, in particular, for $a = b - c.]\!]$

★10. Show that the following three statements are equivalent.

$$\text{(i)} \quad a \perp b, \qquad \text{(ii)} \quad \|a + tb\| = \|a - tb\| \text{ for all scalar } t,$$
$$\text{(iii)} \quad \|a + tb\| \geq \|a\| \text{ for all scalar } t.$$

$[\![$For example, a proof that (iii) implies (i) is given: we may assume that $\|b\| = 1$; then $0 \leq \|a - (a, b)b\|^2 - \|a\|^2 = -|(a, b)|^2$ hence $(a, b) = 0.]\!]$

11. If $a_1, a_2, \ldots, a_n$ are mutually orthogonal, $\|\sum_{k=1}^n a_k\|^2 = \sum_{k=1}^n \|a_k\|^2$. For real inner products, the converse holds for $n = 2$, but not for $n = 3$. [An example may be given in R^3.]

12. Let A, B be inner-product spaces and suppose that $f: A \to B$ is linear and satisfies $\|f(a)\| = \|a\|$ for all $a \in A$. Show that $(f(a), f(b)) = (a, b)$ for all $a, b \in A$.

13. Let E^n be given an inner product. Show that there exists a positive-definite symmetric matrix H such that $(a, b) = aHb' \equiv \sum_{m,k=1}^n a_k h_{km} b_m$.

14. Discuss the codimension of $S^\perp$.

15. Show that C is not an inner-product space.

16. Show that L^p, $1 \leq p \neq 2$, is not an inner-product space.

17. How do the (natural) norms of C, l^p, L^p, $1 \leq p < 2$, compare in strength with the ones derived from the inner products in Example 1. Are the latter complete?

18. Let B be a bilinear functional and f a positive real function, each defined on E^2. About f we shall suppose only that $f(z, w) = 1$ whenever $\|z\| = \|w\| = 1$. (Here z, w are complex numbers.) Suppose that $|B(z, w)| \leq f(z, w)$ for all z, w. Show that $|B(z, w)| \leq \|z\| \cdot \|w\|$ for all z, w.

19. Let $\{a_n\}$ be linearly independent. Show that there exists an orthogonal sequence $\{b_n\}$ of *unit vectors* (that is, $\|b_n\| = 1$) such that for each n, b_n is a linear combination of $a_1, a_2, \ldots, a_n$. (An orthogonal set of unit vectors is called an *orthonormal* set.) $[\![$The *Gram-Schmidt* process may be used. Let $b_1 = a_1/\|a_1\|$ and, inductively, $b_{n+1} = x/\|x\|$, where $x = a_{n+1} - \sum_{k=1}^n (a_{n+1}, b_k)b_k.]\!]$

8.2 The conjugate space

We shall deal with a fixed Hilbert space H and investigate the continuous linear functionals on H. We already know some of them; in Section 1, Theorem 3 we saw that each vector $a \in H$ leads to a continuous linear functional on H by means of the formula $f(x) = (x, a)$. Indeed, $\|f\| = \|a\|$. What we shall now see is that all the continuous linear functionals on H are of this form; the map from H to H^* just described is actually onto. (A possible procedure would be to prove that H^* is uniformly convex and use Section 7.4, Problems 18 through 20.)

THEOREM 1. THE F. RIESZ REPRESENTATION THEOREM. *Let f be a continuous linear functional on a Hilbert space H. Then there exists a unique vector a $\in$ H with f(x) = (x, a) for all x $\in$ H. Moreover $\|a\| = \|f\|$.*

We may assume $f \neq 0$. If such a vector a exists, it will be unique. 〖Suppose $(x, a) = (x, b)$ for all x. Then $(x, a - b) = 0$ for all x. In particular, $(a - b, a - b) = 0$ and so $a - b = 0$.〗

Since H is uniformly convex 〖Section 1, Theorem 2〗, f assumes its maximum at some point b on the unit disk 〖Section 7.4, Corollary 1〗. Thus $\|b\| = 1$, $f(b) = \|f\|$. Let $a = \|f\| \cdot b$. Then $f(a) = \|f\|^2$, $\|a\| = \|f\|$. (This is in accord with the possibility that $f(x) = (x, a)$ for all x.)

Concerning a, we know that $\|a + tx\| \geq \|a\|$ for all $x \in f^{\perp}$ 〖Section 7.4, Lemma 2, with $S = f^{\perp}$, $H = (f = \|f\|^2)$〗, thus $a \perp x$ for all $x \in f^{\perp}$ 〖Section 1, Problem 10〗. What we have proved is that $f(x) = 0$ implies $(x, a) = 0$. Consulting Section 2.10, Corollary 2, we find that for some scalar t, $(x, a) = tf(x)$ for all $x \in H$. Setting $x = a$ yields $\|a\|^2 = t\|f\|^2$ and so $t = 1$. Thus, finally, $f(x) = (x, a)$ for all $x \in H.//$

COROLLARY 1. *Let* H *be a Hilbert space.* *To* f $\in$ H*, *let correspond* a $\in$ H *such that* f(x) = (x, a) *for all* x $\in$ H. *This correspondence is a conjugate-linear isometry onto.*

By Theorem 1, it is an isometry. It is clearly onto 〖given a, define f by $f(x) = (a, x)$〗. Finally, if f, g correspond to a, b and t is a scalar, $(f + tg)(x) = f(x) + tg(x) = (x, a) + t(x, b) = (x, a) + (x, \bar{t}b) = (x, a + \bar{t}b)$, thus $f + tg$ corresponds to $a + \bar{t}b.//$

We see in Section 5 that H, H^* are actually congruent. (Corollary 3.)

Problems 8.2

1. Let a, b, c, be real numbers with $a > 0$, $ac > b^2$. Define a real inner product on R^2 by $(z, w) = (x; y) \begin{pmatrix} a & b \\ b & c \end{pmatrix} \begin{pmatrix} u \\ v \end{pmatrix} \equiv axu + b(xv + yu) + cyv$ for $z = (x; y)$, $w = (u; v)$. Let h, k be real numbers and define f on R^2 by $f(x; y) = hx + ky$. Find the Riesz representation for f. What is $\|f\|$?

2. Show that the Riesz representation theorem fails if the inner-product space is not assumed complete.

3. Let S be a set in a Hilbert space. Show that $S^{\perp\perp}$ is the linear closure of S. 〖If a is not in the linear closure of S, use the Hahn-Banach theorem to conclude that $a \notin S^{\perp\perp}$; see Section 1, Problem 7.〗

8.3   Inner-product norms

As we have seen in Section 1, some norms are not derived from inner products. A norm derived from an inner product must satisfy the parallelogram law

(1) $$\|a + b\|^2 - \|a - b\|^2 = 2\|a\|^2 + 2\|b\|^2.$$

We shall see that this condition is sufficient as well as necessary.

THEOREM 1. JORDAN-VON NEUMANN. *A norm satisfying the parallelogram law is derived from an inner product.*

Case 1: A real linear normed space. Since, for a real inner product, we have $\|a \pm b\|^2 = \|a\|^2 \pm 2(a, b) + \|b\|^2$, we obtain $\|a + b\|^2 - \|a - b\|^2 = 4(a, b)$. Thus, given a norm, if it is derived from an inner product, that inner product must be given by

$$(a, b) = \tfrac{1}{4}(\|a + b\|^2 - \|a - b\|^2). \tag{2}$$

Thus, given a real normed space satisfying the parallelogram law we define, for vectors a, b the number (a, b) by equation (2). We shall prove that it is a real inner product. It is clear that $(a, b) = (b, a)$, and that $(a, a) = \|a\|^2 > 0$ for $a \neq 0$.

Next we prove that $(a + b, c) = (a, c) + (b, c)$. [Making two uses in the second step of the parallelogram law applied respectively, to $a + b$ and $b + c$, $a - c$ and $b - c$, we obtain $(a, c) + (b, c) = \tfrac{1}{4}(\|a + c\|^2 + \|b + c\|^2) - \tfrac{1}{4}(\|a - c\|^2 + \|b - c\|^2) = \tfrac{1}{8}(\|a + c + b + c\|^2 + \|a + c - b - c\|^2) - \tfrac{1}{8}(\|a - c + b - c\|^2 + \|a - c - b + c\|^2) = \tfrac{1}{8}(\|a + b + 2c\|^2 - \|a + b - 2c\|^2) = \tfrac{1}{2}(a + b, 2c)$. This proves, for all a, b, c, that

$$(a, c) + (b, c) = \tfrac{1}{2}(a + b, 2c). \tag{3}$$

In relation (3), set $b = 0$ and obtain, for all a, c, $(a, c) = \tfrac{1}{2}(a, 2c)$. Replacing a by $a + b$ and applying this to relation (3), yields the desired result.] We have now proved that (a, b) is additive as a function of a for each fixed b. Since it is also continuous, it follows from Section 6.1, Theorem 1 that it is linear.

Case 2: Normed space (complex scalars). We use relation (2) to define a product which will turn out to be the real part of an inner product. Let us define $(a, b)_R$ to be the right-hand side of relation (2). For fixed b, this defines a real-valued real linear function. Section 2.11, Theorem 1 provides that there exists, for each b, a linear function (a, b) of a, such that $(a, b)_R = R(a, b)$, indeed we have

$$(a, b) = (a, b)_R - i(ia, b)_R. \tag{4}$$

For each a, $(ia, a)_R = 0$ [relation (2)]; hence $(a, a) = (a, a)_R = \|a\|^2$. We also need the identity $(ia, ia)_R = (a, a)_R$ which follows from relation (2). Finally, making use of this identity, $(b, a) = (b, a)_R - i(ib, a)_R = (a, b)_R - i(b, -ia)_R = (a, b)_R + i(ia, b)_R = \overline{(a, b)}$.//

COROLLARY 1. *If every two-dimensional subspace of a normed space* A *is an inner-product space, then* A *is an inner-product space.*

Given any two vectors a, b, they lie in some two-dimensional subspace of A, hence satisfy the parallelogram law (1). By Theorem 1 the result follows.//

Problems 8.3

1. Show that two linearly dependent vectors in an arbitrary normed space must satisfy the parallelogram law.
2. Every one-dimensional normed space is an inner-product space.
3. In a real normed space define $\{a, b\}$ to be $\tfrac{1}{2}(\|a + b\|^2 - \|a\|^2 - \|b\|^2)$. Show that $\{\ ,\ \}$ has some, but, in general, not all the properties of an inner product. If the norm is derived from an inner product, show that $(a, b) = \{a, b\}$ for all a, b.
4. In Problem 3, $\{a, b\}$ satisfies the inequality $|\{a, b\}| \leq \|a\| \cdot \|b\|$.

5. In a normed space, define M, m as, respectively, sup and inf

$$\left\{ \frac{\|a+b\|^2 + \|a-b\|^2}{2(\|a\|^2 + \|b\|^2)} : a, b \text{ not both } 0 \right\}.$$

Show that $M = 1/m$, that $\frac{1}{2} \le m \le 1$, and that the norm is derived from an inner product if and only if $M = m = 1$.

6. Let a, b be linearly independent vectors in a normed space. The set $\{(x, y) \in R^2 : \|xa + yb\| = 1\}$ is called the *real two-section of the unit circumference*. Show that every such section is an ellipse if the norm is derived from an inner product.

7. Prove the converse of Problem 6. If every two-section of the unit circumference is an ellipse, the norm is derived from an inner product. [Let the ellipse e be $\alpha x^2 + 2\beta xy + \gamma y^2 = 1$. For any x, y,

$$\left\| \frac{xa}{\|xa+yb\|} + \frac{yb}{\|xa+yb\|} \right\| = 1,$$

thus

$$\left(\frac{x}{\|xa+yb\|}, \frac{y}{\|xa+yb\|} \right) \in e$$

and so

$$\frac{\alpha x^2}{\|xa+yb\|^2} + \frac{2\beta xy}{\|xa+yb\|^2} + \frac{\gamma y^2}{\|xa+yb\|^2} = 1.$$

Hence, $\|xa+yb\|^2 = \alpha x^2 + 2\beta xy + \gamma y^2 = \|a\|^2 x^2 + 2\beta xy + \|b\|^2 y^2$. The parallelogram law is now obvious.]

8. Let e be the ellipse $13x^2 + 6\sqrt{3}\, xy + 7y^2 = 13$ in R^2. Give R^2 a norm such that e is the unit circumference [Section 4.2, Theorem 1]. Find the inner product from which this norm is derived. Find the real two-section of the unit circumference through the points $(1, 0)$ and $(0, \sqrt{13/7})$.

9. Show that β in Problem 7 is equal to $R(a, b)$.

10. Let a, b be linearly independent unit vectors in an inner-product space. The real two-section through a, b of the unit circumference is an ellipse with the line $y = x$ as axis, or, if and only if (a, b) is pure imaginary, it is a circle.

11. Let R^n be given a norm. Show that this norm can be derived from an inner product if and only if the unit sphere is an ellipsoid.

8.4 Orthonormal sets in an inner-product space

The material of the next two sections is a generalization of parts of Fourier analysis and, at the same time, of the study of Euclidean spaces.

If the class of orthonormal sets is ordered by inclusion, we may take a maximal chain and thus, as in the construction of a Hamel basis, Section 2.3, Theorem 1, we have, taking the union of the maximal chain, that *there exists a maximal orthonormal set in any inner-product space.* It is clear that *an orthonormal set is maximal if and only if there exists no vector (except 0) which is orthogonal to all of its members.* It is also clear that *if an orthonormal set is fundamental, it is maximal* [for if a is orthogonal to B, it is also orthogonal to the linear closure of B, hence to itself; thus $a = 0$].

★ *Example 1.* In E^n, the set $\{\delta^1, \delta^2, \ldots, \delta^n\}$ is a maximal orthonormal set. [If, for all k, $a \perp \delta^k$, then $0 = (a, \delta^k) = a_k$, thus $a = 0$.]

The same type of argument works in a space of sequences.

★ *Example 2.* In l^2, $\{\delta^n\}$ is a maximal orthonormal set.

★ *Example 3.* Let real $C[-\pi, \pi]$ be given the real inner product $(a, b) = \int_{-\pi}^{\pi} a(t)b(t)\, dt$. Let $s_n(t) = (1/\sqrt{\pi}) \sin nt$. Then $\{s_n\}$ is an orthonormal set. It is not maximal since *cos* is orthogonal to all its members.

DEFINITION 1. *Suppose given an orthonormal set* S *in an inner-product space* A. *For each* a $\in$ A, *the set* $\{(a, b): b \in S\}$ *is called the set of orthogonal coefficients of* a *relative to* S.

We shall omit "relative to S" wherever S is fixed by the context. The familiar Fourier coefficients are a special case of orthogonal coefficients. We may, for instance, use Example 3; then for $a \in C$, $(a, s_n) = (1/\sqrt{\pi}) \int_{-\pi}^{\pi} a(t) \sin nt\, dt$.

★*Example 4.* In Example 1, the orthogonal coefficients of $a = (a_1, a_2, \ldots, a_n)$ are precisely $a_1, a_2, \ldots, a_n$.

If $\{b_1, b_2, \ldots, b_n\}$ is a finite orthonormal set and a is a vector, we have, setting $t_k = (a, b_k)$, $0 \le \|a - \sum_{k=1}^{n} t_k b_k\|^2 = (a - \Sigma t_k b_k, a - \Sigma t_k b_k) = \|a\|^2 - (a, \Sigma t_k b_k) - (\Sigma t_k b_k, a) + (\Sigma t_k b_k, \Sigma t_k b_k) = \|a\|^2 - \Sigma \bar{t}_k(a, b_k) - \Sigma t_k(b_k, a) + \sum_{k=1}^{n} t_k(b_k, \sum_{m=1}^{n} t_m b_m) = \|a\|^2 - 2\Sigma |t_k|^2 + \Sigma t_k \Sigma \bar{t}_m(b_k, b_m) = \|a\|^2 - \Sigma |t_k|^2$.

We have proved that

$$(1) \qquad \|a\|^2 - \sum_{k=1}^{n} |t_k|^2 = \|a - \sum_{k=1}^{n} t_k b_k\|^2, \qquad t_k = (a, b_k).$$

It follows that $\Sigma |t_k|^2 \le \|a\|^2$.

If we have an orthonormal sequence $\{b_n\}$ and a vector a, it follows that for any n, $\sum_{k=1}^{n} |t_k|^2 \le \|a\|^2$ and so finally, $\Sigma |t_k|^2$ is convergent and less than or equal to $\|a\|^2$. To carry the argument further, let B be an orthonormal set, and a a vector. Then all but a countable number of the orthogonal coefficients of a are zero. ⟦Given any $\epsilon > 0$, let $T_\epsilon = \{b \in S: |(a, b)| > \epsilon\}$. Let $b_1, b_2, \ldots, b_n$ be distinct members of T_ϵ. By the above inequality, $\|a\|^2 \ge \sum_{k=1}^{n} |(a, b_k)|^2 \ge n\epsilon^2$, thus $n \le \|a\|^2/\epsilon^2$ and it follows that T_ϵ is finite. Hence $\{b \in B: (a, b) \ne 0\} = \bigcup_{n=1}^{\infty} T_{1/n}$ is countable.⟧

THEOREM 1. *Let* S *be an orthonormal set in an inner-product space and* a *a vector. Then* (a, b) $= 0$ *for all but a countable set of* b $\in$ S, *moreover, arranging those* (a, b) *which are not zero in a sequence, we have*

$$\Sigma |(a, b)|^2 \le \|a\|^2 \qquad (Bessel's\ inequality).$$

Further, we have a $= \Sigma(a, b)b$ *if and only if* a *satisfies*

$$\Sigma |(a, b)|^2 = \|a\|^2 \qquad (Parseval's\ relation).$$

We have just proved Bessel's inequality. Parseval's relation follows from a similar development of relation (1).//

It follows that if $\{b_n\}$ is an orthonormal sequence, $\lim_{n \to \infty} (a, b_n) = 0$ for all a.   (When specialized to Example 3, this yields a special case of the Riemann-Lebesgue lemma.)

Example 5.   In R^3, let $B = \{\delta^1, \delta^2\}$.   Let $a = (1, 2, 3)$, $b = (1, 2, 0)$.   Then $(a, \delta^1) = (b, \delta^1) = 1$, $(a, \delta^2) = (b, \delta^2) = 2$, $\|b\|^2 = 5 = \Sigma_{k=1}^2 |(b, \delta^k)|^2$ and, indeed $b = \Sigma_{k=1}^2 (b, \delta^k)\delta^k$. However, $\|a\|^2 = 14 > \Sigma |(a, \delta^k)|^2$ and, indeed, $a \neq \Sigma(a, \delta^k)\delta^k$, the latter being the projection of a onto the plane spanned by B.

THEOREM 2.   *Any two maximal orthonormal sets in an inner-product space are in one-to-one correspondence.*

Compare this with Section 2.3, Theorem 2, and its proof.   Suppose first that there exists a finite maximal orthonormal set $B = \{b_1, b_2, \ldots, b_n\}$.   Given any vector a, let $d = a - \Sigma_{k=1}^n (a, b_k)b_k$.   Then for each k, $(d, b_k) = 0$.   Hence, $d = 0$.   This shows that B spans the space.   But B is also linearly independent [Section 1, Problem 8] and hence is a Hamel basis.   Any other orthonormal set, being linearly independent has no more than n elements, nor can it have fewer, since we can apply the above argument to it.

Next assume that we have two infinite maximal orthonormal sets B and H.   For each $b \in B$, let $H_b = \{h \in H : (b, h) \neq 0\}$.   Every member of H occurs in at least one H_b [for if, on the contrary, we could find h, a member of H, not in any H_b, we would have $(b, h) = 0$ for all $b \in B$, contradicting the maximality of B].   By Theorem 1, each H_b is countable or finite, hence, since $H = \cup\{H_b : b \in B\}$ as just proved, $|H| \leq |B| \cdot \aleph_0 = |B|$.   By symmetry $|B| \leq |H|$, and the result follows from the Cantor-Bernstein theorem.//

As might be expected, we define the *dimension* of an inner-product space to be the cardinality of a maximal orthonormal set.   The phrases "finite dimensional," and "infinite dimensional" are unambiguous since a finite maximal orthonormal set is a Hamel basis [proof of Theorem 2] and if there exists an infinite orthonormal set, the space has infinite (Hamel) dimension [since every orthonormal set is linearly independent, Section 1, Problem 8].

Example 6.   The dimension of l^2 is $\aleph_0$, since $\{\delta^n\}$ is a maximal orthonormal sequence.

Problems on inner product space 8.4

1.   Let B be the orthonormal subset of R^3 given by $\{\delta^1, \delta^2\}$.   What is the set of points which have the same orthogonal coefficients as the point $(1, 2, 3)$?

2.   Fix n; for $k = 1, 2, \ldots n$, let $w_k = (1/\sqrt{n})e^{2\pi i k/n}$ (that is, $\sqrt{n}\, w_k$ is an nth root of unity). Let $b_k = (w_1^k, w_2^k, \ldots, w_n^k)$.   Show that $\{b_1, b_2, \ldots, b_n\}$ is an orthonormal subset of E^n.

3.   Let B be an orthonormal set.   A vector a is determined by its orthogonal coefficients relative to B if and only if B is maximal.

4.   Let $\{b_1, b_2, \ldots, b_n\}$ be a finite orthonormal set, B its linear span, and a a vector.   Show that $x \equiv \Sigma_{k=1}^n (a, b_k)b_k$ is the point of B closest to a and that $a - x$ is orthogonal to B.   What is x if $a \in B$? Illustrate the situation in R^3 with a diagram.

5.   Use Problem 4 to show that the best mean square $[-\pi, \pi]$ approximation by a sum $\Sigma_{k=1}^n t_k \sin kx(n \text{ fixed})$ to a continuous function f is that in which $t_1, t_2, \ldots, t_n$ are Fourier coefficients of f,

namely $t_k = 1/\pi \int_{-\pi}^{\pi} f(x) \sin kx \, dx$. (The approximation mentioned is that in which the distance from f to g is $\left[\int_{-\pi}^{\pi} \{f(x) - g(x)\}^2 \, dx \right]^{\frac{1}{2}}$.)

6. The dimension of an inner-product space is less than or equal to its Hamel dimension.

7. How does the dimension of an infinite-dimensional Hilbert space compare with its Hamel dimension?

8. Let A be the span (in s) of E^∞ and x, where $x = \{1/n\}$. Give A the inner product $(a, b) = \Sigma a_n \bar{b}_n$. Show that the orthogonal series of x with respect to the orthonormal set $\{\delta^{2n}: n = 1, 2, \ldots\}$ is not convergent. [The *orthogonal series* is $\Sigma(a, \delta^{2n})\delta^{2n}$.]

9. Let $\{a_n\}$, $\{b_n\}$ be the sequences of orthogonal coefficients of two vectors a, b, respectively, with respect to an orthonormal sequence. Show that $\Sigma a_n \bar{b}_n$ is absolutely convergent. If we defined $(a, b)_1$ to be the sum $\Sigma a_n \bar{b}_n$, would this be an inner product?

10. An inner product space A can be extended to a Hilbert space $\bar{A}$, with the inner products of A, $\bar{A}$ agreeing on A, and with A dense in $\bar{A}$. Moreover any *bounded operator* (any continuous linear map from A to itself) can be extended to be a bounded operator on $\bar{A}$.

11. If $\{a_n\}$ is an orthonormal sequence, $a_n \to 0$ weakly. [Bessel's inequality.]

8.5 Orthonormal sets in Hilbert space

The assumption of completeness allows the results of the preceding section to be put into a more satisfactory form.

THEOREM 1. *Let* B *be an orthonormal set in a Hilbert space. For any vector* a, *the orthogonal series* $\Sigma_{b \in B}(a, b)b$ *is convergent.* (*It is understood that the (countable) set of those* b $\in$ B *for which* (a, b) $\neq$ 0 *is arranged in a sequence. The value of the sum does not depend on this arrangement.*) *If* a' *is the sum of the series,* a $-$ a' *is orthogonal to* B.

Compare this with Section 4, Problem 8. Fix a and let $\{b_n\}$ be the members of B which are not orthogonal to a [Section 4, Theorem 1,] (the result is trivial if there are no such members of B) and set $t_n = (a, b_n)$. For any integers p, q, with $q > p > 1$ we have $\|\Sigma_{k=p}^{q} t_k b_k\| = \Sigma_{k=p}^{q} |t_k|^2$. Since Bessel's inequality assures us that $\Sigma |t_k|^2 < \infty$, we see that $\{\Sigma_{k=1}^{n} t_k b_k\}$ is a Cauchy sequence; hence $\Sigma t_k b_k$ is convergent. Let us denote its sum by a'. Then a' has the same orthogonal coefficients as a. [For any b not among the b_n, $(a', b) = 0 = (a, b)$. For each n, $(a', b_n) = \Sigma t_k(b_k, b_n) = t_n = (a, b_n)$.] In particular, $(a - a', b) = 0$ for all $b \in B$; that is, $a - a' \perp B$.

Now assume that a'' is the sum obtained in the above construction by some other ordering of the elements of B which are not orthogonal to a. Both a' and a'' are (infinite) linear combinations of B. Moreover, a'' has the same orthogonal coefficients as a, hence as a'. Thus $a' - a''$ is orthogonal to B, and consequently orthogonal to itself, since it, itself, is a linear combination of B. Thus it is zero.//

COROLLARY 1. *Any maximal orthonormal subset of a Hilbert space is a basis for the space in the sense that every vector is a unique infinite linear combination.*

Any finite linear combination is, by our conventions, also an infinite linear combination.

In Section 6.3, we spoke of the Schauder basis. Any countable maximal orthonormal set is, of course, a Schauder basis for the Hilbert space. When discussing linear metric spaces it is customary to reserve the word basis for finite or countable sets.   In the case of Hilbert space, uncountable bases are allowed.   This is a matter of history and we shall follow usage with the customary admonition that this will cause no confusion.   Theorem 2 shows that a separable Hilbert space has a Schauder basis.

THEOREM 2.   *A Hilbert space has countable (or finite) dimension if and only if it is separable.*

Suppose first that the dimension is uncountable and let B be an uncountable orthonormal set.   For each $b \in B$, the cell $N(b, \frac{1}{2})$ contains no point of B other than b ⟦given b' with $b' \perp b$, we have $\|b - b'\|^2 = \|b\|^2 + \|b'\|^2 = 2$⟧.   Thus there is an uncountable set of disjoint cells, ruling out separability.   Conversely, if the dimension is countable or finite, the space has a Schauder basis and so is separable ⟦Section 6.3, Problem 23⟧.//

We now see how the ideas surrounding the basis have been generalized from Hilbert space to linear metric space.   (The historical order has been reversed in this book.)   Given a basis $\{b_n\}$ for a (separable) Hilbert space, we have the representation $a = \Sigma(a, b_n)b_n = \Sigma l_n(a)b_n$ where l_n is, for $n = 1, 2, \ldots$, a continuous linear functional and $(\{b_n\}, \{l_n\})$ is a biorthogonal pair, since $l_n(b_k) = (b_k, b_n)$.   Thus the coordinate functionals of Section 6.3 appear, and in the Hilbert space setting they are automatically continuous, indeed, $\|l_n\| = \|b_n\| = 1$.

THEOREM 3.   *Let $\{b_n\}$ be an orthonormal sequence in a Hilbert space, and $\{t_n\}$ a sequence of scalars satisfying $\Sigma|t_n|^2 < \infty$.   Then $\Sigma t_n b_n$ is convergent, and its orthogonal coefficients are $\{t_n\}$. Conversely, if $\{t_n\}$ are the orthogonal coefficients of some vector we have $\Sigma|t_n|^2 < \infty$.*

For integers p, q with $q > p > 0$ we have $\|\Sigma_{k=p}^q t_k b_k\|^2 = \Sigma_{k=p}^q |t_k|^2$, thus $\{\Sigma_{k=1}^n t_k b_k\}$ is a Cauchy sequence, hence convergent.   The converse follows from Bessel's inequality.//

The specialization of this result to L^2 and the trigonometric system (see Example 1, below) is called the Riesz-Fischer theorem.

THEOREM 4.   *Two Hilbert spaces with the same dimension are congruent.*

Compare this with Section 2.4, Theorem 4.   (Linear spaces of equal Hamel dimension are isomorphic.)   Let H_1, H_2 be Hilbert spaces with bases B_1, B_2 respectively, of the same cardinality.   Suppose $f: B_1 \to B_2$ is a one-to-one correspondence from B_1 onto B_2.   Given $a \in H_1$ we have $a = \Sigma_{b \in B_1}(a, b)b$.   Define $f(a) = \Sigma(a, b)f(b)$.   ⟦The latter series is meaningful because, according to Section 4, Theorem 1, only a countable number of b is involved. Theorem 3 provides that it converges.⟧

We have $\|f(a)\|^2 = \Sigma|(a, b)|^2 = \|a\|^2$ ⟦Section 4, Theorem 1.⟧   Thus f is norm preserving.   It is clearly linear, thus it is an isometry.   Finally f is onto.   ⟦Suppose given $a \in B_2$. Then, as before, $\Sigma_{b \in B_2}|(a, b)|^2 < \infty$, thus $a_1 \equiv \Sigma_{b \in B_2}(a, b)f^{-1}b$ is a member of H_1, and $f(a_1) = \Sigma_{b \in B_2}(a, b)ff^{-1}b = \Sigma_{b \in B_2}(a, b)b = a$.⟧//

COROLLARY 2.   *Every* n-*dimensional Hilbert space is congruent with* E^n *(or* R^n*).   Every infinite-dimensional separable Hilbert space is congruent with* l^2.

These results follow from Theorem 2 and Section 4, Example 6.//

COROLLARY 3. *Every Hilbert space is congruent with its conjugate space.*

(Various cases of congruence between a normed space and its conjugate were considered in Section 6.4, Problems 6, 7, 8, and 9, and Section 7.2, Problems 17 and 18.) We have seen in Section 2 a conjugate linear isometry between H and H^* such that if f, $g \in H^*$ correspond to a, $b \in H$, respectively, then $(f, g) = (b, a)$. Now let F be a maximal orthonormal set in H^*, and B the set in H corresponding to F under the given correspondence between H^* and H. Then B is an orthonormal set, moreover it is maximal. ⟦If $a \perp B$, we consider that $f \in H^*$ which corresponds to a. Clearly $f \perp F$, hence $f = 0$, and so $a = 0$.⟧ Thus H, H^* have the same dimension.//

Example 1. Let A be the set of all bounded real functions defined on $[-\pi, \pi]$, each of which has a finite number of discontinuities. A is a real linear space and becomes an (incomplete) real inner-product space if we set $(a, b) = \int_{-\pi}^{\pi} a(x)b(x)\,dx$. Let

$$b_n(x) = (1/\sqrt{\pi}) \sin nx \text{ for } n = 1, 2, \ldots$$
$$b_{-n}(x) = (1/\sqrt{\pi}) \cos nx \text{ for } n = 1, 2, \ldots$$
$$b_0(x) = 1/\sqrt{2\pi}.$$

Then $\{b_n\}$, $-\infty < n < \infty$, is an orthonormal set; we may as well call it a sequence. Our aim in this example is to show that $\{b_n\}$ is maximal.

We first examine the behaviour of step functions. In particular we shall see that each step function satisfies Parseval's relation. Let α, β be numbers satisfying $-\pi \leq \alpha \leq \alpha + \beta \leq \pi$, and let a be the step function, $a(x) = 1$ for $\alpha \leq x \leq \alpha + \beta$, $a(x) = 0$ otherwise. Then

$$(1) \qquad \|a\|^2 = \int_{-\pi}^{\pi} a(x)^2\,dx = \int_{\alpha}^{\alpha+\beta} dx = \beta.$$

While

$$\sum_{n=-\infty}^{\infty} (a, b_n)^2 = \sum_{n=1}^{\infty} \left(\int_{\alpha}^{\alpha+\beta} \frac{\cos nx}{\sqrt{\pi}}\,dx \right)^2 + \int_{\alpha}^{\alpha+\beta} (1/\sqrt{2\pi})^2\,dx + \sum_{n=1}^{\infty} \left(\int_{\alpha}^{\alpha+\beta} \frac{\sin nx}{\sqrt{\pi}}\,dx \right)^2$$
$$= \frac{\beta^2}{2\pi} + \frac{2}{\pi} \sum_{n=1}^{\infty} \frac{1}{n^2} - \frac{2}{\pi} \sum_{n=1}^{\infty} \frac{\cos n\beta}{n^2} = \frac{\beta^2}{2\pi} + \frac{\pi}{3} - \frac{2}{\pi} \sum_{n=1}^{\infty} \frac{\cos n\beta}{n^2}.$$

Let us denote this expression by $u(\beta)$. Notice that it is defined for all β and is continuous, since the series is uniformly convergent.

We prove that

$$(2) \qquad u(\beta) \leq \beta \text{ for } 0 \leq \beta \leq 2\pi.$$

⟦In view of relation (1) and the fact that $u(\beta) = \Sigma (a, b_n)^2$, relation (2) is Bessel's inequality, at least for $0 \leq \beta \leq \pi$. For $\pi \leq \beta \leq 2\pi$, we have $0 \leq 2\pi - \beta \leq \pi$, hence $2\pi - \beta \geq u(2\pi - \beta) = 2\pi - 2\beta + u(\beta)$, and so $u(\beta) \leq \beta$.⟧

Now trivial calculation shows that $\int_0^{2\pi} [\beta - u(\beta)]\,d\beta = 0$ and so relation (2) and the continuity of the integrand provide that $u(\beta) = \beta$; thus a satisfies Parseval's relation. It follows from Section 4, Theorem 1, that a is equal to its orthogonal series (in the present context, Fourier series); that is, $a(x) = \sum_{n=-\infty}^{\infty} t_n b_n(x)$ (warning: the series converges in mean of order 2, not necessarily pointwise), where $t_n = (1/\sqrt{\pi}) \int_{-\pi}^{\pi} a(x) \sin nx \, dx$ for $n = 1, 2,$ . . . , and similar formulas for $n = 0, -1, -2, \ldots$. It follows that $\{b_n\}$ is fundamental in A [since the linear closure of $\{b_n\}$ includes the set of step functions, this set being fundamental, indeed, dense in A]. Hence, it is maximal [Section 4, the remark preceding Example 1].

As a corollary, we obtain the result that if all the Fourier coefficients of a (real) continuous function are zero, the function is zero on $[-\pi, \pi]$. [The space A in the example contains real $C[-\pi, \pi]$.]

Example 2. The completion of A in Example 1 is L^2. Since the trigonometric set is fundamental in A, it is also in L^2; hence it is maximal in L^2.

Problems 8.5

This set of problems refers to a Hilbert space A; B is an orthonormal set, $\{b_n\}$ an orthonormal sequence.

1. Let $\{b_n\}$ be maximal. For $x, y \in A$, $(x, y) = \sum_{n=1}^{\infty} (x, b_n)\overline{(y, b_n)}$, the series being absolutely convergent. (Thus, the congruence between A and l^2 preserves inner products, a fact that was noted in Section 1, Problem 12.) Conversely, if the given representation holds for all $x, y \in A$, $\{b_n\}$ is maximal.

2. Suppose $\{b_n\}$ is maximal. Assume $f \in A^*$. Show that $\sum \overline{f(b_n)}b_n$ is convergent and that its sum is the representation of f in A of Section 2, Theorem 1.

3. If $\{b_n\}$ is maximal it is a monotone basis.

4. The linear closure of B in A is a Hilbert space, and B is a basis for it.

5. Give an example of a nonseparable Hilbert space. [Let $l^2(S)$ be the set of complex functions a on a set S such that $a(s) \neq 0$ for only countably many s (depending on a) and $\sum |a(s)|^2 < \infty$.]

6. Any closed maximal linear subspace of A must contain all but a countable subset of B.

7. "Closed" cannot be omitted in Problem 6. [Take $f = 1$ on B.]

8. Every closed subspace of a Hilbert space has a complementary closed subspace. [$S^\perp$.]

9. The result of Problem 8 is false for a Fréchet space, in general. It is possible for a one-dimensional subspace to have no complementary closed subspace. [The complementary subspace would be maximal and lead to a continuous linear functional. Now see Section 7.5, Example 10.]

10. A set S is fundamental if and only if $a \perp S$ implies $a = 0$.

8.6 Operators

A continuous linear map from a Hilbert space H to itself is called a *bounded operator* on the space. The space of bounded operators on H is denoted by $B[H]$. This space has exceedingly rich structure, part of which will be exposed here and generalized in Chapter 14.

$B[H]$ is a Banach space [Section 6.4, Problem 4]. Besides this, members of $B[H]$ may be "multiplied" by composition; that is, if $S, T \in B[H]$, ST is defined by $(ST)a = S(Ta)$ for all $a \in H$. Then $ST \in B[H]$, indeed $\|ST\| \leq \|S\| \cdot \|T\|$. [$\|STa\| \leq \|S\| \cdot \|Ta\| \leq \|S\| \cdot \|T\| \cdot \|a\|$.] The rule $\|ST\| \leq \|S\| \cdot \|T\|$ is called the *multiplicative property* of the norm.

We now examine the adjoint of a bounded operator on H (Section 7.1). By definition, $(T^*g)(a) = g(Ta)$ for $g \in H^*$, $a \in H$. If $b \in H$ is the representative of g, we define T^*b to be T^*g and we have $(a, T^*b) = (Ta, b)$. This relationship defines $T^* \in B(H)$; moreover, it defines T^* uniquely. ⟦If also $(a, T^\#b) = (Ta, b)$ it follows that $(a, T^\#b) = (a, T^*b)$ for all a, b. Since, for each b, this is true for all a, we have, by Section 1, Problem 9, $T^\#b = T^*b$. Since this is true for all b, $T^\# = T^*$.⟧

Several properties of the adjoint were stated in Chapter 7. For example, the adjoint map is linear in the sense that if T_1, $T_2 \colon A \to B$ and s is a scalar, and T_1^*, $T_2^* \colon B^* \to A^*$, then $(T_1 + sT_2)^* = T_1^* + sT_2^*$. Since, for Hilbert space H, the identification from H^* to H is conjugate linear, we have, for operators on H, $(T_1 + sT_2)^* = T_1^* + \bar{s}T_2^*$. Thus *the adjoint map is conjugate linear.*

Another important fact is that $T^{**} = T$. We shall give an easy proof; also, this fact may be extracted from Section 7.2, Problem 14. ⟦For all a, b, $(T^*a, b) = \overline{(b, T^*a)} = \overline{(Tb, a)} = (a, Tb)$. Thus the adjoint of T^* is T. (We are using the fact that the adjoint is unique.)⟧ Because of this property, the map $* \colon B[H] \to B[H]$ (that is, $T \to T^*$) is called an *involution*. It is also known from Section 7.1, Theorem 1 that $\|T^*\| = \|T\|$. In the present setting the proof can be abbreviated. After proving that $\|T^*\| \leq \|T\|$, we simply observe that it follows (replacing T by T^*) that $\|T^{**}\| \leq \|T^*\|$; that is, $\|T\| \leq \|T^*\|$.

LEMMA 1. $\|T^*T\| = \|T\|^2$.

By the multiplicative property of the norm, $\|T^*T\| \leq \|T^*\| \cdot \|T\| = \|T\|^2$. On the other hand, for any $a \in H$, $\|Ta\|^2 = (Ta, Ta) = (a, T^*Ta) \leq \|a\| \cdot \|T^*Ta\|$ ⟦Cauchy's inequality⟧ $\leq \|a\|^2 \cdot \|T^*T\|$. Thus $\|Ta\| \leq (\|T^*T\|)^{1/2} \cdot \|a\|$ and so $\|T\| \leq (\|T^*T\|)^{1/2}$. //

An operator $T \in B(H)$ is said to have an *inverse* T^{-1} *in* $B[H]$ if there exists $T^{-1} \in B[H]$ such that $T^{-1}T = TT^{-1} = I$ (the identity operator, $Ia = a$ for all $a \in H$.) We emphasize that if T has an inverse, T is onto. The phrases *regular operator*, *invertible operator*, and *unit*, are often used to denote an operator with an inverse.

A bounded operator T is said to be *self-adjoint* or *Hermitian* if $T^* = T$. For example, the matrix

$$\begin{pmatrix} 1 & 2+i \\ 2-i & 3 \end{pmatrix}$$

is a self-adjoint operator on E^2 ⟦Problem 5⟧. The operators 0 and I are self-adjoint. (Here 0 is the zero operator $0a = 0$.) Also, for any $T \in B[H]$, T^*T is self-adjoint ⟦Section 7.1, formula (1)⟧.

THEOREM 1. *For every* $T \in B[H]$, $I + T^*T$ *has an inverse in* $B[H]$.

This result will be proved in a different way in Section 14.5, Corollary 2. We here apply Section 7.1, Theorem 3. Since $I + T^*T$ is self-adjoint, it will be sufficient to show that it is norm increasing ⟦for this implies that it is one to one⟧. To this end, suppose $a \in H$. Then $\|(I + T^*T)(a)\| \cdot \|a\| \geq ((I + T^*T)(a), a)$ ⟦Cauchy's inequality⟧ $= (a, a) + (T^*Ta, a) = \|a\|^2 + (Ta, Ta) \geq \|a\|^2$. Thus $\|(I + T^*T)(a)\| \geq \|a\|$. //

DEFINITION 1. *The spectrum* $\sigma(T)$ *of a bounded operator* T *is the set of all scalars* λ *such that* $T - \lambda I$ *has no inverse.*

Historically, the concept of spectrum arose in discussions of linear equations such as $Ax = \lambda x$. If A is a finite matrix, this equation has nonzero solutions if and only if the determinant of $A - \lambda I$ is zero; that is, the matrix $A - \lambda I$ has no inverse.

A scalar λ is called a *characteristic value* of T if there exists a nonzero vector a such that $Ta = \lambda a$. Then a is called a *characteristic vector* corresponding to λ. Each characteristic value lies in the spectrum [since $(\lambda I - T)a = 0$, $\lambda I - T$ is not one to one]. However the spectrum may contain other scalars. [Let T be one to one and not onto. Then 0 is in the spectrum but is not a characteristic value. See Example 1.] For self-adjoint operators we do have a partial converse [Problem 15].

Example 1. Define $T \in B[l^2]$ by $Ta = \{0, a_1, a_2, \ldots\}$, where $a = \{a_1, a_2, \ldots\}$. Then T is not onto [$Ta \neq \delta^1$]; hence T has no inverse and so 0 lies in its spectrum. But 0 is not a characteristic value since T is one to one.

If λ is a characteristic value, and a a corresponding characteristic vector of a self-adjoint operator T, we have $\lambda \|a\|^2 = (\lambda a, a) = (Ta, a) = (a, Ta) = \bar{\lambda}\|a\|^2$. Thus λ is real. This result extends to the whole spectrum [Problem 16; also Section 14.4, Fact (iv)].

Example 2. Some conclusions about a general differential equation associated with the names of Sturm and Liouville are deduced from the following theorem. In this theorem the map T is perfectly general except for a property of the self-adjoint type.

THEOREM 2. *Let* A *be an inner product space,* S *a subset of* A *and* T: S $\rightarrow$ A *a function satisfying* (Ta, b) = (a, Tb) *for all* a, b $\in$ S. *Then two characteristic vectors in* S *corresponding to two different characteristic values of* T *are orthogonal.*

Compare this with Section 7.1, Problem 15. Let $Ta = \lambda a$, $Tb = \mu b$, $\lambda \neq \mu$, $a \neq 0$, $b \neq 0$. The argument just given shows that λ, μ are real. Then $\lambda(a, b) = (\lambda a, b) = (Ta, b) = (a, Tb) = (a, \mu b) = \mu(a, b)$. Thus $(a, b) = 0.//$

We take real C as our space. Fix three members f, g, h of C with $h(x) > 0$ for $0 \leq x \leq 1$. As real inner product on C, let $(a, b) = \int_0^1 a(x)b(x)h(x)\, dx$. Let S be the subset of C consisting of those $a \in C$ such that $D(f \cdot a') \in C$, (here D means derivative; a' is the derivative of a,) and such that $a(0)f(0) = a(1)f(1) = 0$. Finally, let $Ta = [D(f \cdot a') + g \cdot a]/h$. Then T is self-adjoint (in the sense of Theorem 2); that is, $(Ta, b) = (a, Tb)$ for all $a, b \in S$. $[(a, Tb) = \int_0^1 a \cdot D(f \cdot b') + \int_0^1 a \cdot g \cdot b = a \cdot f \cdot b' \Big|_0^1 - \int_0^1 a' \cdot f \cdot b' + \int_0^1 a \cdot g \cdot b = \int_0^1 (a \cdot g \cdot b - a' \cdot f \cdot b')$ and, since this is symmetric in a, b, the result follows.]

We now apply Theorem 2 to the differential equation $D[f(x)y'] + [g(x) - \lambda h(x)]y = 0$ with boundary conditions $f(0)y(0) = f(1)y(1) = 0$.

The result is that if a, b are solutions corresponding to distinct values of λ, then $\int_0^1 a(x)b(x)h(x)\, dx = 0$. This condition is called *orthogonality with weight h*. Note that we need not assume $D(f \cdot y')$ continuous, since that follows from the fact that y is a solution of the equation.

As a special case, consider the equation $y'' - \lambda y = 0$, $y(0) = y(1) = 0$. If λ is not of the form $-n^2\pi^2$, $n = 1, 2, \ldots$, the only solution is $y = 0$. For $\lambda = -n^2\pi^2$ we have $y = \sin n\pi x$. The conclusion is $\int_0^1 \sin m\pi x \sin n\pi x\, dx = 0$ if $m \neq n$.

Problems 8.6

In this set of problems, H is a Hilbert space and $T \in B[H]$.

1. $N(T)$(the null space of T) is defined to be $\{a: Ta = 0\}$; $R(T)$ is the range of T. Show that $N(T) = R(T^*)^\perp$. Hence, if T^* is onto, T is one to one. If T is one to one, the range of T^* is dense. (Compare this with Section 7.1, Theorems 2 and 3 and Problem 8.) 〖For example, let $a \in N(T)$, $y = T^*x$. Then $(a, y) = (a, T^*x) = (Ta, x) = (0, x) = 0$. Thus $a \in R(T^*)^\perp$.〗

2. Show that $R(T) \subset N(T^*)^\perp$, and that the inclusion may be strict. 〖Take T self-adjoint, one to one, but not onto. For example, $T: l^2 \to l^2$ given by $Ta = \{a_n/n\}$. Compare this with Section 7.1, Example 1 and Problem 6.〗

3. $\overline{R(T)} = N(T^*)^\perp$. 〖$N(T^*)^\perp = R(T)^{\perp\perp}$, by Problem 1. Now see Section 2, Problem 3.〗

4. For all T, T^*T is self-adjoint. Is the converse true? That is, if $S \in B[H]$ is self-adjoint, must there exist T such that $S = T^*T$? 〖Use Theorem 1.〗

5. Show that every linear operator on E^n is given by an $n \times n$ matrix. 〖$T(a) = aM$, where $M = (m_{kr})$ is given by $T(\delta^k) = \sum_{r=0}^{n} m_{kr}\delta^r$.〗 Show that the adjoint of the operator is given by the conjugate complex of the transpose of the matrix of the operator.

6. Give a definition for the adjoint in real Hilbert space and obtain the analogues of Problem 5, Lemma 1, and Theorem 1.

7. Check Theorem 1 in the case that $T = iI$, $(i^2 = -1)$.

8. T has an inverse in $B[H]$ if and only if $R(T)$ is dense and some positive multiple of T is norm increasing.

9. $\sigma(I) = \{1\}$.

10. The spectrum of $T \in B[E^n]$ consists exactly of the set of characteristic values.

11. If $(Ta, b) = 0$ for all a, b, then $T = 0$.

12. Let T be self-adjoint and $Ta \perp a$ for all a. Then $T = 0$.

13. For a complex Hilbert space, self-adjoint may be omitted from Problem 12; but it cannot be omitted in the real case. 〖Rotation.〗

14. An *approximate characteristic* value of an operator T is a number λ with the property that to each $\epsilon > 0$ corresponds a unit vector a such that $\|\lambda a - Ta\| < \epsilon$. Show that every approximate characteristic value is in the spectrum. 〖If not, $\|\lambda a - Ta\| \geq 1/\|(\lambda I - T)^{-1}\|$.〗

15. Prove the converse of Problem 14 for a self-adjoint operator. 〖If λ is not an approximate characteristic value, for some $\epsilon > 0$, $(1/\epsilon)(\lambda I - T)$ is norm increasing. Now apply Section 7.1, Theorem 3.〗

16. The spectrum of a self-adjoint bounded operator is real. 〖Use Problem 15 and the technique used in the text to prove that characteristic values are real.〗

17. An operator T is called *normal* if $TT^* = T^*T$. Show that T is normal if and only if $\|Ta\| = \|T^*a\|$ for all a. 〖With $S = TT^* - T^*T$ we have $(Sa, a) = 0$ and Problem 12 applies.〗

18. Prove the converse of Problem 14 for a normal operator. 〖In view of Problem 17 the technique of Problem 15 may be applied.〗

19. The operator T given in Example 2 is linear. Is it continuous?

20. Suppose that $y = u(x)$, $y = v(x)$ are solutions, respectively, of $D[(1 - x^2)y'] - m(m + 1)y = 0$ and $D[(1 - x^2)y'] - n(n + 1)y = 0$, with $m \neq n$; m, n integers, and $u(0) = v(0) = 0$. Show that $\int_0^1 u(x)v(x)\, dx = 0$. (The polynomial solutions of these equations, with $y(1) = 1$, are the Legendre polynomials.)

21. Let $H = $ real L^2 and define $T \in B[H]$ by $(Tf)(x) = xf(x)$ for $0 \leq x \leq 1$, $f \in H$. Show that T has no characteristic values and find its spectrum.

22. Show that a projection (Section 2.8, Problem 6) is perpendicular (that is, $S \perp T$) if and only if it is self-adjoint.

9
TOPOLOGY AND NETS

9.1 Topological space

The name "topology" is used for several almost completely distinct disciplines whose practitioners may have no interest in or knowledge of the ones differing from their own. This situation is reflected in the fact that one may open several books whose titles include essentially only this word, and find offerings whose resemblance to each other is so slight that the common name is unjustified and confusing.

In this chapter we shall study generalized analysis (topology as an abstraction of the limiting process in analysis), together with its concomitants such as continuity and compactness.

A *topology on a set* A is a certain family of subsets of A. Exactly what kind of family is allowed is stated in Definition 1. Once the topology is specified (once the family of sets is specified), a member of the topology (one of the specified sets) will be called an *open set*. Thus "open" means "belonging to the topology," and a set is, by itself, neither open nor nonopen. It is only after the topology is specified that the word, open, has meaning.

DEFINITION 1. *Let a nonempty set* A *be given and let a family* T *of subsets of* A *be specified. The members of* T *are called open sets. Let* T *satisfy the four conditions:*

    (i)   *the empty set is open,*
    (ii) A *is open,*
    (iii) *the union of any collection of open sets is open,*
    (iv) *the intersection of any finite collection of open sets is open.*

Then T *is called a topology for* A. *The pair* (A, T) *is called a topological space.* [Whenever it is clear what T is, we shall refer to the space as A instead of (A, T).]

This definition is clearly inspired by Section 4.3, Problem 14.

★ *Example 1: The discrete topology.* Let A be a set, and let T be the family of all subsets of A; then every subset of A is open.

★ *Example 2: The indiscrete topology.* Let A be a set, and let T contain just two subsets of A: the empty set, and A. Thus only A and $\emptyset$ are open.

★ *Example 3: Semimetric space.* Let A be a semimetric space. Let T be the family of all open subsets of A in the sense of Section 4.3. Then T is a topology for A ⟦Section 4.3, Problem 14⟧. The word, open, is now being used ambiguously; however, a set is open in the semimetric sense if and only if it is open in the topological sense. We say that the semimetric *leads to* the topology; the topology is *given by* the semimetric. All the standard classical spaces, s, c_0, and the rest are now assumed to be topological spaces with the topology given by their natural metrics.

Given a topology, is there a semimetric which leads to it? If there is, we say that the *topology is semimetrizable.* If the topology under discussion is clearly understood to be specified, we say that the *space is semimetrizable.* There is generally more than one semimetric leading to a given semimetrizable topology; indeed, two equivalent semimetrics lead to the same topology ⟦Section 5.1, Theorem 2⟧. A *metrizable* space is one whose topology is given by a metric. The discrete topology is metrizable with the discrete metric. The indiscrete topology is semimetrizable with the indiscrete semimetric.

Example 4: A nonsemimetrizable topology. Let $A = \{a, b, c\}$ (that is, A has three elements) the open subsets of A are $\emptyset$, A, $\{a, b\}$, $\{a, c\}$, $\{a\}$. ⟦Suppose that A is semimetrizable. Let $r = d(a, b)$. Then $r > 0$ since there is an open set containing a and not b; $N(b, r/2)$ is an open set including b but not a. But there is no such open set.⟧

From this discussion we see that the concept of topology is more general than that of semimetric. We shall show that many of the concepts of analysis (for example, continuous function) can be defined and studied in the framework of topology. We begin by mentioning several of these.

A set is called *closed* if its complement is open. A point a is called *interior* to a set S if there exists an open set G with $a \in G \subset S$; and, if so, S is called a *neighborhood* of a. *A set is open if and only if it is a neighborhood of each of its points.* ⟦If G is a neighborhood of each of its points, for each $a \in G$, let $N(a)$ be an open set with $a \in N(a) \subset G$. Then $G = \cup \{N(a): a \in G\}$, a union of open sets. So G is open.⟧

DEFINITION 2. *Let S be a set in a topological space A. We say that a subset of S is S-open if it is the intersection of S with an open set in A. The collection of S-open sets is called the relative topology of A for S.*

It is easy to check that the relative topology of A is a topology for S ⟦Problem 8⟧ and that the relative topology on a subset of a semimetric space is given by the same semimetric ⟦Problem 9⟧.

We now adopt, wholesale, Section 4.3, Definitions 2 (convergence of sequences) and 3 (continuous function), and Section 5.1, Definitions 1 (closure), 2 (homeomorphism), 3 (open map), 4 (dense) and 5 (category). In connection with the first of these definitions, sequences and their convergence are not important in topology. This is partly because Section 4.3, Theorem 1, and Section 5.1, Theorem 1 are false in topological spaces in general ⟦Problems 44, 43⟧. The fourth definition mentions $f[A]$. This is given the relative topology of B.

If a set is given two topologies T, T', we say that T' is *stronger than* T if it is bigger, that is, if $T' \supset T$. T is then said to be *weaker than* T'. This agrees with all earlier usages of strength (Section 5.1, Theorem 2).   The discrete and indiscrete topologies are, respectively, the strongest and weakest of all topologies on a given set.   Clearly T' is stronger than T if and only if every T neighborhood of an arbitrary point a is also a T' neighborhood of a.

THEOREM 1.   *Let a set* A *be given two topologies,* T' *and* T.   *Then* T' *is stronger than* T *if and only if the identity map* i: (A, T') $\rightarrow$ (A, T) *is continuous.*

If i is continuous and $G \in T$, then $i^{-1}[G] = G \in T'$.   Thus T' is stronger than T. Conversely, if T' is stronger than T, and $G \in T$, then also $G \in T'$; that is, $i^{-1}G$ is open. Thus i is continuous.//

DEFINITION 3.   *A local base at a point* a *for a topology* T *is a collection* Σ *of neighborhoods of* a *such that given any neighborhood* N *of* a, *there exists* G $\in \Sigma$ *with* G $\subset$ N.   *A topological space* A *is said to be first countable at* a $\in$ A *if it has a countable local base at* a.   *It is said to be first countable if it is first countable at each of its points.*

★*Example 5.*   A semimetric has as local base at a, the collection of all cells $N(a, 1/n)$, $n = 1$, 2, ...   Thus any semimetric space is first countable.   (Problem 32 shows a space which is not first countable.)

Topologies are most often introduced by means of a subbase.

DEFINITION 4.   *A subbase for a topology* T *is a collection* Σ *of open sets such that given any point* a *and any neighborhood* G *of* a, *there exists a finite collection* {G$_1$, G$_2$, . . . , G$_n$} *of members of* Σ *with* a $\in \cap_{k=1}^{n}$G$_k \subset$ G.

We shall often speak of a subbase for the space, meaning a subbase for the topology. We could have defined base as well as local base, and local subbase as well as subbase, but Definitions 3 and 4 will suffice for our purposes.   Notice that a subbase is made up of open sets, whereas the members of a local base need not be open.

★ *Example 6.*   The Euclidean topology on R^2 has a subbase consisting of all vertical and horizontal open strips of the form $(a < x < b)$ and $(a < y < b)$.   [Let G be a neighborhood of a point $P = (r, s)$.   Then there exists $\epsilon > 0$ such that $N \equiv N(P, \epsilon) \subset G$.   Let H be the strip $\{(x, y): |s - y| < \epsilon/2\}$ and V the strip $\{(x, y): |r - x| < \epsilon/2\}$.   Then $(r, s) \in H \cap V \subset N \subset G$.]

THEOREM 2.   *Let* A *be a nonempty set and* Σ *a collection of sets whose union is* A.   *Then there is a unique topology* T *such that* Σ *is a subbase for* T.   T *is the weakest topology including* Σ.   (*T is called the topology generated by* Σ.)

Let us first show uniqueness.   [If Σ is a subbase for both T and T', let $a \in A$, and let G be a T' neighborhood of a.   By definition, Σ contains a finite collection of sets whose intersection I satisfies $a \in I \subset G$.   Since Σ is made up of T-open sets, I is T-open, being a finite intersection, and so G is a T neighborhood of a.   Thus any set which is T'-open must be a T neighborhood of each of its points, and so must be T-open.   Hence T is stronger than T'.   By symmetry, T' is stronger than T, and so $T = T'$.]

We exhibit T. Let T contain A, $\emptyset$, and besides these T is to contain all unions of finite intersections of members of Σ. This formidable definition means merely that, given a member G of T, with $G \neq \emptyset$, $G \neq A$, there exists a collection J of sets with $G = \cup\{N : N \in J\}$ such that each $N \in J$ is the intersection of a finite number of sets taken from Σ. Conversely, any set formed in this way is, by definition, a member of T. It is clear that Σ is a subbase for T. (In Example 6, the finite intersections are either strips or rectangles and any Euclidean open set is a union of rectangles.) The last part of Theorem 2 is clear.//

DEFINITION 5. *Let a set* A *be given a nonempty collection* Φ *of topologies. The topology generated by* $\{\cup T : T \in \Phi\}$ *is called* $\vee\Phi$, *(pronounced sup of* Φ*). The sup of two topologies* T, T' *will be written* T $\vee$ T', *similarly for a finite number;* $\vee\{T_n\}$ *is written* $T_1 \vee T_2 \vee T_3 \cdots$.

★ *Example 7.* On R^2, let H be the topology generated by the set of horizontal open strips, V the topology generated by the set of vertical open strips. Then $H \vee V$ is the Euclidean topology.

Remark. It will often be convenient to refer to a semimetric d when it is really the topology generated by d that is intended. For example, given two semimetrics d_1, d_2 for a set, we shall speak of $d_1 \vee d_2$, meaning the topology $T_1 \vee T_2$, where T_1, T_2 are the topologies generated by d_1, d_2. We shall see [Section 3, Theorem 2] that $d_1 \vee d_2$ is semimetrizable, however the notation, $d_1 \vee d_2$, does not refer to any particular semimetric which generates its topology. Another such example is the phrase "d_1 is stronger than d_2" which, happily, has the same meaning whether d_1 is a semimetric or the topology generated by it.

To introduce the *separation axioms* we adopt a convenient locution: say that sets S_1, S_2 are *separated by open sets* if there exist disjoint open sets G_1, G_2 such that $S_1 \subset G_1$, $S_2 \subset G_2$; S_1, S_2 are *separated by a continuous function* if there exists a continuous real function f such that $f(a) = 0$ for $a \in S_1$, $f(a) = 1$ for $a \in S_2$. (We may add, without changing the situation, the assumption that $0 \leq f(a) \leq 1$, for if f is given with the other properties, $|f| \wedge 1$ will have the additional property, where $(f \wedge 1)(a) = \min[f(a), 1]$.

A topological space is called by one of the various names given below if it satisfies the condition listed after the name.

T_0 space	given any two distinct points, at least one of them has a neighborhood not containing the other.
T_1 space	given any two distinct points, each has a neighborhood not containing the other.
$\begin{cases} T_2 \text{ space} \\ \text{Hausdorff space} \end{cases}$	any two distinct points can be separated by open sets.
$T_{2\frac{1}{2}}$ space	any two distinct points can be separated by a continuous function.
Regular space	any closed set and any point not in it can be separated by open sets.
T_3 space	regular T_1 space.

Completely regular space	any closed set and any point not in it can be separated by a continuous function.
$\left\{\begin{array}{l} T_{3\frac{1}{2}} \text{ space} \\ \text{Tychonoff space} \end{array}\right.$	completely regular T_1 space.
Normal space	any two disjoint closed sets can be separated by open sets.
T_4 space	normal T_1 space.
$T_{4\frac{1}{2}}$ space	T_1 space obeying the separation condition (1).

(1)   Any two disjoint closed sets can be separated by a continuous function.

Although these definitions have considerable currency, they are not completely standardized in the mathematical literature. For example many writers reserve the name completely regular for what is here called $T_{3\frac{1}{2}}$. The definitions of T_0, T_1, T_2, Hausdorff, are, however, completely standard. Below are listed relationships which hold among these spaces. For example, a T_3 space must be a T_2 space. A T_4 space must be a $T_{4\frac{1}{2}}$ space and conversely.

$$\begin{array}{ccccccccc} T_{4\frac{1}{2}} & \rightarrow & T_{3\frac{1}{2}} & \rightarrow & T_{2\frac{1}{2}} & & & & \\ \updownarrow & & \downarrow & & \downarrow & & & & \\ T_4 & \rightarrow & T_3 & \rightarrow & T_2 & \rightarrow & T_1 & \rightarrow & T_0. \end{array}$$

That $T_{n\frac{1}{2}} \rightarrow T_n$ for $n = 2, 3, 4$ follows from considering $G_1 = (f < \frac{1}{2})$, $G_2 = (f > \frac{1}{2})$. If f is a continuous real function separating two sets, then G_1, G_2 are open sets separating them. Because points are closed in a T_1 space, $T_4 \rightarrow T_3 \rightarrow T_2$. That $T_2 \rightarrow T_1 \rightarrow T_0$ is trivial and the remaining result is Theorem 3.

Example 8: A semimetric space obeys the separation condition (1). *Thus, a metric space is a* $T_{4\frac{1}{2}}$ *space.* Let S_1, S_2 be disjoint closed sets and

$$f(a) = \frac{d(a, S_1)}{d(a, S_1) + d(a, S_2)}.$$

Then f separates S_1, S_2.

★ *Example 9: A* T_0 *semimetric is a metric.* If $d(a, b) = 0$, every neighborhood of a contains b and vice versa.

In the next result, we use the fact that if, *in a normal space,* S, G *are sets with* S *closed,* G *open, and* S $\subset$ G, *then there exists an open set* N *with* S $\subset$ N, $\bar{N} \subset$ G. ⟦S, $\tilde{G}$ are disjoint closed sets. Thus there exist disjoint open sets N and M with $S \subset N$, $\tilde{G} \subset M$. Then $N \subset \tilde{M}$; hence $\bar{N} \subset \tilde{M}$, since $\tilde{M}$ is closed, and so $\bar{N} \subset G$.⟧

Theorem 3 will not be used until Chapter 14.

THEOREM 3. URYSOHN'S LEMMA. *A normal space obeys the separation condition* (1).

Let A be a normal space, S a closed set, G an open set with $S \subset G$. We shall construct a continuous real function f on A with $f = 0$ on S, $f = 1$ on $\tilde{G}$. This will complete the proof. 〚If S, T are disjoint closed sets, let $G = \tilde{T}$.〛 Let D be the set of all numbers in the interval $[0, 1]$ which are of the form $k/2^n$, $n = 0, 1, 2, 3, \ldots , k = 0, 1, 3, 5, 7, \ldots$. We shall define a sequence of open sets, one, $S(d)$, for each $d \in D$ with the property that if $x, y \in D$ and $y > x$, then $S(y) \supset \overline{S(x)}$. Let $S(1) = G$ and let $S(0)$ be open and $S \subset S(0)$, $\overline{S(0)} \subset G$. Proceeding, we define $S(k/2^n)$ by induction on n. Given $k/2^n$ with $n > 0$, $(k - 1)/2^n$ and $(k + 1)/2^n$ have the form $r/2^{n-1}$ and so we may assume that $S[(k - 1)/2^n]$ and $S[(k + 1)/2^n]$ have already been defined. Choose $S(k/2^n)$ so that $S[(k - 1)/2^n] \subset S(k/2^n)$, $\overline{S(k/2^n)} \subset S[(k + 1)/2^n]$.

Now for $a \in G$, define $B_a = \{x \in D: a \in S(x)\}$. Define a real function f on A by $f(a) = 1$ if $a \notin G$, $f(a) = \inf B_a$ if $a \in G$. The proof is completed by showing f continuous. We first observe that for any real number t, $f^{-1}(-\infty, t) = \cup \{S(x): x \in D, x < t\}$ is open, and that $f^{-1}(-\infty, t] = \cap \{\overline{S(x)}: x \in D, x > t\}$ is closed. Thus for any real numbers s, t, $f^{-1}(s, t) = f^{-1}(-\infty, t) \setminus f^{-1}(-\infty, s]$ is open and so f is continuous,//

Problems 9.1

★1. In every topological space, $\emptyset$ is closed.

2. Let A be a set and B a proper subset of A. Let $T = \{\emptyset, B, A\}$. Show that T is a topology for A.

3. In Problem 2, is B open? Is B closed? [In the topological space (A, T).]

★4. The union of a finite collection of closed sets and the intersection of any collection of closed sets are closed.

5. For subsets A, B of a topological space, $\overline{\overline{A}} = \overline{A}$, $\overline{A \cup B} = \overline{A} \cup \overline{B}$, $\overline{A \cap B} \subset \overline{A} \cap \overline{B}$. The latter inclusion may be strict. (Give an example in R.)

★6. The *interior* S^i of a set S is the set of points interior to S. Show that S^i is open and is the union of all open subsets of S.

★7. $S^i = S^{\sim - \sim}$.

★8. The relative topology is a topology.

★9. Let A be a semimetric space and S a subspace (with the same semimetric.) Show that S has the relative topology.

10. A constant function is continuous. [$f(a) = f(b)$ for all a, b.]

11. Any function $f: A \rightarrow B$ is continuous if A has the discrete topology or if B has the indiscrete topology.

12. Let A be a discrete topological space and $f: R \rightarrow A$ a continuous function. Show that f is constant.

★13. A function f is continuous if and only if $f^{-1}[S]$ is closed for every closed set S.

14. $x \in \overline{S}$ if and only if every neighborhood of x contains a point of S.

15. In Problem 2, what is $\overline{B}$?

16. Let S be the unit cell in R^2. Find $\overline{S}$ in (a) the Euclidean topology, (b) the discrete topology, (c) the indiscrete topology, and (d) the topology generated by the set of all horizontal open strips.

17. The discrete and indiscrete topologies are first countable.

★18. Let a set A have two topologies T, T', with T' first countable. Show that T' is stronger than T if and only if $x_n \rightarrow x$ in T' implies $x_n \rightarrow x$ in T. Thus two first-countable topologies are equal if they have the same notion of convergence of sequence. 〚In Section 5.1, Theorem 2, replace $N(x, 1/n)$ by G_n, where $\{G_n\}$ is a T'-local base at x.〛 (See Problem 42.)

19. Two first-countable topologies are equal if they have the same convergent sequences, and at least one of them is a T_1 topology. The assumption T_1 cannot be omitted. 〚If $a_n \rightarrow a$, then $\{a_1, a, a_2, a, a_3, a, \ldots\}$ also converges to a, and only a.〛

20. In Example 6, we may restrict a, b to be rational.

21. A semimetric space has a countable subbase if and only if it is separable.

22. In R^2, let Σ be the collection of all vertical and horizontal lines. Show that Σ generates the discrete topology.

★23. Suppose that a collection Φ of topologies on a set contains a topology T stronger than all the others. Show that $\vee \Phi = T$.

24. In Problem 23, replace "stronger" by "weaker." Now show that $\vee \Phi = \vee (\Phi \setminus \{T\})$. (Assume $\Phi \neq \{T\}$.)

25. What is the topology for a set A which is generated by $\{A\}$?

26. Let T be the topology on R generated by the set of all intervals (x, ∞). Show that T is T_0 but not T_1.

★27. A topology is T_1 if and only if each finite set is closed.

★28. A topology is T_1 if and only if each set with one point is closed.

★29. Let A be a set. Describe the topology for A which has the property that a proper subset of A is closed if and only if it is finite. (The topology is called the *minimal T_1 topology*.)

30. Prove that the minimal T_1 topology is the weakest T_1 topology that can be placed on a given set.

31. In Problem 16, find $\bar{S}$ in the minimal T_1 topology.

32. The minimal T_1 topology on an uncountable set is not first countable.

★33. Any topology stronger than a Hausdorff topology is itself a Hausdorff topology. (Problem 34 improves upon this.)

34. Let A be a topological space and B a Hausdorff space. If there exists a continuous one-to-one function $f: A \to B$, then A is a Hausdorff space.

35. Let u, v be continuous maps from a topological space A to a Hausdorff space. Show that $\{a: u(a) = v(a)\}$ is a closed subset of A.

36. Let A be a $T_{2\frac{1}{2}}$ space. For $a \in A$, define $\hat{a}(f) = f(a)$ for $f \in C[A]$. Show that $\hat{a}$ is a linear functional on $C[A]$ and that $\hat{A} \equiv \{\hat{a}: a \in A\}$ is linearly independent. Can the assumption $T_{2\frac{1}{2}}$ be dropped?

37. A topological space is regular if and only if, given a point x and a neighborhood G of x, there exists a neighborhood N of x with $\bar{N} \subset G$. (This means that the set of closed neighborhoods of x is a local base at x.)

38. A semimetric space is regular and normal.

39. The space of Example 4 is not regular.

40. In Theorem 3, show that it is possible that $\overline{S(0)} = G$. How would the proof proceed?

41. In Problem 29 replace "finite" by "countable." Show that a sequence is convergent in the resulting topology if and only if it is convergent in the discrete topology. (Compare this with Section 5.1, Theorem 2, and the definition of stronger.)

42. In Problem 18, the assumption that T' is first countable cannot be dropped. 〚Problem 41.〛

43. Using the topology of Problem 41, let S be an uncountable proper subset of A. Then S is not closed, but it is *sequentially closed;* that is, $a_n \in S$ for $n = 1, 2, \ldots$ and $a_n \to a$ imply $a \in S$.

44. Let T be the topology of Problem 41, and T' the discrete topology on the same set A. Then the identity map, $i: (A, T) \to (A, T')$ is not continuous, but it is *sequentially continuous;* that is, $a_n \to a$ implies $ia_n \to ia$.

45. In a first-countable topological space a sequentially closed set is closed and a sequentially continuous function is continuous.

46. Extend to topological space the results of Section 4.3, Problems 19 and 20 and Section 5.1, Problems 6, 9, 10, and 16.

47. Extend to a first-countable space the result of Section 5.1, Problem 7 and show that the assumption of first countability cannot be dropped.

48. Let a set S be dense in a set A using each of two topologies T, T'. Must S be dense with $T \vee T'$?

9.2   Nets

There are two short cuts to the theory of convergence in vogue today, nets and filters. This book casts its lot with nets, and a large part of the rest of the text is written in that language.   The reason for this choice is that the language of nets is a faithful imitation of the language of sequences.

Since no mathematician should be ignorant of filters, they are introduced in the problems of this section and several succeeding sections.   Many results are more easily accessible to filter treatment, for example, Theorem 1 of this section.   When this is true, however, the formation of an appropriate net is a short and standard step (Examples 5 and 6) so that very little is lost.   In general, however, the resemblance of nets to sequences is a very fruitful mnemonic for the construction of proofs, and their use is favored by a quorum of practicing mathematicians.

It was a great convenience to work with sequences in semimetric space.   In order to retain this convenience, sequences are generalized to nets.   Like sequences, nets converge or diverge and, as with sequences, topological concepts are definable in terms of nets, for example, $x \in \bar{S}$ if and only if there exists a net of points of S converging to x.   Unlike the corresponding result for sequences (Section 5.1, Theorem 1), the result formulated with nets extends to all topological spaces.

A sequence is a function on ω, and it is the special character of ω which makes sequences too inflexible.   The generalization to nets is accomplished by replacing ω by an arbitrary directed set.   As mentioned in Section 1.5, a directed set is a poset with the property that every two elements have a common upper bound.

DEFINITION 1.   *A net is a function defined on a directed set.   If the range of the function is a set* A, *we refer to it as a net of points of* A *or a net in* A.

Just as there are sequences of points, sequences of functions, *et cetera*, there are nets of points, nets of functions, *et cetera*.

Nets are denoted by the form $(x_\delta: D)$, occasionally $(x_\delta: \delta \in D)$ where D is the directed set.   Whenever D is clear from the context or whenever it is not necessary to know the precise nature of D, we shall write x_δ for the net.   The points x_δ, for various values of δ, are called the *terms* of the net.   Of course, $\{x_\delta: \delta \in D\}$ is the set of terms.   A net $(x_n: \omega)$ is a sequence.   The notation x_n and x_k refer to sequences.

Note.   We shall also use the name "sequence" for any net $(x_\delta: D)$, where D is isomorphic with ω, that is, where D, ω are in one-to-one, order-preserving correspondence.

For example, let e stand for the set of even integers.   Then $(x_n: e)$ is a sequence which we may identify with $(x_{2n}: \omega)$.

DEFINITION 2.   *A net* $(x_\delta: D)$ *is said to be eventually in a set* S *if there exists* $\delta_0 \in D$ *such that* $x_\delta \in S$ *for all* $\delta \geq \delta_0$.   *It is said to be frequently in* S *if, for any* $\delta_0 \in D$, *there exists* $\delta \geq \delta_0$ *with* $x_\delta \in S$.

Thus a sequence x_n is eventually in S if and only if it is in S for all sufficiently large n (that is, for almost all n) and is frequently in S if and only if it is in S for arbitrarily large n (that is, for infinitely many n). Our notation will be $x_\delta \in S$ eventually (or frequently).

The assumption that each pair of elements of D has a common upper bound plays its part entirely by means of Lemma 1. It is Lemma 1, for example, which tells us that if a net converges to two different limits it must be eventually in every neighborhood of each limit and so all neighborhoods of the limits meet (see Definition 3 and Theorem 4).

LEMMA 1. *Let* S_1, S_2, . . . , S_n *be sets and* x_δ *a net such that for each* $k = 1, 2, . . . , n$, $x_\delta \in S_k$ *eventually. Then* $x_\delta \in \cap S_k$ *eventually.*

For $k = 1, 2, . . . , n$, choose δ_k such that $\delta \geq \delta_k$ implies $x_\delta \in S_k$. Since the indices δ, are in a directed set, there exists δ_0 satisfying $\delta_0 \geq \delta_k$ for each k. Then $\delta \geq \delta_0$ implies $\delta \geq \delta_k$ for each k, hence $x_\delta \in S_k$ for each k.//

DEFINITION 3. *Let* x_δ *be a net in a topological space. Then* x_δ *is said to converge to* a; *in symbols,* $x_\delta \to$ a, *if, for any neighborhood* G *of* a, x_δ *is eventually in* G. *If* x_δ *converges to a unique point* a, *we write* a $= \lim x_\delta$ *or* a $= \lim (x_\delta : D)$ *or* a $= \lim_D x_\delta$.

If the net is a sequence, this agrees with the notion of convergence presented in Section 4.3, Definition 2, and $\lim(x_n : \omega) = \lim_{n \to \infty} x_n$.

★ *Example 1.* Let $D = (0, 1)$ with the order of R and let A be a topological space. Then a net in A is a function on $(0, 1)$ with values in A, and $x_\delta \to a$ means $\lim_{\delta \to 1^-} x(\delta) = a$ in the ordinary sense; that is, for any neighborhood G of a, $x_\delta \in G$ for all real numbers δ satisfying $\delta_0 \leq \delta < 1$, δ_0 being some suitably chosen number.

★ *Example 2.* Let D be as in Example 1. Then a net in R is an ordinary real function defined on $(0, 1)$. In this case it is particularly easy to see whether x_δ converges. For example, let $x_\delta = \sin [1/(1 - \delta)]$. Then x_δ does not converge to any limit.

★ *Example 3.* Let $D = [1, 3] \setminus \{2\}$, that is, the set of real numbers between 1 and 3, except 2. For α, $\beta \in D$ define $\alpha \geq \beta$ to mean $|\alpha - 2| \leq |\beta - 2|$, the "$\leq$" being the ordinary inequality. Thus $\alpha \geq \beta$ means that α is closer to 2 than β. For a net on D, $x_\delta \to a$ means $x_\delta \to a$ as $\delta \to 2$ in the usual sense.

★ *Example 4: A net* x_δ *in a semimetric space converges to a point* a *if and only if* $d(x_\delta,$ a$) \to 0$. Of course, $(d(x_\delta, a) : D)$ is a net in R.

Suppose first that $x_\delta \to a$. Let $\epsilon > 0$ be given. Then $x_\delta \in N(a, \epsilon)$ eventually, thus $d(x_\delta, a) < \epsilon$ eventually, and so $d(x_\delta, a) \to 0$. Conversely, if $d(x_\delta, a) \to 0$, let G be a neighborhood of a. Then there exists $\epsilon > 0$ such that $N(a, \epsilon) \subset G$. Now $d(x_\delta, a) < \epsilon$ eventually, thus $x_\delta \in N(a, \epsilon)$ eventually, hence $x_\delta \in G$ eventually.

★ *Example 5.* Let A be a topological space and $a \in A$. Let D be the set of all neighborhoods of a, ordered by inclusion ($\alpha \geq \beta$ means $\alpha \subset \beta$). Then D is a directed set. [It is clearly a poset. Next, given α, $\beta \in A$ (that is, α, β are neighborhoods of a), then $\alpha \cap \beta \in D$, $\geq \alpha$, $\geq \beta$.]

For each $\delta \in D$, let x_δ be a point in δ. Then $(x_\delta : D)$ is a net in A. Furthermore $x_\delta \to a$. [Let G be any neighborhood of A. Then $G \in D$. We have to prove that x_δ is eventually in G. Consulting the definition of "eventually," we see that we must produce δ_0 such that

$\delta \geq \delta_0$ implies $x_\delta \in G$. We take $\delta_0 = G$. Then, if $\delta \geq \delta_0$, this means that $\delta \subset \delta_0$; in other words, $\delta \subset G$. Since $x_\delta \in \delta$, it follows that $x_\delta \in G$.]

Example 6. We now describe another method of constructing a net from a neighborhood system. This is sometimes more useful than that of Example 5, and has the advantage of uniqueness; that is, two applications of the method always yield the same net. This is not true in Example 5, since arbitrary choices are made.

Let A be a topological space and $a \in A$. Let D be the set of all pairs (x, G), where G is a neighborhood of a, and $x \in G$. Define $(x_2, G_2) \geq (x_1, G_1)$ to mean $G_2 \subset G_1$. (Ignore x_1, x_2.) D is a directed set [for example, $(a, G_1 \cap G_2) \geq (x_1, G_1), \geq (x_2, G_2)$]. Now, for $\delta \in D$, that is, $\delta = (x, G)$, define $x_\delta = x$. Then x_δ is a net in A. Furthermore, $x_\delta \to a$. [Given G_0, a neighborhood of a, let $\delta_0 = (a, G_0)$. Then, if $\delta \geq \delta_0$, say $\delta = (x, G)$, we have $x_\delta = x \in G$, by definition of D, and $G \subset G_0$ by definition of "$\delta \geq \delta_0$." Thus $x_\delta \in G_0$].

We now imitate parts of Chapters 4 and 5 with nets instead of sequences. It is remarkable (and encouraging) that the imitation is so faithful, and that the replacement of sequences by nets makes the theorems true for topological spaces.

THEOREM 1. *Let* S *be a set and* a *a point of a topological space. Then* a $\in \bar{S}$ *if and only if there exists a net* x_δ *of points of* S *with* $x_\delta \to$ a.

Section 5.1, Theorem 1 states this for sequences and semimetric space. Suppose first that $a \notin \bar{S}$. Then $\tilde{\bar{S}}$ is a neighborhood of a not meeting S. Since any net in S must lie entirely outside this neighborhood, it cannot converge to a. Conversely, suppose that $a \in \bar{S}$. Each neighborhood of a meets S and so, taking D as in Example 5, and, for each $\delta \in D$, choosing $x_\delta \in \delta \cap S$, we see that $(x_\delta : D)$ is a net of points of S and, by Example 5, $x_\delta \to a$.//

THEOREM 2. *Let* f *be a function from one topological space to another. Then* f *is continuous at* a *if and only if whenever* x_δ *is a net converging to* a, f(x_δ) $\to$ f(a).

Section 4.3, Theorem 1 states this for sequences and semimetric spaces. It goes without saying that if $(x_a : D)$ is a net, so is $(f(x_\delta) : D)$. Let f be continuous at a, $x_\delta \to a$, and let G be a neighborhood of $f(a)$. Then $f^{-1}[G]$ is a neighborhood of a, thus x_δ is eventually in $f^{-1}[G]$; hence $f(x_\delta)$ is eventually in G. Thus $f(x_\delta) \to f(a)$.

Conversely, if f is not continuous at a, there exists a neighborhood G of $f(a)$ such that $f^{-1}[G]$ is not a neighborhood of a. We now choose a net x_δ with $x_\delta \to a$, $f(x_\delta) \nrightarrow f(a)$; namely, let D be as in Example 5, and for each $\delta \in D$, choose $x_\delta \in \delta \setminus f^{-1}[G]$. [This is possible because $\delta \not\subset f^{-1}[G]$, the latter not being a neighborhood of a.] Then $x_\delta \to a$ by Example 5, while $f(x_\delta) \nrightarrow f(a)$ since $f(x_\delta) \notin G$ [because $x_\delta \notin f^{-1}[G]$].//

COROLLARY 1. *If a function* f *is continuous, it satisfies* f[$\bar{S}$] $\subset \overline{f[S]}$ *for all subsets* S *of its domain.*

Suppose that f is continuous. Let $b \in f[\bar{S}]$; that is, $b = f(a)$ for some $a \in \bar{S}$. There exists a net x_δ in A with $x_\delta \to a$ [Theorem 1]. By Theorem 2, $f(x_\delta) \to f(a)$; hence $b = f(a) \in \overline{f[S]}$ [Theorem 1].//

COROLLARY 2.   *Let a set be given two topologies,* T′ *and* T.   *Then* T′ *is stronger than* T *if and only if* $x_\delta \to$ a *in* T′ *implies that* $x_\delta \to$ a *in* T.   *Thus two topologies with the same convergent nets and limits thereof are equal.*

This follows from Theorem 2 and Section 1, Theorem 1.//

Thus we have returned to the definition of strength in terms of convergence (of nets instead of sequences) as given in Section 4.1, Definition 2 and Section 5.1.   It is in this form that we shall most often use it.   One remembers that convergence in the stronger topology forces convergence in the weaker topology.   The use of nets simplifies the idea of relative topology because, in a subspace, the notion of convergence is exactly the same in the relative topology as in the original.

THEOREM 3.   *Let* S *be a set in a topological space* A.   *Let* x_δ *be a net in* S *and* a $\in$ S.   *Then* $x_\delta \to$ a *in the relative topology of* A *if and only if* $x_\delta \to$ a *in* A.

Suppose that $x_\delta \to a$ in the relative topology and let G be a neighborhood of a.   Then $G \cap S$ is a relative neighborhood of a (that is, a neighborhood in the relative topology) and so $x_\delta \in G \cap S$ eventually.   Thus $x_\delta \in G$ eventually and $x_\delta \to a$.   Conversely, if $x_\delta \to a$, let G be a relative neighborhood of a.   Then $G = S \cap N$ for some neighborhood N of a. We have $x_\delta \in N$ eventually; hence, since $x_\delta \in S$, $x_\delta \in G$ eventually.   Thus $x_\delta \to a$ in the relative topology.//

THEOREM 4.   *Every convergent net in a topological space has a unique limit if and only if the space is a Hausdorff space.*

Let $x_\delta \to a$ and $x_\delta \to b$ in a Hausdorff space.   Let G_a and G_b be neighborhoods of a, b respectively.   Then x_δ is eventually in each of them, hence $x_\delta \in G_a \cap G_b$ eventually ⟦Lemma 1⟧.   In particular, G_a meets G_b; hence $a = b$.   ⟦Since any pair of their neighborhoods meet, a, b cannot be distinct.⟧   Conversely, consider a topological space which is not a Hausdorff space, and thus has a pair of distinct points a, b all of whose neighborhoods meet.   We now construct a net which converges to both a and b.   Naturally, we must begin by constructing a directed set.   Let D be the set of all pairs (α, β) where α, β are, respectively, neighborhoods of a, b.   Define $(\alpha, \beta) \geq (\alpha', \beta')$ to mean $\alpha \subset \alpha'$ and $\beta \subset \beta'$. This makes D a directed set ⟦$(\alpha \cap \alpha', \beta \cap \beta') \geq$ both (α, β) and (α', β')⟧.   Now, for any $\delta = (\alpha, \beta) \in D$, choose $x_\delta \in \alpha \cap \beta$ ⟦possible, since $\alpha \cap \beta$ is not empty⟧.   Then $x_\delta \to a$. ⟦Let G be any neighborhood of a.   Let $\delta_0 = (G, N)$ where N is any neighborhood of b, for example, the whole space.   Then $\delta = (\alpha, \beta) \geq \delta_0$ implies that $\alpha \subset G$, hence $x_\delta \in G$. Thus $x_\delta \to a$.⟧   Similarly, $x_\delta \to b$.//

Problems 9.2

1. Let D be a poset with a maximum element.   Show that all nets on D are convergent.
2. Show that the net $((-n)^n : n \in \omega)$ is frequently larger than 100 (that is, this net is frequently in the set $x > 100$).
★3. Let A be a set, B a subset of A, and x_δ a net in A.   Then the statement "x_δ is eventually in B" is false if and only if the statement "x_δ is frequently in $A \setminus B$" is true.

4. Let A be a set, D the set of finite subsets of A ordered by containment. Fix $a \in A$. For $\delta \in D$, let $x_\delta = 1$ if $a \in \delta$, 0 if $a \not\subset \delta$. Show that $x_\delta \to 1$ in R.

5. A convergent net of real numbers need not be bounded $[\![x_\delta = 1/\delta, D = (0, 1)]\!]$. However it is eventually bounded. (Give this a meaning and prove it.)

★6. A set A in a topological space is closed if and only if, whenever x_δ is a net in A converging to x, then $x \in A$.

★7. Let $\{d_n\}$ be a sequence of semimetrics on a set A. Let

$$ d = \sum_{k=1}^{\infty} \frac{1}{2^k} \frac{d_k}{1 + d_k}. $$

Then d is a semimetric and for any net a_δ in A, $a_\delta \to a$ in d if and only if $a_\delta \to a$ in each d_n. $[\![$Part of this is Section 4.3, Problem 9. For the second half, imitate exactly the proof of Section 4.1, Theorem 1.$]\!]$

8. A net $(x_\delta \colon D)$ in a poset is called *isotone* if $\alpha \geq \beta$ implies $x_\alpha \geq x_\beta$. Show that an isotone real net which is bounded above is convergent.

9. Extend Section 5.1, Problem 7 to topological space by replacing sequences with nets.

10. Every constant net converges to a unique limit in and only in a T_1 space.

11. (a) In Section 1, Problem 41, two topologies are given which have the same convergent sequences. Construct a net which is convergent in one but not the other. (b) Perform similar services for Section 1, Problems 43 and 44.

★12. Let Σ be a subbase for a topological space. Show that $a_\delta \to a$ if $a_\delta \in G$ eventually for every $G \in \Sigma$ with $a \in G$. $[\![$Use Lemma 1.$]\!]$

13. Suppose that $x_\delta \to a$, $x_\delta \to b$, and $y_\delta \to a$. Does it follow that $y_\delta \to b$?

14. Solve Section 1, (a) Problem 10, (b) Problem 23 (c) Problem 24, (d) Problem 35 with nets.

15. The quotient topology is the strongest topology such that the natural homomorphism is continuous. (Use the setting of Section 6.5.)

16. Let a_δ be a real net and define $\liminf a_\delta = a$ to mean that for each $\epsilon > 0$, $a_\delta > a - \epsilon$ eventually, and $a_\delta < a + \epsilon$ frequently. Define $\limsup$ by interchanging $a - \epsilon$ and $a + \epsilon$. Show that $\limsup a_\delta = -\liminf(-a_\delta)$.

17. By means of Problem 16, extend the definitions and results of lower semicontinuity (Section 5.1, Problems 17 and 18) to nets and real-valued functions on a topological space.

18. (a) Let S be a set in a linear metric space and D the set of finite subsets of S, ordered by containment. For $\delta \in D$, let $a_\delta = \Sigma\{a \colon a \in \delta\}$. If $a_\delta \to a$ we say that S is *summable* to a. (This is different from matrix summability.) Show that a set S of complex numbers is summable to a if and only if S is countable—say, $S = \{a_n\}$—$\Sigma|a_n| < \infty$, and $\Sigma a_n = a$. (b) A summable set is countable. (c) An orthonormal set S in a Hilbert space is summable if and only if it is countable, say, $S = \{a_n\}$, and $\Sigma\|a_n\|^2 < \infty$. (d) Let S be the set of squares of the orthogonal coefficients of a vector a with respect to an orthonormal set in a Hilbert space. Show that S is summable.

19. Let D be the class of Riemann partitions of $[0, 1]$ and, for $\delta \in D$, let Σ_δ be the ordinary Riemann sum corresponding to a fixed $f \in C$. Show that $\Sigma_\delta \to \int_0^1 f$ if (a) D is ordered by refinement, (b) D is ordered by size of maximum subinterval. (Do not carry through the details. Merely show that the standard procedures, for example, Section 6.4, Example 8, can be phrased in the net language.)

20. Two topologies with the same convergent nets need not be equal, but are equal if at least one of them is T_1 (compare Section 1, Problem 19).

★21. Define *Cauchy net* in a semimetric space as suggested by the definition of Cauchy sequence. Prove that every Cauchy net in a complete semimetric space is convergent. $[\![$For positive integral n, choose $\delta_n \in D$ such that $\delta \geq \delta_n$, $\delta' \geq \delta_n$ implies $d(x_\delta, x_{\delta'}) < 1/n$. Choose $\alpha(n) \in D$ with $\alpha(n) \geq \delta_1, \delta_2, \ldots, \delta_n$. Then $\{x_{\alpha(n)}\}$ is a Cauchy sequence and x_δ converges to any of its limits.$]\!]$

22. A *filter* in a set A is a nonempty collection F of subsets of A such that

(i) $\emptyset \notin F$

(ii)   the intersection of any two members of F belongs to F,

(iii) Any set which includes a member of F belongs to F.

For $a \in A$, let F_a be the collection of all subsets of A containing a, let N_a be the collection of all neighborhoods of a (A being, here, a topological space).   Show that F_a, N_a are filters in A.

23. If F is a filter in A, show that $A \in F$, that any finite intersection of members of F belongs to F, and that no two members of F have empty intersection.

24. Give an example of a filter whose intersection is empty.   〚Consider $(n, n+1, n+2, \ldots)$ $\subset \omega$.〛

25. We say that a filter F *converges to* a, or $F \to a$, if F contains every neighborhood of a; that is, $F \supset N_a$ (Problem 22).   Show that $N_a \to a$, and $F_a \to a$.

26. Let F be the family of all subsets of R which include the interval $[0, 1]$.   Show that F is a filter and does not converge.

27. A topological space is a Hausdorff space if and only if every convergent filter converges to a unique point.   (If $F \to a$ uniquely, we write $\lim F = a$, as usual.)

28. Let F be a filter in a Hausdorff space.   If $F \to a$, then $\bigcap \{S: S \in F\} = \{a\}$, but not conversely.   〚Let $F = \{S \subset R: \tilde{S} \text{ is finite and } 0 \in S\}$.〛

29. A point a is interior to a set S if and only if S belongs to every filter which converges to a.

30. Let N be a net x_δ in a set A.   Let $F_N = \{S \subset A: x_\delta \in S \text{ eventually}\}$.   Show that F_N is a filter, and $F_N \to a$ if and only if $x_\delta \to a$.

31. Let F be a filter in A.   We may form a net from F in two ways.   The first is sometimes more appropriate, for example, when there is a possibility that the resulting net may be a sequence.   The second is usually more natural.   (a) For each $S \in F$, choose $a_S \in S$.   Then $(a_S: F)$ is a net (order F by inclusion).   (Compare this with Example 5.)   (b) Let D be the set of all pairs (a, S), $a \in S \in F$. Define $(a, S) \geq (b, T)$ to mean $S \subset T$.   Finally, for $\delta = (a, S) \in D$, define $x_\delta = a$.   Show that $(x_\delta: D)$ is a net.   We shall refer to the net constructed in (b) as the net *associated with* F.   (Compare this with Example 6.)

32. (a) The net in Problem 31(b) converges to a if and only if $F \to a$.   (b) The net in Problem 31(a) converges to a if $F \to a$ and may converge to a even if F does not (a constant net, for example). (Problems 30 and 32 show that all definitions and results of net theory can be translated into filter language, and conversely.)

33. State and prove analogues for filters of (a) Theorem 1, (b) Theorem 2, (c) Corollary 2, (d) Theorem 3.

9.3 Sup, weak, and product topologies

The history of functional analysis following the introduction of Banach space deals largely with the study and application of various weak topologies.   We introduce and study these topologies in this section, beginning with the sup topologies, and successively specializing to the other two.   We shall often use, without citation, the result of Section 2, Corollary 2, that topologies may be compared by means of net convergence.   Most of our results will follow easily from a characterization of net convergence.

THEOREM 1.   *Let a set be given a collection Φ of topologies.   Let* $T' = \vee \Phi$.   *Then a net* $a_\delta \to a$ *in* T' *if and only if* $a_\delta \to a$ *in every* $T \in \Phi$.

T' is stronger than each $T \in \Phi$; hence half the result is trivial. Conversely, suppose that $a_\delta \to a$ in every $T \in \Phi$ and let G be a T' neighborhood of a. By definition of T' and subbase, there exist finitely many sets G_1, G_2, . . . , G_n, with $a \in \bigcap_{k=1}^n G_k \subset G$, each of which is a neighborhood of a in at least one $T \in \Phi$. Thus a_δ is eventually in each G_k, and so it is eventually in G [Section 2, Lemma 1]. Thus $a_\delta \to a$ in T'.//

In reading the statement of Theorem 2, it may be helpful to consult the remark following Section 1, Example 7. This result shows that semimetrizability is carried to families of topologies when certain countability conditions are met.

THEOREM 2. *Let a set be given a countable collection* $\{d_n\}$ *of semimetrics. Then* $\bigvee \{d_n\}$ *is semimetrizable. Indeed it is given by*

$$d = \Sigma \frac{1}{2^n} \cdot \frac{d_n}{1 + d_n}$$

If the collection is finite, $d = \Sigma d_n$ *may be used instead.*

That d is a semimetric was observed in Section 4.3, Problem 9. That d gives $\bigvee d_n$ follows immediately from Section 2, Problem 7.//

DEFINITION 1. *Let* A *be a set,* B *a topological space, and* f: A $\to$ B. *The topology on* A *generated by* $\{f^{-1}[G]: G$ *open in* B$\}$ *is called the weak topology by* f, *and written* $w(A, f)$.

It is obvious that f is continuous when $w(A, f)$ is put on A. It is also obvious that $w(A, f)$ is the weakest topology on A which makes f continuous. [If T is a topology on A making f continuous and G is an open set in B, $f^{-1}[G]$ is T-open; thus each open set in a basis for $w(A, f)$ is T-open. Hence T is stronger.] Finally, we shall use the remark that $w(A, f)$ is actually equal to $\{f^{-1}[G]: G$ open in $B\}$ since any finite intersection of the form $\bigcap f^{-1}[G_k]$ can be written $f^{-1}[\bigcap G_k]$, and $\bigcap G_k$ is an open set in B.

LEMMA 1. *With the notation of Definition 1, a net* $a_\delta \to a$ *in* $w(A, f)$ *if and only if* $f(a_\delta) \to f(a)$ *in* B.

Suppose that $a_\delta \to a$ in $w(A, f)$. Then $f(a_\delta) \to f(a)$ in B, since f is continuous [Section 2, Theorem 2]. Conversely, if $f(a_\delta) \to f(a)$, let N be a $w(A, f)$ neighborhood of a. Then there exists a neighborhood G of $f(a)$ with $f^{-1}[G] \subset N$. Then $f(a_\delta) \in G$ eventually, hence $a_\delta \in N$ eventually. Thus $a_\delta \to a$.//

DEFINITION 2. *Let* A *be a set,* Ψ *a collection of topological spaces, and for each* B $\in \Psi$, *assume given one or more functions* f: A $\to$ B. *Let the collection of all these functions be called* Φ. *The topology* $\bigvee \{w(A, f): f \in \Phi\}$ *is called the weak topology by* Φ, *and written* $w(A, \Phi)$.

THEOREM 3. *Let a set* A *be given the weak topology* $w(A, \Phi)$ *by a family* Φ *of maps from* A *to a collection of topological spaces. Then a net* $a_\delta \to a$ *in* A *if and only if* f(a_δ) $\to$ f(a) *for every* f $\in \Phi$.

This follows immediately from Theorem 1 and Lemma 1.//

THEOREM 4.   *The weak topology by a sequence* $\{f_n\}$ *of maps from a set* A *to a collection of semi-metric spaces is semimetrizable.*

Since the topology is $\vee \{w(A, f_n): n = 1, 2, \ldots\}$ it will be sufficient, by Theorem 2, to show that $w(A, f)$ is semimetrizable if $f: A \to B$, B a semimetric space.   To show this, set $d_1(a, b) = d[f(a), f(b)]$ for $a, b \in A$.   Then $a_\delta \to a$ in $w(A, f)$ if and only if $f(a_\delta) \to f(a)$ [Lemma 1].   This is true if and only if $d[f(a_\delta), f(a)] \to 0$ [Section 2, Example 4], that is, $d_1(a_\delta, a) \to 0$.   This last is equivalent to $a_\delta \to a$ in d_1; hence $w(A, f)$ is given by d_1.//

★ *Example 1.*   Let n, k be integers with $1 \leq k \leq n$.   Let E^n be given the weak topology w by $(P_1, P_2, \ldots, P_k)$.   *Then w is given by the seminorm* $p(a) = \Sigma_{r=1}^{k}|a_r|$.   *It is also the same as the weak topology w_f by* f: $E^n \to E^k$ *defined by* $f(a) = (a_1, a_2, \ldots, a_k)$.   All three topologies are semimetrizable [Theorem 4], so it is sufficient to compare convergent sequences.   It is clear that $a^n \to a$ in any one of the three topologies if and only if $a_r^n \to a_r$ for $1 \leq r \leq k$. [Use Theorem 3.]   Seminorms other than the one given could have been used (see Section 7.3, Corollary 4).

THEOREM 5.   *With the notation of Definition 2, each* f $\in \Phi$ *is continuous on* A *with* $w(A, \Phi)$ *and* $w(A, \Phi)$ *is the weakest topology on* A *such that this is true.*

If $f: A \to B$, and G is open in B, then $f^{-1}[G]$ is open in A by definition of $w(A, \Phi)$.   Thus is continuous.   To prove the second part, let T be a topology on A making all $f \in \Phi$ continuous.   Let a_δ be a net in A with $a_\delta \to a$ in T.   Then, for every $f \in \Phi$, $f(a_\delta) \to f(a)$ in B, since f is continuous.   Thus $a_\delta \to a$ in $w(A, \Phi)$ [Theorem 3].   Thus T is stronger than $w(A, \Phi)$.//

It is often convenient to have an explicit subbase for $w(A, \Phi)$.

LEMMA 2.   *With the notation of Definition 2, let* Σ(B) *be a subbase for* B, *for each* B $\in \Psi$.   *Let* $\Sigma = \{f^{-1}[G]: f \in \Phi, f: A \to B, G \in \Sigma(B)\}$.   *Then* Σ *generates* $w(A, \Phi)$.

Let T be the topology generated by Σ.   Let a_δ be a net in A with $a_\delta \to a$ in $w(A, \Phi)$, and let N be a T neighborhood of a.   There exist $N_1, N_2, \ldots, N_n \in \Sigma$ with $a \in \cap N_k \subset N$. Each $N_k = f_k^{-1}[G_k]$ for some $G_k \in \Sigma(B_k)$, where $f_k: A \to B_k$.   Now, for each k, $f_k(a_\delta) \to f_k(a)$ [Theorem 3], thus $f_k(a_\delta) \in G_k$ eventually.   Thus $a_\delta \in N_k$ eventually, and so $a_\delta \in N$ eventually.   Hence $a_\delta \to a$ in T, and so $w(A, \Phi)$ is stronger than T.   Conversely, let $a_\delta \to a$ in T and let $f \in \Phi$, say, $f: A \to B$.   Then $f(a_\delta) \to f(a)$ in B.   [Let $f(a) \in G \in \Sigma(B)$. Then $a \in f^{-1}[G] \in \Sigma$.   Thus $a_\delta \in f^{-1}[G]$ eventually, and so $f(a_\delta) \in G$ eventually.   By Section 2, Problem 12, we have the result.]   By Theorem 3, we have $a_\delta \to a$ in $w(A, \Phi)$, and so T is stronger than $w(A, \Phi)$.//

We conclude our present study of weak topologies with two important results in which linearity is assumed.   The first, Theorem 6, is analogous to Theorem 4; the results, however, are far more definitive.

THEOREM 6.   *Let* A *be a linear space and* Φ *a collection of linear functionals on* A.   *Then* $w(A, \Phi)$ *is semimetrizable if and only if* Φ *is of countable Hamel dimension in* $A^{\#}$.   *It is seminormable if and only if* Φ *is of finite dimension.*

Let S be the span of Φ in $A^{\#}$. Assume first that Φ is of countable dimension; that is, there exists a sequence $\{f_n\}$ in S which spans Φ. Then $w(A, \Phi) = w(A, \{f_n\})$. ⟦Each f_n is a linear combination of Φ, and each member of Φ is a linear combination of $\{f_n\}$. Thus each f_n is $w(A, \Phi)$ continuous and each $f \in \Phi$ is $w(A, \{f_n\})$ continuous. It follows from Theorem 3 that net convergence is the same in both topologies.⟧ Theorem 4 provides that $w(A, \Phi)$ is semimetrizable. If Φ is of finite dimension, the same argument shows that $w(A, \Phi) = w(A, \{f_1, f_2, \ldots, f_n\})$ for a certain finite selection of points of S. Then $w(A, \Phi)$ is given by the seminorm p defined by $p(a) = \sum_{k=1}^{n} |f_k(a)|$.

Conversely, suppose that $w(A, \Phi)$ is semimetrizable, hence first countable. Let $\{G_n\}$ be a basic sequence of neighborhoods of 0. For each n, there exist $f_1^n, f_2^n, \ldots, f_{r(n)}^n$ in Φ and $\epsilon_n > 0$ such that $G_n \supset \bigcap\{(|f_k^n| < \epsilon_n): k = 1, 2, \ldots, r(n)\}$ ⟦Lemma 2⟧. Now let f be an arbitrary member of Φ. For some n, $(|f| < 1) \supset G_n$ ⟦since f is continuous and $\{G_n\}$ basic⟧. Thus $\bigcap\{f_k^{n\perp}: k = 1, 2, \ldots, r(n)\} \subset (|f| < 1)$, and so f is a linear combination of $\{f_k^n: k = 1, 2, \ldots, r(n)\}$ ⟦Section 2.10, Corollary 1⟧. Thus Φ is spanned by the countable family of all f_k^n. In the special case of this in which $w(A, \Phi)$ is seminormable, we may take $G_n = (1/n)N(0, 1)$ and so the same set of functions will do for each n. Specifically, choosing $f_1, f_2, \ldots, f_r$, and $\epsilon > 0$ such that $\bigcap(|f_k| < \epsilon) \subset N(0, 1)$, we obtain the fact that $\bigcap f_k^{\perp}$ is included in every neighborhood of 0. Just as before, every $f \in \Phi$ is a linear combination of $f_1, f_2, \ldots, f_r$.//

Consulting Theorem 5, one sees that each $f \in \Phi$ is $w(A, \Phi)$ continuous. Naturally, other functions are continuous as well, for example, f^2, if it is meaningful, is continuous. The problem of discovering exactly which functions are continuous can be solved in a suitably linear environment, as described in Theorem 7. This should be thought of as a representation theorem in the spirit of Section 6.4.

THEOREM 7. *Let A be a linear space and Φ a family of linear functionals. Then any linear functional on A which is $w(A, \Phi)$ continuous is a (finite) linear combination of Φ.*

In this case, the collection Ψ of Definition 2 contains only E. If g is continuous, $G \equiv \{a: |g(a)| < 1\}$ is open. There exists a finite selection $f_1, f_2, \ldots, f_n$ of Φ, and neighborhoods $G_1, G_2, \ldots, G_n$ of 0 in E such that $N \equiv \bigcap_{k=1}^{n} f_k^{-1}[G_k] \subset G$. Now for each k, $f_k^{\perp} \subset f_k^{-1}[G_k]$ ⟦since $a \in f_k^{\perp}$ implies that $f_k(a) = 0 \in G_k$⟧, so $\bigcap_{k=1}^{n} f_k^{\perp}$ is included in N, hence in G. Thus g is bounded on $\bigcap f_k^{\perp}$ and the result follows ⟦Section 2.10, Corollary 1⟧.//

We now turn to the last, and most special of the three types of topology to be treated in this section, namely, the product topology. Recall that a certain (indexing) set B is given and for each $\beta \in B$, a set A_β. Then πA_β is the set of all functions $f: B \to \cup A_\beta$ such that $f(B) \in A_\beta$ for each $\beta \in B$. The maps $P_t: \pi A_\beta \to A_t$, $t \in B$, given by $P_t(f) = f(t)$, are called projections.

DEFINITION 3. *The product topology for a product of topological spaces is the weak topology by the family of all projections.*

This will be taken as the natural topology for the product.

THEOREM 8. *Let a_δ be a net in a product of topological spaces. Then $a_\delta \to a$ if and only if $Pa_\delta \to Pa$ for each projection P onto a factor of the product.*

This follows from Definition 3 and Theorem 3.//

★*Example 2.* Let Y be a topological space and X a set. A member of Y^X is a function $f: X \to Y$. Suppose that a net f_δ in Y^X is given; then $f_\delta \to f$ in the product topology if and only if $f_\delta(x) \to f(x)$ for each $x \in X$, that is, if and only if $f_\delta \to f$ pointwise. [Theorem 8 provides that $f_\delta \to f$ if and only if $P_x f_\delta \to P_x f$ for each $x \in X$. (Recall that $Y^X = \pi\{Y_x: x \in X\}$, where $Y_x = Y$ for each $x \in X$.)] For this reason, the product topology is also called the *pointwise topology.*

★*Example 3.* In Example 1, take $k = n$. The result is that the Euclidean topology on E^n is the product topology [treating E^n as the product E^B, where $B = (1, 2, \ldots, n)$].

★*Example 4: Joint continuity.* Given a function f of two variables in a topological space A, with values in a topological space B, we say that f is *jointly continuous* if $x_\delta \to x$, $y_\delta \to y$ implies $f(x_\delta, y_\delta) \to f(x, y)$. (Note: the nets are defined on the same directed set.) *Then* f *is jointly continuous if and only if* f: A × A → B *is continuous.* [Let f be continuous on $A \times A$, and $x_\delta \to x$, $y_\delta \to y$. Then $(x_\delta, y_\delta) \to (x, y)$ in $A \times A$ by Theorem 8. Thus $f(x_\delta, y_\delta) \to f(x, y)$. The converse is proved in the same way.]

★*Example 5: Addition is jointly continuous.* For example, define $f: R \times R \to R$ by $f(x, y) = x + y$. Let $x_\delta \to x$, $y_\delta \to y$. Then $|x_\delta + y_\delta - (x + y)| \le |x_\delta - x| + |y_\delta - y| < \epsilon$ if $|x_\delta - x| < \epsilon/2$, $|y_\delta - y| < \epsilon/2$, that is, eventually. Thus $x_\delta + y_\delta \to x + y$. *Warning.* Two real nets defined on different directed sets cannot be added.

Example 6: Given a semimetric space A, *the semimetric* d *is jointly continuous; hence* [Example 4] d *is continuous on* A × A. [If $x_\delta \to x$, $y_\delta \to y$, then $|d(x_\delta, y_\delta) - d(x, y)| \le d(x_\delta, x) + d(y_\delta, y) \to 0$.]

THEOREM 9. *A nonempty open set in a product of topological spaces projects onto almost all of the factors; that is,* $P_\beta[G] = A_\beta$ *for all but a finite set of* $\beta \in B$, *where* G *is an open set in* $\pi\{A_\beta: \beta \in B\}$.

By definition of the product topology, there exist $\beta(1), \beta(2), \ldots, \beta(n) \in B$, nonempty open sets $G_k \subset A_{\beta(k)}$, $k = 1, 2, \ldots, n$, such that $\bigcap_{k=1}^n P_{\beta(k)}^{-1} G_k \subset G$. For $t \in B$, $t \ne \beta(k)$, $k = 1, 2, \ldots, n$, we have $P_t G = A_t$. [Assume $x \in A_t$, let $a \in \pi A_\beta$ be defined by $a_t = x$; $a_{\beta(k)}$ is an arbitrary point in G_k for $k = 1, 2, \ldots, n$; a_β is an arbitrary point in A_β for $\beta \ne t$, $\beta \ne \beta(k)$. Then $P_t a = x$, and $P_{\beta(k)} a = a_{\beta(k)} \in G_k$ so that $a \in P_{\beta(k)}^{-1} G_k$ for each k, and so $a \in G$.]//

In the proof of Theorem 9, the fact that the G_k are open was not used. This is to be expected in view of the fact that the topologies on the factors are not restricted in any way. In the case of a finite product, a nonempty open set may project onto no factor, for example, a circle in R^2. This is consistent with Theorem 9.

Theorem 9 implies that a set in a product has empty interior if it projects into (and not onto) all, or even infinitely many factors. This is due, of course, to the way in which the product topology was defined; for example, it would be perfectly feasible, although not useful, to give every product the discrete topology. Theorem 9 would then be false. A hint that the product topology as given in Definition 3 is a reasonable choice is the next result, which gives an analogue of Theorem 9 in an entirely nontopological situation. (But see Section 10.1, Fact (viii).)

If each A_β is a linear space, $A = \pi A_\beta$ is also a linear space with the obvious convention, $(a + tb)_\beta = a_\beta + tb_\beta$ for $a, b \in A$, scalar t. For example, $s = E^\omega$, and $(a + tb)_n = a_n + tb_n$ if $a = \{a_n\}$, $b = \{b_n\}$ are sequences. *The projections are linear* $[\![P_\beta(a + tb) = (a + tb)_\beta = a_\beta + tb_\beta = P_\beta(a) + tP_\beta(b)]\!]$.

THEOREM 10. *An absorbing set in a product of linear spaces projects onto almost all of the factors.*

Let S be an absorbing set in $\pi\{A_\beta : \beta \in B\}$. We have to show that for all but a finite set of $\beta \in B$, $P_\beta[S] = A_\beta$. If not, there can be found a sequence $\{\beta(n)\}$ of members of B, such that $P_{\beta(n)}[S] \neq A_{\beta(n)}$ for $n = 1, 2, \ldots$. Then also $nP_{\beta(n)}[S] \neq A_{\beta(n)}$. For $n = 1, 2, \ldots$, let $x_n \in A_{\beta(n)} \setminus nP_{\beta(n)}[S]$. Define $a \in A$ by $a_\beta = 0$ if β is not one of the sequence $\{\beta(n)\}$, and $a_\beta = x_n$ if $\beta = \beta(n)$. Then $P_{\beta(n)}a = a_{\beta(n)} = x_n \notin P_{\beta(n)}[nS]$ and so $a \notin nS$ and S is not absorbing $[\![$Section 2.5, Problem 13$]\!]$.//

THEOREM 11. *A countable product of semimetric spaces is a semimetric space.*

This follows from Theorem 4 with $f_n = P_n$.//

It is possible for an uncountable product to be semimetrizable; for example, if each factor has the indiscrete topology, the product will be indiscrete. This is essentially the only possibility $[\![$Theorem 12$]\!]$.

LEMMA 3. *Let* $\pi\{A_\beta : \beta \in B\}$ *be an uncountable product of topological spaces which is first countable at one of its points* a. *Then for some* $\beta \in B$, $P_\beta a$ *has no neighborhood except* A_β.

Let $\{G_n\}$ be a countable base of neighborhoods of a. For $n = 1, 2, \ldots$, let $B_n = \{\beta \in B : P_\beta G_n \neq A_\beta\}$. According to Theorem 9, each B_n is finite, and so $\cup B_n$ is countable. Thus there exists $\beta \in B \setminus \cup B_n$. Let G be any neighborhood of $P_\beta a$. Then $P_\beta^{-1}[G]$ is a neighborhood of a; hence it includes some G_n. Thus $G \supset P_\beta[G_n] = A_\beta$ by choice of β.//

THEOREM 12. *An uncountable product of nonindiscrete topological spaces cannot be first countable.*

A point in the product may be chosen, every one of whose projections has a neighborhood which is a proper subset of the range space of the projection. It follows from Lemma 3 that the product cannot be first countable at this point.//

★ *Example 7: s has the product topology,* s $= E^\omega$. This follows immediately from Theorems 8 and 11, the definition of the natural metric for s, and the fact that convergence in s is coordinatewise. $[\![$This was pointed out in Section 4.3, just before Example 1 and in Section 2, Problem 7 of this chapter.$]\!]$ *The natural topology for* s *is* $w(s, s')$. $[\![$By Section 6.4, Example 1, or Example 9, below, any member of s' (any continuous linear functional on s) is a finite linear combination of projections. Thus $w(s, s') = w(s, \{P_n\})$, as proved in the first half of the proof of Theorem 6. But $w(s, \{P_n\})$ is the product topology.$]\!]$ Since we now know that s has the weakest topology such that the coordinates P_n are continuous $[\![$Theorem 5$]\!]$, it follows that *all the sequence spaces* E^n, l^p, c_0, m, *have stronger topologies than* s $[\![$since the coordinates are continuous in each of these spaces$]\!]$. This could, of course, be checked directly in each case.

Example 8. If A is a triangle, c_A has a stronger topology than s 〚Section 6.4, Example 6〛. This will be extended to a general matrix in Section 12.4.

Example 9. Let f be a continuous linear functional on s. It follows from Theorem 7 that f is a finite linear combination of projections. This is the result of Section 6.4, Example 1.

We conclude this section with a remark on the definition of topologies by means of nets. Since Theorem 1 and its specializations, Theorems 3 and 8, are so useful and so easy to state, the reader may have wondered why Theorem 1 was not taken as the definition, instead of the more cumbersome definition given as Definition 5 in Section 1. It seems that if one defines a topology by specifying the convergent nets, much time would be saved. Unfortunately, after specifying which nets are convergent, one has the burden of showing that there actually exists a topology whose convergent nets are the ones which have been specified. In fact, there may be no such topology. For a discussion of this point see reference [5], in Appendix O, pages 73 through 76.

Problems 9.3

★1. Let a linear space A be given the weak topology by $A^{\#}$. Show that there exists no discontinuous linear functional on A.

2. In the space of Problem 1, show that every convergent sequence is included in a finite-dimensional subspace of A. 〚Otherwise, the construction of Section 7.5, Example 2 works.〛

3. In the space of Problem 1, every linear subspace is closed. 〚For such S, every linear functional vanishing on S must vanish on $\bar{S}$. Hence $S = \bar{S}$, by Section 2.4, Theorem 2.〛

4. What is the weak topology by a constant function?

★5. A product of Hausdorff spaces is a Hausdorff space. 〚A convergent net projects onto nets with unique limits. Hence its limit is unique.〛 Problem 6 extends this result.

★6. Let Φ be a family of maps from a set A to a family of Hausdorff spaces. Then $w(A, \Phi)$ is Hausdorff if and only if Φ is separating. 〚See the hint in problem 5.〛

7. Restate Theorem 6 with Φ assumed total. Prove the result. 〚Metric and norm instead of semimetric and seminorm.〛

8. Let $f, g: A \rightarrow E$ be continuous, A being a topological space. Show by means of nets that $f + g$ is continuous.

9. Let a set A be given the weak topology by a family Φ of complex functions (for example, $\Phi = E^A$). Let G be a neighborhood of $a \in A$. Show that there exist $f_1, f_2, \ldots, f_n \in \Phi$, and $\epsilon > 0$ such that $G \supset \{x: |f_k(x) - f_k(a)| < \epsilon$ for $k = 1, 2, \ldots, n\}$.

10. Every projection of a product onto one of its factors is open. 〚In the proof of Theorem 9, for $a \in G$, let the G_k be neighborhoods of $a_{\beta(k)}$. For $t = \beta(k)$, $P_t[G] \supset G_k$, and hence is a neighborhood of $P_t(a)$.〛

11. If πA_β is a Hausdorff space, so is each A_β. 〚Use Problem 10.〛

12. A topological space A is a Hausdorff space if and only if the diagonal in $A \times A$ is closed. 〚The *diagonal* is $\{(a, a): a \in A\}$.〛

13. Obtain the result of Section 1, Problem 35 [$(u = v)$ is closed], from Problem 12, using the map $(u, v): A \rightarrow A \times A$.

★14. Let A be an infinite-dimensional normed space. Show that $w(A, A')$ is not metrizable. 〚Theorem 6, with Section 7.2, Fact (iii); Section 7.3, Problem 3, and Section 6.4, Theorem 1.〛

15. Let a linear space be given the weak topology by a family of linear functionals. Show that every neighborhood of 0 includes a linear subspace of finite codimension. 〚$\bigcap f_k^\perp$ in the proof of Theorem 7. See Section 2.10, Theorem 2.〛

16. Let an infinite-dimensional linear space A be given the weak topology by a family of linear functionals. Show that there is no continuous norm defined on A. In particular, the topology of A cannot be given by a norm. 〚Let p be a continuous seminorm. Since $(p < 1)$ is a neighborhood of 0, Problem 15 implies that p is not a norm.〛

17. Let $A = \pi A_\beta$ be an infinite product of linear spaces A_β, none of which is zero-dimensional. No matter what topology is put on the spaces A_β, A cannot have a continuous norm defined on it. In particular, s has no continuous norm defined on it. 〚Problem 16.〛

★18. The product of relative topologies is the relative topology; that is, given $S_\beta \subset A_\beta$, each S_β having the relative topology of A_β, it follows that πS_β has the relative topology of πA_β. 〚Check convergence of nets, using Section 2, Theorem 3.〛

19. Let A, B, T be topological spaces and $f: A \times B \to T$. Then f is continuous at (a, b) if and only if, for any neighborhood G of $f(a, b)$ in T, there exist neighborhoods M, N of a, b respectively, with $f[M, N] \subset G$.

★20. Let A, B, T be topological spaces and $f: A \times B \to T$ continuous. Fix $b \in B$ and define $g: A \to T$ by $g(a) = f(a, b)$. Show that g is continuous. (Joint continuity implies *separate continuity*.)

21. In contrast with Problem 20, separate continuity in each variable does not imply joint continuity. Give an example in which $f: R \times R \to R$.

22. Let $f: T \to \pi A_\beta$ where T, A_β are topological spaces. Show that f is continuous if and only if $P_\beta \circ f$ is continuous for each β. 〚Theorem 8 and Section 2, Theorem 2.〛

23. In Theorem 12 a countable set of factors may be indiscrete and the result still follows.

24. Does there exist a function $f: R \to R$ such that the weak topology by f is discrete?

25. The product of finitely many discrete spaces is discrete.

26. An infinite product of topological spaces (each with more than one point) cannot be discrete. 〚Theorem 9.〛

27. Let $\{A_n\}$ be a sequence of discrete spaces. Show that $A = \pi A_n$ is metrizable with $d(a, b) = \Sigma\{2^{-n}: a_n \neq b_n\}$, $d(a, a) = 0$.

28. In Problem 27, show that if $\{a^n\}$ is a sequence in A, $a^n \to a$ if and only if for each k, $a_k^n = a_k$ for almost all k. How does this compare with convergence in the discrete topology on A?

29. Let S be the set $\{0, 1, 2, 3, 4, 5, 6, 7, 8, 9\}$. Thinking of infinite decimals suggests that $S^\omega = [0, 1]$. Discuss this possibility, and, giving S the discrete topology, compare convergence in S^ω and $[0, 1]$.

30. Let Φ be a family of functions and f a function, all on a set A. If f is continuous with $w(A, \Phi)$, then $w(A, \Phi \cup \{f\}) = w\{A, \Phi\}$. (Compare this with Theorem 7.) 〚Section 1, Problem 24.〛

31. The result of Theorem 9 is false for maps and weak topology in general; that is, in Definition 2, infinitely many $f \in \Phi$ may map some fixed neighborhood into a proper subset of the range of f.

32. Let A be a set, B a topological space and $f: A \to B$ a map onto. Let A be given the topology $w(A, f)$. Show that f is open.

33. In Problem 32, there may exist a topology for A which is strictly stronger than $w(A, f)$ and which is such that f is open. 〚$f = P_1: R^2 \to R$.〛

34. Fix $z \in A = \pi\{A_\beta: \beta \in B\}$. (For example, if each A_β is a linear space, we can take $z = 0$.) For $\beta \in B$, define $A_\beta(z) = \{a \in A: a_\alpha = z_\alpha \text{ for all } \alpha \neq \beta\}$. We may call this a *copy* of A_β. Show that any copy of A_β with the relative topology of A is homeomorphic with A_β. 〚$P_\beta: A_\beta(z) \to A_\beta$ is a homeomorphism.〛

35. Extend Theorem 9 as follows: fix z as in Problem 34; then the open set includes copies of almost all the factors. 〚The proof given for Theorem 9 works.〛

36. If A is a product of linear spaces A_β, all copies of A_β are isomorphic with A_β and are affine sets.

37. Theorem 10 cannot be extended as was Theorem 9 in Problem 35. 〚Let p be a norm on s (it was pointed out in Section 8.1, Example 2 that one exists); $(p < 1)$ is absorbing but includes no affine set except $\{0\}$.〛

38. Deduce the result (Problem 17) that s has no continuous norm p defined on it from the fact that $(p < 1)$ cannot, by Problem 35, be a neighborhood of 0. 〚See Problem 37.〛

39. Fix z as in Problem 34.   Let $\Sigma A_\beta = \{a \in A : a_\beta = z_\beta$ for almost all $\beta\}$.   Show that ΣA_β is dense in πA_β.

40. $\Sigma E^n = E^\omega = E^\infty$.   (Take $z = 0$ in Problem 39.)

9.4   Subnets

Subnets play the same role as subsequences.   We begin with the concept of a finalizing map from one directed set to another.

DEFINITION 1.   *Let* D$'$, D *be directed sets and* u$: $ D$' \to$ D *a function;* u *is called finalizing if for any* $\delta \in$ D, u$(\delta') \geq \delta$ *eventually.*

Of course, $(u(\delta') : D')$ is a net in D and "$u(\delta') \geq \delta$ eventually" means, as in Section 2, that there exists δ_0' such that $\delta' \geq \delta_0'$ implies $u(\delta') \geq \delta$.   In case $D = D' = \omega$, u is finalizing if and only if $u(n) \to \infty$ as $n \to \infty$.   *The condition, finalizing, should be thought of as a general type of tending to infinity.*

★*Example 1.* $u : D \to R$ is finalizing if and only if $u(\delta) \to \infty$ in the usual sense met with in courses in advanced calculus.

★*Example 2.* $u : D \to (0, 1)$ is finalizing if and only if $u(\delta) \to 1$ in the usual sense.

★*Example 3.*   Let $u : \omega \to R$ be given by $u(n) = n$.   Then u is finalizing.

★*Example 4.*   Let $u : R^+ \to \omega$ be given by $u(x) = [x]$, the largest integer function.   Then u is finalizing.

Example 5.   No function u$: (0, 1] \to (0, 1)$ *can be finalizing.*   This is because, with $\delta = \{1 + u(1)\}/2$, we cannot have $u(\delta') \geq \delta$ eventually [since $u(1) < \delta$].

Example 6.   Let D, D' be directed sets, then $D \times D'$ (Section 1.5, Problem 1) is a directed set, and the projection $P_1 : D \times D' \to D$ is finalizing.   [Given $\delta_0 \in D$, $P_1(\delta, \delta') = \delta \geq \delta_0$, whenever $(\delta, \delta') \geq (\delta_0, \delta_0')$, δ_0' being any arbitrary fixed element of D'.]   Similarly $P_2 : D \times D' \to D'$ is finalizing.

Example 7.   If S is a big enough set of ordinal numbers, no function $u : \omega \to S$ is finalizing.

DEFINITION 2.   *A subset* D$'$ *of a poset* D *is called cofinal if, for any* $\delta \in$ D, *there exists* $\delta' \in$ D$'$ *with* $\delta' \geq \delta$.

For example, the set of even integers is cofinal in ω.   Clearly the inclusion map $i : D' \to D$ (D being a directed set and D' a directed subset) is finalizing if and only if D' is cofinal in D [Problem 6].

DEFINITION 3.   *A subnet of a net* (x$_\delta :$ D) *is a net* (x$_{u(\delta')} :$ D$'$) *where* u$:$ D$' \to$ D *is finalizing.* *More precisely, given nets* (x$_\delta$, D), (y$_{\delta'} :$ D$'$), *where* D, D$'$ *are directed sets, we say that* y$_{\delta'}$ *is a subnet of* x$_\delta$ *if there exists a finalizing map* u$:$ D$' \to$ D, *such that* y $=$ x $\circ$ u; *that is,* y$_{\delta'} =$ x$_{u(\delta')}$ *for* $\delta' \in$ D$'$.

★*Example 8.*   Let $(x_n : \omega)$ be a sequence.   Let e be the set of positive even integers with the usual order.   Then $(x_n : e)$ is a subnet of $(x_n : \omega)$, using the inclusion map from e to ω.

It is also a subsequence [see the Note in Section 2]. Of course it would be possible to obtain essentially the same subnet by considering $(x_{2n}: \omega)$. However, the first method of forming the subnet is more natural in the present context (see Example 12).

★*Example 9.* Given a sequence $(x_n: \omega)$, consider $(x_{[t]}: R^+)$, where $[t]$ is the largest integer $\leq t$. This is a subnet but not a subsequence.

★*Example 10.* Given a net $(x_t: R^+)$, consider $(x_n: \omega)$. Here $u: \omega \to R^+$ is the inclusion map and the subnet is $(x_{u(n)}: \omega)$.

★*Example 11.* As in Section 2, Example 3, let $D = [1, 3] \setminus \{2\}$. As a subnet of $(x_\delta: D)$, consider $(x_{2+1/n}: \omega)$. Here $u: \omega \to D$ is given by $u(n) = 2 + 1/n$. This is finalizing, since $u(n) \to 2$ as $n \to \infty$.

★*Example 12: Natural subnet.* Let $(x_\delta: D)$ be a net, and D' a cofinal subset of D. Then $(x_\delta: \delta \in D')$ is a subnet of D [define $u: D' \to D$ by $u(\delta') = \delta'$, the inclusion map]. Examples 8 and 10 are of this type. Example 11 could be modified to take this form [Problem 9]. We shall refer to this type of subnet as the *natural* subnet corresponding to a cofinal subset.

★ *Example 13.* Suppose that a net $(x_\delta: D)$ in a topological space A does not converge to a certain point $a \in A$. Then, as is the case for sequences, it is useful to know that there exists a neighborhood G of a, and a subnet $(x_{\delta'}: D')$ such that $x_{\delta'} \not\in G$ for all $\delta' \in D'$. [There exists a neighborhood G of a such that $x_\delta \not\in G$ frequently, this being the denial of "$x_\delta \in G$ eventually." Let $D' = \{\delta \in D: x_\delta \not\in G\}$; then the natural subnet (Example 12) is the required subnet.]

Warning. Suppose that $x_\delta \to x$ in a metric space (or, more generally, a first-countable space). It does not follow that x_δ has a subsequence converging to x [mainly because x_δ may not have any subsequences at all; see Example 7].

In Lemma 1, x_δ is a net in some set A. In Theorem 1 and subsequently, A is a topological space.

LEMMA 1. *If* x_δ *is eventually in a set* S, *every subnet of* x_δ *is eventually in* S.

Let $(x_{u(\delta')}: D')$ be the subnet. There exists δ_0 such that $x_\delta \in S$ for $\delta \geq \delta_0$. Since u is finalizing, there exists δ_0' such that $u(\delta') \geq \delta_0$ for $\delta' \geq \delta_0'$, but then $x_{u(\delta')} \in S$.//

THEOREM 1. *Every subnet of a convergent net converges to the same limit as the net.* (In the non-Hausdorff case, this applies to all limits of the net.)

If the limit in question is a and G is a neighborhood of a, the net is eventually in G. By Lemma 1, so is the subnet.//

DEFINITION 4. *The point* a *is a cluster point of a net* x_δ, *if for any neighborhood* G *of* a, $x_\delta \in G$ *frequently.*

LEMMA 2. *If a net is eventually in a set* S, *every cluster point of the net belongs to* $\bar{S}$.

Suppose $a \not\in \bar{S}$. Then $\tilde{\bar{S}}$ is a neighborhood of a not meeting S. Since the net is eventually in S, it is not frequently in $\bar{\bar{S}}$. Thus a is not a cluster point.//

THEOREM 2.   *The point* a *is a cluster point of a net* x_δ *if and only if* x_δ *has a subnet converging to* a.

If a is not a cluster point, it has a neighborhood G such that x_δ fails to be frequently in G; that is, $x_\delta \in \tilde{G}$ eventually.   By Lemma 1, each subnet has the same property, and so does not converge to a.   Conversely, let a be a cluster point of $(x_\delta : D)$.   As expected, we imitate Section 2, Example 5.   This will give a selection of x_δ which will converge to a; unfortunately the selection may not be a subnet, since the finalizing condition may be violated [Example 14, below; also Problem 15].   Thus a few more words need to be said.   Let $D' = \{(\delta, G) : \delta \in D, G \text{ is a neighborhood of } a, x_\delta \in G\}$.   Clearly D' is not empty.   Order D' by defining $(\delta, G) \geq (\delta_1, G_1)$ to mean $\delta \geq \delta_1$ (in D), and $G \subset G_1$.   This makes D' a directed set [Problem 13].

Define $u : D' \to D$ by $u(\delta, G) = \delta$; u is finalizing [Problem 14] and finally $(x_{u(\delta, G)} : (\delta, G) \in D')$ converges to a.   [Let N be a neighborhood of a.   There exists δ_0 with $x_{\delta_0} \in N$.   Let $\delta_0' = (\delta_0, N)$.   Then if $\delta' \geq \delta_0'$, that is, $\delta' = (\delta, G) \geq (\delta_0, N)$, we have $G \subset N$, and $x_\delta \in G$, so $x_\delta \in N$, that is, $x_{\delta'} \in N$, since $x_{\delta'} = x_\delta$.]//

Points sometimes look like cluster points but are not.

★ *Example 14.*   Let $D = (0, 1)$ with the real order.   Let $z = e^{i\pi\delta}$, $w_\delta = e^{2i\pi\delta}$, defining nets in E.   Then 1 is a cluster point of w_δ; in fact, $w_\delta \to 1$.   Also, 1 is a "limit point" of z_δ in the sense that every neighborhood of 1 contains points of z_δ, but 1 is not a cluster point of z_δ; in fact $z_\delta \to -1$.   To emphasize this point, $t_n \equiv e^{i\pi/n} \to 1$; the terms of $\{t_n\}$ are members of z_δ but $\{t_n\}$ is not a subnet of z, since the map $n \to \pi/n$ from ω to D is not finalizing.

Remark.   To simplify the writing, we shall discard the cumbersome subnet notation and write, for example, "x_δ has a subnet y_α."

We now use subnets to describe some topological situations.   The first result is a standard fact about complete regularity which will be used only in Section 14.3.   The subsequent discussion lays groundwork for a development of the basic notion of compactness.

LEMMA 3.   *Let* A *be a completely regular topological space, and* $\Phi = C_1[A]$.   *Then the topology of* A *is* $w(A, \Phi)$

The topology T of A is stronger than $w(A, \Phi)$, since the latter is the weakest making the members of Φ continuous.   Conversely, suppose that a_δ is a net in A which does not converge T to $a \in A$.   There exists a T-neighborhood G of a, and a subnet b_α, with $b_\alpha \notin G$ for all α [Example 13].   By complete regularity, there exists $f \in \Phi$ with $f(a) = 0$, $f(x) = 1$ for $x \notin G$.   Then $f(b_\alpha) \nrightarrow f(a)$ and so $f(a_\delta) \nrightarrow f(a)$ [Theorem 1].   Thus $a_\delta \nrightarrow a$ in $w(A, \Phi)$ [Section 3, Theorem 3] and so $w(A, \Phi)$ is stronger than T [Section 2, Corollary 2].//

DEFINITION 5.   *Let* $(x_\delta : D)$ *be a net in a topological space.   For* $\delta_0 \in D$ *let*

$$T(\delta_0) = \overline{\{x_\delta : \delta \geq \delta_0\}}.$$

We call $T(\delta_0)$ *a tail of the net.*

Clearly, each tail is a closed set.   For example, the tail $T(4)$ of the sequence $\{(-1)^n\}$ is the set $\{-1, 1\}$ containing two members, while for the sequence $\{1/n\}$, $T(4)$ is the set $\{0, \frac{1}{4}, \frac{1}{5}, \frac{1}{6}, \ldots\}$.   (The 0 enters on taking the closure.)

LEMMA 4. *The set of tails of a net* (x_δ: D) *has the finite intersection property; that is, any finite intersection of tails is nonempty.*

If $\delta \geq \delta_k$ for $k = 1, 2, \ldots, n$, then $x_\delta \in \cap_{k=1}^{n} T(\delta_k)$; there always is such a δ, since D is directed.//

LEMMA 5. *The set of cluster points of a net is the intersection of all its tails.*

Each cluster point belongs to every tail, by Lemma 2. Conversely, suppose that a lies in every tail of (x_δ: D) and G is a neighborhood of a. For each $\delta_0 \in D$, a lies in the closure of $\{x_\delta: \delta \geq \delta_0\}$ ⟦since that is $T(\delta_0)$⟧ and so G meets $\{x_\delta: \delta \geq \delta_0\}$. Thus $x_\delta \in G$ frequently and so a is a cluster point.//

Problems 9.4

In this list, D, D' are directed sets unless otherwise specified.

1. Let $D' = D = (0, 2)$ with the real order. Show that $u: D' \to D$ given by $u(\delta) = \delta/2$ is not finalizing.

2. Let $D = [0, 1)$ with the real order. Let $u: \omega \to D$ be given by $u(n) = n[1 + (-1)^n]/(2n + 1)$. Is u finalizing?

3. Let $D = D' = \omega \cup \{\infty\}$ where $\infty \geq n$ for all $n \in \omega$. Define $u: D' \to D$ by $u(n) = 1$ for $n \in \omega$, $u(\infty) = \infty$. Show that u is finalizing.

4. Any two nets have subnets with a common domain; that is, given (x_δ: D), (y_α: A), there exist D' and subnets of x_δ, y_α, each defined on D'. ⟦Let $D' = D \times A$ as in Example 6. Let $u(\delta, \alpha) = \delta$, $v(\delta, \alpha) = \alpha$.⟧

5. Give an example of a net which has no subsequence. ⟦See Example 7.⟧

6. Let $u: D' \to D$ be isotone. Then u is finalizing if and only if $u[D']$ is cofinal in D.

7. Is it possible to have a subnet $x_{u(\delta')}$ of (x_δ: D) which hits the same value infinitely often, that is, such that $u(\delta')$ is the same point in D for infinitely many δ'? ⟦Yes.⟧

★8. A subnet of a subnet of x_δ is a subnet of x_δ.

9. Modify Example 11 so that the given subnet is replaced by a natural subnet. ⟦$D' = \{2 + 1/n: n = 2, 3, \ldots\}$.⟧

10. Deduce from Theorem 1 and Example 11 that if f is a real function with $f(x) \to 5$ as $x \to 2$, then $f(2 + 1/n) \to 5$ as $n \to \infty$.

11. Give $[0, 1]$ the topology in which "closed" equals "countable" (Section 1, Problem 41). Let $D = (0, 1)$ with the real order. Let $x_\delta = \delta$ for $\delta \in D$. Show that x_δ has 1 as a cluster point, but does not converge to 1.

★12. Any cluster point of a subnet of x_δ is a cluster point of x_δ.

★13. Show that D', constructed in the proof of Theorem 2 is a directed set. ⟦Given (δ_1, G_1), (δ_2, G_2), let $G = G_1 \cap G_2$ and $\delta \geq \delta_1$, $\delta \geq \delta_2$, $x_\delta \in G$. Then (δ, G) $\in D'$, $\geq (\delta_1, G_1)$, $\geq (\delta_2, G_2)$.⟧

★14. Show that u, constructed in the proof of Theorem 2 is finalizing. ⟦Given δ, (δ_1, G_1) $\geq (\delta, G)$ implies $u(\delta_1, G_1) \geq \delta$. Choose G, for example, to be the whole space.⟧

15. Let A be a set with three elements a, b, c, and give A the discrete topology. Let D be the set of neighborhoods of a, directed by inclusion. Then D is finite and has a maximum element $\{a\}$. Let $x_n = a$ if n is even, b if n is odd. Then a is a cluster point of (x_n: ω), but the procedure of Section 2, Example 5 does not yield a subnet. What subnet is given by the procedure of the proof of Theorem 2?

16. Prove a result similar to Theorem 2 for a sequence in a semimetric space, obtaining a subsequence instead of a subnet. Observe that this is not a special case of Theorem 2.

17. Must the intersection of two tails of a net be a tail? ⟦No.⟧

18. The tails of any subnet of x_δ are *eventually* included in tails of x_δ, but this is not *always* true; that is, there exists a net x_δ with a subnet one of whose tails is not included in any tail of x_δ.

19. $(n: \omega)$ in R, and $(\delta^n: \omega)$ in c_0 have no convergent subnets.

20. Prove the converse of Section 2, Corollary 1.

21. Let A, B be directed sets and $h: A \to B$. Let $D = A \cup B$ and define $\delta_2 \geq \delta_1$ according to the order in A or B if δ_1, δ_2 both belong to A or to B; while otherwise $\delta_2 \geq \delta_1$ if and only if $\delta_1 \in A$, $\delta_2 \in B$ and $\delta_2 \geq h(\delta_1)$. If $(x_\delta: D)$ is a net, show that A is negligible in the sense that x_δ is eventually of the form x_δ, $\delta \in B$; that $(x_\delta: D)$ and the natural subnet $(x_\delta: B)$ (Example 12) have exactly the same cluster points; that $(x_\delta: D)$ is eventually, or frequently, in a set if and only if (x_δ, B) is. (For example, if $x_\delta = 0$ for $\delta \in A$ and 1 for $\delta \in B$, then $x_\delta = 1$ eventually.)

22. A filter G is said to *refine* a filter F if $G \supset F$. Show that F_S refines F_N if S is a subnet of N. (The language of Section 2, Problem 30 is being used.)

23. Call a a cluster point of a filter F if it is a cluster point of the associated net. Show that a is a cluster point of F if and only if $a \in \cap\{\bar{S}: S \in F\}$. (Section 2, Problem 31(b).)

24. State and prove an analogue, for filters, of (a) Example 12, (b) Theorem 1, (c) Theorem 2

9.5 Compact sets

We make the standard warning that only the aspects of compactness needed later are given here. All the theory of compact metric spaces and of countable and sequential compactness are omitted.

DEFINITION 1. *A set K in a topological space is called compact if, whenever K is included in the union of a family of open sets, it is also included in the union of a finite selection from that family.*

This definition is often phrased thus: a set is called compact if every *open cover* of the set is reducible to a finite *subcover*.

The Heine-Borel theorem states that a subset of R is compact if and only if it is closed and bounded. In a metric space in general, every compact set is closed [Corollary 3, below] and metrically bounded. [Let K be compact and $x \in K$. Then $\{N(x, n): n = 1, 2, \ldots\}$ is an open cover of K. A finite subcover has a largest member which is thus a cell including K.] However a closed, metrically bounded subset of a normed space need not be compact [Example 1]. A topological space with the property that every point has a compact neighborhood is said to be *locally compact*. Locally compact linear spaces play no part in our plans, indeed, Section 12.2, Theorem 5 says (roughly) that the existence of a compact neighborhood forces finite dimensionality. We give, in Lemma 1, a formulation of compactness which is often easier to use than the definition.

DEFINITION 2. *Let A be a set and S a subset. A family Φ of subsets of A is said to have the finite intersection property relative to S if S meets the intersection of every finite subcollection of Φ; and the full intersection property relative to S if S meets the intersection of all members of Φ.*

LEMMA 1. *A set K is compact if and only if any family Φ of closed sets with the finite intersection property relative to K has the full intersection property relative to K.*

Let K be compact, and Φ have the stated property. Then K meets $\cap\{S: S \in \Phi\}$. [If not, $K \subset \cup\tilde{S}$, and so K is included in the union of finitely many $\tilde{S}$, say $K \subset \cup_{k=1}^{n}\tilde{S}_k$. But this means that $K \cap \cap_{k=1}^{n} S_k.$] The converse is proved in exactly the same way [Problem 7].//

Example 1: In c_0, *the disk* $D(0, 1)$ *is not compact*, for if we take, for $n = 1, 2, \ldots, S_n = (\delta^n, \delta^{n+1}, \delta^{n+2}, \ldots)$ we have that $\cap S_n$ is empty, yet any finite intersection surely meets $D(0, 1)$.

LEMMA 2. *A closed subset of a compact set is compact.*

Let S be a closed subset of a compact set K. Let Γ be an open cover of S. Then $\Gamma \cup \{\tilde{S}\}$ is an open cover of K, thus can be reduced to a finite subcover Γ'. Clearly $\Gamma' \setminus \{\tilde{S}\}$ is a cover of S.//

Theorem 1 will be our principal tool for investigating compactness.

THEOREM 1.   *The following three conditions on a set* K *are equivalent:*

  (i)   K *is compact.*
  (ii) *Every net in* K *has a cluster point in* K.
  (iii) *Every net in* K *has a subnet converging to a point in* K.

Conditions (ii) and (iii) are equivalent, according to Section 4, Theorem 2.

Let K be compact and x_δ a net in K. The collection of tails of x_δ has the finite intersection property relative to K [indeed, the collection of sets of the type $\{x_\delta: \delta \geq \delta_0\}$ has this property]; hence, by Lemma 1, K meets the intersection of all tails and so has a cluster point of x_δ [Section 4, Lemma 5].

Conversely, suppose that K has property (ii). Let Φ be a collection of closed sets with the finite intersection property relative to K. Let D be the collection of all finite intersections of members of Φ. Then D is also a collection of closed sets with the finite intersection property relative to K, but, in addition, any finite intersection of members of D belongs to D. Thus D becomes a directed set under inclusion. For each $\delta \in D$ choose $x_\delta \in \delta \cap K$. Then $(x_\delta: D)$ is a net in K. By hypothesis, x_δ has a cluster point $a \in K$. The proof will be completed when it is shown that $a \in \cap\{S: S \in \Phi\}$. Actually we show $a \in \cap\{S: S \in D\}$. Since a is a cluster point of x_δ, $a \in T(\delta)$ for each $\delta \in D$ [Section 4, Lemma 5]. But $T(\delta) \subset \delta$, since D is ordered by inclusion; hence $a \in \delta$ for each $\delta \in D$.//

COROLLARY 1.   *A continuous function preserves compact sets.*

Let A, B be topological spaces, $f: A \to B$ continuous, and K a compact subset of A. Let $(b_\delta: D)$ be a net in $f[K]$. Then for each $\delta \in D$, $b_\delta = f(a_\delta)$ for some $a_\delta \in K$. By Theorem 1, the net a_δ has a subnet x_α with $x_\alpha \to x \in K$. Since f is continuous $f(x_\alpha) \to f(x)$; that is, b_δ has a subnet converging to a point of $f[K]$. By Theorem 1, $f[K]$ is compact.//

It follows from Corollary 1 that a continuous real function on a compact set is bounded and assumes its maximum and minimum.

COROLLARY 2.   *Let* K *be compact and* x_δ *a net in* K *with exactly one cluster point* a.   *Then* $x_\delta \to a$.

If $x_\delta \nrightarrow a$, there exists a neighborhood G of a, and a subnet of x_δ lying outside of G ⟦Section 4, Example 13⟧. This subnet has a cluster point which obviously is not a, but is a cluster point of x_δ ⟦Section 4, Problem 12⟧.//

The rest of this section deals with properties of compactness which are peculiar to Hausdorff spaces.

COROLLARY 3.   *In a Hausdorff space, compact sets are closed.*

Let K be compact, a_δ a net in K with $a_\delta \to a$. By Theorem 1, a_δ has a subnet converging to a point $x \in K$. This subnet also converges to a ⟦Section 4, Theorem 1⟧; hence $a = x$, since limits are unique. Thus $a \in K$ and so K is closed.//

Theorem 2 will not be used until Chapter 14.

THEOREM 2.   *A compact Hausdorff space is* $T_{4\frac{1}{2}}$.

By Urysohn's lemma (Section 1, Theorem 3) it is sufficient to prove the space normal. We first prove the space regular. ⟦Let K be a closed, hence compact, set and $a \notin K$. For each $b \in K$ let $G(b)$, $N(b)$ be disjoint open neighborhoods of a, b, respectively. Since $\{N(b): b \in K\}$ is an open cover of K, it may be reduced to a finite cover, $\{N(b_1), N(b_2), \ldots, N(b_n)\}$. Then $\cap G(b_k)$ and $\cup N(b_k)$ are disjoint open sets including a, K, respectively.⟧ Next, let K, K_1 be closed, hence compact disjoint sets. Repeating the argument which yielded regularity but replacing a by K_1 ⟦possible, since the space is regular⟧ produces the desired separation of K, K_1.//

An amusing and ultimately important remark (Theorem 3) is based on the fact that "compact" and "closed" behave in opposite fashions with respect to strength. Thus, a closed set remains closed if the topology is strengthened, a compact set remains compact if the topology is weakened. (An open cover in a weaker topology is an open cover, hence can be reduced to a finite one. This fact will be used twice in the proof of Theorem 3.) Thus, in situations where closed and compact mean the same thing, the topology can be neither strengthened nor weakened.

THEOREM 3.   *Two comparable compact Hausdorff topologies are equal. A compact Hausdorff space can be given neither a strictly weaker Hausdorff topology nor a strictly stronger compact topology.*

The second sentence follows from the first, since a topology stronger than a Hausdorff topology is Hausdorff ⟦Section 1, Problem 33⟧ and a topology weaker than a compact topology is compact.

To prove the theorem, let T, T' be compact Hausdorff topologies with T' stronger. A T'-closed set is T' compact ⟦Lemma 2⟧, hence T compact, hence T closed ⟦Corollary 3⟧. Thus T is stronger.//

A useful tool of functional analysis is the conclusion that a function of some type has a continuous inverse (see, for example, Section 11.2, Corollary 1). We give a simple result of this form.

THEOREM 4.   *A continuous map* f *from a compact space* K *to a Hausdorff space* H *preserves closed sets. In particular, if it is continuous and one to one, it is a homeomorphism (into).*

If $S \subset K$ is closed, it is compact [Lemma 2], thus $f[S]$ is compact [Corollary 1], hence closed [Corollary 3].//

LEMMA 3. *Let* A *be a set,* B *a topological space, and* f: A $\rightarrow$ B *a function onto. Give* A *the weak topology by* f. *Then, if* K *is a compact subset of* B, $f^{-1}[K]$ *is compact.*

Let a_δ be a net in $f^{-1}[K]$. Then $f(a_\delta)$ is a net in K, hence has a convergent subnet $f(x_\alpha) \rightarrow b \in K$, and $b = f(a)$ for some $a \in A$ since f is onto. Section 3, Lemma 1 provides that $x_\alpha \rightarrow a$. Moreover, $a \in f^{-1}[K]$. The result follows from Theorem 1.//

Problems on topological space 9.5

★1. A finite set is compact.

2. A finite union of compact sets is compact.

3. In the minimal T_1 topology, all sets are compact.

4. In the topology in which "closed" means "countable" (Section 1, Problem 41), a set is compact if and only if it is finite. $[\bigcap_{n=1}^{m} \bigcup_{k=n}^{\infty} \{x_k\}$ is empty if $m = \infty$, not empty if $m < \infty$.]

5. Let Φ be a collection of sets with the finite intersection property and suppose that Φ contains at least one finite set. Then the intersection of all the sets in Φ is nonempty.

6. In Problem 5, replace the second "finite" by "compact," and assume that all the sets in Φ are closed.

7. Prove the converse of Lemma 1.

8. Prove that c_0 is not locally compact.

9. Obtain the result of Example 1 by finding an open cover for $D(0, 1)$ which cannot be reduced to a finite cover.

10. In C, $D(0, 1)$ is not compact.

11. Let K be a compact set in a first-countable space. Then every sequence in K has a subsequence converging to a point of K.

12. Let K be a compact set in a semimetric space, and let a be a point of the space. Then there exists $b \in K$ such that $d(a, b) = d(a, K)$. [The continuous function $d(a, x)$ has a minimum for $x \in K$.]

13. In Corollary 2, the hypothesis that K is compact cannot be dropped. (Give an example in R.)

14. In Corollary 3, the hypothesis Hausdorff cannot be dropped or replaced by T_1. [Problem 3.]

15. Give an example of a set which can be given two different, but comparable compact topologies (this points up Theorem 3). [$[0, 1]$ with R and minimal T_1 topologies.]

16. Every locally compact Hausdorff space can be given a weaker Hausdorff topology which makes it compact.

17. In Theorem 4, the hypothesis that K is compact cannot be dropped. [Identity map from a discrete space.]

18. In Theorem 4, the hypothesis Hausdorff cannot be dropped or replaced by T_1. [Identity map to a space with the minimal T_1 topology.]

19. Let K, B be, respectively, compact and Hausdorff. Let $f: K \rightarrow B$ be continuous, one to one, and onto. Then f is open. (Hence it is a homeomorphism.)

20. In Problem 19, "one to one" cannot be dropped [Section 5.1, Problem 3], nor can "onto."

★21. Let $\{x_n\}$ be a convergent sequence in a topological space, say $x_n \rightarrow x$. Show that $\{x\} \cup \{x_n: n = 1, 2, \ldots\}$ is compact. [Any neighborhood of x includes almost all x_n.]

★22. Let S be a set in a topological space A. A subset of S is compact in A if and only if it is compact in S with the relative topology of A. [Use Theorem 1, Part (iii), and Section 2, Theorem 3.]

23. In Lemma 3, the hypothesis "onto" cannot be dropped.

24. A net in a locally compact space which is eventually outside of any given compact set has no cluster points.

25. In Problem 24, "locally compact" cannot be dropped. ⟦Section 4, Problem 11.⟧

26. A closed set in a product need not project onto closed subsets of the factors (Give an example in $R \times R$). However, if one of the projections of a closed subset of a product of two spaces is compact, its other projection is closed. ⟦Let $P_1 z_\delta \to x$. Then $P_2 z_{u(\delta')} \to P_2 z$, $P_1 z_{u(\delta')} \to x$. Hence $z_{u(\delta')} \to (x, P_2 z) = w$, say, and $x = P_1 w$.⟧

27. A compact set in a semimetric space is *totally bounded*. This means that for any $\epsilon > 0$, the set can be covered by a finite number of cells of radius ϵ. ⟦This follows directly from the definition of compactness.⟧

28. A compact semimetric space must be separable. ⟦Use Problem 27.⟧

29. Can every metric space be given an equivalent metric under which it is totally bounded?

30. A lower semicontinuous real function assumes a minimum on any compact set. ⟦f is bounded from below, otherwise, with $f(a_n) < -n$; a_n has a convergent subnet b_α, yet $f(b_\alpha) \to -\infty$. With $t = \inf f$, let $f(a_n) < t + 1/n$. Then a_n has a subnet $b_\alpha \to b$. Then $f(b) = t$.⟧

31. Must the closure of a compact set be compact? Must the intersection of two compact sets be compact? ⟦Both answers are no, but trivially yes in a Hausdorff space.⟧

32. A topological space is compact if and only if every filter in it has a cluster point.

9.6   Universal nets

The definitions and lemmas used in this section will have no further mention in this book. Tychonoff's theorem, which concludes the section, is, however, an important tool. Observe that no topological ideas occur until after Lemma 3.

DEFINITION 1.   *A net in a set* A *is called universal if, for any subset* S *of* A, *either the net is eventually in* S *or it is eventually in* A \ S.

For example, a constant net is universal. Indeed, an eventually constant net is universal.

LEMMA 1.   *If a universal net is frequently in a set, it is eventually in it.*

If not, it would be frequently in both the set and its complement, hence would not be eventually in either one.//

LEMMA 2.   *Let* A, B *be sets,* $f: A \to B$, *and* a_δ *a universal net in* A. *Then* $f(a_\delta)$ *is a universal net in* B.

Let S be a subset of B. Then a_δ is eventually in either $f^{-1}[S]$ or its complement; thus $f(a_\delta)$ is eventually in either S or $B \setminus S$.//

LEMMA 3.   *Every net has a universal subnet.*

Let A be a set and $(a_\delta: D)$ a net in A. Let Ψ be the set of all "ends" of a_δ, where an end is a set of the form $\{a_\delta: \delta \geq \delta_0\}$. There exists a collection Φ of nonempty subsets of A which (i) is closed under pairwise intersection (that is, $S_1, S_2 \in \Phi$ implies $S_1 \cap S_2 \in \Phi$), (ii) is maximal with respect to this property, and (iii) includes Ψ. ⟦Consider the set of all collections satisfying conditions (i), (iii).   It is not empty, since the collection of all those subsets of A which include at least one end of a_δ satisfies conditions (i), (iii).   Ordering this set by containment, let Φ be the union of a maximal chain.   It is clear that Φ is maximal with respect to conditions (i), (iii), hence with respect to condition (i) alone, since any set including Φ also includes Ψ.]

Now let $D' = \{(\delta, G): G \in \Phi, a_\delta \in G\}$. D' is not empty; indeed, every $G \in \Phi$ occurs in D'.   [Let $G \in \Phi$, $e \in \Psi$.   Then $e \in \Phi$, since $\Phi \supset \Psi$, and e meets G, since Φ is closed under pairwise intersection, that is, for some δ, $a_\delta \in G$.]   We make D' into a directed set by defining $(\delta, G) \geq (\delta_1, G_1)$ to mean $\delta \geq \delta_1$ and $G \subset G_1$.   Finally, let $u(\delta, G) = \delta$.   This gives a finalizing map from D' to D [Section 4, Problem 14].

Our proof is concluded by showing that $(a_{u(\delta')}: \delta' \in D')$ is a universal net.   We first remark that $a_{u(\delta')}$ is universal as far as Φ is concerned, indeed for $G_0 \in \Phi$, $a_{u(\delta')} \in G_0$ eventually.   [As proved above, $(\delta_0, G_0) \in D'$ for some δ_0.   Then $(\delta, G) \geq (\delta_0, G_0)$ implies $a_{u(\delta,G)} = a_\delta \in G \subset G_0$.]   Now suppose that $a_{u(\delta')}$ is not universal; that is, there exists $S \subset A$ such that $a_{u(\delta')}$ is frequently in both S and $A \setminus S$.   Then each $G \in \Phi$ must meet both S and $A \setminus S$ [since if, for example, $G \subset S$, it would follow that $a_{u(\delta')}$ is eventually in S, since it is eventually in G, as just proved].   Thus, in particular $S \not\subset \Phi$ [since a_δ fails to be eventually in S].   Now $\Phi \cup \{S \cap G: G \in \Phi\}$ is closed under pairwise intersection [since each $G \in \Phi$ meets S] and is strictly larger than Φ.   This contradicts the maximality of Φ.//

From now on we work in a topological space.

LEMMA 4.   *Let* a_δ *be a universal net and* a *a cluster point.   Then* $a_\delta \to a$.

Let G be a neighborhood of a.   Then a_δ is frequently in G.   By Lemma 1, it is eventually in G.   Thus $a_\delta \to a$.//

Of course this means that in a Hausdorff space a universal net has at most one cluster point.

LEMMA 5.   *A universal net in a compact set is convergent (to a member of the set).*

By Section 5, Theorem 1, it has a cluster point in the set.   By Lemma 4, it converges to that point.//

THEOREM 1.   TYCHONOFF'S THEOREM.   *A product of compact spaces is compact.*

Let a_δ be a net in πA_β, each A_β being a compact topological space.   By Lemma 3 it has a universal subnet x_α.   For each β, $P_\beta x_\alpha$ is a universal net in A_β [Lemma 2].   By Lemma 5, $P_\beta x_\alpha$ is convergent for each β.   Hence x_α is convergent [Section 3, Theorem 8].   By Section 5, Theorem 1, πA_β is compact.//

★ *Example 1.*   In R^n, let $H(a, b) = \{(x_1, x_2, \ldots, x_n): a \leq x_k \leq b \text{ for } k = 1, 2, \ldots, n\}$, a, b being real numbers.   Call $H(a, b)$ a hypercube.   Then for $a \leq b$, $H(a, b) = [a, b]^n$.   It follows from Tychonoff's theorem that $H(a, b)$ is compact.   [As shown in Section 3, Example 3, R^n has the product topology.   See also Section 3, Problem 18.]   Thus any closed bounded set in R^n is compact [it is a closed subset of a hypercube] and R^n is locally compact.   The same is true for E^n, since $E^n = R^{2n}$, that is, they have the same points and the same topology.

Problems 9.6

1. A universal sequence is eventually constant.

2. Every subnet of a universal net is universal.

3. Show that there exists a universal net in R with no cluster point. ⟦Apply Lemma 3 to $\{n\}$.⟧

4. If a product is compact, so is each factor. ⟦Section 5, Corollary 1.⟧

5. If every projection of a closed set S in a product is compact, S is compact.

6. The unit disk of m is a compact subset of s. ⟦Problem 5.⟧

7. $(0, 1)^n$ is locally compact, but $(0, 1)^\omega$ is not. ⟦Use Section 3, Theorem 9.⟧

8. Apply the proof of Lemma 3 to $((-1)^n : \omega)$. ⟦Ψ has only one member, the set $\{-1, 1\}$. A possible choice of Φ is $\{\{-1, 1\}, \{1\}\}$. Then D' contains points of two types, $(n, \{-1, 1\})$, $n = 1, 2, \ldots$, since $x_n \in \{-1, 1\}$ for all n, and $(2n, \{1\})$, $n = 1, 2, \ldots$. But no set of the second type is followed by a set of the first type. (This is the situation of Section 4, Problem 21.) The net $x_{u(\delta')}$, is eventually 1 since for $\delta'_0 = (2, \{1\})$, $x_{u(\delta')} = 1$ for all $\delta' \geq \delta'_0$.⟧

9. A compact Hausdorff space need not be separable ⟦$[0, 1]^A$⟧. (Recall that a compact metric space must be separable.)

10. An *ultrafilter* is a maximal filter. Show that every filter in a set A is included in an ultrafilter. ⟦Take the union of a maximal chain.⟧

11. For $a \in A$, the collection of all subsets of A containing a is an ultrafilter.

12. Universal nets and ultrafilters correspond under the procedure of Section 2, Problems 30, 31(b).

13. If F is an ultrafilter in A, and S, T are subsets of A with $S \cup T \in F$, then either $S \in F$ or $T \in F$.

14. Every ultrafilter in a compact space is convergent.

15. Write a proof of Theorem 1 by means of filters, using Problems 10 and 14 and analogues of the lemmas.

10
LINEAR TOPOLOGY

10.1 Linear topological space

Linearity and semimetric topology were studied separately in Chapters 2 and 5. They were joined in Chapters 6 and 7. The extension of the subject matter of Chapter 5 in Chapter 9 leads once more to a junction of linear and topological ideas. As pointed out in Section 6.1, some connection should be assumed between them. As usual, it is the assumption that the linear operations are continuous. However, strangely enough, some situations occurred in which interplay between linear and topological ideas seemed to arise without such an assumption. One of these was the result that an absorbing set in a product must be fairly large, Section 9.3, Theorem 10. Also, in Section 9.3, Theorem 6, some conclusions about metrizability of weak topologies were drawn from hypotheses about dimension. Another example is Section 9.3, Theorem 7.

DEFINITION 1. *Let a linear space* A *be given. A linear topology for* A *is a topology* T *with the property that addition and multiplication by scalars are continuous. The pair* (A, T), *or simply* A, *if* T *is understood from the context, is called a linear topological space.*

The continuity condition means that if $(a_\delta: D)$, $(b_\delta: D)$, where both D are the same, are nets of vectors, with $a_\delta \to a$, $b_\delta \to b$, then $a_\delta + b_\delta \to a + b$, and if $(t_\delta: D)$ is a net of scalars with $t_\delta \to t$, then $t_\delta a_\delta \to ta$ (see Section 9.3, Examples 4 and 5 for this phrasing of joint continuity).

In the following, we shall make extensive use of both the net and neighborhood formulations of continuity.

✶ *Example 1.* A linear semimetric space is a linear topological space. For $!a_\delta + b_\delta - (a + b)! \leq !a_\delta - a! + !b_\delta - b! \to 0$, while continuity of ta as a function of t, a follows from Part (v) of the definition of paranorm, Section 4.1. There it was assumed that (with sequences, rather than nets) $t_n a_n \to ta$ whenever $t_n \to t$, $a_n \to a$. Since we are dealing with semimetric spaces, this is sufficient to ensure continuity of ta as a function of $(t, a) \in E \times A$, A being the space [Section 4.3, Theorem 1; that $E \times A$ is semimetrizable follows from Section 9.3, Theorem 11].

★ *Example 2: Let* Φ *be a collection of linear topologies on a linear space* A. *Then* $\vee\Phi$ *is a linear topology.* Suppose that $(t_\delta: D)$ is a net of scalars with $t_\delta \to t$, and that $(a_\delta: D)$, $(b_\delta: D)$ are nets in A with $a_\delta \to a$, $b_\delta \to b$. Then $a_\delta \to a$ and $b_\delta \to b$ in each $T \in \Phi$ [Section 9.3, Theorem 1] and so $t_\delta a_\delta + b_\delta \to ta + b$ in each $T \in \Phi$, since T is a linear topology. Hence, again by Section 9.3, Theorem 1, $t_\delta a_\delta + b_\delta \to ta + b$ in $\vee\Phi$.

★ *Example 3.* A special case of Example 2 is the fact that the weak topology by a collection Φ of linear maps from a linear space to a collection of linear topological spaces is a linear topology. This follows from Example 2, when it is checked that $w(A, f)$ is a linear topology, $f: A \to B$ being a linear map and B a linear topological space. The check is trivial [use Section 9.3, Lemma 1 as in Example 2].

✶ *Example 4.* A special case of Example 3 is the fact that a product of linear topological spaces is a linear topological space.

Facts about linear topological space

(i) If $a_\delta \to a$, then $ta_\delta \to ta$ for any scalar t; in particular, $-a_\delta \to -a$. If $t_\delta \to t$, then $t_\delta a \to ta$ for any vector a. If $a_\delta \to a$, then $a_\delta + b \to a + b$ for any vector b.

(ii) $a_\delta \to a$ if and only if $a_\delta - a \to 0$.

(iii) Translation is a homeomorphism onto; that is, with $f(x) = a + x$ (a fixed), f is a homeomorphism of the space onto itself.

(iv) Multiplication by a nonzero scalar is a homeomorphism onto.

(v) Every translate of an open set is open.

(vi) If G is a neighborhood of x and a is a vector, then $a + G$ is a neighborhood of $a + x$. In particular, $a + N$ is a neighborhood of a if and only if N is a neighborhood of 0.

(vii) Any nonzero multiple of an open set is open. More specifically, if G is a neighborhood of a and $t \neq 0$ is a scalar, tG is a neighborhood of ta.

(viii) Every neighborhood of 0 is absorbing. (Hence, by Fact (vi), a neighborhood of a is absorbing at a.)

(ix) Given a neighborhood G of 0, there exists a neighborhood N of 0 such that $tN \subset G$ for all $|t| \leq 1$.

(x) Every neighborhood of 0 includes a balanced neighborhood of 0.

(xi) Given a neighborhood G of 0, there exists a neighborhood N of 0 such that $N + N \subset G$.

Proofs

(i) These statements merely say that joint continuity implies separate continuity. This is Section 9.3, Problem 20.

(ii) If $a_\delta \to a$, $a_\delta - a \to a - a = 0$. If $a_\delta - a \to 0$, $a_\delta = a_\delta - a + a \to 0 + a = a$.

(iii) By Fact (i), translation is continuous. Its inverse is also a translation.

(iv) By Fact (i) multiplication is continuous. In the case of a nonzero scalar, the inverse is also a multiplication.

(v) This follows from Fact (iii).

(vi) This follows from Fact (v).

(vii) This follows from Fact (iv).

(viii) Let G be a neighborhood of 0, and a a vector. Define $f(t) = ta$ for scalar t. Then f is a continuous map from the scalars into the space. Thus there exists $\epsilon > 0$ such that $|t| \leq \epsilon$ implies $t \in f^{-1}[G]$, that is, $ta \in G$.

(ix) Let A be the space. The map $f: E \times A \to A$ given by $f(t, a) = ta$ is continuous. Thus, given a neighborhood G of 0 in A, there exists a neighborhood M of 0 in $E \times A$ such that $f[M] \subset G$. Then there exist neighborhoods N_1, N_2 of 0 in E, A, respectively, such that $P_1^{-1}[N_1] \cap P_2^{-1}[N_2] \subset M$. Observe that N_1 includes $D(0, \epsilon)$ for some $\epsilon > 0$. Given $|t| \leq \epsilon$, $a \in N_2$ we have $ta = f(t, a) \in f[M] \subset G$. Setting $N = \epsilon N_2$ we have $tN \subset G$ for all $|t| \leq 1$ [since $|t| \leq \epsilon$ implies $tN_2 \subset G$].

(x) Let G be a neighborhood of 0. Choose N as in Fact (ix) and let $N_0 = \cup_{|t| \leq 1} tN$; N_0 is obviously balanced, included in G, and, since it includes N, a neighborhood of 0.

(xi) Let A be the space. The map $f: A \times A \to A$ given by $f(a, b) = a + b$ is continuous. Thus, given a neighborhood G of 0 in A, there exists a neighborhood M of 0 in $A \times A$ with $f[M] \subset G$ and neighborhoods N_1, N_2 of 0 in A such that $P_1^{-1}[N_1] \cap P_2^{-1}[N_2] \subset M$. Let $N = N_1 \cap N_2$. For $a, b \in N$, $(a, b) \in M$ [since $P_1(a, b) = a \in N_1$, $P_2(a, b) = b \in N_2$, so $(a, b) \in P_1^{-1}[N_1] \cap P_2^{-1}[N_2]$]. So $a + b = f(a, b) \in f[M] \subset G.//$

The definition of linear topology is sometimes not well suited to the task of checking that a given topology satisfies it. It is useful to have a criterion in terms of the open sets. It turns out that Facts (v), (viii), (x), and (xi), which are necessary, are also, in their totality, sufficient.

THEOREM 1. *Let a linear space* A *be given a topology such that*

(a) *every translate of an open set is open;*
(b) *every neighborhood of 0 is absorbing;*
(c) *every neighborhood of 0 includes a balanced neighborhood of 0;*
(d) *given a neighborhood* G *of 0, there exists a neighborhood* N *of 0 such that* N + N $\subset$ G.

Then A *is a linear topological space.*

We first observe that Fact (ii) holds. [Suppose that $x_\delta \to x$ and let G be a neighborhood of 0. Then $x + G$ is a neighborhood of x by Assumption (a), so $x_\delta \in x + G$ eventually. Thus $x_\delta - x \in G$ eventually and so $x_\delta - x \to 0$. The proof of the converse is similar.]

To show that addition is continuous, it is sufficient to prove that if $x_\delta \to 0$, $y_\delta \to 0$, then $x_\delta + y_\delta = 0$. [If $x_\delta \to x$, $y_\delta \to y$ then, by Fact (ii), $x_\delta - x \to 0$, $y_\delta - y \to 0$ and, if we prove $x_\delta - x + y_\delta - y \to 0$, we obtain $x_\delta + y_\delta \to x + y$ from Fact (ii).] Let G be a neighborhood of 0. Let N be a neighborhood of 0 satisfying $N + N \subset G$. Eventually $x_\delta \in N$, $y_\delta \in N$, hence, eventually $x_\delta + y_\delta \in N + N \subset G$. Thus $x_\delta + y_\delta \to 0$. This concludes the proof that addition is continuous.

Next we prove that, given a neighborhood G of 0 and a positive integer k, there exists a neighborhood N of 0 such that $2^k N \subset G$. [Choose N with $N + N \subset G$. Then $2N \subset N + N \subset G$. Choose N_2 with $N_2 + N_2 \subset N$. Then $4N_2 \subset 2(N_2 + N_2) \subset 2N \subset G$. Similarly, with $N_4 + N_4 \subset N_2$ we have $8N_4 \subset G$. This easy induction establishes the result.]

We next prove Fact (vii). [Let G be a neighborhood of a, and $t \neq 0$ a scalar. *Case 1:* $a = 0$, $|t| \geq 1$. By Assumption (c), G includes a balanced neighborhood N of 0; then $(1/t)N \subset N \subset G$ and so $N \subset tG$ and tG is a neighborhood of 0. *Case 2:* $a = 0$; $|t| < 1$. Choose a positive integer k with $2^k > |1/t|$. As just proved, there exists a neighborhood N of 0 such that $2^k N \subset G$. Thus $2^{-k}G$ is a neighborhood of 0. Hence, by Case 1, so is

$2^k t(2^{-k}G)$ since $|2^k t| > 1$; that is, tG is a neighborhood of 0. *Case 3: $a \neq 0$.* $G - a$ is a neighborhood of 0 by Assumption (a), hence so is $t(G - a) = tG - ta$; that is, tG is a neighborhood of ta.⟧

Next we prove that

(1) $t_\delta \to 0$ implies $t_\delta a \to 0$ for each vector a.

⟦Let G be a neighborhood of 0 and a a vector. Since G is absorbing, there exists $\epsilon > 0$ such that $ta \in G$ for $|t| \leq \epsilon$. But $|t_\delta| < \epsilon$ eventually; hence $t_\delta a \in G$ eventually.⟧

Finally we wish to prove that multiplication is continuous; that is, $a_\delta \to a$, $t_\delta \to t$ implies $t_\delta a_\delta \to ta$. ⟦*Case 1: $a = 0$.* We have to show that $t_\delta a_\delta \to 0$. Let G be a neighborhood of 0. Assumption (c) allows us to assume that G is balanced. Let $N = [1/(|t| + 1)]G$. It is a neighborhood of 0, by Fact (vii). Thus $a_\delta \in N$ eventually. Since also $|t_\delta| < |t| + 1$ eventually, we have, eventually $t_\delta a_\delta \in t_\delta N \subset G$, since G is balanced. *Case 2: $a \neq 0$.* Then $t_\delta a_\delta - ta = t_\delta(a_\delta - a) + (t_\delta - t)a$. By Case 1 and Fact (ii), $t_\delta(a_\delta - a) \to 0$. By (1), $(t_\delta - t)a \to 0$. Since addition is continuous, $t_\delta a_\delta - ta \to 0$ and so, Fact (ii) provides that $t_\delta a_\delta \to ta$.⟧//

Remark 1: $a + G$ is a neighborhood of a if and only if G is a neighborhood of 0 ⟦Fact (vi)⟧. (Equivalently, N is a neighborhood of a if and only if $N - a$ is a neighborhood of 0.) A set is open if and only if it is a neighborhood of each of its points, or is empty.

In Theorems 2 and 3, only the neighborhoods of 0 will be given in advance. Then the open sets will be *defined* by Remark 1.

Even more useful than Theorem 1 will be the following criterion:

THEOREM 2. *Let* A *be a linear space. Let* Γ *be a nonempty collection of balanced absorbing sets such that*

        (i) *given* G_1, $G_2 \in \Gamma$, *there exists* $G_3 \in \Gamma$ *with* $G_3 \subset G_1 \cap G_2$;
        (ii) *given* $G_1 \in \Gamma$, *there exists* $G_2 \in \Gamma$ *with* $G_2 + G_2 \subset G_1$.

Let any set which includes a member of Γ *be called a neighborhood of 0 and let neighborhood and open set be defined as in Remark* 1. *Then* A *becomes a linear topological space whose neighborhoods are precisely those described above.*

We must first prove that a topology has been defined. Clearly $\emptyset$ is open; so is A ⟦A is a neighborhood of 0; thus, given any a, $a + A$ is a neighborhood of a. But $a + A = A$.⟧ Next, suppose given a collection Φ of open sets, let $G_0 = \cup\{G: G \in \Phi\}$, and let $a \in G_0$. Then $a \in G$ for some $G \in \Phi$; hence G_0, which includes G, is a neighborhood of a, so G_0 is open. Next, suppose G_1, G_2, . . . , G_n are open sets; let $G = \cap_{k=1}^n G_k$, and let $a \in G$. For each $k = 1, 2, . . . , n$, $G_k = a + N_k$, N_k being a neighborhood of 0. By Assumption (i) of Theorem 2, there exists $N \in \Gamma$ with $N \subset \cap_{k=1}^n N_2$. Then $a + N \subset G$; hence G is a neighborhood of a, so G is open.

We have now proved that a topology has been defined. Let us denote by T neighborhood a neighborhood in the sense of this topology. To show that the neighborhoods and T neighborhoods are the same, suppose first that G is a T neighborhood of a. Then, by definition, G includes an open set which includes a. By definition of open, G is a neighborhood of a. Conversely, let G be a neighborhood of a. We must find an open set G_0 such that $a \in G_0 \subset G$. For this purpose, let $G_0 = \{x: G$ is a neighborhood of $x\}$. G_0 is not empty since $a \in G_0$. Let $b \in G_0$, and choose $N \in \Gamma$ such that $N + N \subset G - b$ ⟦possible because $G - b$ is a neighborhood of 0⟧. Then $b + N + N \subset G$ and so $b + N \subset G_0$. ⟦Let $x \in b + N$. Then $x + N \subset G$ and so G is a neighborhood of x; that is, $x \in G_0$.⟧ Hence, G_0 is a neighborhood of b. This shows that G_0 is open ⟦being a neighborhood of all its points⟧ and so G is a T neighborhood of a. Because of the equivalence, we now drop the designation T neighborhood, and speak only of neighborhoods.

Next we turn to the task of showing that the topology is linear. This has been greatly simplified by the presence of Theorem 1. We need only check the hypotheses of that theorem. But these are clearly contained in our four assumptions!//

The culmination of the idea of Theorems 1 and 2 lies in Theorem 3, which will facilitate defining examples of linear topologies.

THEOREM 3. *Let* A *be a linear space. Let* Γ *be a nonempty collection of balanced absorbing sets such that, given* $G_1 \in \Gamma$, *there exists* $G_2 \in \Gamma$ *with* $G_2 + G_2 \subset G_1$. *Let any subset of* A *which includes a finite intersection of members of* Γ *be called a neighborhood of* 0, *and let neighborhood and open set be defined as in Remark* 1. *Then* A *becomes a linear topological space whose neighborhoods are precisely those described above.*

For if we let Γ' be the set of all finite intersections of members of Γ, Γ' will satisfy Conditions (i) and (ii) of Theorem 2.//

DEFINITION 2. *The topology obtained from a collection* Γ *of neighborhoods of* 0 *as in Theorem* 3 *will be called the linear topology generated by* Γ, *and* Γ *will be called the generating subbase of neighborhoods of* 0.

There will be no confusion with the similar concept, the topology generated by a collection of subsets, for we shall never omit the word "linear" in applying Definition 2.

We turn now to the very important concept of weak linear topology by a family of maps of a certain kind. Recall the definition of $w(A, \Phi)$, Section 9.3, Definitions 1, 2. Here we shall combine the two steps of the analogous definition.

DEFINITION 3. *Let* A *be a linear space,* Φ *a family of seminorms on* A *or of linear maps from* A *to a collection of linear topological spaces. The weak linear topology by* Φ, *designated* $\sigma(A, \Phi)$, *or, simply* $\sigma(\Phi)$, *is the linear topology generated by* $\{f^{-1}[G]: f \in \Phi, G$ *a neighborhood of* 0 *in the range space of* $f\}$.

For example, if Φ is a family of seminorms, $\sigma(\Phi)$ is the linear topology generated by $\{(p < \epsilon): p \in \Phi, \epsilon > 0.\}$ In particular, $\sigma(A, p)$ is a seminormed space. [As usual, $\sigma(A, p)$ stands for $\sigma(A, \{p\})$.] The reader should now glance at Problems 8, 9 to verify some obvious suspicions.

The weak topology by a family F of linear functionals can be written as the weak linear topology by a family of seminorms, namely, let $\Phi = \{|f|: f \in F\}$. Then $w(A, F) = \sigma(A, F) = \sigma(A, \Phi)$. However, the converse is false. For example, let p be a norm on an infinite-dimensional linear space. Then $\sigma(p)$, the norm topology, is not given by $\sigma(A, F)$ for any family of linear functionals ⟦Section 9.3, Problem 16⟧.

DEFINITION 4. *A linear topology is said to be locally convex if every neighborhood of* 0 *includes a convex neighborhood of* 0.

★ *Example 5.*   A seminormed space is locally convex, since its cells are convex sets.

★ *Example 6: Let Φ be a family of locally convex topologies on a linear space* A.   *Then* $\vee\Phi$ *is locally convex.*   Any neighborhood of 0 includes a finite intersection G of neighborhoods of 0 in the various member topologies of Φ.   Since the intersection of convex sets is convex, G is convex; moreover, it is a $\vee\Phi$ neighborhood of 0.   See also Example 2.

★ *Example 7: If, in Example 3, the range spaces of the functions in Φ are all locally convex, $\sigma(\Phi)$, the weak topology by Φ (that is, the weak linear topology by Φ) is locally convex.*   By Example 6, it is sufficient to check this for a single function f.   But $f^{-1}[K]$ is convex for any convex set K ⟦Section 2.5, Theorem 3⟧ and the result follows.   In particular, *a product of locally convex spaces is locally convex.*

Various examples of spaces which are not locally convex will be given later, for example, Section 3, Example 2 (l^p, $0 < p < 1$); Section 3, Problem 21 and 22 (M); and Section 12.2 (L^p, $0 < p < 1$).   The spaces l^p and L^p, but not M, have a property resembling local convexity ⟦Section 7.5, Problem 16⟧.

A linear topological space is homogeneous and uniform; that is, it has the same appearance at each of its points, for example the neighborhood system at 0 serves, after translation, as a neighborhood system at any other point.   An important corollary of this is now given.

LEMMA 1.   *Let* A *be a linear topological space.   Then a directed set* D *exists with the following property: given a set* S *and* a $\in \bar{S}$, *there exists a net* a_δ, *defined on* D, *of points of* S *with* $a_\delta \to$ a.

We know that for each given S, a, such a directed set and net exist ⟦Section 9.2, Theorem 1⟧, but in the present context D depends only on A and not on S, a.   We take for D the set of neighborhoods of 0, directed by inclusion.   For $\delta \in D$, choose $a_\delta \in (a + \delta) \cap S$.   Then $a_\delta \to a$ exactly as in Section 9.2, Example 5.//

Problems on linear topological space 10.1

★1. If G is a neighborhood of 0, so are $G \pm G$.

★2. If a set S has an interior point, $S - S$ is a neighborhood of 0.   ⟦If S is a neighborhood of x, $S - S \supset S - x$.⟧

3. Let $(t_\delta : D)$ be a net of scalars which is eventually bounded; that is, for some M, $|t_\delta| < M$ eventually, and let $(a_\delta : D)$ be a net of vectors with $a_\delta \to 0$.   Show that $t_\delta a_\delta \to 0$.

★4. Let a linear space be given two linear topologies T and T'.   Then T' is stronger than T if and only if every T neighborhood of 0 is a T' neighborhood of 0.

★5. Let G be a neighborhood of 0.   Show that $\cap\{tG : |t| = 1\}$ is a neighborhood of 0.   ⟦Fact (ix).⟧

★6. In the linear topology generated by Γ, Definition 2, net convergence is described by, $a_\delta \to 0$ if and only if for each $G \in \Gamma$, $a_\delta \in G$ eventually (together with Fact (ii), of course).   ⟦Use Section 9.2, Lemma 1.⟧

★7. Show that net convergence in $\sigma(A, \Phi)$, Definition 3, is described by $a_\delta \to 0$ if and only if $f(a_\delta) \to 0$ for all $f \in \Phi$.

★8. Show that $\sigma(A, \Phi)$, Definition 3, is the weakest linear topology such that all members of Φ are continuous.   ⟦If each $f \in \Phi$ is continuous and $a_\delta \to 0$, then $a_\delta \to 0$ in $\sigma(\Phi)$, by Problem 7.⟧

★9. If A is a linear space and Φ is a collection of linear maps from A to various linear topological spaces, then $\sigma(A, \Phi) = w(A, \Phi)$.   ⟦Example 3 and Problem 8.⟧

10. If A is a linear space of nonzero dimension and p is a norm, $\sigma(A, p) \neq w(A, p)$.

★11. If, in Definition 2, the members of Γ are convex, the resulting topology is locally convex.

★12. s is locally convex. 〚Example 7.〛

★13. Let A be a linear topological space, and f a linear functional on A which is $\sigma(A, A')$ continuous. Show that f is continuous on A. 〚The A topology is stronger.〛

14. Let the discrete topology be put on a linear space. Show exactly which parts of the definition of linear topology it satisfies, which of the Facts and how much of the hypotheses of Theorem 1 it obeys. (It is not a linear topology. Compare Section 4.3, Problem 21.)

15. Let Γ be the set of all intervals $[0, \epsilon)$, $\epsilon > 0$. Use Γ to give R a topology as in Theorem 2. Show that $1/n \rightarrow 0$, but $- 1/n \nrightarrow 0$. Thus this is not a linear topology. Continue as in Problem 14.

16. Let G be the set described in Section 2.5, Example 2. In R^2, let Γ be the set of all positive multiples of G, and use Γ to define a topology as in Theorem 2. Continue as in Problem 14. 〚Addition is not continuous.〛

17. Give R^2 the topology in which $\{a\}$ is open for each $a \neq 0$, while the neighborhoods of 0 are the Euclidean ones. (The topology is generated by cells centered at 0, and one-point sets.) Carry out the program of Problem 14.

18. Give R the topology generated by the set of all intervals (a, ∞). Carry out the program of Problem 14.

19 Discuss the statement, "Continuity of addition is equivalent to Fact (xi); continuity of multiplication is equivalent to Facts (viii) and (ix)." (Compare Problem 16 in which Fact (xi) fails.)

20. Give F the topology of uniform convergence, that is, a subbase neighborhood of $f \in F$ is $\{g : |g(x) - f(x)| < \epsilon \text{ for } 0 \leq x \leq 1\}$. Show that this is not a linear topology. 〚$f/n \nrightarrow 0$ for some f.〛

21. Show that the collection of balanced absorbing subsets of R^2 does not generate a linear topology on R^2. 〚See Problem 16.〛

22. Show that the collection of balloons in a given linear space generates a linear topology for the space. (This will be called the *balloon* topology.) 〚Theorem 3, see also Section 4.2, Corollary 1.〛 Identify the topology. 〚$\sigma(A, \Phi)$, where Φ is the set of all seminorms on A.〛

23. Let A be an infinite-dimensional normed space. Let T_n, T_w, T_b be, respectively, the norm topology, $\sigma(A, A^\#)$, and the balloon topology of Problem 22. Show that T_b is strictly stronger than the other two and that T_n, T_w are incomparable. 〚If $f \in A^\# \setminus A'$, $f(a_k) \nrightarrow 0$ for some $a_k \rightarrow 0(T_n)$. Also $N(0, 1)$ is not T_w open, by Section 9.3, Problem 15.〛

24. Let A be a linear space, Φ a linear subspace of $A^\#$, and let $R\Phi = \{Rf : f \in \Phi\}$. Show that $\sigma(R\Phi) = \sigma(\Phi)$.

25. Check the truth in linear topological space of (a) Section 4.3, Problem 24; (b) Section 4.3, Problem 25; (c) Section 6.1, Problem 18; (d) Section 6.1, Problem 19; (e) Section 6.1, Problem 21.

26. A *Cauchy net* is a net $(x_\delta : D)$ such that, for each given neighborhood G of 0, there exists $\delta_0 \in D$ such that $\delta \geq \delta_0$, $\delta' \geq \delta_0$ imply $x_\delta - x_{\delta'} \in G$. Show that in a linear semimetric space, the two notions of Cauchy net coincide (Section 9.2, Problem 21).

27. Let Φ be a family of linear topologies on a linear space. Let p be a seminorm which is continuous with $\bigvee \{T : T \in \Phi\}$. Show that there exists a finite selection $T_1, T_2, \ldots, T_n$ of members of Φ such that p is continuous with $T_1 \vee T_2 \vee \cdots \vee T_n$. 〚$(p < 1)$ is a neighborhood of 0; hence it includes the intersection of a finite number of subbase neighborhoods.〛

10.2 Arithmetic

We now seek familiarity with the interplay of linearity and topology, considering such questions as whether or not the closure of a convex set is necessarily convex. We make repeated use of the symmetry arguments presented in Section 2.5, Problem 6. These say, for example, that if S is symmetric, $a \in b + S$ if and only if $b \in a + S$.

Facts

In the following list, A, B, G, K are sets in a linear topological space, t is a scalar, and x a vector.

(i) $\bar{A} + \bar{B} \subset \overline{A + B}$. Equality need not hold, even in R; however, if one of the sets is compact, equality holds.

(ii) If G is open, $A + G$ is open.

(iii) $A + B^i \subset (A + B)^i$. Here B^i denotes the interior of B. Equality need not hold, even in R.

(iv) If G is a neighborhood of 0, $\bar{A} \subset A + G$.

(v) $\bar{A} = \cap \{A + G \colon G \text{ is a neighborhood of } 0\}$.

(vi) If $t \neq 0$, $t\bar{A} = \overline{tA}$. (If the space is T_1, this holds also for $t = 0$.) In particular, $-\bar{A} = \overline{(-A)}$.

(vii) If $t \neq 0$, $tA^i = (tA)^i$.

(viii) Let K be compact. Then (even though $K \neq \bar{K}$ is possible) $\bar{A} + K = \bar{A} + \bar{K} = \overline{A + K}$.

(ix) $x + \bar{A} = \overline{x + A}$.

(x) The sum of a closed set and a compact set is closed.

Proofs

We may assume that all the sets mentioned are nonempty.

(i) Let $x \in \bar{A} + \bar{B}$; that is, $x = a + b$, $a \in \bar{A}$, $b \in \bar{B}$. There exists a directed set D and nets $(a_\delta \colon D)$, $(b_\delta \colon D)$ of points of A, B, respectively, with $a_\delta \to a$, $b_\delta \to b$. [Section 1, Lemma 1]. Then $a_\delta + b_\delta \to a + b$ and $a_\delta + b_\delta \in A + B$, hence $x = a + b \in \overline{A + B}$. An example of inequality is $A = \omega$, $B = \{1/n - n \colon n \in \omega\}$ in R. [$1/n \in A + B$ for each n, but $0 \notin A + B$. Hence $A + B$ is not closed; but A, B are.] The compactness result is given in Fact (viii).

(ii) $A + G = \cup\{a + G \colon a \in A\}$, a union of open sets. [Each $a + G$ is a translation of an open set.]

(iii) $A + B^i \subset A + B$, also $A + B^i$, is open [by Fact (ii)]; thus $A + B^i \subset (A + B)^i$. An example of inequality is $A = $ rationals, $B = $ irrationals $\cup \{0\}$ in R.

(iv) Let $x \in \bar{A}$. Let N be a symmetric neighborhood of 0 with $N \subset G$. Since $x + N$ is a neighborhood of x, it meets A. Hence $x \in A + N \subset A + G$.

(v) By Fact (iv), $\bar{A} \subset \cap(A + G)$. Now if $x \notin \bar{A}$, let G_1 be a neighborhood of 0 such that $x + G_1 \not\pitchfork A$. Let N be a symmetric neighborhood of 0 with $N \subset G_1$. Then $x + N \not\pitchfork A$, hence $x \notin A + N$. Thus $x \notin \cap(A + G)$.

(vi) Let $x \in t\bar{A}$. Then $x/t \in \bar{A}$. There exists $a_\delta \in A$ with $a_\delta \to x/t$, then $ta_\delta \to x$, and $ta_\delta \in tA$. Thus $x \in \overline{tA}$. Conversely, let $x \in \overline{tA}$. Then there exists $b_\delta \in tA$ with $b_\delta \to x$. Say $b_\delta = ta_\delta$, $a_\delta \in A$. Then $a_\delta \to x/t$, and $a_\delta \in A$. Thus $x/t \in \bar{A}$, $x \in t\bar{A}$.

(vii) Using Section 9.1, Problem 7 and Fact (vi), above, we have $(tA)^i = (tA)^{\sim - \sim} = [tA^\sim]^{- \sim} = [tA^{\sim -}]^\sim = tA^{\sim - \sim} = tA^i$.

(viii) From (i), $\bar{A} + K \subset \overline{A + K}$. Now let $x \in \overline{A + K}$. There exists a net in $A + K$, say $a_\delta + k_\delta$ with $a_\delta + k_\delta \to x$, $a_\delta \in A$, $k_\delta \in K$. Since K is compact, k_δ has a subnet $k_{u(\delta')}$ which converges to a point $k \in K$. Then, also, $a_{u(\delta')} + k_{u(\delta')} \to x$, and $a_{u(\delta')} = [a_{u(\delta')} + k_{u(\delta')}] - k_{u(\delta')} \to x - k$. Thus $x - k \in \bar{A}$ and so $x \in \bar{A} + K$.

(ix) and (x) These are special cases of Fact (viii).//

THEOREM 1. *In a linear topological space, the following statements hold:*

(a) *the closure and interior of a convex set are convex;*
(b) *the closure and interior (with 0 adjoined) of a balanced set are balanced;*
(c) *the closure of a linear subspace is a linear subspace;*
(d) *the closure of an affine set is affine.*

The parenthesized phrase in Part (b) means that if S is balanced, $S^i \cup \{0\}$ is balanced. A purely linear analogue of the second part of Part (a) was a similar result for absorbing and convex sets, Section 2.6, Problem 9.

An important special case of Part (c) is that $\overline{\{0\}}$ is a linear subspace.

Interior was not mentioned in Parts (c), (d), since a proper subspace or affine set can have no interior, indeed, must be nowhere absorbing.

To prove the theorem, let S be a set, and u, v scalars. Then

(1) $$u\bar{S} + v\bar{S} \subset \overline{uS + vS},$$

by Facts (i) and (vi), if $u \neq 0$, $v \neq 0$, and trivially otherwise.

Now if S is convex,

(2) $$uS + vS \subset S,$$

for $0 \leq u \leq 1$, $u + v = 1$, and relation (1) implies that $\bar{S}$ obeys the same inclusion, hence is convex. If S is a linear subspace, relation (2) holds for all u, v, and relation (1) implies that $\bar{S}$ obeys the same inclusion. If S is affine, relation (2) holds for all u, v with $u + v = 1$ and again $\bar{S}$ obeys the inclusion. The part of Part (a) which concerns interior is proved in exactly the same way using Facts (iii) and (vi), except that u, v are not allowed to be 0, but if relation (2) holds for $0 < u < 1$, $u + v = 1$, this implies that S is convex, so the proof can be completed.

The proof of Part (b) is entirely similar [Problem 13].//

COROLLARY 1. *A maximal subspace of a linear topological space is either closed or dense.*

Its closure is also a linear subspace, hence can only be the subspace itself or the whole space.//

COROLLARY 2. *Every neighborhood of 0 includes a balanced open neighborhood of 0. In a locally convex space, every neighborhood of 0 includes a balanced convex open neighborhood of 0.*

Let G be a neighborhood of 0, N a balanced neighborhood of 0 with $N \subset G$. Then N^i is a balanced open neighborhood of 0 [Theorem 1, Part (b)].//

THEOREM 2. *A linear topological space is regular.*

Let S be a closed set, and $a \notin S$. Then there exists a neighborhood G of 0 with $a \notin S + G$ [Fact (v)]. Let N be a symmetric open neighborhood of 0 with $N + N \subset G$ [Corollary 2 and Section 1, Fact (xi)]. Let $G_1 = S + N$, $G_2 = a + N$. Then G_1 is open [Fact (ii)] and $G_1 \cap G_2$ [$a \notin S + G \supset S + N + N$; hence $a + N$ does not meet $S + N$].//

If a linear topological space satisfies the very weak T_0 condition, it must perforce be a T_3 space.

THEOREM 3. *The following conditions on a linear topological space are equivalent:*

(i)   *it is a* T_0 *space;*
(ii) *it is a* T_3 *space;*
(iii) $\{0\}$ *is a closed set;*
(iv) *given* a $\neq 0$, *there exists a neighborhood of* 0 *not containing* a.

See also Problem 38.

Condition (i) implies Condition (ii).   Let a, b be distinct vectors.   Let G be an open set which is a neighborhood of one but does not contain the other.   Say for definiteness, G is a neighborhood of a not containing b.   Then $b - G + a$ is a neighborhood of b not containing a.   Thus the space is T_1, hence T_3 〚Theorem 2〛.

Condition (ii) implies Condition (iii).   A T_3 space is T_1 and so all finite sets are closed.   Conditions (iii) and (iv) are equivalent by Fact (v) and the fact that $a \notin \overline{\{0\}}$.

Condition (iii) implies Condition (i).   All one-point sets are closed, since translation is a homeomorphism onto.   Hence the space is T_1.//

DEFINITION 1.   *A linear* T_0 *(hence* T_3*) space is called a separated space.*

In particular, a separated space is a Hausdorff space.

The reader will observe that often, in a theorem in which a space is assumed separated, this requirement can be dropped if certain sets occurring in the statement of the theorem are assumed closed.   Problem 9 is an example of this; in a separated space, the set A would not have to be assumed closed.

Problems 10.2

In this list, A, B, S are sets in a linear topological space.

★1. A symmetric, convex set which has an interior point must be a neighborhood of 0.   〚$S = \frac{1}{2}S + \frac{1}{2}S = \frac{1}{2}S - \frac{1}{2}S$.〛 "Symmetric, convex" cannot be replaced by "balanced."   〚Section 2.5, Example 2.〛

2. $\overline{\bar{A} + \bar{B}} = \overline{A + B}$.   (Hence, if $\bar{A} + \bar{B}$ is closed, it is equal to $\overline{A + B}$.)

★3. Every neighborhood of 0 includes a closed neighborhood of 0.   〚$\bar{N} \subset N + N \subset G$.〛

★4. Every neighborhood of 0 includes a balanced closed neighborhood of 0.   〚Problem 3 and Section 1, Problem 5.〛

★5. In a locally convex space, every neighborhood of 0 includes a balanced convex closed neighborhood of 0.

6. If $na \rightarrow 0$ as $n \rightarrow \infty$, then $a \in \overline{\{0\}}$ and conversely.   (Compare Section 6.1, Problem 11.)

7. Fact (v) expresses $\bar{A}$ as the intersection of open sets including A.   However it is not necessarily true that $\bar{A} = \cap\{G: G \text{ open}, G \supset A\}$.   (Give an example in R.)

8. Compare $\overline{\bar{Z}\bar{A}}$ with $\overline{ZA}$, Z being a set of scalars.   〚Use of Section 9.4, Problem 4 is suggested.〛 Include a discussion of the case in which neither $\bar{Z}$ nor $\bar{A}$ contains 0.   〚Equality!〛

9. If A is closed, $A + \overline{\{0\}} = A$.

10. Prove or disprove, $A + \overline{\{0\}} \neq \bar{A}$ for some A.

11. A proper linear subspace has no interior point (in fact, it is nowhere absorbing).   Hence a closed proper subspace is nowhere dense.   A proper subspace may be somewhere dense 〚$E^\infty \subset c_0$〛, indeed, of second category.   〚Section 7.5, Problem 18.〛

12. Give R^2 the weak topology by P_1. Find $\overline{\{0\}}$.

★13. Prove Part (b) of Theorem 1.

14. The interior of a balanced set need not be balanced. (An example may be found in R^2.)

★15. The *convex balanced closure* of a set is the intersection of all convex balanced closed sets including it. Prove that the convex balanced closure of a set is convex, balanced, and closed.

★16. Let f be a continuous linear functional such that $|f(a)| \leq 1$ for all a in a set S. Show that $|f(a)| \leq 1$ for all a in the convex balanced closure of S. ⟦$(|f| \leq 1)$ is a convex balanced closed set including S, hence includes its convex balanced closure.⟧

17. The linear closure of a set is the closure of its span. ⟦Use Theorem 1, Part (c).⟧

18. In Problem 17, replace "linear" by "convex," "span" by "convex hull."

★19. In Problem 17, replace "linear" by "balanced," "span" by "balanced hull." (Supply definitions for "balanced closure," *et cetera.*)

20. Give an example to show that in Problem 17, "closure of its span" cannot be replaced by "span of its closure." Do the same for Problems 18 and 19.

21. If $A + A \subset 2\bar{A}$, then $\bar{A}$ is convex. ⟦Let $a, b \in \bar{A}$. For real t, let $f(t) = ta + (1 - t)b$. Then $f^{-1}[\bar{A}]$ is dense in $[0, 1]$.⟧

22. Deduce from Problem 21 that the closure of a convex set is convex.

23. Let A be convex and have nonempty interior. Then $\bar{A} = \overline{A^i}$, and $A^i = (\bar{A})^i$.

24. Suppose that $a_n \in S$, $t_n \geq 0$ for $n = 1, 2, \ldots$, that $\Sigma t_n = 1$, and $\Sigma t_n a_n$ is convergent. Show that $\Sigma t_n a_n$ belongs to the convex closure of S. (Assume that the space is separated if you wish.)

25. Let X be a linear space, Y a linear topological space, $f: X \to Y$ a linear map. Assume that the range of f is of second category in Y. Then, for any absorbing set G in X, $f[G]$ is somewhere dense in Y.

26. Let $x \neq 0$ be a point in a separated space. Show that there exists a neighborhood G of 0 such that $x + G \cap G$.

27. Each one-dimensional subspace of a separated space is linearly homeomorphic with E. ⟦Section 6.3, Lemma 1.⟧

28. Let X, Y be, respectively, a linear space and a separated space. Let L be the set of linear maps from X to Y. Show that L is a closed linear subspace of Y^X. ⟦If $f_\delta \in L$, $f_\delta \to f$, then $f(a + b) = \lim\{f_\delta(a) + f_\delta(b)\} = f(a) + f(b)$.⟧

29. Let X, Y be, respectively, a topological space and a separated space. Let C be the set of continuous maps from X to Y. Show that C is a linear subspace of Y^X, but is not necessarily closed. ⟦With $X = Y = R$, C is dense.⟧

30. In a separated space, the balanced closure of a compact set must be compact.

31. (Quotients.) Let S be a closed linear subspace of a linear topological space A. Give A/S the strongest topology such that the natural homeomorphism is continuous. Show that this makes A/S a separated space, and that, if A is a seminormed space, the topology is the same as that given in Section 6.5.

32. In Problem 31, show that A has the weak topology by ϕ, the natural homeomorphism.

33. In the notation of Problem 32, A/S has the unique topology such that ϕ is both continuous and open.

34. In the notation of Problem 31, if A is locally convex, so is A/S.

35. The gauge of a closed balloon is lower semicontinuous.

36. Let X be a linear space, Y a linear topological space, and $f: X \to Y$ a linear map. Can X have two different topologies such that f is continuous, open, and $f^{-1}[\overline{\{0\}}] = \overline{\{0\}}$?

37. A *topological group* is a group with a topology such that the group operations are continuous. Prove Theorem 3 for topological groups.

▲38. A separated space is a $T_{3\frac{1}{2}}$ space.

39. $A/\overline{\{0\}}$ is *complete* (every Cauchy net converges) if A is.

★40. The convex balanced hull of a finite union of compact convex balanced sets is compact. ⟦Section 9.5, Theorem 1.⟧

10.3   Bounded sets

We have seen that the concept of metric boundedness (inclusion in a cell) is not very important, since any semimetric can be replaced by an equivalent one in which the whole space is included in a cell of unit radius $[\![d/(1+d)$ or $d \wedge 1]\!]$.

DEFINITION 1. *A set in a linear topological space is called bounded if it is absorbed by every neighborhood of* 0. (*This means that* S *is bounded if and only if for every neighborhood* G *of* 0, *there exists* $\delta > 0$ *such that* $\epsilon S \subset G$ *for* $0 \leq \epsilon < \delta$.)

Our conventions ensure that the empty set is bounded.

★ *Example 1: A set in a seminormed space is bounded if and only if it is included in a cell.* $[\![$Every cell is bounded; every subset of a bounded set is bounded; every nonzero multiple of a cell is a cell.$]\!]$ Thus, in a seminormed space, boundedness and metric boundedness are the same.

Facts

In this list, S is a set in a linear topological space.

(i) S is bounded if and only if it is absorbed by every balanced neighborhood G of 0.

(ii) S is bounded if and only if, given any neighborhood G of 0 any one of the following is true:

> (a)   There exists $\epsilon > 0$ such that $\epsilon S \subset G$.
> (b)   There exists a scalar t such that $tG \supset S$.
> (c)   There exists an integer n such that $nG \supset S$.

(iii) Each subset of a bounded set is bounded.

(iv) S is bounded if and only if, given any sequence $\{\epsilon_n\}$ of scalars with $\epsilon_n \to 0$ and $\{a_n\}$, $a_n \in S$, we have $\epsilon_n a_n \to 0$.

(v) A linear subspace is bounded if and only if it is included in $\overline{\{0\}}$.   In particular, no linear subspace of a linear separated space may be bounded (except $\{0\}$).

(vi) A bounded set in a linear semimetric space is metrically bounded, but the converse does not hold.

(vii) A finite union of bounded sets is bounded.

(viii) Any finite set is bounded.

(ix) A finite sum of bounded sets is bounded.

(x) Any scalar multiple or translate of a bounded set is bounded.

(xi) If a set is bounded in some stronger linear topology, it is bounded.

(xii) A compact set is bounded; in particular, a convergent sequence is bounded.

(xiii) The balanced closure of a bounded set is bounded.   The convex hull of a bounded set need not be bounded.

(xiv) In a locally convex space, the convex hull of a bounded set is bounded.   (Hence the convex balanced closure is bounded.)

Proofs

(i) A bounded set is absorbed by every neighborhood of 0, hence by every balanced neighborhood of 0. Conversely, suppose that S is absorbed by every balanced neighborhood of 0. Let G be a neighborhood of 0; choose a balanced neighborhood N of 0 with $N \subset G$. Since S is absorbed by N, it is also absorbed by G.

(ii) Condition (a) clearly holds if S is bounded. Conversely, let S satisfy Condition (a) and let G be a balanced neighborhood of 0. There exists $\delta > 0$ such that $\delta S \subset G$. For any ϵ, $0 < \epsilon < \delta$, $\epsilon S = (\epsilon/\delta)\delta S \subset (\epsilon/\delta)G \subset G$. Hence S is bounded [Fact (i)].

Condition (a) clearly implies Condition (b). Conversely, if Condition (b) holds, given G, find a balanced neighborhood N of 0 with $N \subset G$. There exists $t \neq 0$, with $tN \supset S$. Then $|t|N \supset S$, hence $(1/|t|)S \subset N \subset G$ and Condition (a) holds.

Condition (c) clearly implies Condition (b). Conversely, if Condition (b) holds, given, G, find N, t as above. Let $n > |t|$ be an integer. Clearly $nN \supset |t|N$ [N is balanced] hence $nG \supset S$.

(iii) If a neighborhood of 0 absorbs a set, it absorbs every subset thereof.

(iv) Let S be bounded, $\{\epsilon_n\}$, $\{a_n\}$ as mentioned, and G a neighborhood of 0. Choose δ as in Definition 1. There exists k such that $|\epsilon_n| < \delta$ for $n > k$. Thus, for $n > k$, $\epsilon_n a_n \in \epsilon_n S \subset G$. Conversely, suppose that S is not bounded. By Fact (ii), Condition (c), there exists a neighborhood G of 0 such that $nG \not\supset S$ for $n = 1, 2, \ldots$. For each $n = 1, 2, \ldots$, let $a_n \in S \setminus nG$, then $(1/n)a_n \notin G$, so $(1/n)a_n \not\to 0$.

(v) Every neighborhood of 0 includes $\overline{\{0\}}$ [Section 2, Fact (iv)], hence $\overline{\{0\}}$ is bounded. By Fact (iii), so is any subset. Conversely, suppose that $a \in S \setminus \overline{\{0\}}$, S being a linear subspace. Then $na \in S$ for $n = 1, 2, \ldots$. But $(1/n)na \not\to 0$, since $(1/n)na = a \notin \overline{\{0\}}$. By Fact (iv), S is not bounded.

(vi) If S is bounded, we have $S \subset nN(0, 1)$ for some integer $n > 0$. But $nN(0, 1) \subset N(0, n)$ [Section 6.1, Problem 3]. That the converse is false, even in a one-dimensional linear metric space, is shown by defining $!x! = |x|/(1 + |x|)$ for $x \in R$. Then $R \subset N(0, 1)$, and R is not bounded, by Fact (v).

(vii) Let $S = S_1 \cup S_2 \cdots \cup S_n$, each S_k being bounded, and let G be a balanced neighborhood of 0. For $k = 1, 2, \ldots, n$, $\epsilon_k S_k \subset G$ for some $\epsilon_k > 0$. With $\epsilon = \min(\epsilon_1, \epsilon_2, \ldots, \epsilon_n)$, $\epsilon S \subset G$.

(viii) That a set consisting of a single point is bounded is simply the fact that neighborhoods are absorbing. The rest follows from Fact (vii).

(ix) Let S, T be bounded, G a neighborhood of 0, N a balanced neighborhood of 0 with $N + N \subset G$. Let $\epsilon_1 S \subset N$, $\epsilon_2 T \subset N$, $\epsilon = \min(\epsilon_1, \epsilon_2)$. Then $\epsilon(S + T) \subset N + N \subset G$. The extension to any finite number follows by induction.

(x) The first part follows from the fact that a nonzero scalar multiple of a neighborhood of 0 is a neighborhood of 0. The second part follows from Facts (viii) and (ix).

(xi) If A is absorbed by every T' neighborhood of 0 and T' is stronger than T, then, *a fortiori*, A is absorbed by every T neighborhood of 0.

(xii) Let K be compact and G a neighborhood of 0. Let N be a balanced open neighborhood of 0 with $N + N \subset G$ [Section 2, Corollary 2]. Then $\{a + N : a \in K\}$, an open cover of K, can be reduced to a finite subcover; that is, there exist $a_1, a_2, \ldots, a_n \in K$ with $K \subset \cup\{a_k + N : k = 1, 2, \ldots, n\} = S + N$, where $S = \{a_1, a_2, \ldots, a_n\}$. By Facts (ii) and (viii), $S \subset nN$ for some integer $n > 0$. Then $K \subset S + N \subset nN + N \subset$

$nN + nN = n(N + N) \subset nG$. The particular case of a convergent sequence follows from Section 9.5, Problem 21, and from Fact (iii).

(xiii) We first consider the closure. Let S be bounded and G a neighborhood of 0. Let N be a balanced neighborhood of 0 with $N + N \subset G$, and let $S \subset nN$, $n > 0$ an integer. Then, by Section 2, Fact (iv), $\bar{S} \subset S + N \subset nN + N \subset nN + nN = n(N + N) \subset nG$. Thus $\bar{S}$ is bounded.

Next, let us prove that the balanced hull of S is bounded. Let G be a balanced neighborhood of 0. If $S \subset nG$, the balanced hull of S is also included in nG, since nG is balanced. Finally the balanced closure is the closure of the balanced hull [Section 2, Problem 19].

To complete the proof of Fact (xiii), we present an example of a bounded set whose convex hull is not bounded [Example 2].

(xiv) Let S be bounded, and G a neighborhood of 0. Let N be a convex neighborhood of 0 with $N \subset G$. Then $tN \supset S$ for some t, hence tN includes the convex hull of S, since tN is convex. Hence tG, which includes tN, includes the convex hull of S.//

★ *Example 2.* The space l^p, $0 < p < 1$, is a complete linear metric space. We now show that it has *a bounded subset whose convex hull is not bounded.*

It follows from Fact (xiv) that *this space is not locally convex.*

(1)   *A set in l^p, $0 < p < 1$, is bounded if and only if it is metrically bounded.*

Half of this follows from Fact (vi). Conversely, suppose that S is metrically bounded, say, $S \subset N(0, r)$, and let G be a neighborhood of 0. Then $G \supset N(0, \epsilon)$ for some $\epsilon > 0$. Thus $S \subset N(0, r) = r^{1/p}N(0, 1) = (r/\epsilon)^{1/p}N(0, \epsilon) \subset (r/\epsilon)^{1/p}G$. Thus S is bounded.

(2)   *In l^p, $0 < p < 1$, the convex hull* H *of* D(0, 1) *is not bounded.*

We have $\delta^n \in D(0, 1)$ for $n = 1, 2, \ldots$. Let $a_n = (1/n)\Sigma_{k=1}^n \delta^k = (1/n, 1/n, \ldots, 1/n, 0, 0, 0, \ldots)$. Then $a_n \in H$ for $n = 1, 2, \ldots$, and $!a_n! = (1/n)^p !\Sigma_{k=1}^n \delta^k! = n^{1-p} \to \infty$ as $n \to \infty$. Thus H is metrically unbounded and so, by (1), it is unbounded. However, again by (1), $D(0, 1)$ is bounded.//

(Notice that H includes no proper subspaces. This follows from Section 4.2, Problem 23.)

THEOREM 1.   *A continuous linear function preserves bounded sets. A continuous paranorm is bounded on every bounded set.*

Let $f: A \to B$, and let S be a bounded set in A. Let G be a neighborhood of 0 in B. Then, for some $\epsilon > 0$, $\epsilon S \subset f^{-1}[G]$ [since S is bounded, and $f^{-1}[G]$ is a neighborhood of 0]. It follows from this that $\epsilon f[S] \subset G$, and so $f[S]$ is bounded.

Next, let p be a continuous paranorm and S a bounded set. Let p denote also the semi-metric topology induced by p. Then p is weaker than T, the original topology [$a_\delta \to 0(T)$ implies $p(a_\delta) \to 0$]. By Fact (xi), S is p bounded. The result follows by Fact (vi).//

Each half of the theorem can be given a proof similar to that given for the other half.

Although [Example 5] the converse of Theorem 1 is false, in that continuity does not follow from boundedness on bounded sets in general, it will be seen [Section 5, Theorem 4] that, for a wide class of spaces, the converse implication holds.

★ *Example 3.* Let π be an infinite product of linear topological spaces, none of which consists entirely of $\overline{\{0\}}$. In π, *no absorbing set* G *can be bounded*, for all the projections of a bounded set are bounded ⟦Theorem 1⟧, while some of the projections of G are onto ⟦Section 9.3, Theorem 10⟧ and so cannot be bounded ⟦Fact (v)⟧. In particular, s has no bounded neighborhoods, since it has no bounded absorbing set ⟦$s = E^\omega$⟧.

★ *Example 4: Two topologies with the same bounded sets.* For the sake of giving an appropriate example, we present a result which is stated in a more general form in Section 12.3, Corollary 1. The result is that if A is a seminormed space, the seminorm topology and $\sigma(A, A')$ have the same bounded sets. ⟦Since $\sigma(A, A')$ is weaker, half of this follows from Fact (xi). Conversely, let S be $\sigma(A, A')$ bounded. Every $f \in A'$ is bounded on S, by Theorem 1. Hence S is bounded in the seminorm topology, by the uniform-boundedness principle, Section 7.6, Theorem 2.⟧ Now, if A is an infinite-dimensional normed space, the two topologies are different ⟦Section 9.3, Problem 14 or 16 and Section 10.1, Problem 9⟧.

★ *Example 5.* The identity map from (A, σ) to A in Example 4 preserves bounded sets, but is not continuous. Also, the norm which gives A its norm topology is bounded on $\sigma(A, A')$-bounded sets but is not $\sigma(A, A')$ continuous, since the norm topology is not weaker than $\sigma(A, A')$. This yields counterexamples to the converses of both halves of Theorem 1.

Problems on linear topological space 10.3

1. A set is bounded if and only if every one of its countable subsets is bounded.

2. Deduce Fact (viii) from Fact (iv).

★3. If a set is included in a linear subspace, it is bounded if and only if it is bounded in the relative topology of the subspace. ⟦Fact iv.⟧

4. Prove that a Cauchy sequence is bounded. Is this true for Cauchy net? ⟦No, not even in *R*.⟧

5. Deduce Fact (ix) by applying Theorem 1 to the addition function, that is, $f: A \times A \to A$ given by $f(a, b) = a + b$.

6. Deduce Fact (xi) from Theorem 1, applied to the identity map.

7. Let the space A be of second category in itself, and assume that there exists a sequence $\{B_n\}$ of bounded sets such that $A = \cup B_n$. Then A has a bounded neighborhood of 0. (Hence, by Section 4, Corollary 1, A is semimetrizable.)

8. A collection Φ of bounded sets is called a *base* for the bounded sets if every bounded set is included in a member of Φ. If A is of second category in itself and has a countable base for its bounded sets, then A has a bounded neighborhood of 0. ⟦Problem 7.⟧

9. Prove Theorem 1 by means of Fact (iv).

10. An infinite product of separated spaces, none of which is of zero dimension, has no bounded absorbing set.

11. A set in a product is bounded if and only if each projection is bounded.

12. A set in $L^p, p > 0$, is bounded if and only if it is metrically bounded. ⟦Same as the proof of (1).⟧

13. The convex hull of a finite set is bounded.

14. In any infinite-dimensional linear metric space there exists an infinite set which is linearly independent and bounded.

15. If there exists an infinite set which is linearly independent and bounded, there exists a linear discontinuous functional. (Hence, in the topology $\sigma(A, A^\#)$, every infinite bounded subset of A is linearly dependent.) ⟦Let $f(a_n) = n$.⟧ Compare Section 9.3, Problem 2.

16. Let A be infinite dimensional. If there exists a bounded absorbing set, there exists a discontinuous linear functional. ⟦Use Section 2.5, Problem 25.⟧ Hence, in $\sigma(A, A^\#)$ every absorbing set is unbounded.

17. A set A is called *totally bounded* if, for each neighborhood G of 0 there exists a finite subset S of A with $A \subset S + G$. Show that a totally bounded set is bounded. (Compare Section 9.5, Problem 27, and the unifying remarks in Section 7.)

18. Show that a compact set is totally bounded. ⟦Let S be the set, G a neighborhood of 0. Reduce the open cover $\{a + G : a \in S\}$ to a finite one.⟧

19. Give an example of a closed bounded set S and a continuous linear functional f such that $f[S]$ is not closed.

20. Call a set S *pseudo-bounded* if to each neighborhood G of 0, there corresponds n such that $S \subset G + G + \cdots + G$ (n terms). Show that a bounded set is pseudo-bounded.

21. Give an example of a pseudo-bounded set which is not bounded. ⟦Section 7.5, Example 9.⟧

22. In a locally convex space, every pseudo-bounded set is bounded.

23. If there exists a bounded neighborhood of 0, every pseudo-bounded set is bounded. (This is true of L^p, $0 < p < 1$.)

24. Prove Theorem 1 for pseudo-bounded sets. ⟦In Problem 20, take $G = (|f| < 1.)$⟧

25. Every continuous linear functional vanishes on every pseudo-bounded linear subspace. ⟦Problem 24.⟧

26. Give an example of a bounded set whose convex hull includes a proper subspace. ⟦The unit disk in L^p, $0 < p < 1$. Use Problem 12. The gauge of the convex hull is a continuous seminorm, hence it is identically zero by the Hahn-Banach theorem and the fact that L^p has no continuous linear functional except 0. (Section 7.5, Example 11.)⟧

27. Suppose that $\{a_n\}$ is a null sequence in a locally convex space. Show that $(1/n)\sum_{k=1}^{n} a_k \to 0$ as $n \to \infty$.

28. Prove by means of Problem 27 that l^p, $0 < p < 1$, is not locally convex.

10.4   Metrization

A semimetric space must be first countable, but not conversely for topological spaces in general. However, for linear topological spaces, first countability is no longer a more general condition. This is the content of Theorem 2. The same result holds in more general settings. See, for example, Problem 12 and Section 7. Before turning to metrizability, in general, we give a criterion for the existence of a seminorm yielding a given topology. The converse of Theorem 1 is trivial.

THEOREM 1.   *If a linear topological space has a bounded, convex neighborhood of 0, the topology is given by a seminorm.*

There exists a bounded neighborhood N of 0 which is a balloon. ⟦Let G be a bounded, convex neighborhood of 0, N_0 a balanced neighborhood of 0 with $N_0 \subset G$, and N the convex hull of N_0. Then $N \subset G$ since G is convex, and N is bounded since G is.⟧

We now show that the topology is given by a seminorm, namely the gauge of N, (Section 4.2, Theorem 1.) The seminorm topology T_n is stronger than the original topology T. ⟦Let M be a T neighborhood of 0. Then $\epsilon N \subset M$ for some $\epsilon > 0$, since N is bounded. Thus M is a T_n neighborhood of 0.⟧ T is stronger than T_n. ⟦Let M be a T_n neighborhood of 0. It includes a cell $N(0, \epsilon)$. But $N = N(0, 1)$, thus $M \supset N(0, \epsilon) = \epsilon N$; that is, M includes (and hence is) a T neighborhood of 0.⟧//

In preparation for the metrization theorem, we show how to obtain a function obeying the triangular inequality from an arbitrary nonnegative real function. Given a point a in a linear space A, consider a finite set of points $a_0, a_1, a_2, \ldots, a_n$, with $a_0 = 0$, $a_n = a$.

Such a set will be called a *chain* ending at *a*. Given a real nonnegative function D, defined on A, let p be defined by the equation,

$$(1) \qquad p(a) = \inf \left\{ \sum_{k=1}^{n} D(a_k - a_{k-1}) \right\},$$

the inf being taken over all chains ending at *a*. Since D is nonnegative, $p(a) \geq 0$. In particular, $p(a)$ is finite.

LEMMA 1. *With these definitions*, p(a + b) ≤ p(a) + p(b).

Let $\epsilon > 0$ be given. Choose chains $a_0, a_1, \ldots, a_n$; $b_0, b_1, \ldots, b_m$ ending at a, b respectively, so that $\Sigma D(a_k - a_{k-1}) < p(a) + \epsilon/2$, $\Sigma D(b_k - b_{k-1}) < p(b) + \epsilon/2$. Let $c_0 = 0$, $c_1 = a_1$, $c_2 = a_2, \ldots, c_n = a_n = a$, $c_{n+1} = a + b_1$, $c_{n+2} = a + b_2, \ldots, c_{n+m} = a + b$. Then $p(a + b) \leq \Sigma_{k=1}^{m+n} D(c_k - c_{k-1}) = \Sigma_{k=1}^{n} D(a_k - a_{k-1}) + \Sigma_{k=1}^{m} D(b_k - b_{k-1}) < p(a) + p(b) + \epsilon.//$

THEOREM 2. *Let* A *be a first countable linear topological space. Then* A *is semimetrizable, the semimetric being given by a paranorm. If* A *is separated, the semimetric is a metric.*

For locally convex spaces on easy proof is given in Section 12.1, Theorem 4.

Since A is first countable we can construct, by induction, a local base at 0 which is a sequence $\{G_n\}$ of balanced neighborhoods of 0 such that, for each $n = 2, 3, 4, \ldots$,

$$(2) \qquad G_n + G_n + G_n \subset G_{n-1}.$$

If we set $G_0 = A$, we make relation (2) true for $n = 1$ also. To each $a \in A$, $a \notin \overline{\{0\}}$, corresponds a unique non-negative integer $k(a)$ such that $a \in G_{k(a)} \setminus G_{k(a)+1}$. For $a \in \overline{\{0\}}$ we shall take $k(a) = +\infty$. Let $D(a) = 2^{-k(a)}$, taking $D(a) = 0$ if $a \in \overline{\{0\}}$. We shall see that D has many, though not all, of the properties of a paranorm. Clearly,

$$(3) \qquad D(-a) = D(a) \qquad \text{and } D(a) > 0 \quad \text{if} \quad a \notin \overline{\{0\}}.$$

Moreover,

$$(4) \qquad a \in G_m \qquad \text{if and only if} \qquad m \leq k(a).$$

If $k(a)$ is finite, the statement (4) is literally true. If $k(a) = +\infty$, $a \in G_m$ for all m, so that statement (4) remains true with the convention $m < +\infty$ for all m.

We next prove, for a sequence $\{a_n\}$ of vectors

$$(5) \qquad a_n \to 0 \qquad \text{if and only if} \qquad D(a_n) \to 0.$$

[Let $a_n \to 0$. For any integer $m > 0$, $a_n \in G_m$ eventually. Thus $k(a_n) \geq m$ eventually, so $k(a_n) \to +\infty$ and $D(a_n) \to 0$. Conversely, if $D(a_n) \to 0$, for any m, $k(a_n) \geq m$ eventually, so $a_n \in G_m$ eventually. Thus $a_n \to 0$.]

Next we prove

$$(6) \qquad D(a + b + c) \leq 2 \max \{D(a), D(b), D(c)\}.$$

[If a, b, c all belong to $\overline{\{0\}}$, this is trivial. We shall assume that this is not the case. Let $k = \min \{k(a), k(b), k(c)\}$ so that $k < +\infty$ and a, b, c all belong to G_k by statement (4).

Next, $a + b + c \in G_k + G_k + G_k \subset G_{k-1}$ by relation (2), and so $k(a + b + c) \geq k - 1$ by statement (4). Thus, $D(a + b + c) \leq 2^{-(k-1)} = 2 \cdot 2^{-k} = 2 \max \{D(a), D(b), D(c)\}.]$

(7)
$$D(\sum_{i=1}^{n} a_i) \leq 2 \sum_{i=1}^{n} D(a_i), \quad n = 1, 2, \ldots.$$

[For $n = 1, 2,$ and 3, relation (7) is obvious from relation (6). To construct an inductive proof of relation (7), let $n > 3$. Let m be the largest integer such that

(8)
$$\sum_{i=1}^{m} D(a_i) \leq \tfrac{1}{2} \sum_{i=1}^{n} D(a_i).$$

In case $D(a_1) > \tfrac{1}{2}\Sigma D(a_i)$, take m and the left hand side to be 0. Then $0 \leq m < n$, also

$$\sum_{i=1}^{m+1} D(a_i) > \tfrac{1}{2} \sum_{i=1}^{n} D(a_i)$$

and so

(9)
$$\sum_{i=m+2}^{n} D(a_i) < \tfrac{1}{2} \sum_{i=1}^{n} D(a_i).$$

In case $m = n - 1$, the left hand side is taken to be 0. Since the sums in the left-hand sides of relations (8) and (9) contain fewer than n terms (or are 0), we have, by the induction hypothesis,

$$D(\sum_{i=1}^{m} a_i) \quad \leq 2 \sum_{i=1}^{m} D(a_i) \quad \leq \sum_{i=1}^{n} D(a_i),$$

$$D(\sum_{i=m+2}^{n} a_i) \leq 2 \sum_{i=m+1}^{n} D(a_i) \leq \sum_{i=1}^{n} D(a_i),$$

$$D(a_{m+1}) \qquad\qquad\qquad \leq \sum_{i=1}^{n} D(a_i).$$

Applying statement (6) to these three inequalities yields relation (7).]

We are now ready to define our paranorm. It is defined by the formula (1). The triangular inequality has already been checked [Lemma 1].

The other properties of a paranorm are checked as follows:

   (i) $p(0) = 0$ [take $n = 1$ in equation (1)];
   (ii) $p(a) \geq 0$ [since $D(a) \geq 0$ for all a];
   (iii) $p(-a) = p(a)$ [if $a_0 = 0$, $a_n = a$, choose $a'_0 = 0$, $a'_n = a$, $a'_1 = -a_1$, $a'_2 = -a_2$, $\ldots$, then $\Sigma D(a'_i - a'_{i-1}) = \Sigma D(a_i - a_{i-1})$].

Before checking the last property of paranorm (joint continuity of multiplication), we observe that if we set $d(a, b) = p(a - b)$, a semimetric d is defined for A. We turn to the task of showing that the semimetric topology is the same as the original topology. From this, continuity of multiplication follows, since multiplication is continuous using the original topology of A.

For any chain ending at a, we have, by relation (7), $\Sigma D(a_i - a_{i-1}) \geq \tfrac{1}{2}D[\Sigma(a_i - a_{i-1})] = \tfrac{1}{2}D(a)$. Taking inf yields $p(a) \geq \tfrac{1}{2}D(a)$. We also have $p(a) \leq D(a)$ by taking $n = 1$ in equation (1). Thus it follows from statement (5) that $a_n \to 0$ if and only if $p(a_n) \to 0$. Thus $a_n \to a$ if and only if $d(a_n, a) \to 0$. Since the original topology and the semimetric topology are first countable, this implies that they are equal [Section 9.1, Problem 18].//

It follows from Theorem 2 that if a linear topology is given by a semimetric, then it is given by an invariant semimetric, that is, by a paranorm. Conceivably, the space may be complete with one semimetric, but not another 〚Problem 5〛. It turns out that if the topology is given by some complete semimetric, then any invariant semimetric which gives the topology must be complete (see Section 6.1, Problem 43.)

COROLLARY 1. *A linear topological space is semimetrizable if it has a bounded neighborhood of* 0. *However a linear semimetric space need not have a bounded neighborhood, indeed a locally convex space has a bounded neighborhood if and only if the topology is given by a seminorm.*

Let G be a bounded neighborhood of 0, and for $n = 1, 2, \ldots$, let $G_n = (1/n)G$. For any neighborhood N of 0, $G_n \subset N$ for sufficiently large n since G is bounded. Hence $\{G_n\}$ is basic and Theorem 2 gives the result. The space s has no bounded neighborhood 〚Section 3, Example 3, or because, if it did, it would be a normed space by the following argument.〛

A seminormed space has a bounded neighborhood, namely any cell. Conversely, if a locally convex space has a bounded open set G, it has a convex open set $N \subset G$ 〚Section 2, Corollary 2〛, and N, being a subset of G, is bounded. The result follows from Theorem 1.//

Example 1. l^p, $0 < p < 1$, has a bounded neighborhood. This follows from Section 3, Example 2. See also Section 3, Problem 12.

Example 2. Let π be an uncountable product of linear topological spaces, none of which consists entirely of $\overline{\{0\}}$. Then π is not semimetrizable. This follows from Section 9.3, Theorem 12.

Problems on linear topological space 10.4

1. An infinite product of separated spaces cannot be a normed space. 〚Section 3, Example 3.〛 (Assume that no space is zero-dimensional.)

2. If two linear topologies (on the same linear space) have in common a bounded neighborhood of 0, they are equal.

3. If the space has a bounded nonempty open set, then it has a bounded neighborhood of 0, and conversely.

4. Suppose that the topology of A is not given by a seminorm. Let p be a continuous seminorm on A. Show that $(p < 1)$ is not bounded.

5. Give an example of a Banach space which can be given an equivalent incomplete metric. 〚Give R a metric which makes it isometric with $(0, 1)$.〛

6. A nonnormable, or nonmetrizable topology may be normable on a subspace, for example, one-dimensional. Show that the s topology is not normable on c_0. 〚Section 9.3, Problem 16.〛

7. F is not metrizable.

▲8. The F topology on C is not metrizable.

9. Let Q be the set of neighborhoods of 0 ordered by inclusion. If Q has a cofinal chain K, the space is semimetrizable. 〚Let G be a neighborhood of 0. Choose $G_n \in K$ with $nG_n \subset G$. If $\{G_n\}$ is not a local base, there exists $N \in K$, $G_n \not\subset N$. Then $G_n \supset N$ for all n and so G is the whole space.〛

10. If Q, Problem 9, has a chain K such that $\bigcap\{G : G \in K\} = \{0\}$, the space need not be metrizable, even if K is countable. 〚c_0 with $\delta(c_0, c_0')$. $G_n = \{a : |a_k| < 1/n$ for $k = 1, 2, \ldots, n\}$.〛

11. $\{0\}$ may be a G_δ in a nonmetrizable separated space. 〖Problem 10.〗
12. State and prove a theorem like Theorem 2 for topological groups.

10.5   Continuity and equicontinuity

In the first part of this section we deal with linear maps between linear topological spaces and give necessary and sufficient conditions for continuity of f in terms of $f^\perp$ and the behavior of f on open and on bounded sets.

★ *Example 1: Two locally convex separated topologies with the same continuous linear functionals.*   If (A, T) is a linear topological space, T and $\sigma(A, A')$ have the same continuous linear functionals.   〖Any linear functional which is $\sigma(A, A')$ continuous is T continuous since T is stronger than $\sigma(A, A')$.   The converse is trivial, from the definition of $\sigma(A, A')$.〗   To give the required example we may take A to be an infinite-dimensional normed space.   The norm topology and $\sigma(A, A')$ are different as pointed out in Section 3, Example 4.

THEOREM 1.   *If a linear map* f *is continuous at some point, it is continuous everywhere.*

Say f is continuous at $a \in A$.   Let $x \in A$ and let x_δ be a net in A with $x_\delta \to x$.   Then $a + x_\delta - x \to a$ and so $f(x_\delta) - f(x) = f(a + x_\delta - x) - f(a) \to 0$.   Thus f is continuous at x.//

THEOREM 2.   *If a linear map* f: A → B *is bounded on some neighborhood* G *of* 0 (*that is,* f[G] *is bounded*), *then* f *is continuous.*   *The converse is false in general, but is true if* B *has a bounded neighborhood of* 0.

Let N be a neighborhood of 0 in B.   Then, for some $t > 0$, $tN \supset f[G]$; that is, $f^{-1}[N] \supset (1/t)G$.   Thus $f^{-1}[N]$ is a neighborhood of 0, and so f is continuous at 0, hence everywhere. To see that the converse is false, consider $i: s \to s$.   It is continuous but does not map any open set onto a bounded set, since s has no bounded neighborhoods 〖Section 3, Example 3〗. Finally if B has a bounded neighborhood N of 0 and f is continuous, f is bounded on $f^{-1}[N]$, a neighborhood of 0.//

COROLLARY 1.   *A linear functional is continuous if and only if it is bounded on some neighborhood of* 0.

THEOREM 3.   *A linear functional* f *is continuous if and only if* f$^\perp$ *is closed.*

If f is continuous, $f^\perp$ is closed, since it is $f^{-1}[\{0\}]$ and $\{0\}$ is closed.   Now suppose that f is not continuous.   We shall prove that $f^\perp$ is dense.   (We are not being generous.   It must be closed or dense 〖Section 2, Corollary 1〗.)   Let a be an arbitrary vector and G a balanced neighborhood of 0.   Since f is unbounded on G 〖Theorem 2〗 and $f[G]$ is a balanced subset of E, we must have $f[G] = E$.   In particular, $f(g) = -f(a)$ for some $g \in G$. Then $a + g \in f^\perp \cap (a + G)$.   Thus $f^\perp$ meets every open set.//

Example 2. Theorem 3 fails for linear maps in general, even for Banach spaces. For example, let f be a discontinuous automorphism of a Banach space [Section 7.5, Example 3]. Then $f^\perp = \{0\}$ is closed (compare Section 6.3, Problem 16).

The next result is similar to Section 6.3, Lemma 1. We are able to give a much briefer proof by using Theorem 3.

COROLLARY 2. *Let* A *be a separated space and* a $\in$ A, a $\neq$ 0. *Let* f *be a linear functional on* A *and* g: A $\to$ A *be defined by* g(x) = f(x)a. *Then if* g *is continuous, so is* f.

Obviously, $f^\perp = g^\perp = g^{-1}[\{0\}]$, which is closed, g being continuous, and $\{0\}$ closed.//

COROLLARY 3. *A linear functional* f *is continuous if and only if* $f^\perp$ *is not dense.*

This is contained in the proof of Theorem 3.//

We now consider criteria for continuity in terms of the behavior of a function on bounded sets. We have seen in Section 3 (Theorem 1 and Example 5) that preservation of bounded sets is necessary but not sufficient. There is a wide class of spaces in which this condition is actually sufficient.

DEFINITION 1. *A bornivore is a set which absorbs all bounded sets.*

Bornivore is a French neologism meaning "bounded eater." The meaning of the definition is that G is a bornivore if and only if, given any bounded set B, there exists $\delta > 0$ such that $\epsilon B \subset G$ for $0 \leq \epsilon < \delta$. Every neighborhood of 0 is a bornivore, by definition of the word "bounded."

DEFINITION 2. *A linear topological space is said to have the* b *property if every bornivore is a neighborhood of* 0. *A locally convex space is said to be bornological if every convex bornivore is a neighborhood of* 0.

Example 3: An infinite-dimensional normed space A, *with* $\sigma(A, A')$, *is not bornological.* The convex set $N(0, 1)$ absorbs all $\sigma(A, A')$ bounded sets [Section 3, Example 4], but is not a $\sigma(A, A')$ neighborhood of 0. [If it were, the $\sigma(A, A')$ topology would be stronger than, hence equal to, the norm topology, contrary to Section 9.3, Problem 14.] (See Problem 24 for another view of this example.) However, if "normed" is replaced by "Fréchet," this result is no longer true [Example 5].

★ *Example 4: Every linear semimetric space has the* b *property.* Let S be a set which is not a neighborhood of 0. For each positive integer n, $N(0, 1/n) \not\subset nS$ [since nS is not a neighborhood of 0]. Thus, for $n = 1, 2, \ldots$, there exists a_n with $!a_n! < 1/n$, $a_n \notin nS$. Since $a_n \to 0$, $\{a_n\}$ is a bounded set [for example, Section 3, Fact (xii)], but for no integer $k > 0$ is it true that $\{a_n\} \subset kS$ [choose $n = k$]. Thus S does not absorb the bounded set $\{a_n\}$. This example shows that the class of spaces with the b property is a fairly wide one.

Example 5: An infinite-dimensional locally convex Fréchet space A *which, with* $\sigma(A, A')$, *is bornological.* (Compare Example 3.) The example is s. The natural topology is metric, and is also $\sigma(s, s')$ [Section 9.3, Example 7, and Section 1, Problem 9]. The space is locally convex [Section 1, Example 7] and is bornological by Example 4.

The point of introducing the *b* property is the statement of Theorem 4.

THEOREM 4.   (i) *Let* A, B *be linear topological spaces and let* A *have the* b *property.   Then a linear map* f: A → B *is continuous if and only if it preserves bounded sets.*   (ii) *The same result holds assuming* B *locally convex and* A *bornological.*

Half of the result is Section 3, Theorem 1.   Next, assume that *f* preserves bounded sets and let *G* be a neighborhood of 0 in *B*.   (Make *G* convex in case (ii) of the theorem.)   Then $f^{-1}[G]$ absorbs all bounded subsets of *A* [let *S* be one, then $f[S]$ is bounded, hence absorbed by *G*] and so, by hypothesis, it is a neighborhood of 0.   Thus *f* is continuous.//

It is often useful to restrict a discussion of continuous linear functionals to real functions only.   Theorem 5 will be used to justify this on occasion.

THEOREM 5.   *Let a linear space* A *be given two linear topologies* T *and* T'.   *Then*

(i)   *every* T *continuous linear functional is* T' *continuous*

if and only if

(ii)   *every* T *continuous real linear functional is* T' *continuous.*

Assuming (i), let *f* be real linear and *T* continuous.   Setting $g(a) = -if(ia)$, $f + ig$ is linear and *T* continuous [Section 2.11, Theorem 1].   Hence it is *T'* continuous and so *f*, its real part, is *T'* continuous.

Assuming (ii), let *h* be linear and *T* continuous.   Write $h = f + ig$, with *f*, *g* real linear. Then *f*, *g* are *T* continuous, hence *T'* continuous, and so *h* is.//

COROLLARY 4.   *A linear functional is continuous if and only if its real part is.*

This is included in the proof of Theorem 5.//

We conclude this section with a brief discussion of equicontinuity.   A set Φ of linear maps from one linear topological space, *A*, to another, *B*, is called *equicontinuous* if, for each neighborhood *G* of 0 in *B*, $\cap\{f^{-1}[G]: f \in \Phi\}$ is a neighborhood of 0 in *A*; that is, given *G*, there is a single neighborhood *N* of 0 in *A* with $f[N] \subset G$ for all $f \in \Phi$.   The crucial remark about equicontinuity is that it is a generalization of uniform boundedness.

★*Example 6: With the notation of the definition just given, let* B *be a seminormed space; then* Φ *is equicontinuous if and only if it is uniformly bounded on some neighborhood* G *of* 0, *that is, for some* M, $\|f(a)\| < M$ *for all* $a \in G$, $f \in \Phi$.   [*If* Φ *is equicontinuous, take* $G = \cap\{f^{-1}[N(0, 1)]: f \in \Phi\}$.   *Conversely, if* G, M *exist, then for all* $f \in \Phi$ *and any* $\epsilon > 0$, $f[\epsilon G/M] \subset N(0, \epsilon)$.]

As a special case we have the fact that *if* A, B *are seminormed spaces,* Φ *is equicontinuous if and only if it is uniformly bounded, that is, there exists* M *such that* $\|f\| \leq M$ *for all* $f \in \Phi$.

Facts

In this list, all functions mentioned are linear maps between linear topological spaces, *A*, *B*, or linear functionals on a linear topological space *A*; Φ is a family of such functions.

(i) A finite family of continuous linear maps is equicontinuous.

(ii) Suppose that for each neighborhood G of 0 in B, $H(G) \equiv \cap \{f^{-1}[G]: f \in \Phi\}$ has nonempty interior. Then Φ is equicontinuous.

(iii) Let $\{f_n\}$ be a sequence of continuous linear functionals. The following two conditions are equivalent:

(a) $\{f_n\}$ is equicontinuous,

(b) $\{f_n\}$ is pointwise bounded and, if $g: A \to m$ is defined by $g(a) = \{f_n(a)\}$, g is continuous.

(iv) Let $\{f_n\}$ be equicontinuous. Then $\{a: f_n(a) \to 0\}$ is a closed linear subspace of A.

This extends Section 7.6, Problem 10, the same result for functionals on seminormed spaces. See also Section 7.6, Theorem 4.

Proofs

(i) For each neighborhood G of 0 in B, $\cap_{k=1}^n f_k^{-1}[G]$ is, if each f_k is continuous, a finite intersection of neighborhoods of 0. Thus it is a neighborhood of 0.

(ii) Let G be a neighborhood of 0 in B, N a symmetric neighborhood of 0 with $N + N \subset G$. Then $H(G) \supset H(N) + H(N) = H(N) - H(N)$ is a neighborhood of 0 since $H(N)$ has an interior point [Section 1, Problem 2].

(iii) Assume first that $\{f_n\}$ is equicontinuous. Let $G = \cap \{f_n^{-1}[N(0,1)]: n = 1, 2, \ldots\}$. (The cell $N(0,1)$ is in E.) This is a neighborhood of 0 in A; hence, it is absorbing. Suppose that $a \in kG$. Then $|f_n(a)| < k$ for each n. To see that g is continuous, we note that it is bounded on G, since $\|g(a)\| = \sup \{|f_n(a)|: n = 1, 2, \ldots\} \leq 1$ for $a \in G$. By Theorem 2, g is continuous.

Assuming next that (b) holds, let $G = g^{-1}[N(0,1)]$. (The cell $N(0,1)$ is in m.) Then G is a neighborhood of 0 in A. Moreover, $G = \cap \{f_n^{-1}[N(0,1)]: n = 1, 2, \ldots\}$ and so $\{f_n\}$ is equicontinuous.

(iv) Let $S = \{a: f_n(a) \to 0\}$. It is clear that S is a linear subspace. To show S closed, suppose that $x \in \bar{S}$, and let G_0 be an arbitrary neighborhood of 0 in B. Let G be a neighborhood of 0 in B with $G + G \subset G_0$, and let $N = \cap \{f_n^{-1}[G]: n = 1, 2, \ldots\}$. Choose $a \in S$ with $x - a \in N$ [possible, since $x \in \bar{S}$]. Choose an integer k such that $n > k$ implies $f_n(a) \in G$ [possible, since $f_n(a) \to 0$]. Then, finally, for $n > k$ we have $f_n(x) = f_n(a) + f_n(x - a) \in G + f_n[N] \subset G + G \subset G_0$. Thus $f_n(x) \to 0$, and so $x \in S$.//

Problems 10.5

In this list A, B are linear topological spaces, and f, $f_n: A \to B$ are linear. Any paranorm mentioned is defined on A.

★1. Let g be a real subadditive function which is continuous at 0 and satisfies $g(0) = 0$. Then g is continuous everywhere. (Thus Theorem 1 holds for paranorms.) [$-g(a - b) \leq g(b) - g(a) \leq g(b - a)$. Now let $b = a_\delta \to a$.]

2. In Problem 1 "at 0" cannot be replaced by "somewhere."

3. In Problem 1, the assumption $g(0) = 0$ cannot be dropped.

★4. Suppose that $f[N]$ is a neighborhood of 0 in B whenever N is a neighborhood of 0 in A. Show that f is open.

5. Let B be a normed space. Then $f: A \to B$ is continuous if and only if it is bounded on some neighborhood of 0.

6. The result of Problem 5 holds if $B = l^p$, $0 < p < 1$.

7. Suppose that there exists a bounded set G in B such that $f^{-1}[G]$ has nonempty interior.   Show that f is continuous.

8. Suppose that for every nonempty open set G in B, $f^{-1}[G]$ has nonempty interior.   Show that f is continuous.   (This result is false if f is not assumed linear.)

9. Find the mistake in the following "proof" that a continuous linear functional f on a linear metric space must be bounded on $N(0, 1)$.   If not, for $n = 1, 2, \ldots$, there exists a_n with $!a_n! < 1$, $|f(a_n)| > n$.   Then $|f(a_n/n)| = (1/n)|f(a_n)| > 1$, while $a_n/n \to 0$.

10. Show that Section 4.4, Theorem 1 (f is continuous if and only if $\|f\| < \infty$) is a special case of Theorem 2.

11. Prove Corollary 1 for seminorms.

12. Describe explicitly a nonempty open set in s on which P_1 is bounded.   (Corollary 1 asserts its existence.)

★13. A seminorm p is continuous if and only if ($p < 1$) is a neighborhood of 0.   〚With $G = \epsilon(p < 1)$, $p[G] \subset (-\epsilon, \epsilon)$, so that p is continuous at 0.   The result may also be deduced from Problem 11.〛

14. The gauge of the convex hull of the unit disk in l^p, $0 < p < 1$ is a continuous norm.   〚By Problem 13 and Section 4.2, Problem 23.〛

15. A continuous linear function from M or L^p, $0 < p < 1$, into a locally convex separated space B must be identically zero.   〚$f^{-1}[G]$ is convex if G is.   Now see Section 7.5, Problem 12.〛   What if B is not separated?

16. Let f be a linear functional.   Then f is continuous if and only if $|f|$ is continuous.   〚Use of Theorem 3 is suggested.〛

17. Theorem 3 is false for seminorms.

18. Use Theorem 3 to deduce Section 7.3, Theorem 2 from Section 7.3, Corollary 1.

19. The result ($\|f\|_S = \|f\|$ for dense S) of Section 6.1, Problem 27 cannot be extended to the case $\|f\| = \infty$.   〚Let $S = f^\perp$.〛

20. Theorem 3 holds for a linear map into E^n.

21. In Corollary 2, replace "separated" by "linear topological," "$a \neq 0$" by "$a \notin \overline{\{0\}}$," thus generalizing Section 6.3, Lemma 1.

22. A linear functional $f \neq 0$ is continuous if and only if $f^\perp$ is nowhere dense.

23. A locally convex separated space is bornological if and only if it has the strongest locally convex topology with the same class of bounded sets.   〚Any convex bornivore may be added to the topology without decreasing the class of bounded sets.〛

24. Deduce the result of Example 3 from Problem 23.   〚Use Section 3, Example 4.〛

25. In Example 4, suppose that the space is E and that S is the unit disk with 0 omitted.   What will $\{a_n\}$ be?

26. Let A be a seminormed space with $\sigma(A, A')$.   Then (even though A may not be bornological), A has the property that any linear functional which is bounded on bounded sets is continuous.   〚It is continuous in the seminorm topology by Theorem 4, Example 4, and Section 3, Example 4, hence it is $\sigma(A, A')$ continuous.〛

27. Give an example of a linear topological space which does not have the property given in Problem 26.   〚c with the weak topology by all functions $f(a) = \sum_{k=1}^{\infty} t_k a_k$, $\sum |t_k| < \infty$; lim is not continuous.〛

28. A locally convex separated space is bornological if and only if every bounded seminorm is continuous.   (A bounded seminorm is one which is bounded on bounded sets.)

29. Let E^∞ be given $\|a\| = \sup |a_n|$.   Let $f_n = \sum_{k=1}^{n} P_k$.   Show that $\{f_n\}$ is not equicontinuous.

30. If A, B are seminormed spaces, Φ is equicontinuous if and only if it is bounded in $L(A, B)$.

31. If Φ is an equicontinuous set of functions, and f is continuous, then $\Phi \cup \{f\}$ is equicontinuous.

32. If $\{f_n\}$ is equicontinuous and f is continuous, then $\{f_n + f\}$ is equicontinuous.

33. If an equicontinuous sequence of linear functionals converges on a dense set (or even a fundamental set) it converges everywhere.

34. If Φ is a family of continuous linear functions, and for each neighborhood G of 0 in B, $\bigcap\{f^{-1}[G]: f \in \Phi\}$ is somewhere dense, Φ is equicontinuous.

35. In Problem 8 of Section 3, replace "of second category in itself" by "a semimetric space." [There exists a bounded bornivore of the form $\Sigma t_n B_n$, where $\{B_n\}$ is the base.]

36. s has no countable base for its bounded sets. [Problem 35.]

10.6   Finite-dimensional space

The number of linear topologies that can be put on a finite-dimensional space is limited. Indeed, once the subspace $\overline{\{0\}}$ is given, the linear topology is uniquely determined. A special case is that there is exactly one linear separated topology. Thus, the general case is similar to that of seminormed spaces, Section 7.3.

The results of this section explain why, in the study of linear topology, the finite-dimensional case is considered trivial. Several linear topologies of interest can be placed upon infinite-dimensional spaces and, as is shown in Chapter 13, the interplay among these topologies is important. In the finite-dimensional case, there is only one separated topology; indeed, the study of these spaces can be carried forward without any topological notions at all. For example, if A is finite dimensional, $A' = A^{\#}$ and so the (topological) concept of dual can be studied in a purely algebraic way. (For a one-dimensional space A, the result is immediate. If A is not separated, $\overline{\{0\}}$, being a linear subspace, is the whole space and so A is indiscrete. If A is separated, let $a \neq 0$ and define $f(b) = t$ for $b = ta$. Then f is continuous by Section 5, Corollary 2, while f^{-1} is continuous by definition of linear topological space. Thus A is linearly homeomorphic with E.)

LEMMA 1.   *Let* n, k *be integers,* $1 \leq k \leq n$. *Let* T *be a linear topology on* E^n *such that*

(1)
$$\overline{\{0\}} = \{a: a_1 = a_2 = \cdots = a_k = 0\}.$$

Then T *is given by a seminorm, namely,* $p(a) = \Sigma_{r=1}^{k}|a_r|$.

First, p is stronger (that is, its topology is stronger) than T. To prove this let G be a T neighborhood of 0. Let N be a T neighborhood of 0 with $N + N + \cdots + N \subset G$. (There are n terms in the sum.) Since N is absorbing, there exists $\epsilon > 0$ such that $t\delta^r \in N$ for $r = 1, 2, \ldots, k$ if $|t| < \epsilon$. Then the p cell $N(0, \epsilon) \subset G$. [If $|p(a)| < \epsilon$, that is, $\Sigma_{r=1}^{k}|a_r| < \epsilon$, we have $|a_r| < \epsilon$ for each $r = 1, 2, \ldots, k$, hence $a_r\delta^r \in N$; while for $r = k + 1, k + 2, \ldots, n$, $a_r\delta^r \in \overline{\{0\}}$ by hypothesis on T, hence $a_r\delta^r \in N$ by Section 2, Fact (iv). Thus, finally, $a = \Sigma_{r=1}^{n}a_r\delta^r \in N + N + \cdots + N \subset G$.] Thus G is a p neighborhood of 0.

Next we prove that p is weaker. Let Φ be a family of T-closed, balanced T neighborhoods of 0 satisfying $\bigcap\{G: G \in \Phi\} = \overline{\{0\}}$ [in Section 2, see Fact (v) and Problem 4]. The p circumference $C(0, 1)$ is p compact [Section 9.6, Example 1 shows that it is compact in the Euclidean topology, which is stronger], hence, T compact [p is stronger] and $\bigcap\{G: G \in \Phi\}$ does not meet it [$a \in \overline{\{0\}}$ implies $p(a) = 0$ by equation (1)].

Thus Φ does not have the finite intersection property relative to $C(0, 1)$; that is, there exist $G_1, G_2, \ldots, G_n$ in Φ with $V \equiv \bigcap_{k=1}^{n}G_k$ not meeting $C(0, 1)$. Then V is a balanced T neighborhood of 0, since each G_k is, and $V \subset N(0, 1)$ since V is balanced and does not meet $C(0, 1)$. Thus $N(0, 1)$ is a T neighborhood of 0.//

THEOREM 1. *Every finite-dimensional linear topological space is a seminormed space. Furthermore, the topology is uniquely determined by* $\overline{\{0\}}$. *In particular, a finite-dimensional linear space has exactly one linear separated topology, and it is given by a complete norm.*

The linear space is isomorphic with E^n in such a way that the image of $\overline{\{0\}}$ is $\{a : a_1 = a_2 = \cdots = a_k = 0\}$. Thus, the result follows from Lemma 1. The completeness of the norm is given in Section 7.3, Theorem 1.//

Continuing as in the finite-dimensional seminormed theory, Section 7.3, we obtain Corollaries 1 through 5.

Remark. In each case, the result refers to a linear topological space A, not necessarily finite dimensional, unless specified.

COROLLARY 1. *On a finite-dimensional separated space, every linear functional is continuous.*

This follows immediately from Theorem 1, and Section 7.3, Theorem 2.

COROLLARY 2. *The convex hull* H *of any finite set* S *is bounded.*

The set S is bounded in its span, Σ; Σ, being finite dimensional, is seminormed. Thus H is bounded in Σ [Section 3, Fact (xiv)], hence H is bounded [Section 3, Problem 3].//

COROLLARY 3. *Every finite-dimensional subspace* S *of a linear separated space* A *is closed.*

Let x_δ be a net in S, $x_\delta \to a \in A$. By Theorem 1, S is a complete normed space. Now x_δ is a Cauchy net in S. [It is a Cauchy net in A, and Cauchy net is defined entirely in terms of neighborhoods of 0.] Hence x_δ is convergent in S [Section 9.2, Problem 21]. Since the space is separated, a is the only limit x_δ has, thus $a \in S$.//

COROLLARY 4. *Let* A *be a finite-dimensional linear separated space,* B *a linear topological space, and* f: A $\to$ B *a linear function. Then* f *is continuous.*

We shall take $A = E^n$. Let H be the convex hull of $\{\delta^1, \delta^2, \ldots, \delta^n, -\delta^1, -\delta^2, \ldots, -\delta^n, i\delta^1, \ldots, i\delta^n, -i\delta^1, \ldots, -i\delta^n\}$. Then $f[H]$ is bounded [Corollary 2]; moreover, H is a neighborhood of 0; hence f is continuous [Section 5, Theorem 2].//

▲ COROLLARY 5. *The sum of a closed linear subspace* S, *and a finite-dimensional subspace* B *is closed.*

This is remarkable in view of the fact that B need not be closed. $(S + B)/S$ is a finite-dimensional subspace of the separated space A/S [consult Section 2, Problem 31 for quotients]. Hence it is closed. But $S + B = \phi^{-1}[(S + B)/S]$, and ϕ, the natural homomorphism, is continuous; hence $S + B$ is closed.//

Problems 10.6

1. Give R^2 two different topologies in which $\overline{\{0\}}$ is one dimensional.
2. Let two linear topological spaces have the same finite dimension and $\overline{\{0\}}$ of the same dimension. Show that they are linearly homeomorphic.
3. Let A be a finite-dimensional linear space, and S a subspace. Show that A can be given a linear topology making $S = \overline{\{0\}}$.

★4. Let A be a separated space, a a nonzero vector, b a vector, and $\{t_n\}$ a sequence of scalars such that $t_n a \to b$. Show that $b = ta$ and $t_n \to t$ for some scalar t. 〚The subspace S spanned by a is linearly homeomorphic with E under the map $ua \to u$ for $u \in E$. Also $b \in S$, since S is closed.〛

5. If a separated space has countably infinite Hamel dimension, it is of first category in itself. (Hence E^∞ cannot be given a complete invariant metric. This extends Section 7.3, Problem 3.)

6. In Corollary 3, "separated" cannot be omitted.

7. Extend Corollary 5 by allowing $B/\overline{\{0\}}$ to be finite dimensional.

8. Let S be a finite-dimensional subspace of a linear topological space. Show that $S + \overline{\{0\}} = \bar{S}$. 〚Corollary 5 and Section 2, Fact (i).〛 "Finite-dimensional" cannot be omitted.

9. Extend Corollary 3 by removing "separated" and assuming that S includes $\overline{\{0\}}$. 〚By Problem 8, or because A/S is separated and $S = \phi^{-1}[\overline{\{0\}}].$〛

10. Extend Corollary 1 by removing "separated" and assuming that f vanishes on $\overline{\{0\}}$. 〚Problem 9.〛

11. Extend Corollary 4 as in Problem 10.

12. If A is a finite-dimensional linear topological space, its topology is $\sigma(A, A')$. 〚The two topologies have the same $\overline{\{0\}}.$〛

13. In Section 5, Problem 20, replace E^n by any finite-dimensional linear topological space.

14. Show that every finite-dimensional separated space has a certain product topology. 〚See Section 2.3, Problem 10.〛

15. Do Problem 3 with "finite-dimensional" omitted.

16. Some one-dimensional subspaces of a linear topological space are linearly homeomorphic with E and some are not. What property of a vector a puts its span in one class or the other?

17. If a linear functional vanishes on a closed linear subspace of finite codimension, it is continuous. 〚f is continuous on A/S.〛

18. In Problem 17, "subspace of finite codimension" cannot be replaced by "infinite-dimensional subspace."

19. The *boundary* of a set S is defined to be $\bar{S} \cap \bar{\bar{S}}$. Let S be a bounded set in a separated space of nonzero dimension. Show that any line meeting S meets the boundary of S. 〚Let $u = \sup\{t: ta + (1 - t)b \in S\}$. Then $ua + (1 - u)b$ is in the boundary. (The line is homeomorphic with R.)〛

▲10.7   Uniformity

This section presents only a point of view. Precise statements, conditions, and proofs are omitted; it should be read merely to catch a flavor. References are given in Appendix C.

Suppose given a topological space A and a means of associating with each $a \in A$ a neighborhood $N(a)$ of a. (This is, of course, a map $N: A \to 2^A$.) We shall denote a collection of such maps (subject to certain conditions) by U and call it a *uniformity*.

Example 1. Given a semimetric space, for each fixed $r > 0$, let $N_r(a) = N(a, r)$. The collection of all N_r is a uniformity.

Example 2. Given a linear topological space, fix G, a neighborhood of 0, and define $N(a) = a + G$.

Example 3. Given a topological group, proceed as in Example 2, replacing "+" by the group operation.

Example 4. The standard procedure for discussing uniformity is to consider a family Φ of subsets of $A \times A$, each including the diagonal. Each $M \in \Phi$ determines $N \in U$ by the formula $N(a) = \{b: (a, b) \in M\}$. ($M$ is given first; then U is defined. With suitable restrictions on M, U has whatever properties are appropriate.)

A uniformity U generates a topology in the obvious way; a is interior to G if $N(a) \subset G$ for some $N \in U$. A topology is called uniformizable if there is a uniformity which generates it. A compact Hausdorff space is uniformizable. The essential property of a uniformity is that one can compare how far apart pairs of points are separated which are located in different parts of the space. For example $(1, 0)$, $(6, 0)$ are the same distance apart as $(8, 9)$, $(5, 5)$ in R^2. In a topological space in general no such comparison can be made, since there is no way of transferring a neighborhood from one part of the space to another. This is why Cauchy sequence cannot be defined in terms of topological concepts alone. However, in a uniform space we say that $\{x_n\}$ is *Cauchy* if, given $N \in U$, there exists k such that $p > k$, $q > k$ implies $x_q \in N(x_p)$ and $x_p \in N(x_q)$. (At this stage we shall assume, for simplicity, that all members N of U are symmetric; that is, $a \in N(b)$ if and only if $b \in N(a)$. In Example 1, N is symmetric. In Example 2, N is symmetric if G is. Then the definition of Cauchy sequence is simplified in an obvious way.)

For $N \in U$ and S a subset of the uniform space, we define $N[S] = \cup \{N(a): a \in S\}$. In Example 1, this gives an open set including S and whose complement is "far from" S. In Example 2, if $N(a) = a + G$, $N[S] = S + G$. A subset S of a uniform space is called *totally bounded* if for each $N \in U$, there exists a finite subset F of S with $S \subset N[F]$. (Compare Section 3, Problem 17, and Section 9.5, Problem 27.)

The formulas of Section 2 can be proved for uniform space in general. (We have not stated what properties we want U to have, thus they cannot be proved here.) For example, Fact (v) states that $\bar{S} = \cap \{N[S]: N \in U\}$ (although Section 2, Problem 7 reminds us that $\bar{S} \neq \cap \{G: G \supset S, G \text{ open}\}$, in general). Translated into a fact about semimetric spaces, this says $\bar{S} = \cap \{N(S, r): r > 0\}$, where $N(S, r) = \{x: d(x, a) < r \text{ for some } a \in S\}$.

A uniform space is regular. The proof of Section 2, Theorem 2 works in general. Instead of a neighborhood G of 0, choose $G \in U$. Then choose a symmetric $N \in U$ with $NN \subset G$. (Here, $NN(a)$ means $N[N(a)]$, and $NN \subset G$ means $NN(a) \subset G(a)$ for each a. Needless to say, the existence of such N for every G is one of the assumptions we have left out.) Then $G_1 = N[S]$, $G_2 = N[a]$, to complete the proof. A special case is that a semimetric space is regular.

Similarly Section 2, Theorem 3 holds for uniform space; if the space is T_0 it is automatically T_3. Given a, b with $a \notin N(b)$ for some $N \in U$, then $b \notin N(a)$ (choosing N symmetric) and so the space is T_1 *et cetera*. Indeed, we can go further; the space must be $T_{3\frac{1}{2}}$.

A first-countable uniform space is metrizable. This generalizes Section 4, Theorem 2. The concept of uniform continuity can easily be defined.

It should be mentioned in conclusion that a set S in a connected uniform space is (on occasion) called *bounded* if, for every $N \in U$, there exists $a \in S$ such that $S \subset NN \ldots N(a)$ for sufficiently (finitely) many N. For linear topological spaces this reduces to pseudo-boundedness (Section 3, Problem 20), which is equivalent to boundedness in locally convex spaces, but not in general [Section 3, Problems 21, 22]. For semimetric space, boundedness implies metric boundedness, but not conversely.

Linear topology goes beyond uniformity in its use of scalars, for example, in discussions of convexity, boundedness, and linear maps. It is only its additive-group structure that is subsumed within the uniformity theory.

11

THE CLOSED-GRAPH THEOREM

11.1 Closed functions

The closed-graph theorem deals with closed functions. In this section we give the definition and some properties (perhaps more than strictly necessary) of closed functions, especially as relates to compact sets. Linearity does not enter, except momentarily, until Section 2.

DEFINITION 1. *Let* A, B *be sets, and* f: A $\rightarrow$ B *a function. The graph of* f *is* $\{(a, fa): a \in A\}$. *It is a subset of* A $\times$ B.

Thus $(a, b) \in$ graph of f if and only if $b = f(a)$.

DEFINITION 2. *Let* A, B *be topological spaces and* f: A $\rightarrow$ B *a function. Then* f *is called closed if its graph is a closed subset of* A $\times$ B.

This definition is sometimes extended to cover the case in which f is defined on a proper subset of A, in which case a modification of Theorem 1 holds, part of the conclusion being that f is defined at a. We shall have no use for this extension of the definition.

A function which preserves closed sets is referred to as a closed function by many authors. Our usage stems from the fact that a function and its graph are formally identical.

THEOREM 1. *Let* A, B *be topological spaces. Then* f: A $\rightarrow$ B *is closed if and only if whenever* a_δ *is a net in* A *with* $a_\delta \rightarrow$ a, *and* f(a_δ) $\rightarrow$ b, *it follows that* b = f(a). *In particular, if* B *is a Hausdorff space and* f *is continuous, then* f *is closed.*

Let f be closed, $a_\delta \rightarrow a$, and $f(a_\delta) \rightarrow b$. Then $(a_\delta, fa_\delta) \rightarrow (a, b)$ in $A \times B$ [Section 9.3, Theorem 8]. Since the graph of f is closed, it follows that (a, b) belongs to the graph; that is, $b = f(a)$. Conversely, let f satisfy the stated condition. We shall prove that the graph G is closed. Let u_δ be a net in G with $u_\delta \rightarrow v$. Then $u_\delta = (a_\delta, b_\delta)$, $v = (a, b)$ with $b_\delta = f(a_\delta)$, $a_\delta \rightarrow a$, $b_\delta \rightarrow b$. By hypothesis, it follows that $b = f(a)$, hence $(a, b) \in G$, so G is closed.

The particular case mentioned in the statement of the theorem holds because, if f is continuous, $f(a_\delta) \rightarrow f(a)$. Since also $f(a_\delta) \rightarrow b$ and B is a Hausdorff space, it follows that $b = f(a)$. Problem 1 shows that some extra assumption on B is needed.//

▲*Note.* As the discussion develops, it will become clear that "closed" is a more natural assumption than "continuous" for maps between non-Hausdorff spaces. Indeed, certain results proved for Hausdorff spaces remain true without the Hausdorff assumption when the functions involved are assumed closed rather than continuous. The resulting theorems include the earlier ones, since, with the Hausdorff assumption, continuous functions are closed. Examples are Section 6.2, Problems 8 and 9; Section 9.5, Theorem 4, whose generalization is Fact (ii) below; Section 7.1, Problem 14; and, below, Section 2, Corollary 1 compared with the open mapping theorem. It turns out that for linear topological spaces, this is a gain in elegance rather than power, since, for example, if $f: A \to B$ is linear and closed, then B is separated [Problem 18]. We make no use of this remark.

★ *Example 1.* If A, B are semimetric spaces, Theorem 1 is true with sequences instead of nets. [$A \times B$ is semimetrizable.] Thus the definition of closed given in Section 5.3, Problem 20 is the same as the present one.

★ *Example 2.* Define $f: R \to R$ by $f(x) = 1/x$ for $x \neq 0$, $f(0) = 0$. Then f is closed, but not continuous. [If $x_n \to x$ and $f(x_n) \to y$, then $x \neq 0$; hence f is continuous at x and $y = f(x)$.]

Facts

In this list, A, B are topological spaces, and $f: A \to B$ is a closed function.

(i) $f^{-1}: B \to A$ is closed if it exists.
(ii) Let K be a compact subset of A. Then $f[K]$ is closed. (It need not be compact, even if $A = B = R$). Hence a closed function defined on a compact space preserves closed sets.
(iii) Let K be a compact subset of B. Then $f^{-1}[K]$ is closed.
(iv) *The little closed-graph theorem.* Let B be compact. Then f is continuous.
(v) Let A be compact. Then f^{-1} is continuous, if it exists.
(vi) *The little open-mapping theorem.* Let A be compact. Suppose also that f is one to one and onto. Then f is open. ("One to one" cannot be dropped, nor can "onto.")

Proofs

(i) The map $(a, b) \to (b, a)$ is a homeomorphism from $A \times B$ onto $B \times A$ which carries the graph of f to the graph of f^{-1}. Hence, if one is closed, the other is. (Another proof stems from the observation that the condition given in Theorem 1 is symmetric; that is, f satisfies it if and only if f^{-1} does.)

(ii) Let b_δ be a net in $f[K]$ with $b_\delta \to b$. Then $b_\delta = f(a_\delta)$ for some $a_\delta \in K$. Since K is compact, a_δ has a subnet $x_\alpha \to a \in K$ [Section 9.5, Theorem 1]. Then also $f(x_\alpha) \to b$. [It is a subnet of b_δ.] By Theorem 1, $b = f(a) \in f[K]$. Thus $f[K]$ is closed. An example in which it is not compact is given in Problem 5.

(iii) In this proof, the steps are justified as in the proof of Fact (ii). Let a_δ be a net in $f^{-1}[K]$ with $a_\delta \to a$. Since K is compact, $f(a_\delta)$ has a subnet $f a_{u(\delta')} \to b \in K$. Then also $a_{u(\delta')} \to a$. By Theorem 1, $b = f(a)$ and so $a \in f^{-1}[K]$.

(iv) Let K be a closed subset of B. Then K is compact [Section 9.5, Lemma 2], hence $f^{-1}[K]$ is closed [Fact (iii)]. Thus f is continuous [Section 9.1, Problem 13].

(v) This follows from Facts (i) and (iv).

(vi) According to Fact (v), f^{-1} is continuous. For the parenthesized remarks, (one to one) see Section 5.1, Problem 3, and (onto) consider an inclusion map.//

COROLLARY 1. *A closed linear functional on a linear topological space must be continuous.*

Obviously, $f^{\perp}$ is closed [Fact (iii), since it is $f^{-1}[\{0\}]$]. Hence f is continuous [Section 10.5, Theorem 3].//

This trivial but interesting corollary of Fact (iii) presages greater things in Section 2. Example 4 shows that "functional" cannot be replaced by "map between separated linear topological spaces."

★ *Example 3.* Let a set A have two Hausdorff topologies T, T' with T' strictly stronger than T. Then $i: (A, T) \rightarrow (A, T')$ is closed but not continuous. [It is not continuous, since T is not stronger than T'. It is closed by Fact (i), since its inverse is continuous, hence closed.]

★ *Example 4*: *A closed linear map between normed spaces which is not continuous.* Example 3 will do if, for example, $A = l$, T' is the natural topology for l and T is the relative topology of c_0. We shall see in Section 2 that no such example exists in which the normed spaces are both complete.

We shall isolate, in Lemma 1, a key step in applications of the closed-graph theorem. Because of the very frequent reference to this result, we shall bestow a name upon it which the reader should keep in mind. It is often applied in the form given in Problem 9.

LEMMA 1. THE CLOSED-GRAPH LEMMA. *Let* A, B *be topological spaces and let* f: A $\rightarrow$ B *be closed. If* A, B *are both given stronger topologies,* f *remains closed.*

The topology on $A \times B$ is strengthened. [Convergence of a net x_δ in $A \times B$ is equivalent to convergence of $P_1 x_\delta$ and $P_2 x_\delta$.] Thus the graph of f remains closed.//

Problems on topological space 11.1

1. Let A be a topological space which is not a Hausdorff space. Then the identity map from A to itself is continuous but not closed.

★2. A linear function $f: A \rightarrow B$, A, B being linear topological spaces, is closed if and only if $a_\delta \rightarrow 0$, $f(a_\delta) \rightarrow b$ imply $b = 0$.

3. Use Section 9.1, Problem 35 to prove that if $f: A \rightarrow B$ is continuous and B is a Hausdorff space, then f is closed. [$u(a, b) = b$, $v(a, b) = f(a)$, u, $v: A \times B \rightarrow B$.]

4. A closed map need not preserve closed sets.

5. Let f be as in Example 2. Find a compact subset K of R such that $f[K]$ is not compact.

6. Let f be as in Example 2. Find a compact subset K of R such that $f^{-1}[K]$ is not compact.

7. Give the result of Example 4, but with the domain complete instead of the range.

8. Lemma 1 is false if "closed" is replaced by "continuous," even if all topologies mentioned are Hausdorff.

★9. Let A, B be topological spaces, and $f: A \to B$ a function. Suppose that B can be given a weaker Hausdorff topology which makes f continuous. Show that f is closed. ⟦The closed-graph lemma.⟧

10. The sufficient condition that f be closed given in Problem 9 is not necessary, even if f is onto. (The strongest topology on B making f continuous may not be Hausdorff.)

11. Let B be R with the minimal T_1 topology. Is the identity map from R to B closed? ⟦No.⟧

12. Must a closed seminorm be continuous?

13. Let A be the subset of real C consisting of functions with a continuous derivative on $[0, 1]$. Define $D: A \to C$ by $Df = f'$, the derivative. Show that D is closed but not continuous.

14. A closed function of a continuous function is closed.

15. A continuous function of a closed function need not be closed. ⟦Let f be the function given in Example 2. Let $g(x) = 1/(1 + x^2)$ for real x.⟧

16. A continuous linear function of a closed linear function need not be closed (even if all spaces involved are linear metric spaces and the continuous function is a functional). ⟦$\phi: E^\infty \to c$ given by $(\phi a)_n = \sum_{k=1}^n a_k$ (take $E^\infty \subset c_0$). Then ϕ is closed, lim: $c \to E$ is continuous, but lim $\circ$ ϕ is not closed, since, if it were, it would be continuous by Corollary 1.⟧

17. A closed function of a closed function need not be closed. ⟦Problem 15, also Problem 21.⟧

18. If $f: A \to B$ is closed, $f[A]$ must be T_1 in the relative topology of B. (Thus, if there exists a closed map onto B, B must be a T_1 space.) However $\overline{f[A]}$ need not be T_0 in the relative topology of B. ⟦$A = R$, $B = R \cup \{a\} \cup \{b\}$ with $x_\delta \to$ both a and b as $x_\delta \to \infty$ in R in the usual sense.⟧

19. Let $f: A \to B$ be closed, and A compact. Then $f[A] = \overline{f[A]}$ is a Hausdorff space in the relative topology of B. ⟦Nets have unique limits.⟧

20. Let $f: A \to B$ be closed. Then for any finite set $S \subset A$, $f[\bar{S}] \subset f[S]$. (Compare Section 9.2, Corollary 1.)

21. Give an example of two non-Hausdorff spaces A, B and a map $f: A \to B$ which is one to one, onto, closed. They must be T_1, by Problem 18. (This gives another example of Problem 17, namely ff^{-1} is not closed, by Problem 1.)

22. Suppose that a group is given a compact Hausdorff topology such that the group operation is continuous. Show that the operation of taking the inverse is also continuous. ⟦It is closed, by Theorem 1. Now use Fact (iv).⟧

11.2   The closed-graph theorem

Third in order, after the Hahn-Banach theorem and the uniform-boundedness principle, comes the closed-graph theorem, completing the list of the three central themes of this book. In some ways, the closed-graph theorem is the most useful of the three. Indeed, there will often be a rivalry between the closed-graph theorem and the uniform-boundedness principle; either one serving to prove an assertion at issue. Some examples are Corollaries 3 and 4, below, as compared with Section 12.3, Theorems 4 and 5. The setting chosen for the closed-graph theorem is Fréchet space, except for a few of the preliminary computations.

LEMMA 1.   *Let* A, B *be linear metric spaces with* A *complete. Let* f *be a closed linear map from* A *to* B *such that for every neighborhood* N *of* 0 *in* A, $\overline{f[N]}$ *is a neighborhood of* 0 *in* B. *Then* f *is open.* (*In particular,* f *is onto.*)

Let $r > 0$. We are going to show that $f[N(0, r)]$ is a neighborhood of 0 in B. For $n = 0, 1, 2, \ldots$, let $G_n = N(0, r/2^n)$ in A. By hypothesis, $\overline{f[G_n]}$ is a neighborhood of 0;

that is, for some $\epsilon_n > 0$,

$$(1) \qquad \overline{f[G_n]} \supset N(0, \epsilon_n) \text{ in } B.$$

We may assume that $\epsilon_n \to 0$. 〚For example, choose $\epsilon_n < 1/n$ for each n.〛
The result is proved by showing that $f[G_0] \supset \overline{f[G_1]}$; this is not unreasonable, since G_1 is "half as large as" G_0. For $n = 0, 1, 2, \ldots$, let $H_n = N(0, \epsilon_n)$ in B. Then $H_1 \subset f[G_0]$. 〚To prove this, let $y \in H_1$. By relation (1), there exists $x_1 \in G_1$ with $!y - f(x_1)! < \epsilon_2$. From this, it follows that $y - f(x_1) \in H_2$. So, again by relation (1), there exists $x_2 \in G_2$ with $!y - f(x_1) - f(x_2)! < \epsilon_3$. Continuing in this way, we obtain for each n (as we already have for $n = 1, 2$) a point $x_n \in G_n$ with $!y - f(x_1) - f(x_2) - \cdots - f(x_n)! < \epsilon_{n+1}$. This proves that

$$(2) \qquad \sum_{k=1}^{\infty} f(x_k) = y.$$

Moreover, since $x_n \in G_n$, we have $!x_n! < r/2^n$ so that $\sum_{k=1}^{\infty} x_k$ is absolutely convergent, hence convergent, since A is complete. Let

$$(3) \qquad \sum_{k=1}^{\infty} x_k = x.$$

Since f is closed, it follows from relations (2) and (3) that $y = f(x)$. It also follows from relation (3) that $!x! \leq \sum_{k=1}^{\infty} !x_k! < r$, that is, $x \in G_0$. Thus finally $y \in f[G_0]$.〛
Thus $f[G_0]$ is a neighborhood of 0 in B. Since every neighborhood of 0 includes $N(0, r)$ for some $r > 0$, we have shown that f carries neighborhoods of 0 onto neighborhoods of 0. Since f is linear, this implies that it is open. 〚Section 10.5, Problem 4.〛
The fact that f is onto follows easily. 〚$f[A]$ is a linear subspace with an interior point.〛//

LEMMA 2. *With* A, B, f *as in Lemma 1, it is sufficient to suppose that* f[N] *is somewhere dense (instead of* $\overline{f[N]}$ *a neighborhood of* 0.)

Let N be a neighborhood of 0. Let G be a symmetric neighborhood of 0 with $G + G \subset N$. Then $\overline{f[G]}$ has an interior point and so $\overline{f[N]} \supset \overline{f[G]} - \overline{f[G]}$ is a neighborhood of 0. 〚We have used the fact that $G + G = G - G$, Section 10.1, Problem 2 and Section 10.2, Fact (i).〛//

THEOREM 1. THE OPEN-MAPPING THEOREM. *Let* A, B *be Fréchet spaces, and* f: A $\to$ B *a closed linear map onto. Then* f *is open.*

(In the little open-mapping theorem [Section 1, Fact (vi)], it was required also that f be one to one.)
Let N be a neighborhood of 0 in A. Then $\cup\{kN: k = 1, 2, \ldots \} = A$, since N is absorbing; thus $\cup\{kf[N]: k = 1, 2, \ldots\} = f[\cup\{kN\}] = f[A] = B$, since f is onto. Now B is complete, hence of second category in itself 〚Baire category theorem〛, and so not every $kf[N]$ can be nowhere dense. Thus $\overline{f[N]}$ is somewhere dense; that is, $f[N]$ has an interior point. By Lemma 2, the result follows.//

COROLLARY 1. *Let* A, B *be Fréchet spaces and* f: A $\to$ B, *linear, continuous, one to one, and onto. Then* f *is a homeomorphism.*

This follows instantly from the open-mapping theorem, since f is closed.//

COROLLARY 2.   *Let a linear space be given two complete invariant metrics, one of which is stronger.* *Then they are equivalent.   (In other words, two comparable, complete, invariant metrics are equivalent.)*

Compare Section 9.5, Theorem 3 (uniqueness of compact Hausdorff topology).   The identity map from the stronger to the weaker is a homeomorphism, by Corollary 1.//

This result will be greatly improved (Section 3, Corollary 2).   The requirement of completeness cannot be dropped for either of the two metrics, neither can the requirement of comparability.   This is the content of Section 7.5, Examples 6, 7, and 8.

Corollary 2 yields a class of results of which Section 5.3, Problem 14 is typical, namely that certain norms are incomplete.

THEOREM 2.   THE CLOSED-GRAPH THEOREM.   *Let A, B be Fréchet spaces, and* $f: A \to B$ *a closed linear map.   Then* f *is continuous.*

(For $B = E$, we had a trivial proof, Section 1, Corollary 1.)

We remetrize A.   For $a \in A$, define $p(a) = \,!a! + \,!f(a)!$; then p is a paranorm for A. ⟦For example, let $t_n \to t$, and $p(a_n - a) \to 0$.   Then $!a_n - a! \to 0$ and $!f(a_n - a)! \to 0$ by definition of p.   Thus $!t_n a_n - t a! \to 0$ and $!t_n f(a_n) - t f(a)! \to 0$, since A, B are linear metric spaces, and so, again by definition of p, $p(t_n a_n - t a) \to 0$.⟧

Notice also that p is total, so that it actually yields a metric for A.   Moreover, p is complete.   ⟦Let $\{a_n\}$ be a p Cauchy sequence.   Then, by definition of p, it follows that $\{a_n\}$ is a Cauchy sequence in A (original metric) and $\{f(a_n)\}$ is a Cauchy sequence in B.   Since A, B are complete, these sequences are convergent.   Say $a_n \to a$, $f(a_n) \to b$.   Since f is closed, $b = f(a)$, and it follows immediately that $p(a_n - a) \to 0$.⟧

Thus p gives A a new, stronger, complete invariant metric.   By Corollary 2, this is equivalent to the original metric.   Since f is p continuous ⟦$p(a_n) \to 0$ implies $f(a_n) \to 0$⟧, the result follows.//

The immense power of the closed-graph theorem resides in the ease with which a function may be proved closed, as exemplified by the closed-graph lemma, along with various desirable consequences.   For example, (Corollary 3) equicontinuity, a form of uniform boundedness, follows in one context, thus improving Section 10.5, Fact (iii) in the presence of completeness.

COROLLARY 3.   *Let* $\{f_n\}$ *be a pointwise-bounded sequence of continuous linear functionals on a Fréchet space* A.   *Then* $\{f_n\}$ *is equicontinuous.*

Define $g: A \to m$ by $g(a) = \{f_n(a)\}$.   The result will follow when g is proved continuous ⟦Section 10.5, Fact (iii)⟧.   It is sufficient to prove g closed.   This follows from the closed-graph lemma and the fact that $g: A \to s$ is continuous.   ⟦Let $a_k \to 0$ in A, then $f_n(a_k) \to 0$ as $k \to \infty$ for each n; that is, $g(a_k) \to 0$ in s, by the fact that convergence in s is coordinatewise.⟧//

A form of the Banach-Steinhaus closure theorem (Section 7.6, Theorem 3) can also be given.

COROLLARY 4.   *Let* $\{f_n\}$ *be a pointwise convergent sequence of continuous linear functionals on a Fréchet space.   Then* f, *defined by* $f(a) = \lim f_n(a)$ *is continuous.*

The function $g: A \to c$ given in Corollary 3 is continuous, and $f = \lim \circ g$, the composition of two continuous functions.//

Problems 11.2

★1. Let A be a Fréchet space. Let B be a linear metric space and $f: A \to B$ a closed linear map such that $f[A]$ is of second category in B. Show that f is open (hence onto). 〖Same as proof of the open-mapping theorem.〗

2. Deduce from Problem 1 the results of Section 5.1, Problems 11, 12 (second half), and a few other similar results on sequence and function spaces. 〖f is an inclusion map.〗

3. Corollary 1 becomes false if B is allowed to be semimetric and Corollary 2 becomes false if the weaker metric is allowed to be a semimetric. 〖$A = R^2$, $B = R^2$ with $\|(x, y)\| = |x|$, $f = i$.〗

4. Deduce Section 5.3, Problem 14 from Corollary 2.

5. Deduce Corollary 1 from the closed-graph theorem. 〖f is closed. Thus, f^{-1} is closed, hence continuous.〗

6. Deduce the open-mapping theorem from the closed-graph theorem. 〖$f: A/f^{\perp} \to B$ is one to one, closed, onto; hence f^{-1} is closed, thus continuous. So f is open.〗

7. In Section 7.1, Problem 12 assume in addition that A, B are complete. Now the conditions are sufficient.

8. In Problem 7, it is not enough to assume just B complete or just A complete (instead of A and B).

9. Abbreviate the proof of Section 7.3, Theorem 3 by applying the closed-graph theorem as soon as f is proved continuous.

10. Let A, B be Fréchet spaces, and assume that B' is separating over B (for example, if B is a normed space). Let $g: A \to B$ have the property that $f \circ g$ is continuous for all $f \in B'$. Show that g is continuous. 〖With $\sigma(B, B')$, g is continuous, hence, by the closed-graph lemma, Section 1, g is closed.〗

11. "Separating" cannot be omitted in Problem 10. 〖Section 7.5, Example 10.〗

★12. Let $\{f_n\}$ be a sequence of continuous linear functionals on a Fréchet space such that $\Sigma f_n(a)$ is convergent for each a. Show that $\Sigma f_n(a)$ is continuous. 〖Corollary 4.〗

13. There exists no real sequence $\{u_n\}$ such that a necessary and sufficient condition for absolute convergence of a real series Σt_n is that $\{u_n t_n\}$ is bounded. 〖Assume $u_n \neq 0$. $f: m \to l$ given by $f(a) = \{a_n/u_n\}$ would be a homeomorphism.〗

14. A continuous, linear, one-to-one map of s into itself is a homeomorphism into. 〖Section 6.4, Problem 29, and the closed-graph theorem.〗

15. Problem 14 is false for c_0. 〖$f(x) = \{x_n/n\}$.〗

16. Let $0 < p < 1$. Suppose that a sequence $\{a_n\}$ of complex numbers has the property that $\Sigma a_n b_n$ is convergent for every $b \in l^p$. Show that $a \in m$. Compare Section 7.6, Example 2. 〖Let $f(b) = \Sigma a_n b_n$. Use Problem 12. Then $\{f(\delta^n)\}$ is bounded because $\{\delta^n\}$ is bounded.〗

17. Let S_1, S_2 be closed linear subspaces of a Banach space, with $S_1 \cap S_2 = \{0\}$. Define p, a norm on $S_1 + S_2$, by $p(a + b) = \|a\| + \|b\|$. Show that p is a complete norm.

18. In Problem 17, the following three conditions are equivalent: (i) $S + S_2$ is closed, (ii) p is equivalent to the original norm of the space, (iii) there exists a constant $k > 0$ such that $\|a + b\| \geq k\|a\|$ for $a \in S_1$, $b \in S_2$. 〖(i) implies (ii) by Corollary 2; (iii) implies (ii), for $\|a + b\| \leq p(a + b) \leq 2\|a\| + \|a + b\| \leq (2/k + 1)\|a + b\|$.〗

19. Let A be a Fréchet space and let S_1, S_2 be complementary linear subspaces of A. Show that the projection onto S_1 along S_2 is continuous if and only if S_1, S_2 are both closed. If $x_n \to 0$, $Px_n \to y$, then $y \in S_1$. Also $Px_n - x_n \to y$, so $y \in P^{\perp} = S_2$. Thus $y = 0$ and P is closed.

20. Let A be a Banach space, and S a closed, total subspace of A^*. Then S is norming if and only if $\hat{A} + S^{\perp}$ is closed in A^{**}. 〖Problem 18 and Section 7.2, Problem 29.〗

21. Use Problem 20 and Section 7.2, Problem 28, to solve Section 7.5, Problem 19.

22. Let f be a continuous linear functional on A^*, where A is a Banach space. Suppose that $f \notin \hat{A}$. Show that $f^\perp$ is norming. 〚Problem 20, and Section 10.6, Corollary 5.〛

▲23. Give an example of a nonreflexive Banach space A such that every total subspace of A^* is norming. 〚Let $\hat{A}$ have finite codimension in A^{**}. See Appendix H, and Problem 20.〛

24. In the definition of paranorm, Section 4.1, Definition 1, show that if the space is complete, Assumption (v), joint continuity of multiplication by scalars, can be replaced by the assumption that ta is separately continuous in t and in a; that is, prove Assumption (v) from this apparently weaker assumption. 〚For scalar t, $|t| \leq 1$, define $f_t \colon A \to A$ by $f_t(a) = ta$. The family (f_t) is equicontinuous. by an extension of Corollary 3.〛

25. Let A, B be Banach spaces and $T \colon A \to B$ continuous linear and range-closed. Then there exists a number M such that every $b \in T[A]$ can be written $b = T(a)$ with $\|a\| \leq M\|b\|$. 〚$T \colon A/T^\perp \to T[A]$ has a continuous, hence bounded, inverse.〛

11.3 *FH* spaces

In this section we present a framework in which applications of the closed-graph theorem are natural and easy.

Let H be a linear space which is also a Hausdorff space. No connection is assumed between the topology and the linear structure; in particular, H need not be a linear topological space. (However, in all the examples presented here, H is actually a linear separated space.) No results are given about H, yet all the results in this section would be false without it. Thus H acts as a kind of catalyst. It might also be looked upon as a framework within which the arguments occur.

Although applications of the results of this section occur throughout the remainder of the book, the principal applications are in Section 12.4 and a glance at its results would augment the discussion of this section.

DEFINITION 1. *Let* H *be a Hausdorff space and a linear space. An* FH *space is a Fréchet space* X *such that*

    (i)   X *is a linear subspace of* H,
    (ii) *the topology of* X *is stronger than that of* H.

(*The letters* F *and* H *are in honor of M. Fréchet and F. Hausdorff.*)

It goes without saying that one cannot recognize whether a given space is an *FH* space unless H is specified. Since, if X is an *FH* space, $i \colon X \to H$ is continuous, we may speak of X as *continuously embedded in* H.

★ *Example 1: FK spaces.* Let H be s. Then the sequence spaces l^p, $p > 0$, c_0, c, m, E^n, are *FH* spaces. 〚Section 9.3, Example 7.〛 This special kind of *FH* space, in which $H = s$, is called an *FK space.* (The letter K stands for the German word Koordinat.) Thus an *FK* space is a Fréchet sequence space with continuous coordinates 〚Since s has the weakest linear topology such that coordinates are continuous; see Section 9.3, Example 7〛. This means, here, that $a^n \to a$ implies $a_k^n \to a_k$ for each k. The concept of *FK* space is reasonably general. For example, it turns out that every Fréchet space with a basis is an *FK* space 〚Section 4, Corollary 1〛.

Example 2. Let A be a triangle. Then c_A is an *FK* space [Section 9.3, Example 8]. This will be extended to general matrices in Section 12.4.

★ *Example 3.* Let H be real F, the space of real functions on $[0, 1]$. Then real C is an *FH* space. So also are $C^{(n)}$, $n = 1, 2, \ldots$, and $C^{(\infty)}$. To prove this, for $0 \leq t \leq 1$, define $\hat{t}$, a function on F, by $\hat{t}(a) = a(t)$ for $a \in F$. Then F has the weak topology by $\{\hat{t}: 0 \leq t \leq 1\}$ [Section 9.3, Example 2; $F = R^{[0,1]}$]. But each $\hat{t}$ is continuous on C, $C^{(n)}$, $C^{(\infty)}$. [For C, $C^{(n)}$, we have $|\hat{t}(a)| = |a(t)| \leq \|a\|$. For $C^{(\infty)}$, let $a_k \to 0$. This means [Table of Spaces and Section 4.1, Theorem 1] that $\|a_k\|_n \to 0$ for each k; but $|\hat{t}(a_k)| = |a_k(t)| \leq \|a_k\|_0$]. Thus the topology of these spaces is stronger than that of F. With $H = F$, a similar discussion shows that C is an *FH* space.

The fundamental idea from which the main results flow is the following.

THEOREM 1.   *Let* X *be a Fréchet space,* Y *an* FH *space for some* H, *and* g: X $\to$ Y *a linear function.   Then* g *is continuous if and only if it is continuous as a map to* H.

If $g: X \to Y$ is continuous, so is $g: X \to H$ since H is weaker. Conversely, if $g: X \to H$ is continuous, the closed-graph lemma [Section 1, Problem 9] says that $g: X \to Y$ is closed. By the closed-graph theorem, it is continuous.//

Remark. In the following, the notation $X \subset Y$ will mean only that X is a subset of Y, hence, also, X is a linear subspace of Y. The inclusion does not refer to any relation between the topologies of X, Y, although, as a matter of fact, such a relation will follow, as we now see. When comparing the topologies, it is, of course, the relative topology of Y on X that is compared with the topology of X.

COROLLARY 1.   *Let* H *be given.   Let* X, Y *be* FH *spaces with* X $\subset$ Y.   *Then the topology of* X *is stronger than that of* Y.   *In particular an* FH *space has a unique* FH *topology; that is, a linear subspace of* H *has at most one topology which makes it an* FH *space.*

Apply Theorem 1 to the inclusion map from X to Y.

LEMMA 1.   *In Corollary 1, the* X *topology is strictly stronger than the* Y *topology if and only if* X *is not a closed subset of* Y.

Let X_Y denote X with the Y metric. If X is a closed subset of Y, then X_Y is complete, hence an *FH* space. By Corollary 1, X_Y and X have the same topology. Conversely, if X_Y, X have the same topology, X_Y is complete. [X_Y, X have equivalent invariant metrics with X complete. See Section 6.1, Problem 10.] Thus X_Y is a closed subset of Y and so is X, since they are the same set.//

★ *Example 4.* Corollary 1 "explains" why, for example, the topology of l is strictly stronger than that of c_0, for l and c_0 are both *FK* spaces, and $l \subset c_0$. Similarly, $l^{1/2}$ has a stronger topology than l^4, c than m, *et cetera*. Indeed, the list in Section 1.2, Problem 1, omitting E^∞, spells out the order of the natural topologies. Notice that c and m have the same topology; c is a closed subset of m. This illustrates Lemma 1. Some of these results also follow from Jensen's inequality.

★ *Example 5.* $C^{(\infty)} \subset C^{(m)} \subset C^{(n)} \subset$ real C, if $m > n$, and again, by Corollary 1 and Example 3, these topologies strictly decrease in strength, reading from left to right.

Example 6. $L^q \subset L^p \subset M$ for $q > p > 0$.   Since $a_n \to 0$ in L^p implies that $a_n \to 0$ in M, it follows that, with $H = M$, the L^p spaces are *FH* spaces and their topologies are ordered so that L^q has a stronger topology than L^p if $q > p$.   This also follows from an analogue of Jensen's inequality [Section 1.4, Problem 5].

COROLLARY 2.   *Let a linear space be given two topologies with each of which it becomes a Fréchet space.   Suppose that there is a Hausdorff topology which is weaker than both of the given topologies.   Then the two topologies are the same.*

This is the uniqueness part of Corollary 1.//

COROLLARY 3.   *Let a linear space* A *be given two topologies with each of which it becomes a Fréchet space.   Suppose that there is a separating family* Φ *of functionals on* A *(not necessarily linear), each of which is continuous in both topologies.   Then the topologies are the same.*

Apply Corollary 2.   The weaker Hausdorff topology is the weak topology by Φ.   This is Hausdorff since Φ is separating [Section 9.3, Problem 6] and is weaker than the two given topologies since it is the weakest for which all members of Φ are continuous.//

Remark.   These corollaries explain why the natural topologies for the various sequence and function spaces are said to be natural.   In the case of the sequence spaces, they have a unique topology which makes them Fréchet spaces and for which coordinates are continuous.   The case for some of the function spaces is the same except that "coordinates" is replaced by "points" [Example 6].

COROLLARY 4.   *Let* X *be a Fréchet space,* Y *an FK space, and* g: X $\to$ Y *a linear function.   Then* g *is continuous if and only if its components are, that is, if and only if* g(x) = {f$_n$(x)} *for* x $\in$ X, *with each* f$_n$ *continuous.*

This is the form taken by Theorem 1 if $H = s$.//
This result should be compared with Section 9.3, Problem 22, which says that $f: T \to \pi A_\beta$ is continuous if and only if $P_\beta f$ is continuous for each β.   In Corollary 4, this result is shown for certain topologies on the range space stronger than the product topology.

COROLLARY 5.   *Any matrix map between* FK *spaces is continuous.*

Let A be a matrix, and let X, Y be the *FK* spaces involved.   For each $x \in X$, we assume that $Ax \in Y$; that is, $(Ax)_n \equiv \Sigma_{k=1}^{\infty} a_{nk} t_k$ exists for each n and that $\{(Ax)_n\} \in Y$.   Thus, for each n, $(Ax)_n$ is continuous as a function of x [Section 2, Corollary 4].   Hence, by Corollary 4, A is continuous.//

THEOREM 2.   *Let* H *be given.   Let* X, Y, *with* X $\subset$ Y, X $\neq$ Y, *be* FH *spaces.   Then* X *is of first category in* Y.

Corollary 7 extends this result.   The inclusion map $i: X \to Y$ is continuous [Corollary 1], linear, and not onto.   The result follows from Section 2, Problem 1.//

COROLLARY 6. *Let* H *be given. Let* {X$_n$} *be a finite or countably infinite collection of* FH *spaces with no one of them including all the others. Then* $\cup$X$_n$ *cannot be given a topology which makes it into an* FH *space.*

Theorem 2 provides that if it could be given such a topology, it would be of first category in itself.//

Problem 33 extends this, showing that no subset of $\cup X_n$ is an *FH* space unless it is a subset of one of the X_n.

Example 7. Clearly $\cup_{n=1}^{\infty} l^n \subset c_0$. It follows from Corollary 6 that this inclusion is strict. Thus there exists a sequence $\{a_k\}$ of complex numbers such that $a_k \rightarrow 0$ but $\Sigma |a_k|^n$ diverges for every positive integer n. (An example is $a_k = 1/\log k$.)

THEOREM 3. *Let* H *be given. Let* {X$_n$} *be a sequence of* FH *spaces. Then* X $\equiv \cap$X$_n$ *becomes an* FH *space with the weakest topology stronger than all the* X$_n$ *topologies, that is, if* X$_n$ *has topology* T$_n$, $\cap$X$_n$ *is FH with* $\vee$T$_n$.

The given topology is metrizable with an invariant metric [Section 9.3, Theorem 2; Section 4.1, Theorem 1]. The metric is obviously stronger than that of H. Finally, to show completeness, let $\{x_n\}$ be a Cauchy sequence. For each k, $\{x_n\}$ is a Cauchy sequence in X_k [Section 5.3, Problem 15], hence convergent. Say $x_n \rightarrow t_k$ in X_k. Then $x_n \rightarrow t_k$ in H; hence all t_k are the same, say $t_k = x$ for all k. Then $x_n \rightarrow x$ in X_k for every k, and so $x_n \rightarrow x$ in X [Section 9.3, Theorem 1].//

COROLLARY 7. *Let* H *be given. Let* X, Y *be* FH *spaces with* X $\not\subset$ Y. *Then* X $\cap$ Y *is of first category in* X.

$X \cap Y$ is an *FH* space [Theorem 3]. The result follows by Theorem 2.//

Problems 11.3

In this list, H is a fixed Hausdorff space which is also a linear space. In certain problems, H is further specified. X, X_1, X_2, Y, Y_1, Y_2 are *FH* spaces, except where otherwise specified.

★1. Let X be an *FK* space, $\{t_n\}$ a complex sequence such that $f(x) = \Sigma t_n x_n$ converges for all $x \in X$. Show that f is continuous. [Section 2, Problem 12.]

2. If, in Problem 1, X has all the properties of an *FK* space except completeness, f need not be continuous. [$X = E^{\infty} \subset c$, $t_n = 1$.]

3. Give an example of a Fréchet sequence space which is not an *FK* space. [Corollary 1, and Section 7.5, Example 6.]

4. If, in Problem 1, X is a Fréchet sequence space, not necessarily *FK*, f need not be continuous. [$t = \delta^r$.]

5. Let S be a set and $H = F[S]$. Show that a linear subspace of H is an *FH* space if and only if it is given a complete linear metric such that points of S are continuous. [As in Example 3.]

6. Show that A_c is an *FH* space with $H = F[S]$, S being the unit disk in the complex plane.

7. Show that E_c is an *FH* space with $H = F[E]$.

8. Let $X_1 \subset X$, $Y_1 \subset Y$. Let $f: X \rightarrow Y$ be linear and continuous and suppose $f[X_1] \subset Y_1$. Then $f: X_1 \rightarrow Y_1$ is continuous. [Closed-graph lemma.]

9. In Problem 8, replace either X or Y or both by H.

10. The result of Problem 8 is false if, instead of FH, the spaces mentioned are merely Fréchet spaces.

11. In Theorem 1 the assumption that X is complete cannot be dropped.

12. E_C has exactly one topology which makes it a Fréchet space such that the points of E are continuous (see Problem 5).

13. There exists no Hausdorff topology simultaneously weaker than the two (noncomparable) norms given in Section 7.5, Example 6.

14. Let X be a Fréchet space, Y an FH space with $H = F$. Show that a linear function $g: X \to Y$ is continuous if and only if $g(x)(t)$ is a continuous function of x for each t, $0 \le t \le 1$. (In other words, $\hat{t} \circ g$ is continuous.) Compare Corollary 4 and the succeeding remark.

15. The result of Corollary 5 is false if the spaces are not assumed complete. ⟦$i: X \to X$ in which the first X is given the topology of s.⟧

16. Let $H = F$, and let X be an FH space consisting entirely of differentiable functions. Let D be the derivative, that is, $Df = f'$. Then $D: X \to Y$ is continuous for any FH space Y including DX. ⟦Fix t, $0 \le t \le 1$. For $n = 1, 2, \ldots$, let $u_n(f) = n[f(t + 1/n) - f(t)]$. Each u_n is continuous because it is a linear combination of two points; $u_n(f) \to f'(t)$, that is, $u_n \to u$ pointwise, where $u(f) = f'(t)$. Thus u is continuous and the result follows by Problem 14, since $(Df)(t) = u(f)$.⟧

17. Problem 16 implies that $D: C^{(\infty)} \to C^{(\infty)}$ is continuous. Prove this directly.

18. Let $\{f_n\}$ be a sequence of real differentiable functions on $[0, 1]$ such that $f_n \to 0$ uniformly but f_n' does not tend uniformly to 0. Show that there exists a function f which is not continuously differentiable and which can be uniformly approximated by finite linear combinations of $\{f_n\}$. (An example is $f_n(t) = (1/n) \sin n\pi t$.) ⟦Otherwise, let X be the linear closure in real C of $\{f_n\}$. By Problem 16, $D: X \to C$ would be continuous.⟧

19. Most continuous functions are not continuously differentiable. Prove this if the word "most" is interpreted in terms of category; in other words, you are being asked to prove that $C^{(1)}$ and $C \setminus C^{(1)}$ are, respectively, of first and second category in C.

20. Prove the result of Example 5 directly.

21. In the finite case of Corollary 6, $\cup X_n$ is not even a linear space.

22. E^∞ cannot be made into an FK space. ⟦Corollary 6.⟧

23. There exists no complex sequence $\{t_n\}$ such that every complex sequence $\{a_n\}$ satisfies $|\Sigma_{k=1}^n a_k| \le t_n$ for $n = 1, 2, \ldots$. Prove this (a) directly, (b) from Corollary 6. ⟦$s \ne \cup \{a: |\Sigma_{k=1}^n a_k| \le t_n\}$.⟧

24. A set S in $X \cap Y$ is compact if and only if $S = K_1 \cap K_2$, with K_1, K_2 compact sets in X, Y.

25. The result of Problem 24 is false if, instead of FH, the spaces mentioned are merely Fréchet spaces.

26. Let $\{X_n\}$ be a sequence of FH spaces and $X = \cap X_n$. Let p be a continuous seminorm on X. Show that there exists k such that p is continuous if X has the relative topology of $\cap \{X_n: n = 1, 2, \ldots, k\}$. ⟦Section 10.1, Problem 27.⟧ (Use the topology of Theorem 3.)

27. Let $\{X_n\}$ be a decreasing sequence of FH spaces and $X = \cap X_n$. Suppose that X is dense in, and not equal to each X_n. Then the topology of X is not normable. ⟦Problem 26 would force X to be closed in some X_n.⟧

28. $l \ne \cap \{l^{1+1/n}: n = 1, 2, \ldots\}$. Prove this (a) by Problem 27, (b) by giving an example.

29. Show by means of Problem 27 that $C^{(\infty)}$ is not a normed space (with its natural topology).

30. In Problem 27, the density assumption cannot be omitted. ⟦$X_n = \{a \in c_0: a_2 = a_3 = \cdots = a_n = 0\}$.⟧

31. Let $\{a_n\}$ be a sequence in $X \cap Y$. If $a_n \to x$ in X, $a_n \to y$ in Y, then $x = y$ and $a_n \to x$ in $X \cap Y$. (Recall that $X \cap Y$ is an FH space, by Theorem 3.)

32. The result of Problem 31 is false if, instead of FH, the spaces are merely Fréchet spaces.

33. If an FH space is included in the union of a sequence of FH spaces, it is included in one of them. ⟦The space would otherwise be of first category in itself, by Corollary 7.⟧

34. The result of Problem 33 is false if, instead of FH, the spaces mentioned are merely Fréchet spaces.

35. Suppose that $X \subset Y$ and X is closed in Y. Show that for any FH space Z, $X \cap Z$ is closed in $Y \cap Z$. [Let Cl denote closure. $\mathrm{Cl}_{Y \cap Z}(X \cap Z) \subset \mathrm{Cl}_Y(X \cap Z) \subset \mathrm{Cl}_Y X = X$.]

36. Suppose that $X \cap Y$ is closed in Y. Show that $X \cap Z$ is closed in Z for any FH space $Z \subset Y$. [By Problem 35, $X \cap Y \cap Z$ is closed in $Y \cap Z$.]

37. Let Z be an FK space such that $c \cap Z$ is not closed in Z. Show that Z must include some unbounded sequences. [In Problem 36, take $x = c$, $Y = m$.]

38. Any FK space in which E^∞ is dense must consist entirely of convergent sequences or contain some unbounded sequences. [Problem 37.]

39. Let A be a row-finite matrix. Show that $As \cap c$ is a closed subspace of c, hence a normed FK space with $\|x\| = \sup |x_n|$. [Problem 36 and Section 6.4, Problem 28.]

40. Suppose that an SH space is a subset of a Hausdorff space H which is given a topology stronger than that of H. (a) Let X, Y be SH spaces. If a net a_δ in $X \cap Y$ converges to x in X and y in Y, then $x = y$, and $a_\delta \to x$ in $X \cap Y$ with topology $X \vee Y$. (b) Let X, Y be SH spaces and let $X \cap Y$ be given the topology $X \vee Y$. Then a set in $X \cap Y$ is compact if and only if it is the intersection of a compact subset of X with a compact subset of Y. In particular, if two compact topologies have a common Hausdorff lower bound, their sup is compact.

11.4   The basis in Fréchet space

In this section we prove the important result that coordinates are continuous. In addition, some criteria are given for the existence of a basis and, finally, some discussion is given of the properties of the basis in Banach space. Recall that a Schauder basis, or, simply, a basis, is a sequence such that every member of the space is a unique infinite linear combination of the sequence. Also, if $\{b_n\}$ is the basis and $a = \Sigma t_n b_n$, we have defined $l_n(a) = t_n$, and obtained, in Section 6.3, Theorem 1, a sufficient condition that the coordinate functionals l_n be continuous, namely that the basis be monotone.

THEOREM 1.   *Let* $\{b_n\}$ *be a basis for a Fréchet space. Then the coordinate functionals are continuous.*

It is sufficient to replace the metric by another, equivalent, invariant metric such that, with the new metric, $\{b_n\}$ is a monotone basis [then, by Section 6.3, Theorem 1, the coordinate functionals are continuous in the new metric, hence in the old]. For this purpose we define

$$(1) \qquad !a!' = \sup \left\{ ! \sum_{k=1}^{n} t_k b_k !: n = 1, 2, \ldots \right\},$$

where $a = \Sigma t_k b_k$, and $! \cdot !$ is the original paranorm, $! \cdot !'$ the new one. We first observe that in the new metric, $\{b_n\}$ is a monotone basis. [Let $t_1, t_2, \ldots, t_r$ be any r scalars; let $a = \Sigma_{k=1}^{r-1} t_k b_k$, $b = \Sigma_{k=1}^{r} t_k b_k$. Then $!a!' = \sup \{ !\Sigma_{k=1}^{n} l_k(a) b_k !: n = 1, 2, \ldots \} = \sup \{ !\Sigma_{k=1}^{n} t_k b_k !: n = 1, 2, \ldots, r-1 \} \leq \sup \{ !\Sigma_{k=1}^{n} t_k b_k !: n = 1, 2, \ldots, r \} = !b!'.$] Moreover $!a!' \geq !a!$ for all a, thus the new metric is stronger than the old. The closed-graph theorem will show the metrics to be equivalent, completing the proof of Theorem 1, when we prove that the new metric is complete.

The following formula will be useful: if $a = \Sigma t_k b_k$, the series converging in the old metric, then

$$(2) \qquad ! \sum_{k=p}^{q} t_k b_k ! \leq 2 !a!', \qquad p, q \text{ integers}, \qquad q \geq p \geq 1,$$

⟦for,

$$! \sum_{k=p}^{q} t_k b_k ! = ! \sum_{k=1}^{q} - \sum_{k=1}^{p-1} ! \le ! \sum_{k=1}^{q} ! + ! \sum_{k=1}^{p-1} ! \le !a!' + !a!'⟧.$$

Now let $\{a_n\}$ be a Cauchy sequence in the new metric. Then $a_n = \sum_{k=1}^{\infty} t_{nk} b_k$, where $t_{nk} = l_k(a_n)$, the series converging in the old metric. Fix a positive integer k. Then $\{t_{nk} b_k\}$ is a Cauchy sequence in the old metric ⟦for $!t_{pk} b_k - t_{qk} b_k! = !(t_{pk} - t_{qk}) b_k! \le 2 !a_p - a_q!'$ by formula (2)⟧. Thus it is convergent and we write

(3)
$$y_k = \text{old } \lim_{n \to \infty} t_{nk} b_k,$$

thus defining y_k. It follows from Section 10.6, Problem 4, that

(4)
$$\lim t_{nk} = t_k \text{ exists for each } k,$$

and

(5)
$$y_k = t_k b_k \text{ for some scalar } t_k.$$

We next show that $\sum y_k$ converges in the old metric. We have $!\sum_p^q y_k! \le !\sum_p^q (y_k - t_{nk} b_k)! + !\sum_p^q (t_{nk} - t_{mk}) b_k! + !\sum_p^q t_{mk} b_k! = T_1 + T_2 + T_3$, say. Given $\epsilon > 0$, fix m so that $n > m$ implies that $T_2 < \epsilon/3$. ⟦Observe that, it follows from formula (2) that $T_2 < 2 !a_n - a_m!'$.⟧ Next choose N so that $q > N$, $p > N$ imply that $T_3 < \epsilon/3$. (Here m is fixed, and T_3 is a section of a convergent series.) Finally, with fixed $q > N$, $p > N$, choose n so large that $T_1 < \epsilon/3$ ⟦possible, by equation (3)⟧. Let $a = \sum y_k$, converging in the old metric. Thus, from relation (5), $a = \sum t_k b_k$, converging in the old metric, and so, since $\{b_k\}$ is a basis (and *not* because of the as yet undemonstrated continuity of l_k), $l_k(a) = t_k$.

The proof is completed by showing that $a_r \to a$ in the new metric. Given $\epsilon > 0$, choose N such that $q > N$, $p > N$ imply that $!a_p - a_q!' < \epsilon$. Then, for any m and any p, q with $q \ge p > N$, we have $!\sum_{k=1}^{m} (t_{pk} - t_{qk}) b_k! \le 2 !a_p - a_q!' < \epsilon$, by formula (2), and so, letting $q \to \infty$ and using relation (4), we have $!\sum_{k=1}^{m} (t_{pk} - t_k) b_k! \le \epsilon$. Taking the sup of this over all m yields $!a_p - a!' \le \epsilon$ for $p \ge N.$//

Example 1: A separable Fréchet space which has no basis. Examples are M, L^p, $0 < p < 1$. This follows from Theorem 1 and the fact that these spaces have no continuous linear functional except 0 ⟦Section 7.5, Examples 10 and 11⟧.

COROLLARY 1. *Every Fréchet space with a basis is congruent with an* FK *space.*

Let A be the space. To each $a \in A$, $a = \sum t_k b_k$ corresponds the sequence $t = \{t_k\}$. The set of all such t is a sequence space isomorphic with A. We transfer to it the metric of A, that is, we define $!t! = !\sum t_k b_k!$. Theorem 1 says that each t_k is a continuous function of a.//

DEFINITION 1. *A set* S *is called topologically free if, for every* a $\in$ S, a *does not belong to the linear closure of* S $\setminus$ $\{a\}$.

★ *Example 2: A topologically free set is linearly independent, but not conversely.* ⟦Let S be linearly dependent. Then, for some distinct $a, a_1, a_2, \ldots, a_n \in S$, $a = \sum t_k a_k$ for some scalars t. Thus $a \in \text{span}\{a_1, a_2, \ldots, a_n\} \subset \text{span } S \setminus \{a\}.$⟧ That the converse fails is shown in Example 4.

★ *Example 3.* If a set S is topologically free, it satisfies a stronger version of linear independence, namely $\Sigma t_k a_k = 0$, a_1, a_2, $\ldots \in S$ imply that $t_k = 0$ for all k. This means that no linear combination, finite or infinite, may be zero. [If $\Sigma t_k a_k = 0$, $t_r \neq 0$, then

$$(-1/t_r)\Sigma\{t_k a_k: k = 1, 2, \ldots, n; k \neq r\} = a_r,$$

so that a sequence of linear combinations of $S \setminus \{a_r\}$ converges to a_r.] However, the converse is false [Problem 5].

Example 4. In C, let $a_n(x) = x^{n-1}$ for $n = 1, 2, \ldots$, $a_0(x) = 1/(2 - x)$, and $S = \{a_n\}$, $n = 0, 1, 2, \ldots$. Then S is linearly independent. However, it is not topologically free, since $a_0 = \Sigma_{n=1}^{\infty} a_n/2^n$.

As in Section 6.3, we define a set S and a collection Φ of functions to be *biorthogonal* if they are in one-to-one correspondence such that, if $f \in \Phi$ corresponds to $a_f \in S$, then $f(a_f) = 1$, while $f(a) = 0$ for $a \in S$, $a \neq a_f$.

THEOREM 2. *Let* S *be a set in a linear topological space. Suppose that there exists a set* Φ *of continuous linear functionals such that* (Φ, S) *is a biorthogonal pair. Then* S *is topologically free.*

Let $a \in S$. Then $a = a_f$ for some $f \in \Phi$. Since f is continuous and linear and vanishes on $S \setminus \{a_f\}$, it must also vanish on the linear closure of $S \setminus \{a_f\}$. However, it does not vanish at a_f.//

The converse of Theorem 2 is false; that is, if S is topologically free, Φ may not exist. [There may be no continuous linear functionals at all, for example, in the space M.]

With the aid of the Hahn-Banach theorem the converse is seen to hold in a normed space, and, in Section 12.2 Corollary 4, this is extended to an arbitrary locally convex space.

COROLLARY 2. *A basis for a Fréchet space is topologically free.*

Theorem 2 implies this, since Theorem 1 yields a biorthogonal system [the coordinate functionals].//

Completeness cannot be dropped, even in normed space [Section 6.3, Example 4].

The linear result corresponding to Corollary 2 is that a Hamel basis is linearly independent. Conversely, any linearly independent set is a Hamel basis for its span. Is every topologically free set a basis for its linear closure? Example 5 and Problem 20 give two counterexamples.

DEFINITION 2. *A sequence is called basic if it is a basis for its linear closure.*

A basis is, thus, a fundamental basic sequence. A topologically free sequence is basic if and only if its linear closure is equal to the (usually smaller) set of its infinite linear combinations. [Uniqueness of expansion follows from Example 3.]

Example 5. In real C, let $b_n(x) = \cos n\pi x$, $l_n(f) = 2 \int_0^1 f(t) \cos n\pi t \, dt$ for $n = 0, 1, 2,$
$\ldots$. Then $\{b_n\}$ is fundamental. [Every polynomial has a uniformly convergent cosine expansion. Now apply the Weierstrass approximation theorem.] The pair $(\{b_n\}, \{l_n\})$ is biorthogonal, so that $\{b_n\}$ is topologically free. But $\{b_n\}$ is not a basis [Section 7.6,

Application 3]. (Section 6.3, Problem 10 can now be improved by adding "even if the l_n are continuous.")

We now give some criteria for being basic, that is, sufficient conditions that a sequence be basic.

▲ THEOREM 3. *In a Fréchet space, any subsequence of a basic sequence is basic.*

Let $\{b_n\}$ be basic, and $\{l_n\}$ the coordinates relative to $\{b_n\}$. (Each l_n is defined and continuous on the linear closure B of $\{b_n\}$, and all arguments take place in B.) Let $\{b_{n_k}\}$ be a subsequence, and B' its linear closure. For $x \in B'$, we have $x \in B$ hence $x = \Sigma_{n=1}^{\infty} l_n(x) b_n$. If $n \neq n_k$ for each k, we have $l_n(x) = 0$ since l_n vanishes on B' [for l_n is continuous and $l_n(b_{n_k}) = 0$ for each k]. Thus $x = \Sigma_{k=1}^{\infty} l_{n_k}(x) b_{n_k}$.//

Completeness cannot be dropped, even for a normed space [Section 6.3, Problem 12].
For the remainder of this section only Banach spaces will be considered.

▲ THEOREM 4. *Let A be a Banach space, and $(\{b_n\}, \{l_n\})$ a biorthogonal pair in A, A*. Define* $f_n: A \to A$ *by* $f_n(a) = \Sigma_{k=1}^{n} l_k(a) b_k$, $n = 1, 2, \ldots$ *. Then $\{b_n\}$ is basic if and only if $\{f_n\}$ is pointwise bounded on the linear closure B of $\{b_n\}$.*

See Problem 16. Suppose first that $\{b_n\}$ is basic. Then each $x \in B$, the linear closure of $\{b_n\}$, satisfies $f_n(x) \to x$ as $n \to \infty$. Conversely, assume that $\{f_n\}$ is pointwise bounded on B. By the uniform-boundedness principle, it is uniformly bounded on B. Then, by Section 10.5, Fact (iv), $K \equiv \{x \in B: f_n(x) \to x\}$ is a closed linear subspace of B. [Apply the result to the function g_n given by $g_n(x) = f_n(x) - x$. Consider Section 10.5, Example 6 and note that $\|g_n\| \leq \|f_n\| + 1$.] But each $b_n \in K$ [since $f_k(b_n) = b_n$ for $k > n$] and so $K = B$ [since it is a closed linear subspace including a fundamental set].//

▲ COROLLARY 3. *Let $\{b_n\}$ be a basis for a Banach space A. Then $\{l_n\}$ is basic in A*.*

We first find biorthogonal functionals for $\{l_n\}$ in A^{**}. This is easy! Clearly $(\{l_n\}, \{\hat{b}_n\})$ is a biorthogonal pair. We shall apply the criterion of Theorem 4. Let $f_n(g) = \Sigma_{k=1}^{n} \hat{b}_k(g) l_k$ for $g \in A^*$. We must prove that $\{f_n(g)\}$ is bounded for each g. Since each $f_n(g)$ is a point in A^*, it is sufficient [by the uniform-boundedness principle] to prove that $\{f_n(g)a\}$ is bounded for each $a \in A$. This we do by observing that

$$f_n(g)a = \sum_{k=1}^{n} \hat{b}_k(g) l_k(a) = \sum_{k=1}^{n} g(b_k) l_k(a) = g\left(\sum_{k=1}^{n} l_k(a) b_k\right) \to g(a),$$

since $\{b_n\}$ is a basis.//

▲ COROLLARY 4. *Let A be a Banach space, and $(\{b_n\}, \{l_n\})$ a biorthogonal pair in A, A* in which $\{l_n\}$ is a basis for A*. Then $\{b_n\}$ is a basis for A.*

Let $f \in A^*$, $f(b_n) = 0$. Then $f = \Sigma \hat{b}_k(f) l_k = 0$. Thus $\{b_n\}$ is fundamental. By Corollary 3, it is basic. [Strictly, $\{\hat{b}_n\}$ is basic in A^{**}, but this is the same thing.]//

However, given $\{l_n\}$, there may be no $\{b_n\}$ [Problem 17] and, as to a dual result, for $A = l$, we see that $A^* = m$ has no basis at all [Section 6.3, Problem 23, Section 5.1, Problem 27].

The next criterion, which is due to M. M. Grynblyum, is purely internal in that it deals only with $\{b_n\}$ and makes no mention of the biorthogonal set. Neither does it specify that the sequence be topologically free.

▲ THEOREM 5. *A sequence* $\{b_n\}$ *of nonzero points in a Banach space is basic if and only if there exists a number* M *such that for every sequence* $\{t_n\}$ *of scalars and positive integers* p, q *with* q > p, *we have*

(6)
$$\| \sum_{k=1}^{p} t_k b_k \| \leq M \| \sum_{k=1}^{q} t_k b_k \|.$$

Suppose first that $\{b_n\}$ is basic. For $b \in B$, the linear closure of $\{b_n\}$, define $\|b\|'$ by equation (1). (Since $\{b_n\}$ is basic, we do have the coordinate functionals l_n.) By the proof of Theorem 1, this new norm is equivalent to the old, so there exists M such that $\|b\|' \leq M\|b\|$ for all $b \in B$. Let $\{t_n\}$, p, q be as in the statement of the theorem. Then

$$\| \sum_{k=1}^{p} t_k b_k \| \leq \sup \{ \| \sum_{k=1}^{n} t_k b_k \| : n = 1, 2, \ldots, q \} = \| \sum_{k=1}^{q} t_k b_k \|' \leq M \| \sum_{k=1}^{q} t_k b_k \|.$$

⟦The equality mentioned follows because, setting $y = \sum_{k=1}^{q} t_k b_k$, we have $l_n(y) = t_n$ for $n = 1, 2, \ldots, q$; 0 for $n > q$.⟧

Conversely, suppose that relation (6) holds. We shall prove that $\{b_n\}$ is basic; here the fact that the space is complete is not used. The proof is arranged in five sections.

(i) Let B_n be the span of $(b_1, b_2, \ldots, b_n)$, $n = 1, 2, \ldots$; B_{nr} the span of $(b_1, b_2, \ldots, b_{r-1}, b_{r+1}, \ldots, b_n)$, $r < n$. Each B_n and B_{nr} is closed, since it is finite dimensional. Then

(7)
$$d(b^r, B_{r-1}) \leq M d(b^r, B_{nr}),$$

for $r = 2, 3, \ldots, n > r$. ⟦If $x \in B_{nr}$, $x - b_r \in B_n$, that is, $x - b_r = \sum_{k=1}^{n} t_k b_k$ for some scalars $t_1, t_2, \ldots, t_n$ and with $t_r = -1$. Then, by relation (6), $M\|x - b_r\| \geq \|\sum_{k=1}^{r} t_k b_k\| = \|\sum_{k=1}^{r-1} t_k b_k - b_r\| \geq d(b_r, B_{r-1})$.⟧

(ii) The sequence $\{b_n\}$ is linearly independent. ⟦If it were not, for some n and scalars $t_1, t_2, \ldots, t_{n-1}$, we should have $b_n = \sum_{k=1}^{n-1} t_k b_k$. Then relation (6) yields

$$\|b_n\| = \| \sum_{k=1}^{n-1} t_k b_k \| \leq M \| \sum_{k=1}^{n-1} t_k b_k - b_n \| = 0.⟧$$

(iii) The sequence $\{b_n\}$ is topologically free. ⟦For any r, $(b_1, b_2, \ldots, b_r)$, being linearly independent and finite, is topologically free. Thus $d(b_r, B_{r-1}) > 0$ and it follows from relation (7) that $d(b_r, B_{nr}) \geq d(b_r, B_{r-1})/M$. Thus the distance from b_r to B_{nr} is greater than a positive number which is independent of n. Thus the distance from b_r to the span of $\{b_n : n \neq r\}$ is positive, so $b_r \not\in$ linear closure of $\{b_n : n \neq r\}$.⟧

(iv) The biorthogonal functionals l_n exist and are continuous. ⟦According to the Hahn-Banach theorem, for each r there exists a continuous linear functional l_r with $l_r(b_r) = 1$, $l_r(x) = 0$ for $x \in$ linear closure of $\{b_n : n \neq r\}$.⟧

(v) To apply Theorem 4, define f_n as there. Let $x \in$ span $\{b_n : n = 1, 2, \ldots\}$. Then $x = \sum_{i=1}^{r} t_i b_i$ for some $t_1, t_2, \ldots, t_r$, and

$$f_n(x) = \sum_{k=1}^{n} \sum_{i=1}^{r} t_i l_k(b_i) b_k = \sum_{k=1}^{r} t_k b_k = x$$

if $n \geq r$, while if $n < r$,

$$\|f_n(x)\| = \| \sum_{k=1}^{n} t_k b_k \| \leq M \| \sum_{k=1}^{r} t_k b_k \| = M\|x\|.$$

Since the span of $\{b_n\}$ is dense in B, we have that $\{\|f_n\|\}$ is bounded ⟦Section 6.1, Problem 27⟧ and, by Theorem 4, the result follows.//

The concepts required for Lemma 1 were introduced in Section 5.1, Problem 17 and Section 9.2, Problem 17.

▲LEMMA 1.   FATOU'S LEMMA.   *In a seminormed space* A, *the seminorm is lower semicontinuous in the weak topology* $\sigma(A, A')$.

Let $a_\delta \to a$ in the weak topology.   Choose $f \in A^*$ with $f(a) = \|a\|$, $\|f\| = 1$ ⟦the Hahn-Banach theorem⟧.   Then $|f(a_\delta)| \leq \|f\| \cdot \|a_\delta\| = \|a_\delta\|$ and so $\|a\| = |f(a)| = \lim |f(a_\delta)| \leq \lim \inf \|a_\delta\|.//$

▲DEFINITION 3.   *A basis for* A *with* $\sigma(A, A')$ *is called a* weak basis *for* A.

▲THEOREM 6.   *A weak basis for a Banach space is a basis for the space.*

Let $\{b_n\}$ be a weak basis for A.   Then $\{b_n\}$ is fundamental.   ⟦If $f \in A'$, $f(b_n) = 0$ for all n, we have for any $a \in A$ with $\Sigma t_n b_n$ converging to a weakly, that $f(a) = \Sigma t_n f(b_n) = 0$. Thus $f = 0$.   The Hahn-Banach theorem yields the result.⟧   (This follows more easily from a convexity result, Section 12.2, Theorem 4, namely that the weak and strong convex closures of a set are the same.)   Since, for each a, the sequence $\{t_n\}$ is uniquely determined, we have coordinate functionals $\{l_n\}$ such that $(\{b_n\}, \{l_n\})$ is a biorthogonal pair.

To prove that each l_n is continuous we proceed as in Theorem 1, except that, in dealing with a normed space, the details are easier.   For $a \in A$, define $p(a) = \sup \{\|\Sigma_{k=1}^{n} l_k(a) b_k\|: n = 1, 2, \ldots\}$.   Then $p(a) < \infty$ for each a.   ⟦This follows from the uniform-boundedness principle.⟧   Clearly p is a norm.   Moreover, for each a, $\|a\| \leq p(a)$ ⟦Lemma 1⟧, p is a complete norm ⟦Problem 24⟧ and so, by the closed-graph theorem, p is equivalent to the original norm.   But each l_n is continuous with p ⟦since $|l_n(a)| = \|\Sigma_{k=1}^{n} l_k(a) b_k - \Sigma_{k=1}^{n-1} l_k(a) b_k\|/\|b_n\| \leq 2p(a)/\|b_n\|$⟧.   Thus we have proved that the coordinates are continuous.   Finally $\Sigma l_k(a) b_k$, being weakly convergent, is norm bounded ⟦by the uniform-boundedness principle⟧ and the result follows from Theorem 4.//

We conclude the chapter with an interesting criterion for reflexivity, due to R. C. James.   Let us say that a Banach space A with basis $\{b_n\}$ and biorthogonal $\{l_n\}$ *has property* α if $\{l_n\}$ is a basis for A^* (or, equivalently ⟦Corollary 3⟧, if $\{l_n\}$ is fundamental) and A is *boundedly complete* if, for every sequence $\{t_n\}$ for which $\Sigma t_n b_n$ is bounded, it follows that $\Sigma t_n b_n$ is convergent.   The latter property is equivalent to the statement, "$\Sigma t_n b_n$ is bounded if and only if there exists $a \in A$ such that $t_n = l_n(a)$," ⟦namely, $a = \Sigma t_n b_n$⟧.

It is easy to check that c_0 has property α only and l is boundedly complete only ⟦Problem 28⟧.   We are going to prove that a space is reflexive if and only if it has both properties.

▲LEMMA 2.   *Let* A *be a Banach space with basis and biorthogonal functionals* $(\{b_n\}, \{l_n\})$.   *Then, for each* $F \in A^{**}$, $\Sigma F(l_k) b_k$ *is bounded.   Conversely, if* $\{t_n\}$ *is a sequence of scalars such that* $\Sigma t_k b_k$ *is bounded, there exists* $F \in A^{**}$ *with* $F(l_k) = t_k$.

Compare Problem 27. Let $F \in A^{**}$. We make several applications of the uniform-boundedness principle. It is sufficient to prove that, for each $f \in A^*$, $\Sigma F(l_k)f(b_k)$ is bounded. Since F is continuous, it is sufficient to prove that $\Sigma f(b_k)l_k$ is bounded. For this, it is sufficient to prove that for each $a \in A$, $\Sigma f(b_k)l_k(a)$ is bounded. Since f is continuous, it is sufficient to prove that $\Sigma l_k(a)b_k$ is bounded. But this series converges to a.

Conversely, let $\Sigma t_k b_k$ be bounded. Since $\{l_n\}$ is linearly independent, there exists a linear functional F defined on the span of $\{l_n\}$ with $F(l_n) = t_n$, $n = 1, 2, \ldots$. F is continuous. 〖Let $f = \Sigma_{k=1}^{n} s_k l_k$. Then $|F(f)| = |\Sigma_{k=1}^{n} s_k t_k| = |f(\Sigma_{k=1}^{n} t_k b_k)| \leq M\|f\|$, where $M = \sup\{\|\Sigma_{k=1}^{r} t_k b_k\| : r = 1, 2, \ldots\} < \infty$ by hypothesis.〗 By the Hahn-Banach theorem, F may be extended so as to be defined and continuous on all of A^*.//

▲ THEOREM 7. *Let* A *be a Banach space with basis and biorthogonal functionals* $(\{b_n\}, \{l_n\})$. *Then* A *is reflexive if and only if* A *has property* α *and is boundedly complete.*

Suppose first that A is reflexive. Then $\{\hat{b}_n\}$ is a basis for A^{**} and property α follows from Corollary 4. Next, suppose that $\Sigma t_k b_k$ is bounded. By Lemma 2, there exists $F \in A^{**}$ with $F(l_n) = t_n$, $n = 1, 2, \ldots$. Since A is reflexive, $F = \hat{a}$ for some $a \in A$ and $a = \Sigma l_k(a)b_k = \Sigma t_k b_k$; in other words, this series is convergent. Conversely, let A have the two properties. For $F \in A^{**}$, $\Sigma F(l_k)b_k$ is bounded 〖Lemma 2〗, hence convergent by hypothesis. Denote its sum by a. Then $F = \hat{a}$ 〖for if $f \in A^*$, we have $f = \Sigma \hat{b}_k(f)l_k$, since $\{l_n\}$ is a basis for A^*, and so $F(f) = \Sigma \hat{b}_k(f)F(l_k) = f(\Sigma F(l_k)b_k) = f(a)$〗.//

Problems 11.4

In this list $\{b_n\}$ is a basis for a Fréchet space A and $l_1, l_2, \ldots$ are the coordinates relative to the basis.

1. In any linear separated space, a finite linearly independent set is topologically free.
2. A topologically free set remains topologically free if the topology is strengthened.
3. In a finite-dimensional space, every topologically free set is basic.
4. A basic set is topologically free.
5. The set $\{a_n : n = 1, 2, \ldots\}$ given in Example 4 is not topologically free, but satisfies the condition of Example 3. 〖Approximate $\sqrt{x}$ by a polynomial $p(x)$. Then x is approximated by $p(x^2)$.〗
6. Let S_1 be the span of S, S_2 the set of (finite or infinite) linear combinations of S, S_3 the linear closure of S. Show that $S_1 \subset S_2 \subset S_3$ and that both inclusions may be strict.
7. Where does the span of the closure of S fall among the sets listed in Problem 6?
8. The basis for E^∞ in Section 6.3, Example 4, is not topologically free.
9. Where does the proof of Theorem 1 break down in the attempt to prove l_1 continuous in the basis mentioned in Problem 8?
10. A set S in a linear semimetric space is topologically free if and only if, for each $a \in S$, $d(a, \text{span}[S \setminus \{a\}]) > 0$.
11. In an inner-product space an orthogonal set of nonzero vectors is topologically free. 〖$\|a - b\|^2 = \|a\|^2 + \|b\|^2 \geq \|a\|^2$ if b is a linear combination of vectors perpendicular to a. Now see Problem 10.〗
12. If A is a Banach space, there exists a constant K such that $\|l_n\| \leq K/\|b_n\|$ for all n. 〖Use formula (2) with $p = q$.〗
13. In Lemma 2, replace "bounded" by "convergent," "$F \in A^{**}$" by "$F \in \hat{A}$." Compare $A = c$, $A^{**} = m$.

14. Let $a_n(z) = z^n$, $n = 0, 1, 2, \ldots$, define $a_n \in E_C$, A_C. Then $\{a_n\}$ is a basis for E_C but not for A_C.

15. Completeness cannot be omitted in Theorem 4.

16. Extend Theorem 4 to Fréchet space, using equicontinuity instead of boundedness in the proof.

17. Give a basis for c_0^* which has no biorthogonal set in c_0. $[\![b_1 = \delta^1, b_n = \delta^n - (-1)^{n-1}\delta^1.]\!]$

18. A basis for A^* with $\sigma(A^*, \hat{A})$ is called a weak* basis. Show that $l^* = m$ has $\{\delta^n\}$ as a weak* basis.

19. In Corollary 4, it is sufficient to assume that $\{l_n\}$ is a weak* basis.

20. In c_0, let $a_n = \delta^n + \delta^{n+1}$, $n = 1, 2, \ldots$. Show that $\{a_n\}$ is topologically free and fundamental, but not a basis. $[\![l_n(x) = \sum_{k=1}^n (-1)^{n-k} x_k$ gives the biorthogonal set. $\{a_n\}$ is not a basis, either because δ^1 is not a linear combination, or by Problem 12.$]\!]$

21. Deduce from Theorem 5 that the sequences of Example 5 and Problem 20 are not bases.

22. Does the basis of Section 6.3, Example 4 obey relation (6)? [It was pointed out in the proof of Theorem 5 that relation (6) is sufficient without completeness.]

23. In a Banach space, if $a_n \to 0$ weakly, it follows that $\liminf \|a_n + b\| \geq \|b\|$ for all b. The converse is false.

24. In Theorem 6, p is complete.

25. Fix positive integers r, n with $n > r$. Let f be a linear combination of $\{\cos k\pi t: 1 \leq k \leq n, k \neq r\}$. Show that there exists t, $0 \leq t \leq 1$, with $|f(t) - \cos r\pi t| \geq \pi/4$. $[\![1 = l_r(b_r - f) \leq \|l_r\| \cdot \|b_r - f\| = (4/\pi)\|b_r - f\|$, in the notation of Example 5.$]\!]$

26. $\{\cos nt\}$ is topologically free in real $C([0, \pi])$, but not in real $C([0, b])$ if $0 < b < \pi$.

27. Let A be a Banach space. For each $f \in A^*$, $\sum f(b_n)l_n$ is bounded. Conversely, $\sum t_n l_n$ bounded implies $t_n = f(b_n)$ for some $f \in A^*$. (Compare Lemma 2.)

28. The space c_0 has property α but is not boundedly complete; l is boundedly complete but does not have property α.

29. If A is boundedly complete, there exists a continuous projection from A^{**} onto $\hat{A}$. $[\![F \to \sum F(l_k)b_k.]\!]$ (Compare Section 7.2, Problem 21.)

30. A has property α if and only if A^* is boundedly complete. $[\![$Use Problem 27.$]\!]$

31. Let A be boundedly complete. Then A is linearly homeomorphic with B^* for some B. $[\![B$ is the linear closure of $\{l_n\}$; $f \in B^*$ corresponds to $\sum f(l_k)b_k$, a norm-increasing map, hence a homeomorphism, by the closed-graph theorem. Notice that B has property α with basis $\{l_n\}$.$]\!]$

32. If, in Problem 29, the projection has norm 1, the map of Problem 31 is a congruence.

33. In problem 31, B^* is congruent with $A^{**}/\bigcap(l_k^{\perp})$.

34. In a separable linear metric space, every topologically free set is countable.

35. Let A be a conservative triangle. Show that the sequence $(1, \delta^1, \delta^2, \ldots)$ is a basis for c_A (Section 6.4, Example 6) if and only if there exists a constant M such that, for all $x \in c_A$, $|\sum_{k=1}^m a_{nk} x_k| \leq M \sup_r |\sum_{k=1}^r a_{rk} x_k|$ for all m, n. $[\![$Use Theorem 4.$]\!]$

36. Show that the $(C, 1)$ matrix (the Cesàro matrix) has the property of the preceding problem.

37. Find a matrix without the property of Problem 35. $[\![$Any triangle not of type M would do, by Section 6.4, Problem 24.$]\!]$

38. Why cannot the existence of a basis for a separable space be proved by taking the union of a maximal chain of topologically free sets as in Section 2.3, Theorem 1?

▲39. Can a space have property α with one basis and not with another? Can a space be boundedly complete with one basis and not with another?

40. Let H be as in Section 3. Let $\{A_k\}$ be a sequence of FH spaces, each having the same basis $\{b_n\}$ and with $\{l_n\}$ a biorthogonal set of functionals good for every A_k. Show that $\{b_n\}$ is a basis for $\bigcap A_n$ with the topology of Section 3, Theorem 3.

41. In Problem 40, the assumption of a single set $\{l_n\}$, good for every A_k, cannot be omitted. (An example with $H = s$ may be given.)

12
LOCAL CONVEXITY

12.1 Seminorms

Recall that a locally convex linear topological space, which, for short, we shall call a *locally convex space*, is a linear topological space such that each neighborhood of 0 includes a convex neighborhood of 0.   Local convexity carries with it a structure reminiscent of that of a product; namely, its topology can be described by a family of functionals, the seminorms.   (The analogy is carried much further in Problem 13.)   The structure will be described in this section.

We have already met (Section 10.1, Definition 3) a particular locally convex topology, namely, $\sigma(A, \Phi)$, or $\sigma(\Phi)$, where A is a linear space, and Φ is a family of seminorms defined on A.   We now see that this is the only kind there is.

THEOREM 1.   *Every locally convex linear topology for a linear space* A *is* $\sigma(A, \Phi)$ *for some family* Φ *of seminorms defined on* A.

Let Γ be the set of convex balanced neighborhoods of 0, and Φ the set of gauge functions of the members of Γ.   If G is a neighborhood of 0, it includes a member of Γ, hence $G \supset$ $(p < 1)$ where p is the gauge of that member.   Conversely, given $\epsilon > 0$, $p \in \Phi$, let $G = (p < 1)$.   Then G is a neighborhood of 0 [in fact, $G \in \Gamma$] and $\epsilon G \subset (p < \epsilon)$.   What we have just shown are, respectively, that the linear topology generated by Φ is stronger than, and weaker than, the original topology.//

We now adopt the program of describing a locally convex space by means of a family Φ of seminorms which generates its topology.   For example, we shall show that a set S is bounded if and only if $p[S]$ is bounded for each $p \in \Phi$, a net $a_\delta \to a$ if and only if $p(a_\delta - a) \to 0$ for each $p \in \Phi$.   Also, one can tell from Φ whether or not the topology is given by a semimetric or seminorm and whether or not it is separated.

DEFINITION 1.   *A family* Φ *of seminorms is said to be determining, or to determine the topology of* A, *if the topology of* A *is* $\sigma(\Phi)$.

Facts

In this list Φ, Ψ are families of seminorms on a linear space A.

(i) $a_\delta \to a$ in $\sigma(\Phi)$ if and only if $p(a_\delta - a) \to 0$ for every $p \in \Phi$.

(ii) $\sigma(\Phi) = \vee \{\sigma(p) : p \in \Phi\}$. [$\sigma(p)$ is an abbreviation for $\sigma(\{p\})$.]

(iii) If $\Phi = \cup\Phi_\beta$, then $\sigma(\Phi) = \vee\sigma(\Phi_\beta)$. [Fact (ii) is a special case.]

(iv) If $\Phi \supset \Psi$, $\sigma(\Phi)$ is stronger than $\sigma(\Psi)$.

(v) $\sigma(\Phi)$ is stronger than $\sigma(\Psi)$ if and only if every $p \in \Psi$ is continuous in $\sigma(\Phi)$.

(vi) Call $p \in \Phi$ *superfluous* if it is continuous in $\sigma(\Phi \setminus \{p\})$. Any superfluous seminorm can be removed from Φ without changing $\sigma(\Phi)$. More precisely $\sigma(\Phi) = \sigma(\Psi)$ if $\Phi = \Psi \cup \{p\}$ and p is $\sigma(\Psi)$ continuous.

(vii) $\sigma(\Phi)$ is separated if and only if Φ is total.

(viii) $\sigma(p_1, p_2, \ldots, p_n) = \sigma(\Sigma_{k=1}^n p_k)$.

(ix) Let q be a seminorm on A. Then q is $\sigma(\Phi)$ continuous if and only if there exist a finite subset $(p_1, p_2, \ldots, p_n)$ of Φ, and a scalar M such that $q \leq M\Sigma_{k=1}^n p_k$. The inequality is to be interpreted pointwise. (A special case is Section 4.4, Theorem 1, in which Φ has one member. Compare also Section 9.3, Theorem 7, the same result for linear functionals.)

Proofs

(i) Let $a_\delta \to a$, $p \in \Phi$, and $\epsilon > 0$. Then $a_\delta - a \in (p < \epsilon)$ eventually, since $(p < \epsilon)$ is a neighborhood of 0; that is, $p(a_\delta - a) < \epsilon$ eventually. Conversely, if $p(a_\delta - a) \to 0$ for every $p \in \Phi$, let G be a neighborhood of 0. Then there exist $\epsilon > 0$, $p_1, p_2, \ldots, p_n \in \Phi$ such that $G \supset \cap_{k=1}^n (p_k < \epsilon)$. Since $p_k(a_\delta - a) \to 0$ for each k, we have $p_k(a_\delta - a) < \epsilon$ for all k, eventually, and so $a_\delta - a \in G$ eventually.

(ii) This is a special case of Fact (iii).

(iii) Suppose that a_δ is a net in A and $a_\delta \to 0$ in $\sigma(\Phi)$. Then $p(a_\delta) \to 0$ for each $p \in \Phi$, hence for each $p \in \Phi_\beta$ for each β. Thus $a_\delta \to 0$ in $\sigma(\Phi_\beta)$ for each β and hence in $\vee\sigma(\Phi_\beta)$. Conversely, that $a_\delta \to 0$ in $\vee\sigma(\Phi_\beta)$ implies $a_\delta \to 0$ in $\sigma(\Phi)$ is proved similarly.

(iv) $a_\delta \to 0$ in $\sigma(\Phi)$ implies $p(a_\delta) \to 0$ for every $p \in \Phi$, hence, for each $p \in \Psi$.

(v) If $\sigma(\Phi)$ is stronger than $\sigma(\Psi)$, each $p \in \Psi$ is continuous in $\sigma(\Phi)$, since it is continuous in $\sigma(\Psi)$. To prove the converse, let $a_\delta \to 0$ in $\sigma(\Phi)$. Then $p(a_\delta) \to 0$ for every $p \in \Psi$. Thus $a_\delta \to 0$ in $\sigma(\Psi)$.

(vi) $\sigma(\Phi)$ is stronger than $\sigma(\Phi \setminus \{p\})$ by Fact (iv). But if $a_\delta \to 0$ in the latter topology, we have $q(a_\delta) \to 0$ for all $q \in \Phi$, $q \neq p$. But then $p(a_\delta) \to 0$ as well and so $a_\delta \to 0$ in $\sigma(\Phi)$.

(vii) If Φ is total; for any vector $a \neq 0$, choose $p \in \Phi$ with $t \equiv p(a) \neq 0$. Then $(p < t/2)$ is a neighborhood of 0, excluding a. Thus the topology is separated. Conversely, if Φ is not total, there exists a vector $a \neq 0$ with $p(a) = 0$ for all $p \in \Phi$. Then $a \in (p < \epsilon)$ for every $\epsilon > 0$; hence a lies in every neighborhood of 0. Thus the topology is not separated.

(viii) This is clear from Fact (i).

(ix) If the inequality holds, q is continuous at 0, hence everywhere. If q is continuous, $(q < 1)$ is a neighborhood of 0, hence includes $\cap_{k=1}^n (p_k < \epsilon)$ for a certain finite selection $p_1, p_2, \ldots, p_n$ of Φ, $\epsilon > 0$. By Section 4.2, Theorem 2, Fact (ix) follows.//

THEOREM 2. *Let* S *be a set in a locally convex space* A, *with topology* $\sigma(\Phi)$. *Then* S *is bounded if and only if* p[S] *is bounded for each* p $\in \Phi$.

If S is bounded, so is $p[S]$ for each $p \in \Phi$ [Section 10.3, Theorem 1]. Conversely, let $p[S]$ be bounded for every $p \in \Phi$. Let G be a neighborhood of 0. Then $G \supset \cap_{k=1}^n (p_k < \epsilon)$ for some $p_1, p_2, \ldots, p_n \in \Phi$, $\epsilon > 0$. There exists M such that $p_k(a) < M$ for $a \in S$, $k = 1, 2, \ldots, n$ and so $(\epsilon/M)S \subset (\epsilon/M) \cdot \cap\{(p_k < M), k = 1, 2, \ldots, n\} = \cap\{(p_k < \epsilon)\} \subset G$. Thus S is bounded.//

THEOREM 3. *Let* A, B *be linear topological spaces in which the topology of* B *is* $\sigma(\Phi)$, *and let* f: A $\rightarrow$ B *be linear. Then* f *is continuous if and only if* p $\circ$ f *is continuous for each* p $\in \Phi$.

(Compare Section 9.3, Problem 22, a similar result for products.)

If f is continuous, each $p \circ f$ is continuous since each p is. If each $p \circ f$ is continuous, let $a_\delta \rightarrow 0$. Then $p \circ f(a_\delta) \rightarrow 0$ for each $p \in \Phi$. Thus $f(a_\delta) \rightarrow 0$ by Fact (i) and so f is continuous at 0, hence everywhere.//

We now examine criteria for semimetrizability and seminormability in terms of the cardinality of determining families of seminorms. The situation should be compared with what is actually a special case, Section 9.3, Theorem 6.

DEFINITION 2. *If* $\Psi \subset \Phi$, *and* $\sigma(\Psi) = \sigma(\Phi)$, *we say that* Φ *is reducible to* Ψ. *If* Φ *is not reducible to a proper subset of itself, we call* Φ *irreducible.*

THEOREM 4. *Let* Φ *be a family of seminorms on a linear space. Then if* Φ *is countable,* $\sigma(\Phi)$ *is semimetrizable. Conversely, if* $\sigma(\Phi)$ *is semimetrizable,* Φ *is reducible to a countable set. If* Φ *is finite,* $\sigma(\Phi)$ *is seminormable. Conversely, if* $\sigma(\Phi)$ *is seminormable,* Φ *is reducible to a finite set.*

If $\Phi = \{p_n\}$, $\sigma(\Phi) = \vee \sigma(p_n)$ [Fact (ii)], which is semimetrizable [Section 9.3, Theorem 2]. For reference we mention that the paranorm which yields the invariant semimetric for $\sigma(\{p_n\})$ is given by

$$(1) \qquad !a! = \sum \frac{1}{2^n} \cdot \frac{p_n(a)}{1 + p_n(a)}$$

[see Section 9.3, Theorem 2]. Next, suppose that $\sigma(\Phi)$ is semimetrizable. Let $\{G_n\}$ be a basic sequence of neighborhoods of 0. For each n, there exist $p_1^n, p_2^n, \ldots, p_{r(n)}^n$ in Φ, and $\epsilon_n > 0$, such that $G_n \supset \cap\{(p_k^n < \epsilon_n): k = 1, 2, \ldots, r(n)\}$.

Let Ψ be the family of all p_k^n, $n = 1, 2, \ldots, 1 \leq k \leq r(n)$. If a net a_δ has the property that $p(a_\delta) \rightarrow 0$ for all $p \in \Psi$, it obviously follows that for each n, $a_\delta \in G_n$ eventually, hence that $a_\delta \rightarrow 0$. Thus $\sigma(\Psi)$ is stronger than $\sigma(\Phi)$. It is also weaker, since $\Psi \subset \Phi$. But Ψ is countable.

If $\Phi = (p_1, p_2, \ldots, p_n)$, $\sigma(\Phi)$ is seminormable, by Fact (viii). Conversely, suppose that $\sigma(\Phi)$ is seminormable, say $\sigma(\Phi) = \sigma(q)$. Fact (ix) provides that $q \leq M \Sigma_{k=1}^n p_k$ for certain $p_1, p_2, \ldots, p_n \in \Phi$ and M. Let $\Psi = (p_1, p_2, \ldots, p_n)$. Then $\sigma(\Psi)$ is stronger than $\sigma(q)$ by Fact (v) and weaker than $\sigma(\Phi)$ by Fact (iv).//

COROLLARY 1. *A locally convex semimetric space has defined on it a sequence* $\{p_n\}$ *of seminorms such that its topology is* $\sigma(\{p_n\})$ *and is given by the paranorm defined in equation* (1). *The semimetric is a metric if and only if a total sequence* $\{p_n\}$ *can be found, in which case all determining sequences are total.*

This follows from Theorem 4.   The corresponding result for seminormed space is trivial.

COROLLARY 2.   *Let $\{p_n\}$ be an increasing family of seminorms on a linear space (that is, p_{n+1} is stronger than p_n for each n) such that no p_n is stronger than all the others.   Then $\sigma(\{p_n\})$ is not seminormable.*

If $\sigma(\{p_n\})$ were seminormable, it would be reducible to a finite set [Theorem 4] from which we select the strongest.//

Example 1.   For $a \in s$, define $p_n(a) = |a_n|$, $q_n(a) = \sum_{k=1}^{n}|a_k|$, $n = 1, 2, \ldots$.   According-ing to Fact (ix), each q_n is $\sigma(p_1, p_2, \ldots, p_n)$ continuous and each p_n is $\sigma(q_k)$ continuous for $k \geq n$.   Thus $\sigma(\{p_n\}) = \sigma(\{q_n\})$.   The q_n are increasing and there is no strongest, since q_{n+1} is strictly stronger than q_n [$q_{n+1} \geq q_n$ and $q_{n+1}(\delta^{n+1}) = 1$, $q_n(\delta^{n+1}) = 0$].   By Corol-lary 2, we see again that s is not a normed space.

Example 2: E_C. $p_n(f) = \max \{|f(z)|: |z| \leq n\}$ for $n = 1, 2, \ldots, f \in E_C$.   By Corol-lary 2, E_C is not a normed space.   [It is sufficient to show that no p_n is stronger than all the others.   For any integers $r > 0$, $n > 0$, let $f(z) = (z/n)^r$.   Then $p_n(f) = 1$, $p_{n+1}(f) = (1 + 1/n)^r$ and so $p_{n+1} \nless Mp_n$.   In other words, p_n is not stronger than p_{n+1}.]

Example 3: $C^{(\infty)}$. $p_n(f) = \max \{|f^{(k)}(t)|: 0 \leq t \leq 1, 1 \leq k \leq n\}$ for $n = 1, 2, 3, \ldots$. By Corollary 2, $C^{(\infty)}$ is not a normed space.   [With $f(t) = e^{rt-r}$, we have $p_n(f) = r^n$, $p_{n+1}(f) = r^{n+1}$ and so $p_{n+1} \nless Mp_n$.   Another proof is given in Section 11.3, Problem 29.]

Problems 12.1

In this list, Φ is a family of seminorms on a linear space A.

1. Every linear topology lies (in strength) between two locally convex linear topologies.   [Indis-crete and balloon topologies.]

2. Show that R^2 has two irreducible determining families of seminorms with different cardinality.

3. $\{|P_n|\}$ is irreducible on c_0.

4. $\{|P_n|\}$ is not determining on c_0 (for the natural topology).

5. A sequence in $[A, \sigma(\Phi)]$ is a Cauchy sequence if and only if it is a p Cauchy sequence for each $p \in \Phi$.

6. Deduce Section 9.3, Theorem 6 from Theorem 4.

7. Any sequence of seminorms can be replaced by an increasing sequence which determines the same linear topology.   [$q_n = \sum_{k=1}^{n}p_k$.]

8. Let A be a locally convex space with topology $\sigma(\Phi)$ and let S be a set in A.   Show that $a \in \bar{S}$ if and only if, for each $\epsilon > 0$, $p_1, p_2, \ldots, p_n \in \Phi$, there exists $b \in S$ with $\sum p_k(a - b) < \epsilon$.

★9. Let S be a set in a locally convex space.   Show that S is bounded if and only if every continuous seminorm is bounded on S.

10. Let A be the set of analytic functions in $(|z| < 1)$.   For $f \in A$, $0 < r < 1$, let $\|f\|_r = \max \{|f(z)|: |z| \leq r\}$.   Let Φ be the set of these norms.   Then A, with $\sigma(\Phi)$, is metrizable, but not norm-able.   [Restrict r to be $n/(n + 1)$, $n = 1, 2, \ldots$.]

11. With A as in Problem 10, $D: A \to A$, the differentiation operator, is continuous.

12. Define $u: A_C \to E_C$ by $uz^n = z^n/n!$, (thus $u\sum a_n z^n = \sum a_n z^n/n!$).   Show that u is continuous.

13. Each locally convex space is linearly homeomorphic into a product of seminormed spaces. [$\pi\{A_V: V \in \Phi\}$, Φ as in Theorem 1; A_V is A with the gauge of V; the map is $a \to f$, where $f_V = a$.]

14. For $(x, y) \in R^2$, $n = 1, 2, \ldots$, let $p_n(x, y) = n|x| + |y|/n$. Show that $\sigma(\{p_n\})$ is the Euclidean topology for R^2.

15. In Problem 14, is $\{p_n\}$ reducible?

16. Let A, B be Fréchet spaces, Φ a total family of continuous seminorms on B, and $f: A \to B$, a linear map. Then f is continuous if and only if $p \circ f$ is continuous for all $p \in \Phi$. 〔The latter condition implies that f is closed. Or consider B as an FH space, $H = B$ with $\sigma(\Phi)$.〕 (This is the criterion of Theorem 3 in a setting possibly not locally convex, for example, $B = l^p$, $\Phi = \{P_n\}$.)

17. Resolve the following contradiction: Let D be the unit disk in C^*; for $f \in C^*$, $a \in C$, $n = 1, 2, \ldots$, define $p_a(f) = |f(a)|$, $q_n(f) = |f(n)|$ (n is the constant function, $n(t) = n$ for $0 \leq t \leq 1$). Then for $f \in D$, $a \in C$, $p_a \leq q_n$ for some n. Thus $\sigma(\{q_n\})$ is stronger on D than $\sigma(\{p_a : a \in C\})$. But the latter is Hausdorff and the former not, since, for all n, $q_n(u) = 0$ where $u(a) = a(0) - a(1)$ for $a \in C$.

12.2   Separation

For the first time, the results of Chapter 3 will be used extensively. A striking property which local convexity brings to linear topological spaces is the existence of many continuous linear functionals. This may be contrasted with the behavior of those spaces which have none at all, except 0 〔Section 7.5, Examples 9, 10, and 11〕. This rich supply of functionals will be useful in describing properties of the space; for example, we shall prove (Corollary 3) that a set is fundamental if and only if every continuous linear functional vanishing on it vanishes identically and that the closed, convex, and bounded sets are determined by the dual space. Another consequence is that the weak topology is not too weak to be useful; for example we shall see (Chapter 13) that a normed space is reflexive if its unit disk is weakly compact. Such a result could not hold for a space A with $A' = \{0\}$ (even if a suitable definition of reflexivity is made), since the weak topology is so weak (it is indiscrete) that all sets are compact. As in Chapter 3, we turn to the separation of convex sets. The work consists essentially of copying the results of Chapter 3 and making, in every case, the amusing observation that the separating functional f is continuous, since $f^\perp$ cannot be dense.

LEMMA 1. *Let* S, T *be sets in a linear topological space* A *at least one of which has an interior point. If* S, T *can be separated by a linear functional* f, *then* f *is continuous.*

Suppose that S has an interior point. For some real t, the hyperplane $(f = t)$ does not meet the interior S^i of S. 〔By definition, $Rf(a) \leq t \leq Rf(b)$ for $a \in S$, $b \in T$. (If the opposite inequalities hold, the argument is the same.) If $f(a) = t$ for some $a \in S^i$, then, choosing $x \in A$ such that $f(x) = 1$ we obtain the relations, $Rf(a + \epsilon x) = f(a + \epsilon x) = t + \epsilon > t$ and $a + \epsilon x \in S$ for sufficiently small $\epsilon > 0$.〕 Hence $(f = t)$ is not dense, $f^\perp$ is not dense, and f is continuous 〔Section 10.5, Corollary 3〕.//

For the separation of convex open sets we need not assume local convexity (Theorem 1). However, when we need to produce a convex open set by our own efforts (for example, Theorem 2), this cannot always be done without local convexity.

THEOREM 1. *Let* A *be a linear topological space, and* S, T *disjoint convex sets, at least one of which has an interior point. Then* S, T *can be separated by a continuous linear functional.*

S, T can be separated by a linear functional ⟦Section 3.2, Theorem 1⟧.   By Lemma 1, the functional is continuous.//

It was pointed out in Chapter 3 that the assumption of an interior point cannot be dropped.

Example 1.   Two sets in a space A, with $A' = \{0\}$, cannot be separated by a continuous linear functional.   It follows that any convex set with an interior point must be the whole space.

THEOREM 2.   *Let* A *be a locally convex space,* S *a convex set and* a *a vector not in* $\bar{S}$.   *Then* a, S *can be strictly separated by a continuous linear functional.*

Let G be a convex open neighborhood of 0 with $(a + G) \cap S$.   Then, Theorem 1 provides that $a + G$, S can be separated.   This separates a, S strictly ⟦compare Section 3.2, Theorem 2⟧ and the separating functional is continuous, by Lemma 1.//

Even if A is locally convex, it does not follow from Theorem 2 that two points can be strictly separated ⟦for example, if $a \in \overline{\{0\}}$, a cannot be strictly separated from 0⟧.   However, if A is also a separated space, two points can be strictly separated.   In particular, *if A is locally convex and separated, A' is total over A.*   It is possible for A' to be total over A without local convexity; for example, $\{P_n\}$ is total over l^p, $0 < p < 1$, which is not locally convex.

An interesting special case of Theorem 2 is that a locally convex space always has defined on it a continuous linear functional, not identically zero, with the one trivial exception in which the topology is indiscrete.

COROLLARY 1.   *Let* A *be a locally convex space, and* S, T *disjoint convex sets such that* S − T *is closed.   Then* S, T *can be strictly separated by a continuous linear functional.*

This follows from Theorem 2 with Section 3.2, Fact (v).//

COROLLARY 2.   *Let* A *be a locally convex space, and* S, K *disjoint convex sets such that* S *is closed and* K *is compact.   Then,* S, K *can be strictly separated by a continuous linear functional.*

This follows from Corollary 1, since $S - K$ is closed ⟦Section 10.2, Fact (x)⟧.//
Notice that K need not be closed.

THEOREM 3.   *Let* S *be a linear subspace of a locally convex space and* a *a vector,* a $\notin \bar{S}$.   *Then there exists a continuous linear functional* f *with* f(a) = 1, f(x) = 0 *for* x $\in$ S.

Let G be a convex open neighborhood of 0 with $(a + G) \cap S$.   Then S can be extended to a maximal linear subspace S_0 not meeting $a + G$ ⟦Section 3.1, Theorem 1⟧.   As in Lemma 1, S_0 is closed, so $S_0 = f^\perp$ with f continuous and linear.   Since $a \notin S_0$, $f(a) \neq 0$, and we may assume that $f(a) = 1$.   ⟦Multiply f by a scalar.⟧//

COROLLARY 3.   *A set in a locally convex space is fundamental if and only if every continuous linear functional vanishing on it is identically zero.*

Apply Theorem 3 to the linear closure of any set which is not fundamental.//

A set is topologically free if it allows a biorthogonal set [Section 11.4, Theorem 2]. In the presence of local convexity, the converse holds.

COROLLARY 4. *Let* S *be a topologically free set in a locally convex space* A. *Then there exists a subset* Φ *of* A' *such that* (Φ, S) *is a biorthogonal pair.*

For any $a \in S$, $a \notin$ linear closure of $S \setminus \{a\}$. Choose f as in Theorem 3, and let Φ be the collection of all such f.//

Given a sufficiently rich supply of continuous linear functionals, the class of closed convex sets is determined [Theorem 4]. In particular, the class of closed linear subspaces, hence the class of topologically free sets, is determined. We cannot proceed further and assert that the class of closed sets is determined, for this would mean that the topology is determined; but this is not so, since, for example, a normed space has the same continuous linear functionals with its weak topology and its norm topology [Section 10.5, Example 1]. However, Section 11.3, Corollary 3 gives one case in which the topology is determined. In Section 3, we shall see that the class of bounded sets is also determined by the dual.

THEOREM 4. *Let a linear space* A *be given two locally convex topologies* T_1, T_2 *such that* $(A, T_1)'$ $\subset (A, T_2)'$. *Then every convex set which is* T_1 *closed is also* T_2 *closed. Also each* T_1 *topologically free set is* T_2 *topologically free. In particular, two locally convex topologies with the same dual have the same closed convex sets, closed linear subspaces, and topologically free sets.*

Since a linear subspace is convex, and "topologically free" is defined by means of linear closure, only the first assertion needs to be proved. Let S be a T_1 closed convex set, and let a be a vector not in S. By Theorem 2, there exists a real number t and a T_1 continuous linear functional f with $Rf(a) > t$, $Rf(x) \leq t$ for $x \in S$. Now Rf is also T_2 continuous [Section 10.5, Theorem 5] and so the set $(Rf \leq t)$ is T_2 closed, and includes S but not a. Thus a is not in the T_2 closure of S. Since a is arbitrary, it follows that S is T_2 closed.//

A trivial special case of the first part of the theorem would be that in which T_2 is stronger than T_1. Then "convex" could be omitted.

COROLLARY 5. *Let* A *be a locally convex space. Then* A *and* $\sigma(A, A')$ *have the same closed convex sets, closed linear subspaces, and topologically free sets.*

This follows from Theorem 4 and Section 10.5, Example 1.//

The section is concluded with an example in which the richness of A' is used to draw conclusions about A.

▲ THEOREM 5. *Suppose that a locally convex separated space* A *has a compact neighborhood* G *of* 0. *Then* A *is finite dimensional.*

The boundary K of G ($\equiv \bar{G} \cap \bar{\tilde{G}}$) is a closed subset of G, hence is compact. For each $f \in A'$, let $Z(f) = f^\perp \cap K$. Then $\cap\{Z(f): f \in A'\} = \emptyset$. [If $f(a) = 0$ for all f, $a = 0$, since A' is total. But $0 \notin K$, since $G^i \cap \bar{\tilde{G}}$.] Compactness of K now implies that the intersection of some finite subfamily of the closed sets $Z(f)$ is empty. Say $\cap\{Z(f_k):$ $k = 1, 2, \ldots, n\} = \emptyset$.

Then $(f_1, f_2, \ldots, f_n)$ is separating over A. [Let $a \neq 0$. Then, for some scalar t, $ta \in K$, Section 10.6, Problem 19. Thus, $f_k(ta) \neq 0$ for some k, since otherwise $ta \in \cap$ $Z(f_k) = \emptyset$.] Thus A, having a finite separating family of linear functionals, is finite dimensional [Section 2.10, Theorem 1].//

A special case is the fact that disks in an infinite-dimensional normed space cannot be compact. "Locally convex" may be omitted and "compact" replaced by "totally bounded" in Theorem 5. See Appendix O, [13], p. 62.

Problems 12.2

In this list, A is a linear topological space, not necessarily locally convex.

1. There exists a convex neighborhood of 0 other than A if and only if there exists a nonzero continuous linear functional.

2. L^p, $0 < p < 1$, has only two convex open sets. [Section 7.5, Example 11.]

3. If S is fundamental in A, $\hat{S}$ is total over A'.

4. Let A be locally convex. A set S in A is fundamental if and only if $\hat{S}$ is total over A'.

5. In Problem 4, "locally convex" cannot be omitted.

6. Let the alc (associated locally convex) topology be the linear topology generated by the set of convex neighborhoods of 0. Show that if T is the alc topology of A, $A' = (A, T)'$.

7. Show that S is fundamental in the alc topology if and only if $\hat{S}$ is total over A'.

8. Name a separated space whose alc topology is indiscrete.

9. The alc topology is the strongest locally convex topology weaker than the given topology.

10. What is the alc topology for l^p, $0 < p < 1$?

11. Compare the alc topology with $\sigma(A, A')$. Could they ever be equal?

12. A' is total over A if and only if the alc topology is separated.

13. Let T_1, T_2 be two locally convex topologies for A such that $(A, T_1)' = (A, T_2)'$. Show that $\overline{\{0\}}$ is the same in the two topologies. (Thus, if one is separated, both are.)

14. "Locally convex" cannot be omitted in Problem 13. [Problems 6 and 12.]

15. Deduce Section 4.4, Problem 43 from Corollary 5 and Section 5.1, Problem 17.

16. "Locally convex" cannot be omitted in Theorem 4. [Let $A' = \{0\}$; consider Corollary 5.]

17. Give an example of an infinite-dimensional separated space A such that A' is of finite positive dimension.

18. A locally convex separated space is locally compact if and only if it is finite dimensional.

19. If a locally convex separated space has a bounded neighborhood of 0 with compact boundary, it is finite dimensional.

20. In Problem 19, "bounded" cannot be omitted.

21. In Theorem 5, "separated" cannot be omitted.

22. State and prove an analogue of Section 3.2, Theorem 2 for locally convex spaces.

23. In Corollary 2, "compact" cannot be replaced by "closed," even if the word "strictly" is removed.

24. Let S_1, S_2 be disjoint (except for 0) linear subspaces of A'. Prove that A has no locally convex separated topology weaker than both $\sigma(A, S_1)$, $\sigma(A, S_2)$. [No linear functional could be continuous on it.]

25. Let $\{f_n\}$ be a uniformly bounded sequence of continuous real functions on $[0, 1]$ which is pointwise convergent to 0. Then there exists a sequence of (finite) linear combinations of $\{f_n\}$ tending uniformly to 0. [$f_n \to 0$ weakly in real C. Thus 0 belongs to the linear norm closure of $\{f_n\}$ by Corollary 5.]

26. Let A be locally convex. A Cauchy sequence in A is convergent if it is weakly convergent, that is, convergent in $\sigma(A, A')$. ⟦Assume $x_n \to 0$ weakly. Let G be a closed convex neighborhood of 0. Then $x_m - x_n \in G$ for large m, n. Let $n \to \infty$. Since G is weakly closed, by Corollary 5, $x_m \in G$.⟧

12.3 Uniform boundedness

The uniform-boundedness principle had a dual appearance for seminormed spaces in Section 7.6. The forms were: (A) A pointwise bounded family of continuous seminorms is uniformly bounded, and (B) A weakly bounded set (that is, $f[S]$ bounded for all $f \in A'$) is bounded. (A) requires completeness, but (B) does not. Of course, (B) cannot be extended to an arbitrary space; for example, it would be false in a separated space A with $A' = \{0\}$; however, it does extend to locally convex spaces. On the other hand, (A) does not require local convexity, but extends to spaces which have what is called the t property. Uniform boundedness is replaced by equicontinuity, which, for seminormed spaces is equivalent ⟦Section 10.5, Example 6.⟧ We begin with the extension of (B).

THEOREM 1. *Let* S *be a set in a locally convex space* A *such that for each* f $\in$ A', f[S] *is bounded. Then* S *is bounded.*

The result will follow if we can show that every continuous seminorm p is bounded on S ⟦Section 1, Problem 9⟧. Thus we have to show that S is a bounded set in the space A with $\sigma(A, p)$. For this it is sufficient to show that S is weakly bounded in this seminormed space; that is, $f[S]$ is bounded for each p-continuous f ⟦by (B), applied to $\sigma(A, p)$⟧. But any p-continuous f is continuous on A. ⟦The p topology is weaker than the topology of A.⟧ Thus $f[S]$ is bounded by hypothesis.//

An attempt to prove Theorem 1 by imitating the earlier proof of (B) runs afoul of the fact that we have not, as yet, defined a topology for A'.

We shall now see that topologies with larger dual spaces have fewer bounded sets and that the class of bounded sets depends only on the dual. In Section 2, Theorem 4 and Corollary 5, the analogous result for closed convex sets was given.

COROLLARY 1. *Let a linear space* A *be given two locally convex topologies,* T_1, T_2, *such that* $(A, T_1)' \subset (A, T_2)'$. *Then every* T_2 *bounded set is* T_1 *bounded. In particular, two locally convex topologies with the same dual have the same bounded sets.*

If S is T_2 bounded, then for every T_2 continuous linear functional f, $f[S]$ is bounded ⟦Section 10.3, Theorem 1⟧. By hypothesis, the same is true for every T_1 continuous linear functional. By Theorem 1, S is T_1 bounded.//

COROLLARY 2. *Let* A *be a locally convex space. Then* A *and* $\sigma(A, A')$ *have the same bounded sets.*

This follows from Corollary 1 and Section 10.5, Example 1.//

In order to extend the other half of the uniform-boundedness principle, we introduce a class of spaces.

DEFINITION 1.   *A linear topological space is said to have the* t *property if every absorbing set is somewhere dense.   A locally convex space is said to be tunneled, or a* t *space if every convex absorbing set is somewhere dense.*   (The *t* stands for the French word *tonneau*, which is used to denote "closed balloon.")

LEMMA 1.   *In a space with the* t *property, every closed balloon is a neighborhood of* 0.

This is a convenient consequence of the *t* property.   Such a balloon is somewhere dense and closed, hence has interior points, and so is a neighborhood of 0 by Section 10.2, Problem 1.

Example 1.   Give E^∞ the norm of c_0.   Then $B \equiv \{a \colon |a_n| \leq 1/n$ for $n = 1, 2, \ldots\}$ is a closed balloon but is not a neighborhood of 0, since $2\delta^n/n \notin B$.   Thus E^∞ is not a *t* space with this norm, by Lemma 1.

The class of spaces with the *t* property is, however, a fairly wide one.

★ *Example 2: Every complete linear semimetric space has the* t *property.*   Let B be an absorbing set. Then $\bigcup\{nB \colon n = 1, 2, \ldots\}$ is the whole space, thus is of second category in the space by the Baire category theorem.   Hence, at least one nB is somewhere dense, so B is.   Example 1 shows that the assumption of completeness cannot be dropped, even for a normed space.

Theorem 2 says roughly that a *t* topology is the strongest with the given dual space.   This should be compared with an analogous result for bornology in Section 10.5, Problem 23.

THEOREM 2.   *Let* A *be a* t *space, and let* T *be any locally convex topology on* A *such that* $(A, T)' = A'$ *[that is,* A, (A, T) *have the same continuous linear functionals], then the topology of* A *is stronger than* T.

Let G be a T neighborhood of 0.   Then G includes a T closed, convex, balanced set B which is a T neighborhood of 0 [Section 10.2, Problem 5].   The set B is also closed in A [for from $(A, T)' = A'$, it follows that (A, T), A have exactly the same closed convex sets; this was proved in Section 2, Theorem 4], so B is a neighborhood of 0 in A [since A is a *t* space].   Thus G is a neighborhood of 0 in A.//

Thus, given a collection of locally convex linear topologies, all with the same continuous linear functionals, at most one would be *t*, the strongest.   (There may be none which is *t*, see Section 13.5, Problem 8.)

Examples 3 and 4 are reminiscent of Section 10.5, Examples 3 and 5, which give the same results for bornology.

Example 3: An infinite-dimensional normed space A *with* $\sigma(A, A')$ *is not a* t *space.*   It has the same continuous linear functionals as, but is strictly weaker than, the norm topology [Section 10.5, Example 1].   The result follows from Theorem 2.   (Alternatively, it is easy to check that the unit disk is nowhere dense. This follows from Section 2, Theorem 4, and Section 9.3, Problem 15.)

Example 4: An infinite-dimensional linear metric space A *which, with* $\sigma(A, A')$ *is a* t *space.* The example is *s*. The rest proceeds as in Section 10.5, Example 5.

The extension of the uniform-boundedness principle, part (A), proceeds.

THEOREM 3. *Let* Φ *be a pointwise bounded family of continuous seminorms on either a* t *space or a linear topological space with the* t *property.* *Then there exists a neighborhood* G *of 0 such that* $p(a) \leq 1$ *for all* $p \in \Phi$, $a \in G$.

Let $G = \{a : p(a) \leq 1$ for all $p \in \Phi\}$. Then G is closed, balanced, and convex [for, $G = \cap\{(p \leq 1) : p \in \Phi\}$ and each $(p \leq 1)$ is closed, balanced, and convex]. Also, G is absorbing. [Given a, let $t > \sup\{p(a) : p \in \Phi\}$. Then $p(a/t) < 1$ for all $p \in \Phi$, that is, $a/t \in G$, so $a \in tG$.] Thus G is a closed balloon and so it is a neighborhood of 0.//

THEOREM 4. (i) *Let* A *be a linear topological space with the* t *property,* B *a linear topological space and* Φ *a pointwise bounded family of continuous linear functions from* A *to* B. *Then* Φ *is equicontinuous.* (ii) *The same result holds assuming that* A *is a* t *space and* B *is locally convex.*

Let N be a closed neighborhood of 0 in B. (Make N convex in Case (ii) of the Theorem.) Let $G = \{a \in A : f(a) \in N$ for all $f \in \Phi\}$. Then G is closed [since it is $\cap\{f^{-1}[N] : f \in \Phi\}$ and each $f^{-1}[N]$ is closed]. Also G is absorbing. [Given $a \in A$, $\{f(a) : f \in \Phi\}$ is bounded, hence absorbed by N; that is, for some $t > 0$, $f(a) \in tN$ for all $f \in \Phi$. Thus $a/t \in G$ and so $a \in tG$.] Since G is a closed absorbing set [and convex in case (ii)], it has an interior point and so Φ is equicontinuous [Section 10.5, Fact (ii)].//

THEOREM 5. THE BANACH-STEINHAUS CLOSURE THEOREM. (i) *Let* A *be a linear topological space with the* t *property,* B *a linear topological space, and* $\{f_n\}$ *a pointwise convergent sequence of continuous linear functions from* A *to* B. *Let* $f(a) = \lim_{n\to\infty} f_n(a)$. *Then* f *is continuous.* (ii) *The same result holds for* A *a* t *space and* B *locally convex.*

Clearly, f is linear. Let G be a neighborhood of 0 in B. Let G_0 be a neighborhood of 0 in B with $G_0 + G_0 \subset G$ and N a neighborhood of 0 in A with $f_n[N] \subset G_0$ for $n = 1, 2, \ldots$ [possible because, by Theorem 4, $\{f_n\}$ is equicontinuous]. Then $f[N] \subset G$. [Let $a \in N$. Choose an integer n so that $f(a) - f_n(a) \in G_0$. Then $f(a) = [f(a) - f_n(a)] + f_n(a) \in G_0 + G_0 \subset G$.] Thus f is continuous.//

Problems 12.3

1. A bornological space need not be a *t* space. [Example 1.]
2. A linear topological space which is of the second category in itself must have the *t* property.
3. Let A be an infinite-dimensional normed space. Then $[A, \sigma(A, A')]$ is of first category in itself. [Problem 2 and Example 3, or observe that $A = \cup_{n=1}^{\infty} D(0, n)$.]
4. An absorbing set may be somewhere dense without having 0 in the interior of its closure.

5. A locally convex space is a t space if and only if every lower semicontinuous seminorm is continuous. 〚Section 7.6, Problem 3; Section 10.2, Problem 35.〛

6. Deduce the result of Example 3 from Problem 5, and Section 4.4, Problem 43.

7. Extend Theorem 2 by replacing " $=$ " by " $\subset$ ".

8. "Locally convex" cannot be omitted in Corollary 1. 〚See Section 2, Problem 16.〛

9. Is Theorem 1 true for l^p, $0 < p < 1$?

10. Write out a proof of Theorem 1 using the following outline: with p as in the given proof, $(A, p)'$ $\subset A'$; hence $\sigma[A, (A, p)']$ is weaker than $\sigma(A, A')$; thus S is $\sigma[A, (A, p)']$ bounded; consequently, S is p bounded.

11. In Theorem 4, it is sufficient to assume that Φ is pointwise bounded on a set which is of second category in the space.

12. Theorem 4 fails for a Banach space A with $\sigma(A, A')$.

13. Let $\{p_n\}$ be a pointwise bounded sequence of continuous seminorms on a t space. Then if $a_n \to 0$, also $p_n(a_n) \to 0$.

14. Resolve the following contradiction: let $p(x) = \sup |x_n|$; then p is lower semicontinuous on s. 〚Section 5.1, Problem 18.〛 By Problem 5 and Example 2, p is continuous, but s has no continuous norm. 〚Section 9.3, Problem 17.〛

15. Extend Section 11.4, Theorem 4 to spaces with the t property. 〚Use Section 10.5, Fact (iv) and Problem 33.〛

16. Show that the balloon topology makes every linear space into a t space.

12.4 Locally convex *FK* spaces

This section contains some standard results on infinite systems of linear equations, and some further development of locally convex *FK* spaces. Much of the theory extends to *FH* spaces and does not depend on local convexity; however, for simplicity, we shall work throughout in the locally convex *FK* setting. (The results derived here are not used in Chapters 13 and 14.)

Note 1. The abbreviation (X, Φ) will be used for $(X, \sigma(\Phi))$, where Φ is a family of seminorms.

Whenever an *FK* space is denoted by (X, Φ), it is, of course, locally convex.

Note 2. We shall make frequent use, without further citation, of the fact that a Cauchy sequence in a linear semimetric space is a Cauchy sequence in any weaker linear semimetric 〚Section 6.1, Problem 10〛.

Note 3. If Φ is a countable family $\{p_n\}$ of seminorms, we shall usually think of $\sigma(\Phi)$ purely as a topology. However, if metric concepts should occur, such as an isometric map, then $\sigma(\Phi)$ is to be interpreted as being given by the usual metric, $!x! = \Sigma(1/2^n) \cdot [p_n(x)/(1 + p_n(x))]$, the Fréchet combination.

We begin by showing that almost every sequence space which arises in a natural way is an *FK* space.

THEOREM 1. *Let* (X, Φ), (Y, Ψ) *be* FK *spaces, and* u: $X \to$ s *a continuous linear map. Then* $(u^{-1}[Y], \Phi \cup \Psi u)$ *is an* FK *space and* u: $u^{-1}[Y] \to Y$ *is continuous. In case* u *is one to one and onto* Y, *only the seminorms* Ψu *need be used. By* Ψu, *we mean* $\{p \circ u: p \in \Psi\}$.

The linear topology generated by $\Phi \cup \Psi u$ is clearly stronger than that generated by Φ, hence stronger than the relative topology of s. To prove completeness, let x be a $\Phi \cup \Psi u$

Cauchy sequence in $u^{-1}[Y]$. Then x is a Φ Cauchy sequence in X, hence converges, say $x_n \to a$ in X. Also, x is a Ψu Cauchy sequence, hence ux is a Cauchy sequence in Y, hence converges, say $u(x_n) \to b \in Y$. Since $u: X \to s$ is continuous, we have $u(x_n) \to u(a)$ in s. Since Y is an *FK* space, we have $u(x_n) \to b$ in s. Thus $b = u(a)$. From this, $a \in u^{-1}[Y]$ and, since $x_n \to a$ in Φ and in Ψu, we have $x_n \to a$ in $\Phi \cup \Psi u$. This proves completeness.

That u is continuous is clear; indeed u is obviously continuous when $u^{-1}[Y]$ is given the weaker topology $\sigma(\Psi u)$.

Now let us consider the case in which u is one to one and onto Y. Observe that $u: (u^{-1}[Y], \Psi u) \to (Y, \Psi)$ is a congruence onto (see Note 3). Thus Ψu yields a complete metric for $u^{-1}[Y]$. Since $\Phi \cup \Psi u$ is also complete, and stronger, it follows from the closed-graph theorem (Section 11.2, Corollary 2) that they are equivalent.//

As this theorem illustrates, one attempts to make a given sequence space into an *FK* space by piling on seminorms with two thoughts in mind. First, enough seminorms are put on to make the coordinates continuous; certainly, the set $\{|P_n|\}$ is sufficient for this. If the space is now complete, for example, if it is a closed subset of s, the task is finished. If not, more seminorms are added to eliminate divergent Cauchy sequences until the space is complete. (This may fail, of course, since adding new seminorms also eliminates convergent sequences. For example, E^∞ cannot be made into an *FK* space.) After this process is concluded, an inventory of the seminorms may reveal some that are superfluous and so can be dropped. Sometimes, as in the second part of Theorem 1, the superfluity lies very deep and has important consequences (see Theorem 3).

★ *Example 1.* Consider the linear space m. To make coordinates continuous, place the seminorms $|P_1|$, $|P_2|$, . . . upon it. This does not make m complete; indeed this is the s topology and m is dense in s. ⟦It includes E^∞.⟧ One might, by luck or intuition, add the seminorm p, given by $p(x) = \sup |x_n|$. The set $(p, |P_1|, |P_2|, . . .)$ makes m complete and so the task is finished. However, the observation $|P_n| \leq p$ for all n shows that each P_n is superfluous; thus, in conclusion m is a normed *FK* space with p.

We apply Theorem 1 to an infinite matrix $A = (a_{nk})$, $n, k = 1, 2, ...$ For a sequence x, $Ax = \{(Ax)_n\}$, where $(Ax)_n = \sum_{k=1}^\infty a_{nk}x_k$ and, by definition, $c_A = \{x: Ax \in c\}$. Say that A is *row finite* if each row of A is in E^∞.

COROLLARY 1. *Let A be a row-finite matrix. Then* c_A *is an FK space with seminorms* $\{|P_n|\}$ *and* p, *where* $p(x) = \sup\{|\sum_{k=1}^\infty a_{nk}x_k|: n = 1, 2, . . .\}$.

The summation mentioned is actually finite for each n. In Theorem 1, take $u = A$, $X = s$, $Y = c$. The map is continuous, by Section 11.3, Corollary 5.//

Some other sequence spaces which arise naturally are now considered, culminating in the result that c_A is an *FK* space for an arbitrary matrix A.

LEMMA 1. *Let* $a \in S$. *Let* $D = \{x \in s: \sum a_n x_n$ *is convergent*\}. *Then* D *is an FK space with seminorms* $\{|P_n|\}$ *and* h, *given by* $h(x) = \sup\{|\sum_{k=1}^r a_k x_k|: r = 1, 2, . . .\}$.

In Corollary 1, take A to be the matrix whose rth row is $(a_1, a_2, . . . , a_r, 0, 0, . . .)$ so that $D = c_A$.//

LEMMA 2.   *Let* A *be a matrix.   Then* $d_A \equiv \{x: Ax$ *exists*$\}$ *is an* FK *space with seminorms* $\{|P_n|\}$, $\{h_n\}$, *where* $h_n(x) = \sup \{|\Sigma_{k=1}^r a_{nk}x_k| : r = 1, 2, \ldots\}$.

Let $D_n = \{x: \Sigma_{k=1}^\infty a_{nk}x_k$ is convergent$\}$.   Each D_n, $n = 1, 2, \ldots$, is an *FK* space [Lemma 1] and $d_A = \cap D_n$ is, by Section 11.3, Theorem 3, an *FK* space with all the seminorms of each D_n.   These may be copied from Lemma 1.//

THEOREM 2.   *Let* A *be a matrix.   Then* c_A *is an* FK *space with seminorms* $\{|P_n|\}$, $\{h_n\}$ (*given in Lemma 2*), *and* p, (*given in Corollary 1*).   *If* A *is row finite, use only* $\{|P_n|\}$ *and* p.

In Theorem 1, take $u = A$, $X = d_A$, $Y = c$.   The matrix map is continuous, by Section 11.3, Corollary 5.   The seminorms of d_A are given in Lemma 2.   The last part of the theorem is Corollary 1.//

Next, we give a standard result on infinite systems of linear equations.   Such a system may be written in the form $y = Ax$, where A is a matrix and one faces the problem of solving it for x, given y.

THEOREM 3.   *Let* Y *be an* FK *space and* A *a matrix such that, for each* $y \in Y$, *there exists a unique sequence* x *with* $y = Ax$.   *For each* $n = 1, 2, \ldots$, *define* f_n, *a linear functional on* Y *by* $f_n(y) = x_n$ *where* $Ax = y$.   *Then each* f_n *is continuous.*

In Theorem 1, take $u = A$, $X = d_A$ (Lemma 2).   The second half of Theorem 1 applies in which $u: u^{-1}[Y] \to Y$ is a congruence onto.   Now for $y \in Y$, $f_n(y) = x_n$ where $Ax = y$, that is, $x = u^{-1}(y)$ (the inverse map is not written A^{-1} so that confusion with the inverse matrix will be avoided).   Thus $f_n(y) = P_n[u^{-1}(y)]$; that is, $f_n = P_n \circ u^{-1}$, the composition of two continuous functions.   [P_n is continuous, since $u^{-1}[Y]$ is an *FK* space by Theorem 1].//

Notice that the set of seminorms on $u^{-1}[Y]$ was not mentioned in this proof.   The fact that this space is an *FK* space was sufficient.

The most important special case of Theorem 3 is that in which $Y = c$.

DEFINITION 1.   *A matrix* A *is said to be reversible if the equation* $y = Ax$ *has a unique solution* x *for each* $y \in c$.

A triangle is, of course, reversible.

Example 2.   Let the transformation $x \to y$, x, y being sequences, be defined by $y_n = x_1 + \Sigma_{k=n+1}^\infty x_k$, for $n = 1, 2, \ldots$.   Thus $y = Ax$ with

$$A = \begin{pmatrix} 1 & 1 & 1 & 1 & \cdots \\ 1 & 0 & 1 & 1 & \cdots \\ 1 & 0 & 0 & 1 & \cdots \\ & & \cdots & & \end{pmatrix}.$$

A is one to one [$Ax = 0$ implies $0 = \Sigma x_n = \Sigma x_n - x_2 = \Sigma x_n - x_2 - x_3 = \ldots$, thus $x_2 = x_3 = \cdots = 0$ and, finally, $x_1 = 0$] and onto c.   [Given $y \in c$, let $x_1 = \lim y$, $x_n = y_{n-1} - y_n$ for $n = 2, 3, \ldots$.   Then $y = Ax$.]   Thus A is reversible.

Example 3. Let

$$A = \begin{pmatrix} 2 & 1 & 0 & 0 & \cdots \\ 0 & 2 & 1 & 0 & \cdots \\ 0 & 0 & 2 & 1 & \cdots \\ & & & \cdots & \end{pmatrix}$$

then

$$A^{-1} = \begin{pmatrix} \frac{1}{2} & -\frac{1}{4} & \frac{1}{8} & -\frac{1}{16} & \cdots \\ 0 & \frac{1}{2} & -\frac{1}{4} & \frac{1}{8} & \cdots \\ 0 & 0 & \frac{1}{2} & -\frac{1}{4} & \cdots \\ & & & \cdots & \end{pmatrix}$$

is a two-sided inverse. However, A is not reversible, for it is not one to one. [Let $x = \{(-2)^n\}$. Then $Ax = 0$.]

Example 4. (*M. S. MacPhail*). Let the transformation $x \rightarrow y$, x, y being sequences, be defined as follows: for $n = 1, 2, \ldots$

(1) $$y_{2n} = \sum_{k=1}^{n} x_{2k}$$

(2) $$y_{2n-1} = \frac{1}{2n-1} x_{2n-1} + \sum_{k=1}^{\infty} x_{2k}.$$

This defines a row-infinite matrix A, the transformation being $y = Ax$. For example, the fifth row of A is gotten by putting $n = 3$ in equation (2). It is $(0, 1, 0, 1, \frac{1}{5}, 1, 0, 1, 0, \ldots)$, since $y_5 = x_2 + x_4 + (\frac{1}{5})x_5 + x_6 + x_8 + \cdots$. This transformation is one to one since, if $y = 0$, equation (1) shows that $x_2 = x_4 = \cdots = 0$ and then equation (2) shows that $x_{2n-1} = 0$ for each n. Thus $x = 0$. The transformation is onto c, for, given $y \in c$, define $x_2, x_4, x_6 \ldots$ by equation (1), and set

(3) $$x_n = -n \lim y + n y_n \quad \text{for } n = 1, 3, 5, \ldots.$$

Then $y = Ax$. Thus A is reversible.

LEMMA 3. *Let* A *be a reversible matrix. Then* c_A *is a normed FK space with*

(4) $$\|x\| = \sup |(Ax)_n|.$$

The most general continuous linear functional on c_A *is given by* $f(x) = \alpha \lim_A x + \Sigma t_r (Ax)_r$, $\Sigma |t_r| < \infty$.

For the first part, we imitate the proof of Theorem 2, using the last part of Theorem 1. The functional representation follows trivially from the corresponding representation for c and the fact that $A: c_A \rightarrow c$ is a congruence onto.//

THEOREM 4. *Let* A *be a reversible matrix. Then there exists a matrix* B *satisfying* $\Sigma_{k=1}^{\infty} |b_{nk}| < \infty$ *for each* n, *and a sequence* v *such that* y = Ax *has, for each* y $\in$ c, *the unique solution* x, *given by*

(5) $$x = v \lim y + By.$$

Since c_A is an *FK* space the functions P_n are continuous. By Lemma 3, for $n = 1, 2,$ $\ldots$, $x_n = P_n(x) = v_n \lim_A x + \Sigma b_{nk}(Ax)_k = v_n \lim y + \Sigma b_{nk} y_k$, where $y = Ax$.//

Example 5. In Example 2, $v = \delta^1$.

In Example 4, $v_{2n} = 0$, $v_{2n-1} = -(2n - 1)$; in particular, v is unbounded.

We turn finally to the representation theorem for c_A and begin with the setting of Theorem 1.

THEOREM 5. *With the notation of Theorem 1, let* f *be a continuous linear functional on* $u^{-1}[Y]$. *Then there exist* $F \in X'$, $G \in Y'$, *such that* $f = F + G \circ u$.

Since adjoining to Φ, Ψ, respectively, the set of all finite linear combinations of their members does not change the topologies $\sigma(\Phi)$, $\sigma(\Psi)$, we may assume that any finite linear combination of Φ, Ψ, respectively, belongs to Φ, Ψ. We have $|f| \leq p + q \circ u$ for some $p \in \Phi$, $q \in \Psi$ [Section 1, Fact (ix)]. Now, applying Section 4.4, Problem 30, we have $f = F + \phi$, with $F \in X'$, $\phi \in X'$, $|F| \leq p$, $|\phi| \leq q \circ u$. Define G on $u[X] \cap Y$ by setting $G(y) = \phi(x)$ whenever $y = u(x)$. To see that G is well defined, suppose that $y = u(x) = u(x')$. Then $|\phi(x') - \phi(x)| = |\phi(x' - x)| \leq q[u(x' - x)] = q(0) = 0$. Thus $\phi(x) = \phi(x')$. Since $|G| \leq q$, G may, by the Hahn-Banach theorem (Section 4.4, Theorem 2), be extended to all of Y, still satisfying this inequality.//

COROLLARY 2. *Let* A *be a row-finite matrix, and* $f \in c_A'$. *Then*

$$(6) \qquad\qquad f(x) = \alpha \lim_A x + \Sigma t_r(Ax)_r + \Sigma \beta_r x_r.$$

Here $\Sigma |t_r| < \infty$, *and* $\beta_r = 0$ *for almost all* r.

This follows from Theorem 5, exactly as Corollary 1 follows from Theorem 1. Here we use the representations of s' and c', Section 6.4, Examples 1 and 5.//

In extending this to a general matrix, we are saved much agony by the fortunate circumstance that d_A has a convenient basis.

THEOREM 6. *Let* A *be a matrix, and* $f \in c_A'$. *Then* f *is given by equation* (6), *with* $\Sigma |t_r| < \infty$. *If* A *is row finite,* $\beta_r = 0$ *for almost all* r. *If* A *is reversible,* $\beta_r = 0$ *for all* r.

Since d_A has $\{\delta^n\}$ as basis [Problem 21], we have $g(x) = g(\Sigma x_n \delta^n) = \Sigma \beta_n x_n$ for $g \in d_A'$. Now we apply Theorem 5 in the same way that Theorem 1 was applied to obtain Theorem 2. The second part of the theorem is Corollary 2 and the last part is Lemma 3.//

Problems 12.4

1. Deduce Lemma 1 directly from Theorem 1 by setting $u(x) = \{\Sigma_{k=1}^n a_k x_k\}$, $Y = c$.
2. In Lemma 1, suppose that for a certain r, $a_r \neq 0$. Show that $|P_r|$ may be omitted. $[\![|P_r(x)| = |x_r| \leq 2h(x)/|a_r|.]\!]$
3. In Lemma 2, suppose that for a certain r, the rth row of A is of finite length. Show that h_r may be omitted. $[\![D_r = s.]\!]$

4. In Lemma 2, suppose that for a certain r, the rth column of A contains at least one nonzero term. Show that $|P_r|$ may be omitted. 〚$|x_r| \leq 2h_n(x)/|a_{nr}|$ if $a_{nr} \neq 0$.〛

5. Resolve the following contradiction: Let A be the matrix whose first column consists entirely of ones and all of whose other terms are 0. Clearly $d_A = s$. According to Problem 4, $|P_1|$ is superfluous, but this is surely false for s.

6. Let A be a row-finite and one-to-one matrix. ($Ax = 0$ implies $x = 0$.) Then c_A is a normed *FK* space with p, given in Corollary 1. 〚In Theorem 1, take $Y = c \cap As$. Then Y is a normed *FK* space by Section 11.3, Problem 39.〛

7. Deduce results for c_A similar to those given in Problems 3 and 4. (Bear in mind the warning implicit in Problem 5.)

8. Every reversible matrix has a unique right inverse. 〚Solve $Ax = \delta^n$.〛

9. Not every reversible matrix has a left inverse. 〚Example 2.〛

10. A row-finite matrix which has a row-finite inverse must be reversible. (Compare Example 3.)

11. If A is reversible and row finite, the equation $y = Ax$ can be solved for all y. 〚As is dense in s since $As \supset c$. But As is closed, Section 6.4, Problem 28.〛

12. In Problem 11, "row finite" cannot be omitted.

13. Let A be reversible. For each $y \in c$, we have $y = A(v \lim y + By)$. For each $x \in c_A$, we have $x = v \lim_A x + B(Ax)$.

14. In Theorem 4, B is the right inverse of A. 〚Take $y = \delta^k$ in Problem 13.〛

15. In Example 2, $A(BA) \neq (AB)A$ where B is the matrix given by Theorem 4. 〚Otherwise $B + BA - I$ is a right inverse for A so that $BA = I$, from Problem 8. Now see Problem 9.〛

16. In Theorem 4, if $A(B1) = (AB)1$, and $v \in d_A$, it follows that $v = 0$. 〚Take $y = 1$ in Problem 13.〛

17. In Theorem 4, if A is row finite, $v = 0$. 〚Problem 16.〛

18. Suppose that A is reversible and has convergent columns, say $\lim a_{nk} = a_k$. Show that, with B as in Theorem 4, $BA = I - D$ where $d_{nk} = v_n a_k$. 〚Take $x = \delta^k$ in Problem 13.〛

19. In Lemma 3, show that $t_r = f(b^r)$, where b^r is the rth column of B, and that $\alpha = f(v + B1) - \Sigma f(b^r)$. 〚Putting $y = 1$ in Problem 13 yields $\lim_A (v + B1) = 1$.〛

20. Express P_5 in the form given in Lemma 3, if A is the matrix given in Example 4.

21. For any matrix A, $\{\delta^n\}$ is a basis for d_A. 〚Check that $q(x - \Sigma_{k=1}^n x_k \delta^k) \to 0$ for each x, where q is any one of the seminorms mentioned in Lemma 2.〛

22. The result of Problem 21 is false for c_A. 〚Take $A = I$.〛

23. Obtain the result of Section 6.3, Problem 7 by observing that B is an *FK* space with basis $\{\delta^n\}$; thus, it cannot be c or m. 〚See Section 11.4, Corollary 1.〛

24. If A is a conservative matrix, $\Sigma|\beta_r| < \infty$ in Theorem 6. 〚The series converges for all $x \in c$.〛

25. Let A be a conservative matrix and $f \in c_A'$. Let $\alpha_A(f)$ denote α in equation (6). Show that $\chi(f) = \alpha_A(f)\chi(A)$. 〚Imitate Section 6.4, Problem 20.〛

26. Extend Section 6.4, Problem 18 by replacing "triangle" with "matrix." 〚Use the Banach Steinhaus closure theorem.〛

27. Extend Section 6.4, Problem 21 as in Problem 26 above. 〚Theorem 6; Section 12.2, Corollary 3.〛

28. Extend Section 6.4, Problem 23 as in Problem 26 above.

29. Extend Section 6.4, Problem 25 as in Problem 26 above.

30. If $c_A \subset c_B$ and A is conull, then B is conull also. 〚Use Problem 25 with $f = \lim_B$, continuous by Problem 26.〛

31. If a conservative matrix sums a bounded divergent sequence, it sums an unbounded one. ("A sums x" means "$Ax \in c$.") 〚If $c \subset c_A \subset m$, the topology of c_A is the same as that of m, Section 11.3, Corollary 1. Hence A is coregular, Problem 25. Also c is closed in c_A, since it is closed in m and they have the same topology. Problem 28 provides that $c \supset c_A$.〛 Compare Section 11.3, Problems 36 and 37.

32. If a conservative triangle A has an inverse B with $\|B\| < \infty$, then B is conservative and $c_A = c$. 〚For $x \in c_A$, $x = BAx \in m$. Now see Problem 31, also Section 1.2, Problem 19.〛

33. If a conservative matrix A has a left inverse B with $\|B\| < \infty$, then $c_A \cap m = c$. (This result is due to J. Copping.) 〚Let p be as in Corollary 1. On c, $\|x\| = \|BAx\| \leq \|B\| \cdot p(x)$, hence the p topology is the natural topology for c. Now see Problem 28.〛

34. In Problem 32, replace "triangle" with "matrix" and omit "and $c_A = c$." 〚Let $x \in c$. Then $Bx \in c_A \cap m = c$, Problem 33.〛

35. Let A be a coregular reversible matrix. Then in Theorem 4, $v = 0$. 〚$v_n = \alpha_A(P_n) = \chi(P_n)/\chi(A) = 0$.〛

36. Let X be an *FH* space, and p a lower semicontinuous function on X satisfying all the properties of a seminorm except that $p(x) = +\infty$ is allowed. Show that $(p < \infty)$ is an *FH* space with the sup of the X topology and the p topology.

▲37. Give two reversible matrices whose product is not reversible.

▲38. Let A be a conservative matrix. Then $c_A \cap m = c$ if and only if c is closed in c_A. (If A is coregular, half of this follows from Problem 28.)

13
DUALITY

13.1 Duality

The reader who is interested in Banach algebra may read Definition 3 and Lemma 1 below, then turn immediately to the Banach-Alaoglu theorem, Section 3, Theorem 1. After reading Corollary 1, and Example 1 of Section 3, he may proceed to Chapter 14.

A successful duality theory is one in which a linear topological space A, and its dual A' enjoy a perfect symmetry; that is, A stands in the same relation to A' as A' does to A. In particular, we must be able to identify A'' with A under the natural embedding. Obviously, the central issue is the choice of topology for A', a so-called compatible topology, a topology compatible with the duality.

If A is a reflexive Banach space, we have A^{**} congruent with A under the natural embedding. However, since there are nonreflexive spaces, the norm topology for A' is not entirely satisfactory.

As an example of what might happen, let $A = c_0$, $B = E^\infty$ with $\|x\| = \sup |x_n|$. Then $A' = B' = l$ under a natural identification [Section 6.4, Example 4 and Problem 3]. A topology on l compatible with the duality of B, B', would be one such that $l' = B$, for example, the relative topology of s. Certainly, the natural topology for l would not do, since it yields $l' = m$. One topology on l compatible with the duality of A, A' is given below (Theorem 1). There are some limitations on what it could be, due to the fact that c_0 is not a conjugate space [Section 7.2, Problem 21].

As pointed out on several occasions, we may consider $f(a)$ for $a \in A$, $f \in A'$, as either a function of a or a function of f. In the latter case we have written $\hat{a}(f)$. To achieve symmetry in the notation we write $u(a, f) = f(a)$, defining a bilinear functional u on $A \times A'$. A further generalization of this idea is given in Definition 1. A *bilinear* function u on $A \times B$, where A, B are linear spaces, is one such that $u(a, b)$ is linear in a for each b, and in b for each a. Recall the notation $A^{\#}$ for the set of all linear functionals.

DEFINITION 1. *Let* A, B *be linear spaces and* u *a bilinear functional on* A $\times$ B *with the property that, for each* a $\neq$ 0, *there exists* b *such that* u(a, b) $\neq$ 0, *and for each* b $\neq$ 0, *there exists* a *such that* u(a, b) $\neq$ 0. *Then* A, B *are said to be in duality with respect to* u.

★ *Example 1.* Let $B = A^{\#}$, $u(a, f) = f(a)$ for $a \in A$, $f \in B$. Then A, B are in duality with respect to u. [If $f \neq 0$, there exists a with $f(a) \neq 0$. This is trivial. For $a \neq 0$, there exists f with $f(a) \neq 0$ by Section 2.4, Theorem 2.⟧   Indeed, it is important to observe that if B is any linear subspace of $A^{\#}$ which is total over A, then A, B are in duality with respect to u.   Example 2 shows an important special case.

★ *Example 2.*   Let A be a locally convex separated space, $B = A'$, $u(a, f) = f(a)$ for $a \in A$, $f \in B$.   ⟦Section 12.2, Theorem 3 provides that for each $a \neq 0$, there exists $f \in A'$ with $f(a) \neq 0$.⟧

Example 3.   Let A be a Hilbert space and $B = A$, $u(a, b) = (a, b)$, the inner product ⟦$u(a, a) \neq 0$ if $a \neq 0$⟧.   Admittedly, u is not bilinear, since $u(a, tb) = \bar{t}u(a, b)$ for scalar t. One could define u on $A \times A'$ by $u(a, f_b) = (a, b)$ or extend the duality theory to include such functionals as u, the so-called *sesquilinear* functionals.

The map $a \to \hat{a}$ given by $\hat{a}(b) = u(a, b)$ is by Definition 1 an isomorphism from A into $B^{\#}$.   It is called the *natural embedding*, or the *natural embedding with respect to* u.   Similarly, there is a natural embedding from B into $A^{\#}$ given by $\hat{b}(a) = u(a, b)$ for $b \in B$.

Consider, in Example 1, the natural embedding from B into $A^{\#}$.   For $f \in B$, $\hat{f}(a)$ is, by definition, $u(a, f)$, that is, $f(a)$.   Thus $\hat{f} = f$ and the natural embedding is the identity map. Similarly, in Example 2, the natural embedding of B into $A^{\#}$ is the inclusion map.   In general, the reader would do well to think of B as a subspace of $A^{\#}$, that is, to identify b and $\hat{b}$.

DEFINITION 2.   *Let* A, B *be in duality with respect to* u.   *A locally convex separated topology for* A *is called compatible with the duality if, with this topology, the image of* B *under the natural embedding of* B *into* A^{\#} *is precisely* A'.   *Thus, for any compatible topology on* A, B *is the dual of* A.

Similarly a *compatible topology for* B is defined as one such that A is its dual.

In Example 2, the topology of A is compatible with the duality by the very definition, since B is A' by definition.   Thus any locally convex separated topology is compatible with some duality.   As yet, however we have not faced the problem of placing a topology upon A' (Example 2) which is compatible with the given duality, or of finding other compatible topologies for A.   A complete solution of this problem is given in the Mackey-Arens theorem, Section 5, Theorem 1.

DEFINITION 3.   *Let* A *be a linear space.*   *The weak star topology for* A^{\#}, *also written* $\sigma(A^{\#}, A)$, *is defined to be* $\sigma(A^{\#}, \hat{A})$, *where* $\hat{A}$ *is, as usual,* $\{\hat{a}: a \in A\}$, *and* $\hat{a}(f) = f(a)$ *for all* f $\in$ A^{\#}.   *For any linear subspace* S *of* A^{\#}, *the weak star topology for* S, $\sigma(S, A)$, *is the relative topology of* $\sigma(A^{\#}, A)$.

The weak star topology is locally convex and separated, since $\hat{A}$ is total over $A^{\#}$ ⟦see Section 10.1, Example 7, and Section 9.3, Problem 6⟧.   If we recall that E^A means the set of *all* functionals on A, we see that $A^{\#} \subset E^A$.

LEMMA 1.   *Let* A *be a linear space, and* S *a linear subspace of* A^{\#}.   *Then the weak star topology on* S *is the relative topology of* E^A.

A net f_δ in S converges to 0 in either topology if and only if $f_\delta(a) \to 0$ for each $a \in A$ ⟦Section 9.3, Theorems 3 and 8⟧.//

For this reason, the weak star topology is also called the pointwise or product topology.

Remark 1. The two uses of the symbol $\hat{a}$ are consistent if we have $u(a, f) = f(a)$ for $a \in A, f \in A^{\#}$; for then $\hat{a}(f) = u(a, f) = f(a)$.

THEOREM 1. *Let* A *be a linear space and* B *a linear subspace of* $A^{\#}$ *which is total over* A. *Then* A, B *are in duality with respect to* u *defined by* $u(a, f) = f(a)$ *for* $a \in A, f \in B$. *Furthermore, the weak star topology for* B, $\sigma(B, A)$ *is compatible with the duality.*

Checking Definition 1, we have, if $a \neq 0$, then $u(a, f) = f(a) \neq 0$ for some $f \in B$, since B is total. That $u(a, f) \neq 0$ for some a, if $f \neq 0$, is trivial. Next, place the given topology on B and assume that $F \in B'$; that is, F is a linear functional on B which, with the topology $\sigma(B, A)$, is continuous. Since, by definition, $\sigma(B, A) = \sigma(B, \hat{A})$, it follows from Section 9.3, Theorem 7 that $F \in \hat{A}$, that is, $F = \hat{a}$ for some $a \in A$. By Remark 1, $a \to \hat{a}$ is the natural embedding. Thus it is onto.//

★*Example 4.* Let A be a locally convex separated space, $B = A'$ (see Example 2). Any linear functional F on A' which is $\sigma(A', A)$ continuous is $\hat{a}$ for some $a \in A$ [Theorem 1]. Thus, with the weak star topology on A', $A'' = A$.

Example 5. Let A be a nonreflexive normed space. Placing the norm topology on $B = A'$, we have $B' \neq A$ (strictly, $B' \neq \hat{A}$). Thus the norm topology is not compatible with the duality. However, weakening the topology on B to $\sigma(A', A)$, we reduce sharply the number of linear functionals which are continuous. Indeed Theorem 1 yields $B' = A$.

It should be mentioned that if A is a linear topological space, the topology $\sigma(A, A')$ is often called the *weak topology* for A. Historically, this name is of most interest in the case of a Banach space A. The dual space A' has the three topologies: the norm topology, the weak topology, and the weak star topology, in decreasing order of strength. The norm and weak topologies give A' the same dual [Section 10.5, Example 1]. The dual of A' with the weak star topology is $\hat{A}$ [Theorem 1], thus, in the case of a nonreflexive space, this is smaller.

We can define the weak and weak star topologies in the framework of a duality. Because of the symmetry of the situation, it is inappropriate to use these names; we shall use the σ designation.

DEFINITION 4. *Let* A, B *be linear spaces in duality with respect to* u. *The topology* $\sigma(A, B)$ *for* A *is defined to be the weak linear topology by* $\hat{B}$, *that is, the weakest linear topology such that* $u(a, b)$ *is a continuous function of* a *for each* $b \in B$. *Similarly,* $\sigma(B, A)$ *is defined.*

Thus a net a_δ in A converges to 0 in $\sigma(A, B)$ if and only if $u(a_\delta, b) \to 0$ for each $b \in B$. As before, these topologies are shown to be locally convex and separated. Exactly as in Theorem 1, it is proved that they are compatible with the given duality.

Observe that in Definition 4, $\sigma(A, B)$ is the relative topology of $\sigma(B^{\#}, B)$, the weak star topology for $B^{\#}$, when we identify A with $\hat{A}$ and consider A to be a linear subspace of $B^{\#}$. [If a_δ is a net in A, $a_\delta \to 0$ in $\sigma(A, B)$ if and only if $u(a_\delta, b) \to 0$ for every $b \in B$. For $\hat{a}_\delta \in B^{\#}$, $\hat{a}_\delta \to 0$ in the weak star topology if and only if $\hat{a}_\delta(b) \to 0$ for every $b \in B$, that is, if and only if $u(a_\delta, b) \to 0$ for every $b \in B$, since $\hat{a}_\delta(b) = u(a_\delta, b)$.]

Example 6.   Let A be a linear space and B a linear subspace of $A^{\#}$ which is total over A. Then A has a locally convex separated topology such that $A' = B$, namely, $\sigma(A, B)$ [since it is compatible with the duality given by $u(a, f) = f(a)$].

The study of the topology $\sigma(A, B)$ is continued in Section 3.

Problems 13.1

In this list, A, B are linear spaces in duality with respect to a bilinear functional u.

1. B, A are in duality with respect to v, given by $v(b, a) = u(a, b)$ for $a \in A$, $b \in B$.

★2. Let A have a locally convex separated topology.   Show that the topology is compatible if and only if (i) $u(a, b)$ is continuous as a function of a for each $b \in B$ and (ii) every continuous linear functional f on A is given by the formula $f(a) = u(a, b)$ for some $b \in B$.

★3. Any locally convex topology lying between two compatible topologies is compatible.

4. Any two compatible topologies on A have the same bounded sets [Section 12.3, Corollary 1] and the same closed linear subspaces, and convex sets [Section 12.2, Theorem 4].

5. If A is finite dimensional, so is B, and it has the same dimension as A.   If A is infinite dimensional, so is B.

6. If A is finite dimensional, every separated topology for A (there is only one) is compatible with the duality.

★7. $\sigma(A, B)$ is compatible.

8. Let $B = A^{\#}$, $u(a, f) = f(a)$, and suppose that T is a topology for A which is compatible with the duality.   Show that any stronger locally convex topology is also compatible.

9. Show that duality can be discussed in the following setting which is not locally convex: Let $0 < p < 1$, $A = l^p$, $B = m$, $u(a, b) = \Sigma a_n b_n$.   Show that the natural topology of l^p is compatible with this duality if in Definition 2 we omit "locally convex."   [See Section 6.4, Problem 11.]

10. At most one topology compatible with a given duality can be metrizable.   [Problem 4; Section 10.5, Example 4; and Section 10.5, Problem 23.]

11. Give an example of a duality with which no metrizable topology is compatible.   [A, $A^{\#}$, see Section 7.5, Example 2.]

13.2   Polars

Various significant topologies for spaces in duality are defined most conveniently by means of the polars, a device for associating sets in B with sets in A and vice versa.

DEFINITION 1.   *Let* A, B *be linear spaces in duality with respect to* u.   *For* S $\subset$ A, *define* S°, *the polar of* S, *by* S° = {b $\in$ B: |u(a, b)| $\leq$ 1 *for all* a $\in$ S.}   *A similar definition is given for* S° *if* S $\subset$ B.

Notice that if $S \subset A$, $S^{o} \subset B$, $S^{oo} \subset A$, where S^{oo} means $(S^{o})^{o}$.

★ *Example 1.*   Let A be a linear space, B a linear subspace of $A^{\#}$ which is total over A, and $u(a, f) = f(a)$.   For $S \subset A$, $S^{o} = \{f \in B: |f(a)| \leq 1 \text{ for all } a \in S\}$.   For $S \subset B$, $S^{o} = \{a \in A: |f(a)| \leq 1 \text{ for all } f \in S\}$.

We first study nontopological properties of the polars.

Facts

In this list, A, B are linear spaces in duality with respect to u; S, S_1, S_2 are sets in A or in B.

(i) For $x \in A$ or B, let x^o stand for $\{x\}^o$. Then $S^o = \cap\{x^o \colon x \in S\}$.

(ii) $S_1 \subset S_2$ implies $S_1^o \supset S_2^o$.

(iii) $S \subset S^{oo}$.

(iv) $S^{ooo} = S^o$.

(v) S^o is convex and balanced.

(vi) S^{oo} includes the convex balanced hull of S.

(vii) Let H be the convex hull, the balanced hull, or the convex balanced hull of S. Then $H^o = S^o$.

(viii) For scalar $t \neq 0$, $(tS)^o = (1/t)S^o$.

(ix) If S is finite, S^o is absorbing.

Proofs

In the proofs we shall assume that S, S_1, S_2 are in A. The proofs for the other case follow by symmetry.

(i) This follows immediately from the definition.

(ii) By Fact (i), S_2^o is an intersection over a wider class.

(iii) Let $a \in S$. For $b \in S^o$, $|u(a, b)| \leq 1$. Thus $a \in S^{oo}$.

(iv) $S^{ooo} \supset S^o$, by Fact (iii). Conversely, in Fact (ii), we may, using Fact (iii), take $S_1 = S$, $S_2 = S^{oo}$ and obtain $S^o \supset S^{ooo}$.

(v) Fix $a \in A$ and set $g(b) = u(a, b)$. Then g is a linear functional on B and $a^o = g^{-1}[D]$, where D is the unit disk in the complex plane. Thus a^o is convex and balanced ⟦Section 2.5, Theorem 3⟧ and so also is S^o, by Fact (i).

(vi) This follows from Facts (iii) and (v).

(vii) According to Fact (vi), we have $S \subset H \subset S^{oo}$. Thus, by Facts (ii) and (iv), $S^o \supset H^o \supset S^{ooo} = S^o$.

(viii) Let $b \in (1/t)S^o$. For $a \in tS$, we have $a = tx$ with $x \in S$; also $b = (1/t)y$ with $y \in S^o$. Thus $|u(a, b)| = |u(x, y)| \leq 1$ and so $b \in (tS)^o$. This proves that $(1/t)S^o \subset (tS)^o$. The opposite inclusion follows from this by the following reasoning: $(tS)^o = (1/t)t(tS)^o \subset (1/t)[(1/t)tS]^o = (1/t)S^o$.

(ix) Let $b \in B$. Let $t = \sup\{|u(a, b)| \colon a \in S\}$. If $t = 0$, $b \in S^o$. Suppose that $t > 0$. For $|\delta| < 1/t$, we have $\delta b \in S^o$. ⟦Let $a \in S$, then $|u(a, \delta b)| = |\delta| \cdot |u(a, b)| \leq |\delta| t < 1$.⟧ Thus S^o is absorbing.//

We next consider topological properties of polars.

Facts

In this list, A, B are linear spaces in duality with respect to u. We shall assume that A has a linear topology such that for each $b \in B$, $u(a, b)$ is continuous in a. Thus each point of B "is" a member of A'. We do not assume that the topology is compatible with the duality (that is, $B = A'$), or that B has any topology.

(x) For $S \subset B$, S^o is closed.

(xi) For $S \subset A$, S^{oo} includes the convex balanced closure of S.

(xii) For $S \subset A$, let H be the convex closure, the balanced closure, or the convex balanced closure of S. Then $H^o = S^o$.

(xiii) If S is a bounded set in A, S^o is absorbing.

Proofs

(x) Let a_δ be a net in S^o, $a_\delta \to a$. Then, for $b \in S$, $1 \geq |u(a_\delta, b)| \to |u(a, b)|$. Thus $a \in S^o$. [A proof like that of Fact (v) would also be easy to write.]

(xi) This follows from Facts (vi) and (x).

(xii) Imitate the proof of Fact (vii), using Fact (xi) instead of Fact (vi).

(xiii) The proof of Fact (ix) works here too, since $t < \infty$ [Section 10.3, Theorem 1].//

★ *Example 2.* Let A be a locally convex separated space, $B = A'$ (or a subspace of A' that is total over A) and $u(a, f) = f(a)$. Then the hypotheses of Facts (x) to (xiii) are satisfied.

In the presence of compatibility, Fact (xi) takes on a definitive form.

THEOREM 1. *Let* A, B *be linear spaces in duality with respect to* u *and let* A *have a compatible topology. Then, for* S ⊂ A, S^oo *is the convex balanced closure of* S.

Let H be the convex balanced closure of S. Half of our result is Fact (xi). Now let $x \in A \setminus H$. Section 12.2, Theorem 2, provides that x, H can be strictly separated; that is, there exists $f \in A'$ and a real number t such that $Rf(x) > t$ and $Rf(h) < t$ for all $h \in H$. It follows that $|f(h)| \leq t$ for all $h \in H$, since H is balanced [Section 2.11, Theorem 2]. Since A has a compatible topology, there exists $b \in B$ with $u(a, b) = f(a)$ for all $a \in A$. (We might have said $f \in B$, making an obvious identification.)

From the above, $|u(h, b)| \leq t$ for all $h \in H$, and so $b/t \in H^o$ [$t > 0$, since $0 \in H$]. Thus $b/t \in S^o$ [Fact (ii)]. Now $|u(x, b/t)| = |(1/t)f(x)| > 1$. Thus $x \notin S^{oo}$. But x is arbitrary; hence $S^{oo} \subset H$.//

The reader should observe the similarity between this proof and that of Section 12.2, Theorem 4. Indeed, the results are related. Theorem 1 shows that the convex balanced closure of a set is the same for all topologies with the same dual, since they are all compatible with the same duality, and S^{oo} is defined in terms of the bilinear functional and the space B only; see also Problem 14(d).

Problems 13.2

In this list, A, B are linear spaces in duality with respect to u. When the assumption $B = A'$ is listed, take $u(a, f) = f(a)$. S, S_1, S_2 are sets in A or B. For $S \subset A$, $S^\perp = \{b \in B: u(a, b) = 0$ for all $a \in S\}$. A similar definition is made for $S \subset B$.

1. Let $A = R^2$, $B = A'$. Find S^o if S is (a) a point, (b) a line segment, (c) the square $0 \leq x \leq 1$, $0 \leq y \leq 1$, (d) a circle.

2. Find S^{oo} in each part of Problem 1.

3. Find A^o.

4. If $S_1 \subset S_2$, then $S_1^{oo} \subset S_2^{oo}$.

5. Where was the fact that S is finite used in the proof of Fact (ix)?

★6. Let α, β be positive real numbers. Show that

$$\left(\frac{1}{\alpha}S\right)^o + \left(\frac{1}{\beta}S\right)^o = \left(\frac{1}{\alpha+\beta}S\right)^o.$$

In particular, $(2S)^o + (2S)^o = S^o$. [$\alpha S^o + \beta S^o = (\alpha + \beta)S^o$ since S^o is convex.]

7. $S^\perp \subset S^o$ and, if S is a linear subspace $S^\perp = S^o$. (Compare Section 8.1, Problem 7.)

8. $S^{oo} \subset S^{\perp\perp}$.

9. Prove Facts (i), (ii), (iii), (iv), (v), and (x), for $S^\perp$.

10. Modify and give proofs for Facts (vi), (vii), (xi), and (xii) so that they apply to $S^\perp$. [For example, substitute "span" for "convex hull."]

11. State and prove a result analogous to that of Theorem 1 for $S^{\perp\perp}$. (Compare Section 8.2, Problem 3.)

12. Let A have a compatible topology and $S \subset A$. Show that S is equicontinuous if and only if S^o is a neighborhood of 0.

13. Let Σ be a collection of sets in A or in B. Show that $(\cup S: S \in \Sigma)^o = \cap\{S^o: S \in \Sigma\}$.

14. (a) Fix $J \subset E$. For $S \subset A$, let $S^\natural = \{b \in B: u(a, b) \in J \text{ for all } a \in S\}$. Prove Facts (i), (ii), (iii), and (iv) for $S^\natural$. (b) If J is respectively, balanced, convex, $\{0\}$, $S^{\natural\natural}$ includes the balanced hull, the convex hull, the span, of S. (c) If A has a compatible topology and J is, respectively, closed, $\{0\}$, $S^{\natural\natural}$ includes the closure, the linear closure of S. (d) Let A be a real linear space, let A have a compatible topology, and let $J = (-\infty, 1]$. Show that $S^{\natural\natural}$ is the convex closure of S and deduce Section 12.2, Theorem 4 as a corollary. (e) Let $J = E$. Find $S^\natural$, $S^{\natural\natural}$.

13.3 σ topologies

We begin this section with an important result on weak star compactness. For the sake of those whose interests lie in Banach algebra, we present it first in the case of a normed space, later, in the setting of duality. The latter proof is obtained by modifications of the former one.

THEOREM 1. THE BANACH-ALAOGLU THEOREM. *Let* A *be a normed space. The unit disk* D_1 *in* A* *is weak star compact.*

Consider the following collection of disks in the complex plane. For each $a \in A$, let $D(a)$ be the disk $D(0, \|a\|)$, of center 0, radius $\|a\|$. Then $D_1 \subset \pi\{D(a): a \in A\}$. [Each $f \in D_1$ is a function from A to E satisfying $|f(a)| \leq \|a\|$; that is, $f(a) \in D(a)$, for each $a \in A$.] Moreover, the product topology has, as its relative topology on D_1, the weak star topology [Section 1, Lemma 1]. By Tychonoff's theorem (Section 9.6, Theorem 1), $\pi D(a)$ is compact. The proof is completed by showing that D_1 is a closed subset of $\pi D(a)$ (and appealing to Section 9.5, Lemma 2). To this end, let f_δ be a net of elements of D_1, that is, continuous linear functionals on A satisfying

$$(1) \qquad\qquad |f_\delta(a)| \leq \|a\| \qquad \text{for all } a,$$

and let $f_\delta \to f \in \pi D(a)$ [that is, f_δ is a functional on A satisfying relation (1), and $f_\delta(a) \to f(a)$ for each a]. Then f is linear [for example, $f(a + b) = \lim f_\delta(a + b) = \lim f_\delta(a) + \lim f_\delta(b) = f(a) + f(b)$]. Also, $|f(a)| \leq \|a\|$ for all a [take the limit in relation (1)] and so $f \in D_1$.//

The first step into a representation theory is taken on the basis of Theorem 1 by means of the natural embedding, Section 7.2.

COROLLARY 1.   *Let* A *be a normed space.   There exists a compact Hausdorff space* H *and a congruence from* A *into* C[H].   *Specifically,* H *may be taken to be the unit disk in* A* *with the weak star topology.*

The congruence is $a \to \hat{a}|H$.   (Recall that $\hat{a} \in A^{**}$.)   The map $a \to \hat{a}|H$ is clearly linear.   Moreover, it is an isometry, since $\|\hat{a}|H\| = \sup\{|\hat{a}(h)|: h \in H\} = \|\hat{a}\| = \|a\|$. Finally, $\hat{a}|H$ is a continuous function on H, since, by definition of $\sigma(A', A)$, each $\hat{a}$ is $\sigma(A', A)$ continuous on $A'.//$

Corollary 1 would be useful as a representation theorem if there were some hope that the congruence would be onto.   In Chapter 14, H is replaced by a smaller space for which the hope is reasonable; for the present we see that it is not.

★ *Example 1.*   With $A = E$, $A^* = E$, and H (Corollary 1) is the unit disk in the complex plane.   Thus $C[H]$ is much larger than E.

We now return to the duality theory.   A convenient way to define linear topologies is to have them generated by collections of polars.   Let us show first that the pointwise topology can be obtained in this way.

THEOREM 2.   *Let* A, B *be linear spaces in duality with respect to* u.   *Then* σ(A, B) *is the linear topology generated by* $\{S^o: S$ *a finite set in* B.$\}$

We first check, using Section 10.1, Theorem 3, that the given collection generates a linear topology.   This follows from the observations that each S^o is balanced and absorbing [Section 2, Facts (v) and (ix)] and that for each finite S, $2S$ is also finite and $(2S)^o + (2S)^o = S^o$ [Section 2, Problem 6].

Denote this topology by T.   Now let a_δ be a net in A with $a_\delta \to 0$ in $\sigma(A, B)$.   Then $u(a_\delta, b) \to 0$ for each $b \in B$ [Section 9.3, Theorem 3].   Thus $|u(a_\delta, b)| \leq 1$ eventually. Thus, given a finite set $S \subset B$, eventually $|u(a_\delta, b)| \leq 1$ for all $b \in S$; that is, $a_\delta \in S^o$ eventually.   Thus $a_\delta \to 0$ in T [Section 10.1, Problem 6].   Conversely, suppose that $a_\delta \to 0$ in T. Let $b \in B$, and $\epsilon > 0$.   Since $\{b/\epsilon\}$ is a finite set [it has one member], $a_\delta \in (b/\epsilon)^o$ eventually; that is, $|u(a_\delta, b)| < \epsilon$ eventually.   Thus, $u(a_\delta, b) \to 0$ for each $b \in B$ and so $a_\delta \to 0$ in $\sigma(A, B).//$

Next is given the more general setting of the Banach-Alaoglu theorem.

THEOREM 3.   *Let* A, B *be linear spaces in duality with respect to* u, *and let* A *be given a compatible topology.   For any neighborhood* G *of 0 in* A, G^o *is* σ(B, A) *compact.*

This, of course, continues the tradition that large sets have small polars; see, for example, Section 2, Facts (ii) and (ix).

Theorem 1 is a special case of Theorem 3, obtained by taking $B = A'$ and G the unit disk in A.   To prove Theorem 3, we may assume that G is convex, balanced, and closed [Section 2, Fact (xii)].   Let p be the gauge of G [Section 4.2, Theorem 1].   Then G^o is the set of all $b \in B$ satisfying

(2) $$|u(a, b)| \leq p(a) \qquad \text{for all } a \in A.$$

⟦For $b \in B$ satisfying relation (2), we have, for $a \in G$, $|u(a, b)| \leq p(a) \leq 1$. Thus $b \in G^o$. Conversely, let $b \in G^o$. Define a seminorm q on A by $q(a) = |u(a, b)|$ and apply Section 4.2, Theorem 2, with $n = \epsilon = M = 1$.⟧ Now we identify B with A' and observe that G^o is the set of all $f \in A'$ satisfying

$$(3) \qquad\qquad |f(a)| \leq p(a) \text{ for all } a \in A;$$

this is implied by relation (2).

Define $D(a)$ as in the proof of Theorem 1, replacing $\|a\|$ by $p(a)$. Now $G^o \subset \pi D(a)$ and $\sigma(B, A)$ is the relative topology of the product topology. Again, all comes to showing G^o closed. Let $f_\delta \to f$ as in Theorem 1 and, in the same way, we obtain the fact that f is linear and satisfies (3).

Finally f is continuous, since it is bounded on G, a set with interior ⟦Section 10.5, Theorem 2⟧. Thus $f \in G^o$.//

We now ask a rather natural question. One is usually interested in criteria for continuity of a linear functional. One such criterion is boundedness on a neighborhood G of 0 ⟦Section 10.5, Theorem 2⟧. How big must a set G be so that every linear functional bounded on G is continuous? Recognizing that bigness of G in A corresponds to smallness of G^o in A', ⟦Section 2, Fact (ii)⟧, we ask, as an equivalent question, when is G^o so small that every linear functional bounded on G is continuous? One answer is, roughly, that it is sufficient that G^o be weak star compact. (By the Banach-Alaoglu theorem, this improves Theorem 2 of Section 10.5.)

LEMMA 1. *Let* A *be a locally convex separated space so that* A, A' *are in duality with respect to* u, $u(a, f) = f(a)$. *Let* G *be a convex balanced closed set in* A *such that* G° *is weak star compact. Then any linear functional* f *on* A *which is bounded on* G *is continuous.*

A, $A^{\#}$ are also in duality with respect to u. Let us write G^p for the polar of G in $A^{\#}$. For a set $S \subset A'$, $S^o \subset A$ is unambiguous; that is, if we consider the same S to be a subset of $A^{\#}$, S^o will be the same set in A.

We shall first prove that

$$(4) \qquad\qquad (G^o)^{op} = G^o.$$

⟦G^o is a weak star compact set in $A^{\#}$, since it is weak star compact in A' (see Section 9.5, Problem 22). Thus G^o is weak star closed in $A^{\#}$. By Section 2, Theorem 1, equation (4) follows, since G^o is already convex, balanced, and closed, and since the weak star topology on $A^{\#}$ is compatible, as insured by Section 1, Theorem 1 (take $B = A^{\#}$).⟧ But also $G^{oo} = G$, by Section 2, Theorem 1, since G is already convex balanced and closed (in A) and surely the topology of A is compatible, since it is A' with which we have set up the duality. Applying this to equation (4) yields $G^p = G^o$. In particular, $G^p \subset A'$, a relation which obviously implies the result.//

Problems 13.3

In this list, A, B are linear spaces in duality with respect to a bilinear functional u; X is a linear topological space with topology T, not necessarily locally convex or separated.

★1. Let $S \subset B$.   Then $\sigma(A, S)$ is the linear topology generated by $\{ b^o : b \in S \}$.

2. What is the weak topology for L^p, $0 < p < 1$.   ⟦Section 7.5, Example 11.⟧

3. Let Y be X with the weak topology.   Show that X, Y have the same weak topology.

4. Let Y be a Banach space.   The weak and weak star topologies for Y^{**} agree on $\hat{Y}$; that is, they have the same relative topology.   ⟦Let y_δ be a net in Y and assume that $\hat{y}_\delta \to 0$ in the weak star topology.   Given $\phi \in Y^{***}$, define $f \in Y^*$ by $f(y) = \phi(\hat{y})$, that is, $f = \phi|Y$.   (Compare Section 7.2, Problem 21.)   Then $\phi(\hat{y}_\delta) = f(y_\delta) = \hat{y}_\delta(f) \to 0$.   Thus $\hat{y}_\delta \to 0$ in the weak topology.⟧

5. Let Y be a Banach space.   Show that transferring the weak topology from Y to $\hat{Y}$ by means of the natural embedding gives $\hat{Y}$ the relative topology of the weak topology of Y^{**}.   ⟦$\hat{y}_\delta \to 0$ in the weak star topology if and only if $\hat{y}_\delta(f) \to 0$ for every $f \in Y^*$; that is, $f(y_\delta) \to 0$ for every $f \in Y^*$. Now use Problem 4.⟧

6. Show that every pseudo-bounded set in X is bounded in the weak topology.

7. If a linear topological space is pseudo-bounded, its weak topology must be indiscrete.   ⟦Problem 6.⟧

8. The weak topology by the set of all continuous linear functionals on X is, in general, weaker than T.   What can you say about the weak topology by the set of all continuous seminorms?   ⟦Section 12.1, Theorem 1; Section 12.2, Problem 6.⟧

9. A linear subspace S of B is called *regularly closed* if, for each $b \in B \setminus S$, there exists $a \in A$ such that $u(a, b) = 1$, $u(a, x) = 0$ for $x \in S$.   Show that S is regularly closed if and only if it is $\sigma(B, A)$ closed.   ⟦If S is regularly closed and $b \notin S$, consider $\{ x : |u(a, x)| \leq \frac{1}{2} \}$.   If S is weakly closed and $b \notin S$, use Section 12.2, Theorem 3.⟧

10. Write a proof of Theorem 3 which contains no reference to Theorem 1.

11. In the proof of Theorem 3, show that $G^o = \{ f \in A^\# : |f(a)| \leq p(a) \text{ for all } a \in A \}$.

12. Show that the hypotheses of Lemma 1 do not imply that G has an interior point.   ⟦Let G be a neighborhood of 0 in some stronger compatible topology.⟧

13. Lemma 1 becomes false if the word "closed" is omitted.   ⟦$G = f^\perp$.⟧

14. (a) Lemma 1 becomes false if G is not assumed convex.   (b) However, it is sufficient to assume instead that the convex hull of G is closed.

15. State and prove a version of Lemma 1 which refers to a pair of spaces in duality.

16. Let X be a Fréchet space.   Then X' is weak star sequentially closed in $X^\#$.   ⟦Section 11.2, Corollary 4.⟧

17. In Problem 16, "Fréchet" may not be replaced by "linear metric space."   ⟦Section 7.6, Problem 7, a normed space!⟧

18. Let X be a t space.   A set in X' is equicontinuous if and only if it is weak star bounded.   ⟦Section 12.3, Theorem 4.⟧

19. Let A be a t space with a compatible topology.   Place the topology $\sigma(B, A)$ upon B.   Then every closed and bounded set S in B is compact.   ⟦S^o is a neighborhood of 0, by Problem 18.   Now apply Theorem 3 with $G = S^o$.⟧

20. Let X be a t space.   Place the weak star topology upon X'.   Then every closed and bounded set in X' is compact.   ⟦Problem 19.⟧

21. Let X be a locally convex Fréchet space such that the weak star topology on X' is metrizable. Show that X is finite dimensional.

22. In Problem 21, "locally convex" cannot be omitted.   ⟦Section 7.5, Example 10 or 11.⟧

23. In Problem 21, "Fréchet" cannot be replaced by "linear metric" or by "normed."   ⟦$X = E^\infty$.⟧

24. In Problem 21, "Fréchet" cannot be replaced by "complete linear semimetric."

25. In Problem 21, may we omit "star" and replace X' by X?   ⟦No, consider s.⟧   Compare Section 9.3, Problem 14.

26. Let S be a balloon in X.   Then $S^o (\subset X^\#)$ is $\sigma(X^\#, X)$ compact.   ⟦Theorem 3.⟧

27. Let S be a balloon in A.   Then S^o may not be $\sigma(B, A)$ compact, but is totally bounded in that topology.   ⟦Problem 26.⟧

28. Let S be a linear subspace of B which is total over A.   Then S is $\sigma(B, A)$ dense in B.   ⟦$S^{oo} = B$.⟧

29. Let X' be given any linear topology. Then $\hat{X}$ is weak star dense in X''. 〚Problem 28.〛

30. Is there any linear topology for X' which is weaker than the weak star topology? 〚Section 6.4, Problem 3.〛

31. Let X, Y be linear topological spaces, and $f: X \to Y$ a linear function. Say that f is *weakly continuous* if it is continuous when X, Y both have their weak topology. Show that if f is continuous, it is weakly continuous. 〚Let $x_\delta \to 0$ weakly, $g \in Y'$. Then $g \circ f(x_\delta) \to 0$, since $g \circ f \in X'$.〛

32. A weakly continuous linear map (Problem 31) need not be continuous. 〚$X = Y$ with the weak topology, $f = i$.〛

33. Let X, Y be Fréchet spaces with Y locally convex. Then, in Problem 31, if f is weakly continuous, it is continuous. 〚Section 11.2, Theorem 2; Section 11.1, Lemma 1.〛

34. In Problem 33, "locally convex" cannot be dropped. 〚$Y' = \{0\}$.〛

35. In Problem 31, let f be called RW continuous if it is continuous when Y has its weak topology. (a) Show that if Y is a normed space and f is RW continuous, $\|f(x)\|$ is lower semicontinuous as a function of $x \in X$. (b) Let Y be locally convex, let f be RW continuous, and let S be a convex set in X. Show that $f[\bar{S}] \subset \overline{f[S]}$. 〚Section 9.2, Corollary 1; Section 12.2, Theorem 4.〛

36. Let $\{x_n\}$ be a sequence in X. Then $x_n \to x$ weakly if and only if x belongs to the convex T closure of every subsequence of $\{x_n\}$.

37. (a) Let X be separable. Then it is separable with the weak topology. However, (b) let X be an infinite-dimensional Banach space. Then X is not perfectly separable with the weak topology. (A topology is called *perfectly separable* if it has a countable base.) 〚Section 10.4, Theorem 2; Section 9.3, Problem 14.〛

38. We may consider $l = c_0'$ and $l = c'$. 〚Section 6.4, Examples 4 and 5.〛 Show that the two resulting weak star topologies are incomparable. 〚Consider l' in each case, Section 7.2, Example 2.〛 Why is it wrong, in this context, to say that $\sigma(l, c)$ is stronger than $\sigma(l, c_0)$ because $c \supset c_0$?

39. Find two sequences in l, neither of which converges in both topologies of Problem 38, and each of which converges in one of the topologies.

40. Let $S = \{n^{1/4}\delta^n: n = 1, 2, \ldots\}$ in l^2. Show that in the weak topology $0 \in \bar{S}$, but no sequence of points of S converges to 0.

41. Arrange the following topologies for the space m in order (where they are comparabe): the natural topology; the weak topology; the weak star topology ($m = l'$); the relative topology of s; the weak star topology ($m = E^\infty$, $E^\infty \subset l$); the norm topology given by p, where $p(a) = \Sigma|a_n|/2^n$.

▲42. A sequence in l is weakly convergent if and only if it is convergent. (Compare Section 9.1, Problem 41.)

43. Let A be a multiplicative matrix. Show that A is *coercive*, that is, $m \subset c_A$ if and only if $\Sigma_{k=1}^\infty |a_{nk} \to 0$ as $n \to \infty$. 〚Problem 42.〛

13.4 Normed space

Recall that X^* stands for X' with the norm topology (Section 6.4, Definition 1). Let X be a normed space, and $u(x, f) = f(x)$ for $x \in X$, $f \in X'$. Then X, X' are in duality with respect to u 〚Section 1, Example 2〛. The norm topology for X is compatible, by definition of X'. The weak topology for X is also compatible 〚Section 10.5, Example 1〛, as is the weak star topology for X'. However, the norm and weak topologies for X' are not compatible if X is not reflexive. Thus we are not surprised when the norm and weak star topologies turn out to have different bounded sets 〚Problem 1〛 and closed convex sets and linear subspaces 〚Problem 4〛. (We are thinking of Section 1, Problem 4.)

The norm and weak topologies for X' again have the same bounded and closed convex sets, since they are compatible with a higher duality, that between X' and $X^{*'}$.

Consideration of the Banach-Alaoglu theorem, Section 3, Theorem 1, leads naturally to the question of whether the unit disk is weakly compact, that is, compact in the weak topology. For a reflexive space the answer is clear, since the weak and weak star topologies are then the same. [We may write $Y = X^*$, then $X = Y^*$ and the unit disk in X is weak star compact.] It turns out (Theorem 1) that this condition is also sufficient for reflexivity.

We use the notations D, D_1, D_2 for the unit disks in X, X^*, X^{**}. For $S \subset X$, S^o will have its obvious meaning, $\{f \in X^*: |f(x)| \leq 1 \text{ for all } x \in S\}$. For $S \subset X^*$, S^o shall denote $\{x \in X: |f(x)| \leq 1 \text{ for all } f \in S\}$. Finally, for $S \subset X^{**}$, $S^o = \{f \subset X^*: |G(f)| \leq 1 \text{ for all } G \in S\}$. Thus $S^o = (\hat{S})^o$ for $S \subset X$.

Note. In the following, X is a normed space, and D, D_1, D_2, S^o, have the meanings just described.

LEMMA 1. $D^o = D_1 = (\hat{D})^o = D_2^o$.

For $f \in D_1$, $G \in D_2$, we have $|G(f)| \leq \|G\| \cdot \|f\| \leq 1$. This proves that $D_1 \subset D_2^o$. On the other hand, $\hat{D} \subset D_2$ and so $(\hat{D})^o \supset D_2^o$ [apply Section 2, Fact (ii), using the duality between X^*, X^{**}]. Thus $D^o = D_1 \subset D_2^o \subset (\hat{D})^o = D^o$; the first equality follows by definition of D_1 and the meaning of $\|f\|$ for $f \in X^*$; the two inclusions were just proved; the last equality follows from the definition of $(\hat{D})^o$.//

COROLLARY 1. $\hat{D}$ *is weak star dense in* D_2. *Indeed* D_2 *is the weak star closure of* $\hat{D}$.

The weak star topology cited is that of X^{**} as the dual space of X^*.

Let $A = X^*$, $B = X^{**}$ with the weak star topology, $u(f, G) = G(f)$ for $G \in B$, $f \in A$. Then A, B are in duality with respect to u and B has a compatible topology. Let us write S^p for the polar of S in this duality. For $S \subset B$, $S^p = S^o$, but for $S \subset A$, $S^p \neq S^o$. By Section 2, Theorem 1, $(\hat{D})^{pp}$ is the convex, balanced closure of $\hat{D}$. Since $\hat{D}$ is already convex and balanced, $(\hat{D})^{pp}$ is its closure.

By Lemma 1, $(\hat{D})^p \equiv (\hat{D})^o = D_2^o \equiv D_2^p$. Thus $\overline{\hat{D}} = (\hat{D})^{pp} = D_2^{pp} = D_2$; the first two equalities were just proved; the last one follows from Section 2, Theorem 1 since D_2 is already convex, balanced, and closed. (Indeed, it is compact, by Section 3, Theorem 1.)//

THEOREM 1. *A Banach space is reflexive if and only if its unit disk is compact in the weak topology.*

(This may be compared with norm compactness, which is equivalent to finite dimensionality [Section 12.2, Theorem 5].)

As pointed out before Lemma 1, if X is reflexive, its unit disk is weakly compact. Next, suppose that D is weakly compact. Then $\hat{D}$ is weak star compact in X^{**}. Thus $\hat{D}$ is weakly closed in X^{**} [Section 9.5, Corollary 3]. By Corollary 1, $\hat{D} = D_2$. From this it follows that X is reflexive. [If $f \in X^{**} \setminus \hat{X}$, then $f/\|f\| \in D_2 \setminus \hat{D}$.]//

▲ COROLLARY 2. *Every closed convex set in a reflexive Banach space has a point of minimum norm.*

Let K be the intersection of the set with D. We may assume that K is not empty, since, in the following arguments, D could be replaced by a larger disk. The intersection K is closed and convex, thus is weakly closed [Section 12.2, Corollary 5]. Thus K is a weakly closed subset of the set D which is, by Theorem 1, weakly compact. Hence K is weakly compact ⟦Section 9.5, Lemma 2⟧. Now, the norm is weakly lower semicontinuous ⟦Section 11.4, Lemma 1⟧, thus it assumes a minimum on K ⟦Section 9.5, Problem 30⟧.//

Problems 13.4

In this list, X is a normed space, sometimes further restricted; D, D_1, and D_2 are the unit disks in X, X^*, and X^{**}, respectively.

1. Let $X = E^\infty$ with $\|x\| = \sup |x_n|$. Let $S = \{nP_n : n = 1, 2, \ldots\} \subset X'$. Show that S is weak star bounded, but not bounded in $X^* = l$. ⟦Section 10.3, Fact (xii).⟧

2. Let X be a Banach space. Then, in X', the norm, weak, and weak star topologies all have the same bounded sets. ⟦Section 3, Problem 18.⟧ Problem 1 shows that we cannot omit the assumption of completeness.

3. Show that if $f \in X^{**} \setminus \hat{X}$, then f is not weak star continuous. ⟦Section 1, Theorem 1.⟧

4. With f as in Problem 3, show that $f^\perp$ is norm closed, but not weak star closed. ⟦Problem 3 and Section 10.5, Theorem 3.⟧

5. Find the mistake in the following "proof" that every normed space is reflexive: $\hat{D}$ is weak star compact, by the Banach-Alaoglu theorem. Hence it is weakly compact, by Section 3, Problem 4. Thus D is weakly compact by Section 3, Problem 5. By Theorem 1, X is reflexive.

6. Can "Banach" be replaced by "normed" in Corollary 2?

7. X is weak star dense in X^{**}. ⟦Section 3, Problem 28.⟧

8. X is reflexive if and only if every closed linear subspace of X^* is weak star closed. ⟦Consider $f^\perp$ for $f \in X^{**}$.⟧

9. Give an explicit construction of a closed linear subspace of l which is not weak star closed, considering $l = c_0'$.

10. Any weak star closed, norm-bounded set in X^* is weak star compact.

11. Let X be infinite dimensional. Show that the unit circumference in X cannot be weakly closed. (Thus it certainly cannot be weakly compact.) ⟦It must be weakly dense in D, by Section 9.3, Problem 15.⟧

12. The unit circumference in X is sequentially closed in the weak topology if and only if X has the same convergent and weakly convergent sequences. (Compare Section 3, Problem 42.) ⟦Let $\|x_n - x\| \geq \epsilon > 0$, and $x_n \to x$ weakly. Let $y_n = (x_n - x)/\|x_n - x\|$. Then $y_n \to 0$ weakly, $\|y_n\| = 1$.⟧

13. Use the hint in Problem 12 to obtain the result of Problem 11. ⟦Replace x_n by x_δ.⟧

14. If X is not complete, then, even though $X^* = (\bar{X})^*$, the two weak star topologies on X^*, namely $\sigma(X^*, X)$, $\sigma(X^*, \bar{X})$ are different. (Here, $\bar{X}$ is the completion of X.)

15. Let X be reflexive. Apply Theorem 1 to obtain the results that every closed subspace of X and every normed space linearly homeomorphic with X are reflexive.

16. The norm on X^* is lower semicontinuous in the weak star topology. ⟦Imitate the proof of Section 11.4, Lemma 1.⟧

17. A weak star closed, convex set in X^* has a point of minimum norm. ⟦Imitate the proof of Corollary 2, using Problem 16.⟧

18. In problem 17 "weak star" cannot be omitted.

19. Let X be given the weak topology. A closed bounded set in X need not be compact, even if X is a Banach space in its original topology. ⟦D, if X is not reflexive.⟧ (We cannot apply Section 3, Problem 19, because X^* may have no compatible t topology.) The next problem gives a positive result for total boundedness rather than compactness.

20. Let A be a linear space, and S a linear subspace of $A^\#$. If A is given the topology $\sigma(A, S)$, every bounded set K is totally bounded. ⟦Given a neighborhood G of the form $(|f| < \epsilon)$, $f \in S$, cover

$f[K]$ by cells N_i of diameter ϵ.   If possible, choose $a_i \in K$ with $f(a_i) \in N_i$; otherwise, choose a_i at random.   Then $K \subset \cup(a_i + G)$.⟧

21. In s, every closed bounded set is compact.   ⟦Problem 20; Section 10.5, Example 5.⟧   Thus again, s has no bounded neighborhoods.   ⟦Section 12.2, Theorem 5.⟧

22. Suppose that $F \in X^{**}$, $\|F\| = 1$, and $\delta > 0$.   Show that there exists $a \in D$ such that $\|F + \hat{a}\| > 2 - \delta$.   ⟦Choose $f \in X^*$, $\|f\| = 1$, $|F(f)| > 1 - \delta$.   By Corollary 1, there exists $a \in D$ such that $|F(f) - \hat{a}(f)| < \delta$.   Then $\|F + \hat{a}\| \geq |F(f) + \hat{a}(f)| \geq 2\,|F(f)| - |F(f) - \hat{a}(f)| > 2 - 3\delta$.⟧

23. Deduce the theorem that a uniformly convex Banach space is reflexive from Problem 22. ⟦For $F \in X^{**}$ with $\|F\| = 1$, application of the definition of uniform convexity to F, $\hat{a}$, as given in Problem 22, yields $d(F, \hat{D}) = 0$.   Hence $F \in \hat{D}$.   Thus $D_2 = \hat{D}$.   This argument is due to J. R. Ringrose.⟧

24. Let S be a linear subspace of X^* which is total over X, but not norming.   Show that $S \cap D_1$ is not weak star dense in D_1.   (Even though, according to Section 3, Problem 28, S is weak star dense in X^*.)   ⟦Otherwise, let $\|x\| = 1$; let $f \in D_1$; $f(x) = 1$.   Choose $g \in S \cap D_1$ with $|f(x) - g(x)| < \epsilon$. Then $|g(x)| \geq 1 - \epsilon$.   Thus $\|x\|_S \geq 1 - \epsilon$.⟧

25. Let K be a closed, bounded, balanced, convex neighborhood of 0 in X^*.   Show that K is weak star compact.   ⟦Renorm.⟧   (In Section 3, Problem 20, "closed" means "weak star closed.")

▲26. Let X be a Banach space and S a linear subspace of X^* such that $S \cap D_1$ is weak star closed. Show that S is weak star closed.

27. In Problem 25, "neighborhood of 0" cannot be replaced by "set."   ⟦$S \cap D_1$, where S is a linear subspace which is not weak star closed.   See Problem 26.⟧

13.5   Two more topologies

We begin with the strong topology for the dual of a linear topological space X.   This will be dismissed briefly.   Its chief interest lies in the fact that it specializes to the norm topology for the dual of a normed space.   In general, then, it is not compatible with the duality of X, X'.

DEFINITION 1.   *Let* **X** *be a locally convex separated space.   The strong topology for* **X**′ *is the linear topology generated by the set of all* S°, S *a bounded subset of* **X**.   *The neighborhoods will be called strong neighborhoods.*

We have to check that this definition is meaningful, that is, the set of all $S°$ satisfies the conditions of Section 10.1, Theorem 3.   Each $S°$ is balanced and absorbing ⟦Section 2, Facts (v) and (xiii)⟧.   Also, given S, $(2S)° + (2S)° \subset S°$ ⟦Section 2, Problem 6⟧.   The check is complete.

Facts

In this list, X is a locally convex separated space.

(i) The strong topology is stronger than the weak star topology.

(ii) Given a strong neighborhood N of 0, there exists a bounded set $S \subset X$ with $S° \subset N$. (Conversely, any such $S°$ is a strong neighborhood of 0.)

(iii) The strong topology is locally convex and separated.

(iv) If f_δ is a net in X', $f_\delta \to 0$ in the strong topology if and only if $f_\delta \to 0$ uniformly on each bounded set in X.

(v) If X is a normed space, the strong topology on X' is the norm topology.

Proofs

(i) This follows from the fact that finite sets are bounded, together with Section 3, Theorem 2.

(ii) Let $S = \cup S_k$, where S_1, S_2, . . . , S_n are bounded sets satisfying $N \supset \cap S_k^o$.

(iii) Each S^o is convex. Also the strong topology is stronger than the weak star topology, which is separated.

(iv) Let $f_\delta \to 0$. Let S be bounded. Let $\epsilon > 0$ be given. Then S/ϵ is bounded, hence $f_\delta \in (S/\epsilon)^o$ eventually, say for $\delta \geq \delta_0$. For $a \in S$, $\delta \geq \delta_0$, $|f_\delta(a)| = \epsilon|f_\delta(a/\epsilon)| \leq \epsilon$. Conversely, if $f_\delta \to 0$ uniformly on every bounded set, let G be a strong neighborhood of 0. By Fact (ii), there exists bounded $S \subset X$ with $S^0 \subset G$. There exists δ_0 such that $\delta \geq \delta_0$ implies that $|f_\delta(a)| < 1$ for all $a \in S$. Thus $f_\delta \in S^o$ eventually, $f_\delta \in G$ eventually.

(v) If G is a cell $N(0, r)$ in X^*, $G = N(0, 1/r)^o$, so G is a strong neighborhood of 0. Conversely, if G is a strong neighborhood of 0, $G \supset S^o$ for some bounded $S \subset X$ ⟦Fact (ii)⟧, and S is included in a cell N. Then N^o is a cell and $G \supset N^o$.//

Finally we come to the long-awaited solution of the problem of determining exactly which topologies are compatible with a given duality.

Note. In the remainder of this section, A, B are linear spaces in duality with respect to u,

We have seen that all compatible topologies have the same bounded sets ⟦Section 12.3, Corollary 1⟧ and closed convex sets ⟦Section 12.2, Theorem 4⟧.

We first observe that the weakest compatible topology for A is $\sigma(A, B)$; that is, every compatible topology is stronger than $\sigma(A, B)$ ⟦for $\sigma(A, B)$ is, by definition, the weakest topology such that the members of B are continuous, that is, such that $u(a, b)$ is continuous in a for each b⟧. This fact will be used without further citation.

Now suppose that T is a compatible topology for A, and that G is a convex, balanced, closed neighborhood of 0. Then, *there exists a convex balanced $\sigma(B, A)$ compact set S in B such that $G = S^o$* ⟦namely, $S = G^o$, using the Banach-Alaoglu theorem (Section 3, Theorem 3) and Section 2, Theorem 1⟧.

Thus essentially only polars of convex balanced $\sigma(B, A)$ compact sets are admissible as neighborhoods of 0. It is natural to consider the topology generated by all of these, which will, then, provided it is compatible at all, obviously be the strongest compatible topology. Thus we shall have a weakest and a strongest compatible topology as soon as we show that the topology given in the next definition is compatible.

DEFINITION 2. *$\tau(A, B)$ is the linear topology for A generated by $\{S^o: S$ is a convex, balanced, $\sigma(B, A)$ compact set in $B\}$; $\tau(B, A)$ is defined by interchanging A, B in this definition.*

Notice that A, B are linear spaces, and that no topology is needed for them in Definition 2. For example, if A is given two different topologies for which it has the same dual A' then $\tau(A, A')$ is the same, whichever of the two topologies on A one starts with. Just as for Definition 1, it is checked that these are linear topologies, the main points being that, if S is convex, balanced, and $\sigma(B, A)$ compact, so is $2S$, and S^o is absorbing ⟦Section 2, Fact (xiii); and the fact that a compact set is bounded, Section 10.3, Fact (xii)⟧.

Facts

In this list, A, B are linear spaces in duality with respect to u. In each Fact, A, B may be interchanged.

(vi) For each $\tau(A, B)$ neighborhood N of 0, there exists a convex balanced $\sigma(B, A)$ compact set $K \subset B$ with $K^o \subset N$.

(vii) $\tau(A, B)$ is stronger than $\sigma(A, B)$

(viii) $\tau(A, B)$ is separated.

(ix) Let N be a $\tau(A, B)$ neighborhood of 0. Then N includes a set G which is convex, balanced, $\sigma(A, B)$ closed, and is such that G^o is $\sigma(B, A)$ compact. [This implies a "Banach-Alaoglu theorem," namely that if N is a neighborhood, N^o is $\sigma(B, A)$ compact. If we knew, already, Fact (x), this would follow from Section 3, Theorem 3. All this makes Fact (x) seem plausible.]

(x) $\tau(A, B)$ is compatible with the duality.

Proofs

(vi) In the proof of Fact (ii), replace "bounded" by "convex, balanced, $\sigma(B, A)$ compact." (Replace S by K.) Finally, apply Section 10.2, Problem 40.

(vii) By Section 3, Problem 1, $\sigma(A, B)$ is generated by the polars of singleton sets of B (sets with one point). The convex balanced closure of each such set is $\sigma(B, A)$ compact, thus $\tau(A, B)$ is generated by a larger class of polars.

(viii) Fact (vii) applies, since $\sigma(A, B)$ is separated.

(ix) Choose K as in Fact (vi). Let $G = K^o$. Then G is convex, balanced, and $\sigma(A, B)$ closed [Section 2, Facts (v) and (x)]. Next, $G^o = K^{oo} = K$ [Section 2, Theorem 1], which is $\sigma(B, A)$ compact by definition of K.

(x) For each $b \in B$, $u(a, b)$ is a $\sigma(A, B)$-continuous function of a. By Fact (vii), it is $\tau(A, B)$ continuous. (Thus, with $\tau(A, B)$, $A' \supset B$. Next we prove that $A' \subset B$. This is the program outlined in Section 1, Problem 2.)

Let A be given the topology $\tau(A, B)$, and let $f \in A'$. Let $N = (|f| < 1)$. Choose G with the properties in the statement of Fact (ix). Now let A be given the topology $\sigma(A, B)$. Referring to Section 3, Lemma 1, we see that G satisfies its hypotheses. Moreover f is bounded on G since $G \subset N$. Thus f is $\sigma(A, B)$ continuous. Since $\sigma(A, B)$ is compatible with the duality, this means that for some $b \in B$, $f(a) = u(a, b)$ for all $a \in A$, that is, $f \in B$.//

THEOREM 1. THE MACKEY-ARENS THEOREM. *Let* A, B *be linear spaces in duality with respect to a bilinear functional* u. *Let* T *be a locally convex separated topology for* A. *Then* T *is compatible with the duality if and only if* T *lies between* $\sigma(A, B)$ *and* $\tau(A, B)$.

It has already been made clear that every compatible topology lies between $\sigma(A, B)$ and $\tau(A, B)$ (see the discussion between the Note, and Definition 2). On the other hand, if T lies between $\sigma(A, B)$ and $\tau(A, B)$, it is compatible since they are [Fact (x); Section 1, Problem 3].//

It is amusing to take a locally convex separated space (A, T) and compute $\sigma(A, A')$ and $\tau(A, A')$. These will be, respectively, weaker and stronger than T. The following examples show some special cases of this. We remark that a linear topological space A is called *relatively strong* if its topology is equal to $\tau(A, A')$.

Example 1: If (A, T) *is a t space*, $\tau(A, A') = T$; *that is, a t space is relatively strong.* Section 12.3, Theorem 2, says that T is stronger. Theorem 1 provides that T cannot be strictly stronger.

Example 2. Let A be a Banach space, with dual A'. Then the norm topology, being $\tau(A, A')$, by Example 1, is the strongest and the weak topology is the weakest locally convex topology for A for which the dual is A'. The norm topology for A^* is not, in general, $\tau(A^*, A)$. This does not contradict Example 1, since the norm topology is, in such a case (namely, when A is not reflexive), not compatible with the duality. The norm topology for A^* is, however equal to $\tau(A^*, A^{**})$, by Example 1.

Example 3: For the space s, *all compatible topologies coincide.* We refer to compatibility with the duality between s and $s' = E^\infty$ (Section 6.4, Example 1). The natural topology is $\tau(s, s')$, by Example 1. It is also $\sigma(s, s')$, by Section 10.5, Example 5.

Example 4. If A is an infinite-dimensional normed space with its weak topology which we shall call T, we have $T = \sigma(A, A')$, $T \neq \tau(A, A')$.

Problems 13.5

In this list, A, B are linear spaces in duality with respect to a bilinear functional u; (X, T) is a locally convex separated space, sometimes further restricted.

1. Suppose that A has a compatible topology. Define the strong topology for B, and prove the result corresponding to Fact (i).

2. The strong topology for X' is stronger than $\tau(X', X)$. 〖A weakly compact set is weakly bounded, hence bounded, since T and the weak topology are both compatible.〗

3. Give examples in which the strong topology for X' is (a) equal to, (b) strictly stronger than $\tau(X', X)$.

4. Let Y be a linear space. Show that $\tau(Y, Y^\#)$ is the balloon topology.

5. Let Y be an infinite-dimensional normed space. Show that the norm topology is not comparable with $\sigma(Y, Y^\#)$, but is weaker than $\tau(Y, Y^\#)$. 〖Section 9.3, Problem 16.〗

6. Every bornological space is relatively strong. 〖Section 10.5, Problem 23.〗

7. Give an example of a locally convex separated space which is relatively strong, but is not a t space. 〖Problem 6; Section 10.5, Example 4.〗

8. Give an example of a duality with which no t topology is compatible. 〖Problem 7.〗

9. Let X be a t space. Then there exists a locally convex separated space Y such that $X = Y'$, the topology of X being $\tau(Y', Y)$. 〖Take $Y = X'$.〗 Compare Section 7.2, Problem 21.

10. Let G be a neighborhood of 0 in X. Then G^o is strongly bounded. 〖Strong neighborhoods absorb G^o because their polars are absorbed by G.〗

11. Let X be a locally convex Fréchet space for which the strong topology is metrizable. Show that X is a Banach space. 〖If $\{G_n\}$ is a basic sequence of convex balanced closed neighborhoods of 0 in X', then $X = \cup G_n^o$, each G_n^o is bounded and Section 10.3, Problem 8, applies.〗 Compare Section 3, Problem 21.

12. Let Y be a normed space. Let S be a convex balanced weak star compact set in Y'. Then S is norm bounded. 〖S^o is a neighborhood of 0 in Y in the norm topology, by Problem 6 and Section 10.5, Example 4. Hence $S = S^{oo}$ is norm bounded.〗

13. In Problem 12, "convex balanced" may not be omitted. 〖Let $Y = E^\infty$, $\|y\| = \sup |y_n|$, $S = \{nP_n\} \cup \{0\}$. S is weak star compact because $nP_n \to 0$ in the weak star topology.〗

14. In Problem 12, "convex balanced" may be omitted if Y is assumed complete; indeed, "compact" may be replaced by "bounded." 〖Section 3, Problem 18.〗

15. The topology for A generated by $\{S^o: S$ is a $\sigma(B, A)$-compact set in $B\}$ may be strictly stronger than $\tau(A, B)$. 〖Let $A = E^\infty$, $\|a\| = \sup|a_n|$, $B = A' = l$. Let $S = \{n\delta^n\} \cup \{0\}$. Then S is weak star compact since $n\delta^n \to 0$ in the weak star topology. But S^o is not a $\tau(A, B)$ neighborhood of 0, by Section 3, Theorem 3, because S^{oo} is not $\sigma(B, A)$ compact, by Problem 12.〗

16. The *bidual* of X is the dual of X' when X' is given the strong topology. Let the bidual have the strong topology. (a) Show that the natural embedding of X in the bidual has a continuous inverse (defined only on $\hat{X}$, of course). 〖Let G be a neighborhood of 0 in X. By Problem 10, G^o is strongly bounded, so G^{oo} is a strong neighborhood in the bidual.〗 (b) If X is a t space, the natural embedding is a homeomorphism into.

17. Obtain the results of Section 11.3, Problem 40 for pairs of compatible topologies on A. 〖$H = \sigma(A, B)$.〗

14

BANACH ALGEBRA

14.1 Algebra

In this section we give the algebraic background leading up to the Gelfand representation theory. No results in topological algebra occur in this section, although discussions of algebras of functions on a topological space occur in the examples. For simplicity, we assume that our algebras have an identity. In Section 5, it is pointed out how to remove this assumption. Extended discussion of the various radicals will be avoided.

A *ring* A is a set for which are defined an addition, making A a commutative group, and an associative multiplication which satisfies the distributive laws.

An *algebra* is a ring and a linear space such that $t(ab) = (ta)b = a(tb)$ for scalar t, vectors a, b.

If $ab = ba$ for all a, b, the algebra is called *commutative*.

If the scalars are real, the algebra is called a *real algebra*.

An *identity* is a vector, 1, satisfying $a1 = 1a = a$, for all a. An algebra may have at most one identity. [If 1, e are identities, $1 = 1e = e$.] The complex numbers, E, form a commutative algebra with identity; R is a real algebra.

For sets S, T in an algebra, ST is the set of products ab, $a \in S$, $b \in T$, and for $n = 1, 2,$
$\ldots$, $S^n = \{a^n : a \in S\}$.

If the algebra has an identity 1, we shall identify a scalar t with the vector $t1$. Thus for scalar t, vector a, $t + a$ has a meaning, namely $t1 + a$, provided, as stated, that the algebra has an identity. The phrase, a set of scalars, will mean a set of scalar multiples of 1, and E becomes a one-dimensional subalgebra of any algebra with identity. A function f on an algebra with identity is also defined on E, namely, $f(z) = f(z1)$ for scalar z.

★ *Example 1.* Let X be a topological space. Then $C[X]$, $C_1[X]$ are commutative algebras with identity.

[Multiplication is pointwise, for example, for a, $b \in C[X]$, $(ab)(x) = a(x)b(x)$.]

Note. To avoid trivialities, we shall always assume, in discussing $C[X]$ and $C_1[X]$, that X has more than one point.

Example 2. The set of n-by-n matrices of real numbers, $n > 1$, is a real noncommutative algebra with identity.

The following definitions presuppose a fixed algebra A.   A *left ideal* is a linear subspace I satisfying $AI \subset I$.   Similarly, a *right ideal* satisfies $IA \subset I$.   These are called *one sided ideals*. A left ideal which is also a right ideal is called, simply, an *ideal;* sometimes, for emphasis, a *two-sided ideal*.   (Of course, every two-sided ideal is a one-sided ideal.)   A *proper ideal* is an ideal I which is not the whole algebra.   A *maximal ideal* is a maximal proper ideal.   Finally, an *ideal maximal subspace* is an ideal which is also a maximal linear subspace.   (It will be a maximal ideal, of course.)

★ *Example 3.*   Let A be an algebra and $a \in A$.   Than aA is a right ideal, Aa is a left ideal. If A is commutative, $aA = Aa$ is an ideal.

★ *Example 4.*   Let X be a $T_{2\frac{1}{2}}$ space.   In the following, we shall refer to $C[X]$; exactly the same considerations apply to $C_1[X]$.   For each $x \in X$, let $I_x = \{a : a(x) = 0.\}$ Each I_x is a maximal linear subspace.   [If we define $\hat{x}$ by $\hat{x}(a) = a(x)$ for $a \in C[X]$, $\hat{x}$ is a linear functional on $C[X]$ and $I_x = x^{\perp}$.   The result follows from Section 2.10, Fact (iv) and the observation that $\hat{x} \neq 0$, because $\hat{x}(1) \neq 0$.]   Moreover, each I_x is an ideal.   [For $a \in I_x$, $b \in C[X]$, $(ba)(x) = b(x)a(x) = 0$.   Thus $ba \in I_x$.]   Thus, *each I_x is an ideal maximal subspace*.

If A has an identity and a, $b \in A$ satisfy $ab = ba = 1$, we write $b = a^{-1}$, calling b the *inverse* of a.   A vector could have at most one inverse.   [If $ab = ca = 1$, $b = (ca)b = c(ab) = c$.]   This same proof shows that *if a has a right inverse b (that is, $ab = 1$) and a left inverse c, then $b = c = a^{-1}$*.   Any vector which has an inverse is called a *unit*.   All nonzero scalars are units [$t \cdot (1/t) = 1$].

LEMMA 1.   *In an algebra with identity, a proper ideal contains no units.*

This may be compared with Section 2.7, Problem 25, a similar result for order ideals. If I is an ideal and $a \in I$ is a unit, then for any vector b, $b = ba^{-1}a \in ba^{-1}I \subset I$ and so I is not proper.//

★ *Example 5.*   Let X be a compact topological space, and I a proper ideal in $C[X] = C_1[X]$. *There exists $x \in X$ such that $a(x) = 0$ for all $a \in I$; that is, $I \subset I_x$ for some $x \in X$.* Our assertion is that $\{a^{\perp} : a \in I\}$ has the full intersection property, Section 9.5, Definition 2.   Since X is compact, this will follow when we prove that this set has the finite intersection property, since it is a collection of closed subsets of X.   Thus, let $(a_1, a_2, \ldots, a_n)$ be any finite subset of I and let $u = \sum_{k=1}^{n} |a_k|^2$.   Then $u \in I$.   [$|a_k|^2 = \bar{a}_k a_k \in \bar{a}_k I \subset I$. Here $\bar{a}_k$ is the complex conjugate of a_k, that is, $\bar{a}_k(x) = \overline{a_k(x)}$ for $x \in X$; and $|a_k|(x) = |a_k(x)|$ for $x \in X$.]   By Lemma 1, u is not a unit, thus $u(x) = 0$ for some x [otherwise, $1/u \in C[X]$]. This shows that $u^{\perp}$ is not empty.   Since $u^{\perp} = \bigcap \{a_k^{\perp} : k = 1, 2, \ldots, n\}$, it follows that the collection of all sets $a^{\perp}$, $a \in I$, has the finite intersection property.

★ *Example 6.*   Let X be a compact Hausdorff space and I a maximal ideal in $C[X]$.   By Example 5, $I \subset I_x$ for some $x \in X$.   By Example 4, I_x is a proper ideal.   Thus $I = I_x$. Since $I_x \neq I_y$, if $x \neq y$ [choose $a \in C[X]$ with $a(x) = 0$, $a(y) = 1$.   A compact Hausdorff space is $T_{2\frac{1}{2}}$, by Section 9.5, Theorem 2], we have given a one-to-one correspondence between X and the set of maximal ideals of $C[X]$, namely $x \leftrightarrow \hat{x}^\perp$. One says, informally, that *the maximal ideals are points*. Notice also that each maximal ideal of $C[X]$ is an ideal maximal subspace.

We have seen (Lemma 1) that a proper ideal must contain no unit. Theorem 1 is in the converse direction.

THEOREM 1. *Let* A *be a commutative algebra with identity. Every vector which is not a unit is contained in a maximal ideal.*

Let a be a vector with no inverse. Let P be the collection of all proper ideals containing a. P is not empty, since $aA = Aa \in P$ [aA is proper, since $1 \notin aA$, a having no inverse]. Order P by containment and let I be the union of a maximal chain. I is an ideal. [For example, let $u \in I$, $b \in A$. Then $u \in J$ for some ideal J in the maximal chain, so $bu \in J$ and, therefore, $bu \in I$.] I is proper [for 1 belongs to no member of P, thus $1 \notin I$] and I is maximal [otherwise the maximal chain could be enlarged].//

A *multiplicative* function f is one which satisfies $f(ab) = f(a)f(b)$. A multiplicative linear function is called a *homomorphism* (an *isomorphism into* if it is one to one) and a scalar-valued homomorphism (that is, a multiplicative linear functional) is called a *scalar homomorphism*.

LEMMA 2. *Let* A *be an algebra with identity. Let* f $\neq$ 0 *be a scalar homomorphism of* A. *Then* f(1) = 1, f(t) = t *if* t *is a scalar*, f(a) $\neq$ 0 *if* a *is a unit*, f(a) = 0 *if* a *is nilpotent (that is, if* a^n = 0 *for some positive integer* n), *and* f(a) = 0 *or* 1 *if* a *is idempotent (that is, if* a^2 = a).

If $a^2 = a$, $f(a) = f(a^2) = [f(a)]^2$ so that $f(a) = 0$ or 1. If $f(1) = 0$, we have, for all a, $f(a) = f(a)f(1) = 0$. If $ab = 1$, we have $1 = f(a)f(b)$ and so $f(a) \neq 0$. If $a^n = 0$, $0 = f(a^n) = [f(a)]^n$, so that $f(a) = 0$.//

Example 7. Let A be the set of all 2-by-2 matrices B of complex numbers satisfying $b_{12} = 0$. This is a noncommutative algebra with identity. As a linear space, A is three dimensional, for example, with

$$u = \begin{pmatrix} 1 & 0 \\ 0 & 1 \end{pmatrix}, \qquad v = \begin{pmatrix} 0 & 0 \\ 1 & 0 \end{pmatrix}, \qquad w = \begin{pmatrix} 0 & 0 \\ 0 & 1 \end{pmatrix},$$

we have, uniquely,

$$\begin{pmatrix} a & 0 \\ b & c \end{pmatrix} = au + bv + (c - a)w.$$

A linear functional f on A is given by

$$f\begin{pmatrix} a & 0 \\ b & c \end{pmatrix} = \alpha a + \beta b + \gamma(c - a),$$

where $\alpha = f(u)$, $\beta = f(v)$, $\gamma = f(w)$. If f is multiplicative, we have, by Lemma 2, $\alpha = 1$, $\beta = 0$, $\gamma = 0$ or 1, and so

$$f\begin{pmatrix} a & 0 \\ b & c \end{pmatrix} = c \quad \text{or} \quad a.$$

Defining

$$g\begin{pmatrix} a & 0 \\ b & c \end{pmatrix} = a, \qquad h\begin{pmatrix} a & 0 \\ b & c \end{pmatrix} = c$$

we see that g, h are actually scalar homomorphisms, and the argument shows that they are the only nonzero scalar homomorphisms on A.

LEMMA 3. *Let* A *be an algebra with identity and* f $\neq 0$ *a linear functional. Then* f *is multiplicative if and only if* $f^{\perp}$ *is a subalgebra of* A *and* $f(1) = 1$.

If f is a scalar homomorphism $f(1) = 1$ ⟦Lemma 2⟧ and $f^{\perp}$ is a linear subspace. It is also an algebra, indeed it is an ideal. ⟦If $a \in A$ and $x \in f^{\perp}$, $f(ax) = f(a)f(x) = 0$, $f(xa) = f(x)f(a) = 0$, since $f(x) = 0$. Thus ax and $xa \in f^{\perp}$.⟧ Conversely, suppose that $f(1) = 1$ and that $f^{\perp}$ is a subalgebra. Let a, b be vectors. Then $a - f(a) \in f^{\perp}$ ⟦$f[a - f(a)] = f(a) - f(a)f(1) = 0$⟧. Also $b - f(b) \in f^{\perp}$, and so, by hypothesis, $f^{\perp}$ contains the product p of these two expressions, namely $p = [a - f(a)][b - f(b)] = ab - f(b)a - f(a)b + f(a)f(b)$. From $p \in f^{\perp}$ follows $0 = f(p) = f(ab) - f(b)f(a) - f(a)f(b) + f(a)f(b)$ and so $f(ab) = f(a)f(b)$.//

The relationship between scalar homomorphisms and ideal maximal subspaces is inherited from and similar to the relationship between linear functionals and maximal linear subspaces. It is, however, simpler, because, in the present context, it is a one-to-one correspondence.

THEOREM 2. *Let* A *be an algebra with identity and* f $\neq 0$ *a scalar homomorphism of* A. *Then* $f^{\perp}$ *is an ideal maximal subspace. Conversely, if* I *is an ideal maximal subspace, there exists a unique scalar homomorphism* f *with* I $= f^{\perp}$.

The first half follows from the proof of Lemma 3, in the course of which it was shown that $f^{\perp}$ is an ideal. That $f^{\perp}$ is a maximal subspace is a familiar fact ⟦Section 2.10, Fact (iv)⟧. Conversely, since I is a maximal linear subspace, there exists a unique linear functional f with $f^{\perp} = I$ and $f(1) = 1$. ⟦$1 \notin I$, by Lemma 1. The existence and uniqueness of f was given in Section 2.10, Fact (v)⟧. By Lemma 3, f is multiplicative.//

★ *Example 8.* Let X be a compact Hausdorff space. Example 6 shows a one-to-one correspondence between X and the set M of maximal ideals of $C[X]$, namely $x \leftrightarrow \hat{x}^{\perp}$. By Theorem 2, $x \leftrightarrow \hat{x}$ sets up a one-to-one correspondence between X and the set of nonzero scalar homomorphisms of $C[X]$. One says, informally, that *every nonzero scalar homomorphism on* C[X] *is a point.*

A *division ring* (or *algebra*) is a ring (or algebra) with identity in which every nonzero vector is a unit. A commutative division ring is called a *field*. R^2 with complex multiplication, and the space of quaternions are real division algebras of dimension greater than 1.

Now let A be an algebra and I an ideal. We give A/I a multiplication by defining $(a + I)(b + I) = ab + I$. (In Section 2.8, we made A/I a linear space.) This multiplication is well defined ⟦for if $a + I = a' + I$, $b + I = b' + I$, then $a - a' \in I$, $b - b' \in I$ and so $ab - a'b' = a(b - b') + (a - a')b' \in I$, that is, $ab + I = a'b' + I$⟧. It is easy to check that A/I is an algebra. If A is commutative, so is A/I, and if A has an identity, so has A/I, namely $1 + I$.

LEMMA 4. *Let* A *be a commutative algebra with identity, and* I *a maximal ideal. Then* A/I *is a field.*

The converse is also true, but we shall not need it. Let $x \in A/I$, $x \neq 0$; that is, $x = b + I$, $b \notin I$. Let $J = I + bA$. Then J is an ideal. [For $a \in A$, $a(I + bA) = aI + abA = aI + baA \subset I + bA$. Also, J is a linear subspace, since I and bA are.] Moreover, $I \subset J$ [$I = I + b0 \subset I + bA$] and $I \neq J$, since $b \in J$ [$b = 0 + b1 \in I + bA$]. Since I is maximal, $J = A$. In particular $1 \in J$, that is, $1 = u + ba$ for some $u \in I$, $a \in A$. Then $(a + I)x = (a + I)(b + I) = ab + I = 1 - u + I = 1 + I$, since $u \in I$. Thus $a + I = x^{-1}$. Since every nonzero element of A/I has an inverse, A/I is a field.//

Let A be an algebra with identity. The *spectrum* of a vector a, written $\sigma(a)$, is the set of all scalars z such that $a - z$ has no inverse. If $\sigma(a)$ is not empty, we define the *spectral radius* of a, written $r(a)$, as sup $\{|z|: z \in \sigma(a)\}$. This may be infinite, of course.

★ *Example 9.* Let A be a division algebra which is of dimension greater than 1. Then every $a \in A$ which is not a scalar, that is, not a scalar multiple of 1, has empty spectrum. [For any $z \in E$, $a - z \neq 0$; hence $a - z$ is a unit.] For such a, $r(a)$ is meaningless.

★ *Example 10.* For $a \in C[X]$, X a topological space, *the spectrum of a is its range.* [If $a(x) = t$ for some x, $a(x) - t = 0$ and so $a - t$ has no reciprocal, thus $t \in \sigma(a)$. Conversely, if $a(x) \neq t$ for all x, $a - t$ is never zero and so has a continuous reciprocal, thus $t \notin \sigma(a)$.] For $C_1[X]$, $\sigma(a)$ is the closure of the range of a. This is proved similarly [Problem 16].

In each case, the spectral radius of a is sup $\{|a(x)|: x \in X\}$. There may be $a \in C[X]$ with $r(a) = \infty$ [for example, let $X = (0, 1)$, $a(x) = 1/x$]. However, for $a \in C_1[X]$, $r(a) = \|a\| < \infty$. (This is the natural norm for $C_1[X]$.)

LEMMA 5. *Let* $f \neq 0$ *be a scalar homomorphism on an algebra with identity. Then for each vector* a, $f(a) \in \sigma(a)$.

Here, $f[a - f(a)] = 0$, thus by Lemma 2, $a - f(a)$ has no inverse.//

★ *Example 11.* For $a \in C[X]$, $x \in X$, $\hat{x}(a) \in \sigma(a)$ by Lemma 5. Thus $a(x) \in \sigma(a)$. This was already observed in Example 10.

LEMMA 6. *Let* A *be an algebra with identity and* $a \in A$. *Then* $[\sigma(a)]^n \subset \sigma(a^n)$ *for each positive integer* n. *In particular, if* a *is nilpotent,* $r(a) = 0$.

Let $z \in \sigma(a)$ and consider $u \equiv a^n - z^n = (a - z)v = v(a - z)$, where $v = a^{n-1} + a^{n-2}z + \cdots + z^{n-1}$. Now, if u had an inverse, it would follow that $(a - z)vu^{-1} = 1 = u^{-1}v(a - z)$, that is, $a - z$ has a right and a left inverse. Hence it has an inverse, contrary to $z \in \sigma(a)$. Thus, in fact, $a^n - z^n$ has no inverse and $z^n \in \sigma(a^n)$.//

DEFINITION 1. *The* G *radical of an algebra is the set of points at which all scalar homomorphisms are* 0. *The algebra is called* G *semisimple if its* G *radical is* $\{0\}$. (The letter G is used in honor of I. M. Gelfand.)

Letting S be the set of scalar homomorphisms (not empty, since $0 \in S$), the G radical is $\bigcap\{f^\perp: f \in S\}$. It is not empty, since it contains 0. In Example 7, the G radical is

$$\left\{ \begin{pmatrix} 0 & 0 \\ x & 0 \end{pmatrix} : x \in E \right\},$$

while, if X is a compact Hausdorff space, $C[X]$ is G semisimple. 〚By Example 8, each non-zero scalar homomorphism is given by $\hat{x}$ for some $x \in X$. Thus, if a is in the G radical, for every $x \in X$, $0 = \hat{x}(a) = a(x)$ and so $a = 0$.〛

LEMMA 7. *Let* A *be an algebra with identity. The* G *radical of* A *contains all commutators, that is, vectors of the form* ab $-$ ba, *and all vectors whose spectral radius is* 0, *in particular, all nilpotent vectors.*

For any scalar homomorphism f, $f(ab - ba) = f(a)f(b) - f(b)f(a) = 0$. Also, if $r(a) = 0$, it follows from Lemma 5 that $f(a) = 0.//$

It follows that a G semisimple algebra is commutative. It turns out that for noncommutative algebras, the G radical is a very unnatural object to study; in any case we shall be mainly interested in commutative algebras.

DEFINITION 2. THE GELFAND REPRESENTATION. *Let* A *be a commutative algebra with identity for which* H, *the set of nonzero scalar homomorphisms, is not empty. For a* $\in$ A, *define* â, *a complex function on* H, *by* â(f) = f(a) *for* f $\in$ H. H *is given the topology* σ(H, A).

Thus A is mapped into $C[H]$, the algebra of continuous functions on the Hausdorff space H 〚H has the weak star topology, the relative topology of $\sigma(A^{\#}, A)$〛. The map from A into $C[H]$ is a homomorphism 〚$(ab)^{\wedge}(f) = f(ab) = f(a)f(b) = \hat{a}(f)\hat{b}(f)$ for $f \in H$, a, $b \in A$, so that $(ab)^{\wedge} = \hat{a}\hat{b}$; similarly $(ta + b)^{\wedge} = t\hat{a} + \hat{b}$ for scalar t〛. The *kernel* of the homomorphism, that is, the set of elements a of A for which $\hat{a} = 0$, is precisely the G radical of A, so that the representation is an isomorphism into if and only if A is G semisimple. In this extremely general framework, we are unable to do much more with the Gelfand representation than acknowledge its existence.

One remark of interest is that for each $a \in A$, $\sigma(a)$ includes the range of $\hat{a}$ 〚if $\hat{a}(f) = t$ for some $f \in H$, it follows that $t = f(a) \in \sigma(a)$, as provided by Lemma 5〛.

We shall now see that the Gelfand representation has the desirable feature that if $A = C[X]$, X a compact Hausdorff space, then H may be identified with X and the representation is an isomorphism onto.

★ *Example 12.* Let X be a compact Hausdorff space. Each $a \in C[X]$ goes into $\hat{a} \in C[H]$ given by $\hat{a}(\hat{x}) = a(x)$ for all $x \in X$ 〚Example 8 and $\hat{a}(\hat{x}) = \hat{x}(a) = a(x)$〛. Conversely, given $u \in C[H]$, for $f \in H$, $f = \hat{x}$ for some $x \in X$; let $a(x) = u(f)$, then $u = \hat{a}$. Thus the representation is an identification of $C[X]$ with $C[H]$. The representation has the additional pleasant feature that H, X are also identified as topological spaces; that is, they have the same topology. Strictly speaking, the map $x \to \hat{x}$ of Example 8 is a homeomorphism onto. 〚If x_{δ} is a net in X, $x_{\delta} \to x$, then $a(x_{\delta}) \to a(x)$, since each $a \in C[X]$ is continuous, that is, $\hat{x}_{\delta}(a) \to \hat{x}(a)$ for each a, and so $\hat{x}_{\delta} \to \hat{x}$ in $\sigma(H, A)$. Thus the representation is continuous. Since X is compact and H Hausdorff, it is a homeomorphism, by Section 9.5, Theorem 4. A briefer proof runs thus: identify H, X; now, H has the weakest topology such that each a is continuous, hence weaker than that of X; by Section 9.5, Theorem 3, the topologies are equal.〛

COROLLARY 1. *Let* X *and* Y *be compact Hausdorff spaces such that* C[X] *and* C[Y] *are (algebraically) isomorphic. Then* X, Y *are homeomorphic.*

In Example 12, H and its topology are determined by the algebra [namely, H is the set of scalar homomorphisms on A with topology $\sigma(H, A)$]. Example 12 provides that each of X, Y is homeomorphic with H.//

Problems 14.1

In this list, any problem whose data are unspecified refers to an algebra A with identity; a, b, c are vectors; t, z are scalars.

★1. If a, b are units, $a^{-1} - b^{-1} = a^{-1}(b - a)b^{-1}$.

2. If $a^2 = 1$, $\sigma(a) = \{1\}$, $\{-1\}$, or $\{-1, 1\}$. In particular, $r(a) = 1$.

3. If a is idempotent, $\sigma(a) = \{0\}$, $\{1\}$, or $\{0, 1\}$.

4. Let X be the union of two disjoint subintervals of R. Give examples, in $C[X]$, which realize all the possibilities of Problems 2 and 3. Would this be possible if X were an interval?

5. $\sigma(ta) = t\sigma(a)$ for scalar $t \neq 0$. The result holds also for $t = 0$, if $\sigma(a) \neq \emptyset$. Deduce from this that $r(ta) = |t|r(a)$ for all scalar t if $\sigma(a) \neq \emptyset$.

6. Give an example in which r is not a seminorm (see Problem 5). [Try 2×2 matrices, using Problem 2 and Lemma 6.]

★7. If $ab = ba$ and a is a unit, then $a^{-1}b = ba^{-1}$.

8. Let a, b be idempotents. Then (i) $a + b$ is idempotent if and only if $ab = ba = 0$, (ii) $a - b$ is idempotent if and only if $ab = ba = b$, (iii) if $ab = ba$, then ab is idempotent. (Compare Section 2.8, Problem 10.)

9. Let A be commutative. Suppose that a, b, c and $a + b + c$ are all idempotent. Show that $ab = 0$. ▲Can "commutative" be dropped?

★10. In the Gelfand representation, show that $\hat{A} \equiv \{\hat{a}: a \in A\}$ is separating over H.

11. Show that any vector with unique left inverse is a unit and that any vector with a left inverse, but no right inverse, has infinitely many distinct left inverses. [If $ba = 1 \neq ab$, then $ua = 0$, where $u = ab - 1$. Now, consider $b + nu$.]

★12. $\sigma(ab)$ and $\sigma(ba)$ are the same, with the possible exception that only one contains 0. [Let $u = (1 - ab)^{-1}$. Then $(1 - ba)^{-1} = 1 + bua$ because $(1 - ba)(1 + bua) = 1 - ba + b(1 - ab)ua$.]

13. The exceptional case in Problem 12 may occur. [a, b: $c_0 \to c_0$ given by $a\delta^n = \delta^{n+1}$, $b\delta^n = \delta^{n-1}$, $b\delta^1 = 0$.]

14. Given an algebra B without identity, show that B can be embedded as an ideal maximal subspace in an algebra A with identity. [Let $A = B \times E$. Define $(a, u) \cdot (b, v)$ to be $(ab + va + ub, uv)$.]

15. Let B have trivial multiplication, that is, $BB = \{0\}$, and let A be as in Problem 14. Show that B is the G radical of A.

16. Let X be a topological space. For $a \in C_1[X]$, $\sigma(a)$ is the closure of the range of a.

17. A proper left ideal contains no vector with a left inverse.

18. The algebra of $n \times n$ complex matrices has no proper ideals. It has proper one-sided ideals. [Example 3.]

19. "Commutative" cannot be omitted in Theorem 1. [Problem 18.]

★20. Let B be a subalgebra of A and suppose that $1 \in B$. Show that $\sigma(b) \subset \sigma_B(b)$ for $b \in B$. [$\sigma_B(b)$ denotes the spectrum of b as an element of B.]

21. Give an example of inequality in Problem 20. [Polynomials in C.]

★22. In Problem 20, suppose that B *contains its inverses*, that is, $b \in B$, b a unit in A implies $b^{-1} \in B$. Then $\sigma(b) = \sigma_B(b)$.

23. If A contains a vector a with empty spectrum, then A has no nonzero scalar homomorphism. What is the G radical?

24. The G radical in Example 7 is made up entirely of commutators.

25. Let K be the G radical of A. Then A/K is G semisimple.

26. Theorem 2 is false if the assumption of an identity is omitted. ⟦Let $ab \equiv 0$. Then for all f, $f^\perp$ is an ideal, but no $f \neq 0$ is multiplicative.⟧

27. (a) Let $W = \{a: 1 - ab$ is a unit for all $b\}$. Then W is included in the G radical. (b) Show that W is $\{a: 1 - ba$ is a unit for all $b\}$. ⟦Problem 12.⟧

28. If A is a division algebra, W of Problem 27, is $\{0\}$. If, in addition, the dimension of A is more than one, the G radical of A is all of A (hence not equal to W). ⟦0 is the only scalar homomorphism.⟧

29. Let B be a linear space of dimension greater than 1, $f \in B^\#$, $f \neq 0$. Define $ab = f(a)b$. Show that B is a noncommutative algebra with no identity, that f is the only nonzero scalar homomorphism on B, that every linear subspace is a left ideal, and that the proper right ideals are the linear subspaces of $f^\perp$.

30. With B, f as in Problem 29, fix $u \in B$ with $f(u) = 1$ and define $ab = f(a)b + f(b)a - f(a)f(b)u$. Show that B is a commutative algebra with identity and B has a maximal linear subspace S on which multiplication is trivial that is, $SS = \{0\}$. (Thus S is an ideal by Lemma 3 and Theorem 2.) ⟦$S = f^\perp$.⟧

31. Suppose that a linear topological space is made into an algebra with identity in such a way that the set of units has an interior point. Show that every scalar homomorphism is continuous. ⟦By Lemma 2, $f^\perp$ is not dense.⟧

32. An ideal I is called *regular* if A/I has an identity. (Do not assume that A has an identity.) Show that, if A has an identity, every ideal is regular. Give an example of a nonregular ideal. ⟦$ab = 0$ for all a, b.⟧

33. (a) Let A be an algebra (with or without identity). Let f be a nonzero scalar homomorphism. Show that $f^\perp$ is a regular ideal. ⟦If $f(u) = 1$, $u + f^\perp$ is an identity in $A/f^\perp$.⟧ (b) Conversely, if I is a regular ideal maximal subspace, $I = f^\perp$ for some scalar homomorphism f.

34. Take as known that the product of two conull matrices is a conull matrix; deduce from Lemma 3 that χ is a scalar homomorphism on the algebra of conservative matrices.

35. Let S be the square $(0 \leq x \leq 1, 0 \leq y \leq 1)$ in the complex plane. Define $j \in C[S]$ by $j(z) = z$ for $z \in S$. Show that (a) $J \equiv jC[S]$ is an ideal and that $\bar{j} \notin J$ (here $\bar{j}(z) = \bar{z}$, the complex conjugate); (b) $\bar{j}$ is in the closure of J.

36. Let J be an ideal in $C[X]$, X a compact Hausdorff space. Show that $J^{\perp\perp}$ is an ideal which includes J, perhaps, properly. (Note: take $J^\perp \subset X$.) ⟦Problem 35.⟧ See also Problem 44.

37. Let X be a topological space. If $C_1[X]$ contains an idempotent other than 0, 1, X is not connected. (Thus topological properties of X follow from algebraic properties of $C_1[X]$, as implied by Corollary 1.)

38. Let A be the algebra of all continuous real functions f on $[0, 1]$ satisfying $f(0) = 0$. Is $\{f: f'(0) = 0\}$ a maximal ideal?

39. Let $X = (0, 1)$, an open interval in R. Find a maximal ideal in (i) $C[X]$, (ii) $C_1[X]$, which is not of the form I_x. ⟦Extend (i), $\{a: a(x) = 0$ on a neighborhood of 0$\}$; (iii), $\{a: \lim_{x \to 0} a(x) = 0\}$ to a maximal ideal (not including 1).⟧

40. Let B be a two-dimensional real noncommutative algebra. Show that there exists $f \in B^\#$ such that either $ab = f(a)b$ for all a, b, or $ab = f(b)a$ for all a, b.

41. Let D be the algebra of conservative triangular matrices. Show that, for each n, $f(A) = a_{nn}$ is a scalar homomorphism. Hence every matrix in the G radical has zero diagonal.

▲42. For D, Problem 41, the set W, Problem 27, is the set of coercive matrices with zero diagonal.

▲43. Let X be a compact Hausdorff space. Then every closed ideal in $C[X]$ is $\{a: a(x) = 0$ for all $x \in S\}$ for some $S \subset X$. (Problem 35 shows that "closed" cannot be dropped.) ⟦$S = \bigcap\{a^\perp: a \in I\}$, see Example 5.⟧

44. Deduce from Problem 43 that in Problem 36, $J^{\perp\perp} = \bar{J}$. [Problem 35(b) is a corollary.]

45. Set up a correspondence between filters on ω and proper ideals in s. For example, for I a proper ideal in s, let $x^\perp = \{n: x_n = 0\}$, $I^\perp = \{x^\perp: x \in I\}$. Show that $I^\perp$ is a filter. Conversely, if F is a filter on ω, let $F_0 = \{x \in s: x^\perp \in F\}$. Show that F_0 is a proper ideal.

14.2   Banach algebra

In this section we introduce topological considerations by means of a complete norm. The main object is the study of the Gelfand representation.

A *Banach algebra* is a Banach space on which is defined a multiplication making it an algebra such that for all vectors a, b, $\|ab\| \leq \|a\| \cdot \|b\|$. This inequality is called the *multiplicative property* of the norm.

We say that the Banach algebra has an identity 1 if 1 is an identity for the algebra and, in addition, $\|1\| = 1$. In particular, a *Banach algebra with identity cannot be zero dimensional*.

Note. Much of the theory described in the following pages is valid for complex algebras only. When no specification is made, results will apply for both real and complex algebras. On the other hand, certain results will specify complex algebras; these will depend strongly on the fact that the scalars are complex.

Some of the spaces listed in the Table of Spaces are commutative Banach algebras with identity, the multiplication in each case being coordinatewise, or pointwise, that is, $(ab)(t) = a(t)b(t)$ or $(ab)_n = a_n b_n$. These are $C_1[X]$, R^n, E^n, c_0, c, $l^p (p \geq 1)$, A_C. (The multiplicative property of the norm of l^p follows easily from Hölder's inequality. Check it first for unit vectors.) These and some of the others are Banach algebras with other (equivalent) norms or other multiplications. An example is the convolution for l and L which will be mentioned in Section 3, Application 1.

The *maximal group* $G(A)$ of a Banach algebra A with identity, is the set of units.

The *algebraic closure* of a set S is the smallest closed subalgebra which includes S. The *algebraic hull* of S is the smallest subalgebra which includes S.

Facts

In this list, A is a Banach algebra with identity.

(i) Multiplication is continuous (as a function: $A \times A \to A$).

(ii) $N(1, 1) \subset G(A)$, that is, $\|a - 1\| < 1$ implies that a is a unit. Moreover, if $\|a - 1\| < 1$, a^{-1} lies in the algebraic closure of $\{1, a\}$, and $\|a^{-1}\| \leq 1/(1 - \|a - 1\|)$.

(iii) The maximal group $G(A)$ is open. In fact, if g is a unit and $\|a - g\| < 1/\|g^{-1}\|$, then a is a unit. Moreover, a^{-1} lies in the algebraic closure of $\{1, a, g^{-1}\}$, and $\|a^{-1}\| \leq \|g^{-1}\|/(1 - \|g - a\| \cdot \|g^{-1}\|)$.

(iv) If g is a unit and $\|a - g\| < 1/2\|g^{-1}\|$, then a is a unit and $\|a^{-1}\| < 2\|g^{-1}\|$. In particular, $\|a - 1\| < \frac{1}{2}$ implies $\|a^{-1}\| < 2$.

(v) a^{-1} is continuous as a function of a on $G(A)$.

(vi) If a_n is a unit for $n = 1, 2, \ldots$, and $a_n \to a$, a not a unit, then $\|a_n^{-1}\| \to \infty$.

(vii) The closure of a proper ideal is a proper ideal.

(viii) A maximal ideal is closed.

Proofs

(i) Let $a_n \to a$, $b_n \to b$. Then for some K, $\|a_n\| < K$ for all n. Thus $\|a_n b_n - ab\| \leq \|a_n b_n - a_n b\| + \|a_n b - ab\| \leq \|a_n\| \cdot \|b_n - b\| + \|a_n - a\| \cdot \|b\| < K\|b_n - b\| + \|a_n - a\| \cdot \|b\| \to 0$.

(ii) Since $a = 1 - \epsilon$ with $\|\epsilon\| = \|1 - a\| < 1$, it is natural to think of expanding $(1 - \epsilon)^{-1}$ in a power series in ϵ. We adapt this suggestion to the realities of the situation. First consider the series $\Sigma_{k=0}^{\infty}\epsilon^k$, where $\epsilon = 1 - a$, and $\epsilon^0 = 1$ (the identity). This series converges. [$\|\epsilon^k\| \leq \|\epsilon\|^k$, and $\|\epsilon\| < 1$, thus the series is absolutely convergent. Since the space is complete, the series converges. This was proved in Section 6.2, Theorem 1.]

Next, for $n = 1, 2, \ldots$, let $b_n = \Sigma_{k=0}^n \epsilon^k$. Then $ab_n = (1 - \epsilon)\Sigma_{k=0}^n \epsilon^k = 1 - \epsilon^{n+1} \to 1$ as $n \to \infty$ [since $\|\epsilon^{n+1}\| \leq \|\epsilon\|^{n+1} \to 0$.] Similarly, $b_n a \to 1$. Since multiplication is continuous [Fact (i)], with $b = \Sigma\epsilon^k$, we have $ab = ba = 1$. Thus $b = a^{-1}$. Next, ϵ, each ϵ^k, and each b_n all lie in the algebraic hull of $\{1, a\}$. Thus $b = \lim b_n$ lies in the algebraic closure. Finally $\|b\| \leq \Sigma\|\epsilon\|^k = 1/(1 - \|\epsilon\|)$.

(iii) Let $\epsilon = 1 - ag^{-1} = (g - a)g^{-1}$. We apply the preceding argument to $b = g^{-1}\Sigma_{k=0}^{\infty}\epsilon^k$. Let $b_n = g^{-1}\Sigma_{k=0}^n \epsilon^k$. Then, since $a = (1 - \epsilon)g$, we have

$$ab_n = 1 - \epsilon^{n+1},$$
$$b_n a = g^{-1}(1 - \epsilon^{n+1})g,$$

and so, since $\|\epsilon\| < 1$ and multiplication is continuous, we have $ab = ba = 1$. Also

$$\|a^{-1}\| = \|b\| \leq \frac{\|g^{-1}\|}{1 - \|\epsilon\|} \leq \frac{\|g^{-1}\|}{1 - \|g - a\| \cdot \|g^{-1}\|}.$$

(iv) This follows from Fact (iii).

(v) Suppose that $a_n \to a$, and that $a_n \in G(A)$, $a \in G(A)$, that is, a_n and a have inverses. Then $\|a_n^{-1} - a^{-1}\| = \|a_n^{-1}(a - a_n)a^{-1}\| \leq \|a_n^{-1}\| \cdot \|a - a_n\| \cdot \|a^{-1}\| \leq 2\|a^{-1}\| \cdot \|a - a_n\| \cdot \|a^{-1}\|$, whenever n is sufficiently large that $\|a_n - a\| < 1/2\|a^{-1}\|$ [Fact (iv).] Thus $a_n^{-1} \to a^{-1}$.

(vi) Fact (iii) provides that $\|a - a_n\| \geq 1/\|a_n^{-1}\|$.

(vii) For $S \subset A$, $a \in A$, we have $a\bar{S} \subset \overline{aS}$. [Let $x \in a\bar{S}$. Then $x = ay$, $y \in \bar{S}$. There exists a sequence $\{y_n\}$ of points of S with $y_n \to y$. Then $ay_n \to ay = x$, and $ay_n \in aS$. Thus, $x \in \overline{aS}$.] Thus if I is an ideal and $a \in A$, $\bar{I}$ is a linear subspace [Section 10.2, Theorem 1] and $a\bar{I} \subset \overline{aI} \subset \bar{I}$. $\bar{I}$ is proper, since I is not dense [$I \cap G(A)$, by Section 1, Lemma 1, and $G(A)$ is a nonempty open set, according to Fact (iii)].

(viii) The closure of a maximal ideal I is a proper ideal including I [Fact (vii)]; hence, it is equal to I.//

Concerning Fact (ii), $\|a - 1\| \leq 1$ would not be sufficient [take $a = 0$]. Moreover, the next example shows that completeness cannot be dropped.

Example 1. Let A be the set of polynomials on D, the unit disk in the complex plane, as a normed subspace and subalgebra of $C[D]$. The space A does not satisfy Fact (ii). [For example, let $a(z) = 1 + \frac{1}{2}z$. Then $\|a - 1\| = \frac{1}{2}$ but $1/a(z)$ is not a polynomial.] Here, $G(A)$ is one dimensional [all nonzero multiples of 1].

The quotient algebra discussed in Section 1 extends to Banach algebras. Let I be a closed ideal in a Banach algebra. With $\|a + I\| = \inf\{\|a + u\| : u \in I\}$, A/I is a Banach space. [Section 6.5, Theorem 1]. Thus we have only to check that $\|(a + I)(b + I)\| \leq \|a + I\| \cdot \|b + I\|$; that is, $\|ab + I\| \leq \|a + I\| \cdot \|b + I\|$. [$\|ab + I\| = \inf\{\|ab + u\| : u \in I\} \leq \inf\{\|ab + aw + vb + vw\| : v \in I, w \in I\}$ (since $aw + vb + vw \in I$, that is, $\{aw + bv + vw : v \in I, w \in I\} \subset \{u : u \in I\}$; inf, when taken over a larger set is smaller).

Thus $\|ab + I\| \le \inf \{\|(a + v)(b + w)\|: v \in I, w \in I\} \le \inf \{\|a + v\| \cdot \|b + w\|: v \in I, w \in I\} = \inf \{\|a + v\|: v \in I\} \cdot \inf \{\|b + w\|: w \in I\}$ (since v, w are chosen independently) $= \|a + I\| \cdot \|b + I\|.\}$

If $I = A$, then $A/I = \{0\}$. In the following, we shall assume that $I \ne A$.

If A has an identity, so has A/I, namely $1 + I$. $\{(1 + I)(a + I) = (a + I)(1 + I) = a + I$, clearly. Also, $\|1 + I\| = \inf \{\|1 + u\|: u \in I\} \le 1$ (take $u = 0$). The opposite inequality is clear [Problem 12], and so $\|1 + I\| = 1$.

At various stages in the development, topological results will follow from purely algebraic assumptions. For example, from algebraic isomorphism between $C[X]$, $C[Y]$, follows homeomorphism of X, Y [Section 1, Corollary 1]. The next result is also of this form.

THEOREM 1. *Let* f $\ne 0$ *be a scalar homomorphism on a Banach algebra with identity. Then* $\|f\| = 1$. *(In particular,* f *is continuous.)*

This may be compared with Section 4.4, Problem 48, a similar result for ordered spaces.

Let a be an arbitrary vector. If $f(a) = 0$, then $|f(a)| \le \|a\|$. If $f(a) \ne 0$, $1 - a/f(a) \in f^\perp$, hence is not a unit [Section 1, Lemma 2]. By Fact (ii), $\|a/f(a)\| \ge 1$, that is, $|f(a)| \le \|a\|$. Thus $\|f\| \le 1$. Since, also, $f(1) = 1 = \|1\|$, it follows that $\|f\| \ge 1.//$

Example 2. Let A be as in Example 1. Define $f(a) = a(2)$ for $a \in A$. Then f is a scalar homomorphism, yet $\|f\| = \infty$. [For integer $n > 0$, let $a(z) = z^n$. Then $\|a\| = 1$, $f(a) = 2^n$. Thus $\|f\| \ge 2^n$ for any n.] Thus, in Theorem 1, completeness cannot be dropped.

The space H in the Gelfand representation, Section 1, will be called the *carrier space of* A.

Recall that H is the set of nonzero scalar homomorphisms on A. Theorem 1 shows that H is a subset of the unit disk in A^* and we recall that H was given the topology $\sigma(H, A)$ in Section 1, this being the relative topology of the weak star topology on A^*.

THEOREM 2. *Let* A *be a Banach algebra with identity. Then the carrier space* H *is a compact Hausdorff space.*

Since the unit disk D in A^* is weak star compact [Banach-Alaoglu theorem, Section 13.3, Theorem 1], it is sufficient to show that H is closed in this disk.

Suppose then that f_δ is a net in H, $f_\delta \to f \in D$; f is linear and continuous on A [since $f \in D$]. For any a, $b \in A$, $f(ab) = \lim f_\delta(ab) = \lim f_\delta(a)f_\delta(b) = f(a)f(b)$. Thus, f is multiplicative. Also, $f \ne 0$, since $f(1) = \lim f_\delta(1) = 1$; hence, $f \in H.//$

In studying the spectrum, each result should be compared with the situation in $C[X]$, X a compact Hausdorff space. For $a \in C[X]$, $\sigma(a)$ is the range of a, thus is compact. Theorem 3 generalizes this.

THEOREM 3. *Let* A *be a Banach algebra with identity. For each* a $\in$ A, σ(a) *is a compact set of scalars.*

The set $\sigma(a)$ is bounded; in fact,

$$(1) \qquad\qquad z \in \sigma(a) \qquad \text{implies} \qquad |z| \le \|a\|.$$

⟦If $|z| > \|a\|$, then $\|a/z\| < 1$, causing $1 - a/z$ to be a unit, as provided by Fact (ii). Thus, $a - z$ is a unit and so $z \notin \sigma(a)$.⟧ Next, $\sigma(a)$ is closed. ⟦Let $z \notin \sigma(a)$. Then $z - a$ is a unit. By Fact (iii), if w is a scalar sufficiently close to z (namely, $|w - z| < 1/\|(z - a)^{-1}\|$), $w - a$ is a unit and so $w \notin \sigma(a)$. Consequently, $z \notin \overline{\sigma(a)}$. (A briefer proof runs, $\sigma(a) = [(a + G) \cap E]^{\sim}$, where $G = G(A)$ is open.)⟧//

THEOREM 4.   *In a complex Banach algebra* A *with identity, the spectrum of every vector is nonempty.*

The result is false for real Banach algebras, even if they are assumed commutative ⟦Problem 13 and Section 1, Example 9⟧.

Assume that $\sigma(a)$ is empty. Then, in particular, a has an inverse. Let f be a continuous linear functional on A satisfying $f(a^{-1}) = 1$ ⟦Hahn-Banach theorem⟧. For complex z, define $g(z) = f[(a - z)^{-1}]$. This defines g on all of E ⟦since $\sigma(a) = \emptyset$⟧, moreover, g is an entire function in the sense of the theory of functions of a complex variable.

$$\left\llbracket \frac{g(z + h) - g(z)}{h} = f \left\{ \frac{(a - z - h)^{-1} - (a - z)^{-1}}{h} \right\} \right.$$

and, since f is continuous, it is sufficient to prove that the vector inside the braces tends to a limit as $h \to 0$. This we do in exactly the way one differentiates $1/(c - x)$ in elementary calculus. Using Section 1, Problem 1, we obtain

$$\frac{(a - z - h)^{-1} - (a - z)^{-1}}{h} = (a - z - h)^{-1}(a - z)^{-1} \to \{(a - z)^{-1}\}^2 \text{ as } h \to 0$$

by Fact (v).⟧ Also, $|g(z)| \leq \|f\| \cdot \|(a - z)^{-1}\|$, and, for $|z| > 2\|a\|$, we have $\|(a - z)^{-1}\| = \|(a/z - 1)^{-1} \cdot (1/z)\| < 2/|z|$, from Fact (iv). Consequently, $|g(z)| \leq 2\|f\|/|z| \to 0$ as $|z| \to \infty$. Thus, g is an entire function which vanishes at infinity. Liouville's theorem provides that $g = 0$, contradicting $g(0) = f(a^{-1}) = 1$.//

COROLLARY 1.   MAZUR'S THEOREM.   *If a complex Banach algebra* A *is a division algebra, then* A *is one dimensional.*

The result is false for real Banach algebras, even if assumed commutative ⟦Problem 13⟧. The algebra A cannot be zero dimensional because of our blanket assumption that $\|1\| = 1$. The proof consists of observing that, if A is more than one dimensional, it has an element with empty spectrum ⟦Section 1, Example 9⟧, contradicting Theorem 4.//

Example 3: Suppose that a complex Banach algebra A *with identity satisfies* $\|a^{-1}\| = 1/\|a\|$ *for all* $a \in G(A)$; *then* A *is one dimensional.* For any points $a_n \in G(A)$, $n = 1, 2, \ldots$, satisfying $a_n \to a$, $a \neq 0$, we have $\|a_n^{-1}\| = 1/\|a_n\| \to 1/\|a\|$. By Fact (vi), $a \in G(A)$; hence, $G(A)$ is closed in $A \setminus \{0\}$. It is also open {Fact (iii)}. Thus, $G(A) = A \setminus \{0\}$ ⟦since $A \setminus \{0\}$ is connected; in fact, any two points can be joined by a path made of two line segments⟧. By Corollary 1, A is one dimensional.

We are now able to remove the rather inelegant distinction between ideal maximal subspaces and maximal ideals, provided we restrict our attention to commutative algebras. (In a noncommutative Banach algebra, there may be no proper ideals at all ⟦Section 1,

Problem 18]. (It is not difficult to see, from this, that the following result becomes false if "commutative" is dropped.)

COROLLARY 2. *Let* A *be a commutative complex Banach algebra with identity. Then every maximal ideal* I *is a maximal linear subspace, that is,* I $=$ f$^\perp$ *for some* f $\in$ H.

We saw above that A/I is a Banach algebra with identity [note that I is closed, by Fact (viii)]. In Section 1, Lemma 4, it was proved that A/I is a field. Thus, A/I is one dimensional [Corollary 1].//

Remark 1. For $A = C[X]$, X a compact Hausdorff space, this result was obtained in Section 1, Example 6.

Remark 2. If A is a commutative complex Banach algebra with identity, there always exists a nonzero scalar homomorphism on A; that is, H is not empty. This follows from Corollary 2, and Section 1, Theorem 1.

We have seen that in $C[X]$, X a compact Hausdorff space, the maximal ideals are the points; thus X is the carrier space of $C[X]$. If $A \subset C[X]$, the points will still be maximal ideals of A, but A may have others.

Example 4. Let K be the plane circumference $x^2 + y^2 = 1$. Let A be the subalgebra of $C[K]$ consisting of those functions which are restrictions to K of members of A_C. This is a closed subalgebra of $C[K]$. [If $a_n \in A$, $a_n \to a$, the maximum modulus theorem yields that $\{a_n\}$ is a Cauchy sequence in A_C.] Now, each member of A has a unique extension to a member of A_C; hence, points in the cell $x^2 + y^2 < 1$ are maximal ideals of A which are not points of K.

The crucial point in certain applications is the proof that a specific subalgebra still has the property that all of its maximal ideals are points. We give an example of this, reserving applications for the next section.

Example 5: *Maximal ideals in* A$_C$. Notice that A_C is a closed subalgebra of $C[D]$, D being the unit disk in the complex plane. Define $j \in A_C$ by $j(z) = z$ for $|z| \leq 1$. Let f be a nonzero scalar homomorphism on A_C and set $w = f(j)$. We shall prove that $f = \hat{w}$, that is, $f^\perp = I_w$. First, $|w| \leq 1$ [since $|w| = |f(j)| \leq \|f\| \cdot \|j\| = 1$, according to Theorem 1]. Next, $f(a) = a(w)$ if a is a polynomial (that is, $a(z)$ is a polynomial in z) [$a(z) = \Sigma t_k z^k = \Sigma t_k \{j(z)\}^k$; thus, $a = \Sigma t_k j^k$ and so $f(a) = \Sigma t_k w^k = a(w)$]. But the set of polynomials is dense in A_C. [Given $a \in A_C$, $\epsilon > 0$, choose $r < 1$, but so near 1 that $|a(rz) - a(z)| < \epsilon/2$ for $|z| \leq 1$. Then $a(rz)$ is analytic for $|z| \leq 1$ [in contrast to $a(z)$, which may not be analytic for $|z| = 1$]; thus, the power series for $a(rz)$ converges uniformly for $|z| \leq 1$. A segment of this series will be a polynomial $b(z)$, satisfying $|a(rz) - b(z)| < \epsilon/2$ for $|z| \leq 1$. Thus, $|a(z) - b(z)| < \epsilon$ for $|z| \leq 1$; that is, $\|a - b\| < \epsilon$.] Hence, $f(a) = a(w)$ for all a. [Both f and $\hat{w}$ are continuous on A_C, and equal on a dense subset, the polynomials.]

We have thus proved that the maximal ideals in A_C are points in D, the same as for $C[D]$ [Section 1, Example 8]. Thus H, the carrier space, is D. (The topologies agree too, see Section 1, Example 12.) Notice that $H = \sigma(j)$. For a further remark on this, see Problem 25.

COROLLARY 3. *Let* A *be a commutative complex Banach algebra with identity, and* a $\in$ A. *Then* z $\in$ σ(a) *if and only if* f(a) = z *for some nonzero scalar homomorphism* f.

If $f(a) = z$, then $z \in \sigma(a)$ ⟦this was proved in Section 1, Lemma 5⟧. Conversely, suppose that $z \in \sigma(a)$. Then $a - z$ has no inverse, hence is included in a maximal ideal ⟦Section 1, Theorem 1⟧. This ideal is $f^{\perp}$ for some $f \in H$ and $f(a - z) = 0$, so that $f(a) = z.//$

It follows from Theorem 4 that $r(a)$, the spectral radius of a, is defined for each a. An important formula for $r(a)$ will now be given.

THEOREM 5. *Let* A *be a complex Banach algebra with identity, and* a $\in$ A. *Then* r(a) = $\lim_{n \to \infty} \|a^n\|^{1/n} = \inf \{\|a^n\|^{1/n} : n = 1, 2, \ldots\}$ (*The limit always exists.*)

The result is trivial if $a = 0$. Now assume $a \neq 0$. Let $z \in \sigma(a)$. Then, for any n, $z^n \in \sigma(a^n)$ ⟦Section 1, Lemma 6⟧, thus $|z|^n \leq \|a^n\|$, from relation (1). Hence, $z \in \sigma(a)$ implies $|z| \leq \|a^n\|^{1/n}$ for $n = 1, 2, \ldots$, from which it follows that

$$(2) \qquad\qquad r(a) \leq \|a^n\|^{1/n} \qquad \text{for } n = 1, 2, \ldots.$$

Next, for an arbitrary continuous linear functional f on A, set $g(z) = f[(1 - za)^{-1}]$ for $z \in E$. This defines $g(z)$ for all z, if $r(a) = 0$ and, for $|z| < 1/r(a)$, if $r(a) \neq 0$. ⟦Obviously, $g(0)$ is defined. If $|1/z| > r(a)$, then $1/z \notin \sigma(a)$ so that $(1/z) - a$ is a unit. Thus, $1 - za$ is a unit and $g(z)$ is defined.⟧ Moreover, for such z, $g(z)$ is analytic (as in the proof of Theorem 4).

We now obtain a power series expansion for g. The circle $|z| < 1/\|a\|$ is included in the circular region (which may be the whole complex plane) in which g is analytic. Within the circle $|z| < 1/\|a\|$ we have $(1 - za)^{-1} = \sum_{n=0}^{\infty} z^n a^n$ ⟦since $\|za\| < 1$; compare this with the proof of Fact (ii)⟧. Thus, $g(z) = \sum_{n=1}^{\infty} f(a^n) z^n$. Since g is analytic in the larger region, this power series must converge in it; that is, it must converge for $|z| < 1/r(a)$ or for all z, if $r(a) = 0$. It follows that, for any such z, $f(a^n) z^n \to 0$. This holds for arbitrary $f \in A^*$, and so, by the uniform-boundedness principle, $\|z^n a^n\| < K$ for some $K = K(z)$ and $n = 1, 2, \ldots$. From this follows $\|a^n\|^{1/n} < K^{1/n}/|z|$ and so

$$(3) \qquad\qquad\qquad \limsup \|a^n\|^{1/n} \leq 1/|z|.$$

If $r(a) = 0$, relation (3) holds for all z and so $\|a^n\|^{1/n} \to 0$. If $r(a) \neq 0$, relation (3) holds for all $|z| < 1/r(a)$, thus $r(a) \geq \limsup \|a^n\|^{1/n}$, and this, with relation (2), yields the result.//

We now return to the Gelfand representation for commutative complex Banach algebras with identity. It is permissible to discuss it because Remark 2 provides that H, the carrier space, is not empty.

Facts

In this list, A is a commutative complex Banach algebra with identity; H is the set of nonzero scalar homomorphisms on A (the carrier space), with $\sigma(H, A)$, the weak star topology. The set H is a compact Hausdorff space. The map $a \to \hat{a}$ refers to the Gelfand representation, a homomorphism from A into $C[H]$.

(ix) The map $a \rightarrow \hat{a}$ is norm reducing, hence continuous.

(x) a has an inverse if and only if $\hat{a}$ has, and

$$(4) \qquad\qquad (a^{-1})^{\wedge} = 1/\hat{a}.$$

(xi) $\sigma(a) = \sigma(\hat{a}) =$ range of $\hat{a}$. [$\sigma(\hat{a})$ is computed for the algebra $C[H]$.]

(xii) The spectral radius of a, $r(a)$, is $\|\hat{a}\|$. Thus r is a seminorm on A.

(xiii) The map $a \rightarrow \hat{a}$ is an isometry into if and only if $\|a^2\| = \|a\|^2$ for all a.

Proofs

(ix) For any $f \in H$, $|\hat{a}(f)| = |f(a)| \leq \|f\| \cdot \|a\| = \|a\|$. Thus $\|\hat{a}\| \equiv \sup \{|\hat{a}(f)| : f \in H\} \leq \|a\|$.

(x) If a has an inverse, so has $\hat{a}$ and relation (4) holds because the map $a \rightarrow \hat{a}$ is a homomorphism. If $\hat{a}$ has an inverse, this means $\hat{a}(f) \neq 0$ for all f. Thus, $f(a) \neq 0$ for all f, thus $0 \notin \sigma(a)$ [Corollary 3] and so a is a unit.

(xi) If $z \in \sigma(a)$, then, by Corollary 3, for some $f \in H$, $z = f(a) = \hat{a}(f)$. Conversely, if $\hat{a}(f) = z$ for some $f \in H$, $z \in \sigma(a)$, from Section 1, Lemma 5. That $\sigma(\hat{a})$ is the range of $\hat{a}$ was pointed out in Section 1, Example 10.

(xii) This follows from Corollary 3 and the definition of $r(a)$. (See Section 1, Problem 6.)

(xiii) If the map is an isometry, $\|a^2\| = \|a\|^2$, since this is true in $C[H]$. Conversely $\|a^2\| = \|a\|^2$ for all a implies, for all a, $\|a\| = \|a^{2^n}\|^{2^{-n}}$ for $n = 1, 2, \ldots$. Thus, by Theorem 5, $\|a\| = r(a) = \|\hat{a}\|.//$

DEFINITION 1.   *The radical* K *of a commutative complex Banach algebra with identity is*

$$\{a : \hat{a} = 0\}.$$

This was called the G radical in Section 1. It was not called the radical, since, for algebras in general, other definitions are commonly used (see Section 1, Problem 27, for one). In the present context, however, all definitions of radical reduce to the one given here (see, for example, Problem 21).

Clearly, K is the intersection of all maximal ideals.

An algebra is called *semisimple* if $K = \{0\}$, that is, if H is total over A. The Gelfand representation of a semisimple commutative complex Banach algebra with identity is one to one and so such an algebra is mapped, by means of a norm-reducing isomorphism, into a subalgebra of $C[H]$, H a compact Hausdorff space. If we knew $\hat{A}$ to be closed, we could deduce from the closed-graph theorem that the map is also a homeomorphism. This is not always so [Problem 34]. A sufficient condition is given in Fact (xiii). (Since that condition implies that the representation is one to one, it is also a sufficient condition that the algebra be semisimple.) Any subalgebra of $C[X]$, X a compact Hausdorff space, is semisimple, since $\hat{X}$ is total.

THEOREM 6.   *Let* A *be a commutative complex Banach algebra with identity. The radical is a closed ideal. A vector* a *is in the radical if and only if* $\sigma(a) = \{0\}$, *that is,* r(a) = 0.

The radical is the intersection of all maximal ideals, each of which is closed. A vector a is in the radical if and only if $\hat{a} = 0$, that is, $\sigma(a) = \sigma(\hat{a}) = 0$ [Fact (xi)]; and $\sigma(\hat{a}) = 0$ if and only if $r(a) = 0.//$

Problems 14.2

In this list, A is a Banach algebra, not necessarily commutative, and H is its carrier space, when appropriate. If the words "spectrum" or "unit" are mentioned, it is assumed that A has an identity.

1. A maximal ideal in A is either closed or dense.

2. Let $\{a_n\}$ be a sequence of units. Then $a_n \to 0$ implies $\|a_n^{-1}\| \to \infty$, but not conversely.

3. Extend Fact (ii) by showing that if $r(a - 1) < 1$, then a is a unit. 〖Same proof, using Theorem 5.〗

4. If $\|a - 1\| < 1$, a has a square root. 〖Expand $(1 + \epsilon)^{\frac{1}{2}}$.〗

5. In Fact (xiii), "=" may be replaced by "$\geq$."

6. For (u, v), $(u', v') \in E^2$, set $(u, v) \cdot (u', v') = (uu', vv')$. (a) Show that E^2 is a commutative, semisimple Banach algebra with identity. (b) Find H. Give all values of $\hat{a}(f)$ for $f \in H$ if $a = (2, 1 + i)$. (c) Show that the Gelfand representation is onto, but not an isometry. (d) Give E^2 a norm that makes the representation an isometry.

7. For $(u, v) \in E^2$, set $\|(u, v)\| = |u| + |v|$. Define $(u, v) \cdot (u', v') = (uu', uv' + vu')$. Find the radical and H, and evaluate $(u, v)^{\wedge}(f)$ for $f \in H$.

8. A continuous scalar homomorphism f on a normed algebra has $\|f\| \leq 1$. 〖If $\|a\| < 1$, then $a^n \to 0$, thus $[f(a)]^n \to 0$.〗

9. Deduce Theorem 1 from Problem 8 and Section 1, Problem 31.

10. Give an example of a complex commutative Banach algebra with identity in which the Gelfand representation is not one to one.

11. In Problem 10, replace "one to one" by "onto." 〖Example 5.〗

12. Suppose that A contains an element 1 satisfying $1a = a1 = a$ for all $a \in A$. Show that $\|1\| \geq 1$. 〖$\|1\| = \|1^2\| \leq \|1\|^2$.〗

13. There exists a 4-dimensional real Banach algebra which is a division algebra 〖the quaternions〗, also, a 2-dimensional real commutative Banach algebra which is a division algebra 〖R^2 with complex multiplication〗.

14. Corollary 1 becomes false if "complex" is dropped. 〖Problem 13.〗

15. The set of harmonic functions on the unit square S in R^2 as a normed subspace of $C[S]$ does not satisfy Fact (ii). Hence, it is not a Banach algebra. Which parts of the definition does it not satisfy?

16. If A has an identity and satisfies $\|ab\| = \|a\| \cdot \|b\|$ for all a, b, then A is one dimensional. 〖Example 3.〗 (This result is due to S. Mazur.)

17. Theorem 4 fails for real algebras because there is no Liouville's theorem for real analytic functions. Show that the construction of Theorem 4 applied to i in E with real scalars leads to the bounded analytic function $- 1/(x^2 + 1)$. [Take $f(x, y) = - y$.]

18. For a unit g, let (α) stand for $\|a - g\| < 1/\|g^{-1}\|$ and let (β) stand for $\|g^{-1}a - 1\| < 1$. Show that (α) implies (β), but not conversely, and that (β) implies that a is a unit. Thus, Fact (iii) is improved.

19. $\|a^n\|^{1/n}$ need not be a monotone function of n. 〖$a^2 = 1 \neq a$.〗

20. Deduce that $\|a^n\|^{1/n}$ tends to a limit as $n \to \infty$, from Section 2.4, Problem 32. 〖$u_n = \log \|a^n\|$.〗 (A need not be assumed complete.)

21. Let A be a commutative complex Banach algebra with identity. Then W, Section 1, Problem 27, is equal to the radical. 〖If $a \notin W$, let $f(1 - ab) = 0$. Then $f(a) \neq 0$. An alternative proof runs thus: If a is in the radical, $r(a) = 0$. Thus for all b, $r(ab) = 0$, by Theorem 5 or 6 and so $\Sigma(ab)^n$ is convergent. Its sum is $(1 - ab)^{-1}$.〗

22. In Problem 21, "complex" cannot be omitted. 〖Section 1, Problem 28.〗

23. (Compare Section 1, Problems 20, 21, 22.) Let A be a Banach algebra with identity, B a closed subalgebra, $1 \in B$. Show that for $b \in B$, any boundary point of $\sigma_B(b)$ is also a point of $\sigma(b)$. Hence, if $\sigma_B(b)$ has no interior, it follows that $\sigma(b) = \sigma_B(b)$. 〖Let $t \in \sigma_B(b)$, $t_n \notin \sigma_B(b)$, $t_n \to t$; $\|(t_n - b)^{-1}\| \to \infty$, by Fact (vi). Thus, $t - b$ has no inverse in A, by Fact (v).〗

24. Let A be commutative and with identity. For $a \in A$ define $g: H \to \sigma(a)$ by $g(f) = f(a)$. Show that g is continuous, onto, but not necessarily one to one.

25. If in Problem 24, A is the algebraic closure of $\{1, a\}$ then g is one to one, hence a homeomorphism, that is, $H = \sigma(a)$.

26. Evaluate H, $\sigma(j)$ for (a) A_C with $j(z) = z$, (b) real C with $j(x) = x$. Compare Problem 25.

27. Let X be the 2 sphere, $x^2 + y^2 + z^2 = 1$ in R^3. Then $C[X]$ is not the algebraic closure of $\{1, a\}$ for any $a \in C[X]$. 〚Problem 25.〛

28. If $ab = ba$, then r has the multiplicative property, $r(ab) \leq r(a)r(b)$. 〚$(ab)^n = a^n b^n$. Now use Theorem 5.〛

29. The spectral radius is upper semicontinuous. 〚Theorem 5.〛

▲ 30. The spectral radius is not necessarily continuous.

31. If A is commutative, the spectral radius is a continuous seminorm. 〚$r(a) = \|\hat{a}\|$; see also Problem 29 and Section 6.1, Problem 37.〛 It is a norm if and only if A is semisimple.

32. Let A be semisimple and commutative. The spectral radius is equivalent, in the sense of Section 4.1, Definition 2, to the norm if and only if $\hat{A}$ is closed in $C[H]$. (See Problem 31.) 〚Use the closed-graph theorem.〛

33. Let A be semisimple, commutative, and with identity. Then $\hat{A}$ is closed in $C[H]$ if and only if there exists a constant K such that $\|a\|^2 \leq K \|a^2\|$ for all $a \in A$. 〚Use Problem 32 and $r(a^2) = r(a)^2$. Conversely, $\|a\| \leq K^{1/2 + 1/4 + \cdots + 2^{-n}} \|a^{2^n}\|^{2^{-n}} \to Kr(a)$.〛

34. Let l have the multiplication $(ab)_n = a_n b_n$. Let A be the algebra obtained by adjoining an identity (Section 1, Problem 14, also $\|(a, u)\| = \|a\| + |u|$). Show that A is a semisimple commutative Banach algebra with identity, but $\hat{A}$ is not closed in $C[H]$. 〚Let $a = \sum_{k=1}^n \delta^k$. Then $\|a\|^2 \leq K\|a^2\|$ is false for large n. Use Problem 33.〛

35. (The following definitions are due to R. Arens.) Let A be a Banach algebra. For $f \in A^*$, $a \in A$ define $f_a \in A^*$ by $f_a(x) = f(ax)$. For $f \in A^*$, $F \in A^{**}$, define $f_F \in A^*$ by $f_F(x) = F(f_x)$. Show that (a) $f_{\hat{a}} = f_a$ (here $\hat{a} \in A^{**}$ the natural embedding); (b) $\|f_a\| \leq \|f\| \cdot \|a\|$; (c) $\|f_F\| \leq \|f\| \cdot \|F\|$. For $F, G \in A^{**}$, define FG by $(FG)(f) = F(f_G)$. Show that (d) A^{**} is a Banach algebra; (e) the natural embedding: $A \to A^{**}$ is an isomorphism into; and (f) if A is commutative, $\hat{A}$ is in the *center* of A^{**}, that is, $ab = ba$ for $a \in A^{**}$, $b \in \hat{A}$.

36. The maximal group is dense in C, but not in real C.

37. Let D be the unit disk in E. Then the maximal group is not dense in $C[D]$. 〚Let $a(z) = z$; then $\|b - a\| < 1$ implies $b \notin G$.〛

38. Call a a *left topological divisor of zero* if for each $\epsilon > 0$, there exists b such that $\|b\| = 1$, $\|ab\| < \epsilon$; and make similar definitions with "right" and "two-sided" for "left." Show that a unit cannot be a topological divisor of zero.

39. A vector in the boundary of the maximal group must be a two-sided topological divisor of zero. 〚Let $a_n \to a$, $b_n = a_n^{-1}/\|a_n^{-1}\|$. Then $ab_n \to 0$, by Fact (vi).〛

40. Let $A = B[X]$, X a Banach space. Let $T \in A$ be one to one and range closed. Show that T is not a left topological divisor of zero. 〚If $\|S\| = 1$, $\|TS\| < \epsilon$, let $\|a\| = 2$, $\|Sa\| > 1$, $b = Sa$. Then $\|b\| > 1$, $\|Tb\| < \epsilon$. This violates the closed-graph theorem.〛

41. With A as in Problem 40, let $T \in A$ be onto. Show that T is not a right topological divisor of zero. 〚If $\|S\| = 1$, $\|ST\| < \epsilon$, let $\|b\| = 2$, $\|Sb\| > 1$, $b = Ta$. Then $1 < \|STa\| < \epsilon \|a\|$, contradicting Section 11.2, Problem 25.〛

14.3 Applications

The Banach algebra theory given in Section 2 has applications, both internally, to further investigation of Banach algebras, and to classical analysis. We shall show a few of these.

THEOREM 1.   *The norm of a semisimple commutative Banach algebra with identity is unique. This means that an algebra with identity whose set of scalar homomorphisms is total has at most one norm which makes it a Banach algebra (in other words, any two norms are equivalent).*

This follows immediately from Section 11.3, Corollary 3, since all scalar homomorphisms are continuous ⟦Section 2, Theorem 1⟧.//

The word "commutative" was not used in the restatement of the theorem, since an algebra whose set of scalar homomorphisms is total must be commutative ⟦$f(ab - ba) = 0$ for all f⟧.

Application 1.   *Absolutely convergent Fourier series*

Let H be the unit circumference, $|z| = 1$, in the complex plane.   Let A be the set of complex functions on H of the form

$$a(z) = \sum_{n=-\infty}^{\infty} \alpha_n z^n, \qquad \sum_{-\infty}^{\infty} |\alpha_n| < \infty.$$

Clearly, A is a linear subspace of $C[H]$.   It is also a subalgebra.   ⟦If $a, b \in A$, $a = \Sigma \alpha_n z^n$, $b = \Sigma \beta_n z^n$, we have $a(z)b(z) = \Sigma(\alpha * \beta)_n z^n$, where

$$(\alpha * \beta)_n = \sum_{k=-\infty}^{\infty} \alpha_k \beta_{n-k}$$

and

$$\Sigma |(\alpha * \beta)_n| \leq \sum_{n=-\infty}^{\infty} \sum_{k=-\infty}^{\infty} |\alpha_k \beta_{n-k}| = \sum_k |\alpha_k| \sum_n |\beta_{n-k}| = \Sigma |\alpha_k| \Sigma |\beta_k| < \infty,$$

interchange of summations being justified by absolute convergence.   (The sequence $\{(\alpha * \beta)_n\}$ is called the *convolution* of $\{\alpha_n\}$ and $\{\beta_n\}$.)⟧

A is a commutative algebra with identity d^0 given by $d^0(z) = 1$.   (We chose the notation d^0 because $1 = \Sigma_{n=-\infty}^{\infty} \delta_{n0} z^n$.   Similarly, $d^n(z) = z^n$, $n = \pm 1, \pm 2, \ldots$)

We now look for the maximal ideals in A.   It turns out, as usual, that they are precisely the points of H.   Our task will be greatly simplified if A can be made into a Banach algebra, since then the maximal ideals will be maximal linear subspaces ⟦Section 2, Corollary 2⟧.   This is easy.   We define $\|a\| = \Sigma |\alpha_n|$ where $a(z) = \Sigma \alpha_n z^n$.   The inequality $\|ab\| \leq \|a\| \cdot \|b\|$ was proved a moment ago.   Also $\|d^0\| = 1$.   As to completeness, we observe that the map $a \to \{\alpha_n\}$, where $a(z) = \Sigma \alpha_n z^n$, is an isometry of A onto the space of bisequences $\alpha = \{\alpha_n : n = 0 \pm 1, \pm 2, \ldots\}$ with $\|\alpha\| = \Sigma |\alpha_n|$.   This is proved complete exactly as in Section 5.3, Example 2.

Let f be a nonzero scalar homomorphism on A.   Let $t = f(d^1)$.   (Of course, $d^1(z) = \Sigma \delta_{n1} z^n = z$.)   Then $|t| \leq \|f\| \cdot \|d^1\| = 1$.   But $(d^1)^{-1} = d^{-1}$, thus

$$|t| = \frac{1}{f(d^{-1})} \geq \frac{1}{\|f\| \cdot \|d^{-1}\|} = 1.$$

Thus finally $|t| = 1$, and we shall show that $f = \hat{t}$; that is, $f(a) = a(t)$ for all $a \in A$.   This follows from the facts that $f(d^1) = d^1(t)$ ⟦since each is t⟧, that $\{(d^1)^n : n = 0, \pm 1, \pm 2, \ldots\}$ is a basis for A, and that $f[(d^1)^n] = [f(d^1)]^n = t^n = (d^1)^n(t)$.

We have now identified the carrier space of A as the unit circumference H in the complex plane. We shall deduce Theorem 2 from this fact.

THEOREM 2. (N. WIENER). *Let* $h(\theta)$ *be defined for* $-\pi \leq \theta \leq \pi$ *and have the absolutely convergent Fourier series* $\Sigma_{-\infty}^{\infty}\alpha_n e^{i\theta n}$. *Suppose also that* $h(\theta) \neq 0$ *for* $-\pi \leq \theta \leq \pi$. *Then* $1/h(\theta)$ *also has an absolutely convergent Fourier series.*

Let $a(z) = \Sigma\alpha_n z^n$ define $a \in A$. Our hypothesis is, as proved above, that $\hat{a}(f) \neq 0$ for all $f \in H$, the carrier space of A [$\hat{a}(f) = f(a) = a(t)$ for some $t \in H$ and with $t = e^{i\theta}$ we have $a(t) = h(\theta) \neq 0$]. By Section 2, Fact (x), a has an inverse in A.//

Application 2. *The Stone-Čech compactification,* βX

Let X be a $T_{3\frac{1}{2}}$ space. Let $A = C_1[X]$ and, as usual, let H be the carrier space. If X is not compact, $H \neq X$, that is, A has maximal ideals which are not given by points of X (nonzero scalar homomorphisms not given by $\hat{x}$, $x \in X$). This is true since H is compact [A is a commutative, complex Banach algebra with identity]. Of course, $H \supset X$. [Every $\hat{x}$ is a nonzero scalar homomorphism. Since X is $T_{3\frac{1}{2}}$, the map $x \rightarrow \hat{x}$ is one to one. We are identifying x with $\hat{x}$, X with a subset of H.]

The topology induced on X by H is the same as the original topology of X. [Since X is $T_{3\frac{1}{2}}$, its topology is the weak topology by $C_1[X]$ (Section 9.4, Lemma 3). For every $\hat{a} \in C[H]$, $\hat{a}|X = a$ and so this is the topology $\sigma(H, A)$.]

Every function $a \in C_1[X]$ can be extended to a continuous function on H, namely $\hat{a}$ [for $x \in X$, $\hat{a}(x) \equiv \hat{a}(\hat{x}) = \hat{x}(a) = a(x)$]. This shows, already, that H has a very peculiar structure; for example, if $X = (0, 1)$ and $a(x) = \sin 1/x$, $\hat{a}$ is continuous on the compact set H, and $\hat{a}|X$ is a function whose graph clusters everywhere in the interval $[-1, 1]$ on the Y axis. Thus H must have many points; also H is not metrizable [if it were, $\hat{a}$ would be uniformly continuous, thus, also $\hat{a}|X$].

By taking the closure of X in H—call it βX—we have the result that *every* $T_{3\frac{1}{2}}$ *space* X *can be embedded as a dense subset in a compact Hausdorff space* βX *such that each bounded continuous complex function on* X *has a unique extension to a continuous function on* βX. Here, X is called the *Stone-Čech compactification* of X.

It is worth observing that X is actually dense in H; thus, in fact, βX is the carrier space of $C_1[X]$ and, in a sense, $C_1[X] = C[\beta X]$. Suppose, on the contrary, that X is not dense in H. (Strictly speaking, that $\hat{X}$ is not dense in H.) For some $f \in H$ we can find a neighborhood N of f not meeting X. There exist $g_1, g_2, \ldots, g_n \in C_1[X]$, $\epsilon > 0$, such that $N \supset \{f_0 \in H: |g_k(f_0) - g_k(f)| < \epsilon$ for $k = 1, 2, \ldots, n\}$. [H has the topology $\sigma[H, C_1[X]]$.] Since $N \cap X$, for each $x \in X$, there exists $k(x)$ such that $|g_{k(x)}(x) - g_{k(x)}(f)| \geq \epsilon$. Treating f as a scalar homomorphism on $C_1[X]$, this says

(1) $$|g_{k(x)}(x) - f(g_{k(x)})| \geq \epsilon \qquad \text{for each } x \in X.$$

For $k = 1, 2, \ldots, n$, define $a_k \in C_1[X]$ by $a_k(x) = g_k(x) - f(g_k)$ for $x \in X$.

Then $f(a_k) = f[g_k - f(g_k)1] = 0$, that is, $a_k \in f^{\perp}$. Exactly as in Section 1, Example 5, we set $u = \Sigma_{k=1}^{n}|a_k|^2$ and find that $u \in f^{\perp}$. Yet $u(x) \geq \epsilon^2$ for all $x \in X$ by relation (1);

thus, u is a unit in $C_1[H]$ and so $f(u) \neq 0$ [Section 1, Lemma 2]. This contradiction establishes the result.

Application 3

The Stone-Čech compactification may be used to construct measures, integrals, and generalized limits of various types. For example, consider $m = C_1[\omega]$. Now choose $t \in \beta\omega \setminus \omega$ and for $a \in m$, set $\lim a = \hat{a}(t)$, where $\hat{a}$ is the unique extension of a to $\beta\omega$. The use of the terminology "lim" is justified, since, if a is convergent, $\lim a$ is its ordinary limit. [We may suppose that $a_n \to 0$. Given $\epsilon > 0$, let G be a neighborhood of t such that $n \in \omega \cap G$ implies $|a_n| < \epsilon$. It follows that $|\hat{a}(t)| \leq \epsilon$, since ω is dense in $\beta\omega$.] We have thus extended lim from c to m in such a way that the following five conditions are satisfied:

> (i) $\lim (ta + b) = t \lim a + \lim b$ for scalar t,
> (ii) $\lim ab = \lim a \cdot \lim b$,
> (iii) $\lim a \geq 0$ if $a_n \geq 0$ for all n,
> (iv) $\lim a$ is the ordinary limit if $a \in c$,
> (v) $|\lim a| \leq \sup |a_n|$.

Of course, the Hahn-Banach theorem also provides an extension of the limit, but not with the given list of properties.

If X is a compact Hausdorff space, we may consider a subalgebra A of $C[X]$ and inquire whether it may be given a norm which makes it a Banach algebra. If A is closed in $C[X]$ and contains 1, A has exactly one such norm, that which is inherited from $C[X]$ [Theorem 1]. In general, however, one considers nonclosed subalgebras of $C[X]$; for example, with $X = [0, 1]$, consider the space $C^{(1)}$ of continuously differentiable functions in real C; this space is a real Banach algebra with the norm $\|a\| = \max \{|a(x)| : 0 \leq x \leq 1\} + \max \{|a'(x)| : 0 \leq x \leq 1\}$. Again, this norm is unique, according to Theorem 1.

It is interesting that if A is any subalgebra, with identity, of $C[X]$ and A is then made into a Banach algebra, *the points of* X *are continuous on* A. [They are scalar homomorphisms; see Section 2, Theorem 1.] Thus A is an FH *space with* $H = E^X$. Furthermore, *the norm for* A *must satisfy* $\|a\| \geq \max \{|a(x)| : x \in X\}$; in other words, *the norm given to* $C[X]$ *is minimal among norms of subalgebras of the type under discussion*. [Given $x \in X$, $|a(x)| = |\hat{x}(a)| \leq \|\hat{x}\| \cdot \|a\| = \|a\|$, as provided by Section 2, Theorem 1.] This, of course, is consistent with the fact that smaller *FH* spaces have stronger topologies [Section 11.3, Corollary 1].

Example 1. Consider $C^{(\infty)}$, the space of real infinitely differentiable functions on $[0, 1]$ as a subalgebra of real C. This is a real algebra with identity. We now observe that *there is no way to make* $C^{(\infty)}$ *into a Banach algebra*. We already know [Section 12.1, Example 3] that $C^{(\infty)}$ cannot be made into a Banach space if the points of $[0, 1]$ are to be continuous. Here, remarkably enough, we do not need the extra condition, for the points are scalar homomorphisms and are thus automatically continuous, if $C^{(\infty)}$ is made into a Banach algebra [Section 2, Theorem 1].

Problems 14.3

Where X is unspecified, it is a $T_{3\frac{1}{2}}$ space.

1. The Gelfand representation of the space A of Application 1 is not an isometry.

2. Let $a(z) = \sum_{n=0}^{\infty}\alpha_n z^n$, $\sum|\alpha_n| < \infty$, for $|z| \leq 1$. Suppose that $a(z) \neq 0$ for $|z| \leq 1$. Show that $1/a(z) = \sum\beta_n z^n$ for $|z| \leq 1$ for some sequence $\{\beta_n\}$ satisfying $\sum|\beta_n| < \infty$.

3. Let $X = (0, 1)$ and $A = C_1[X]$. Define $a \in A$ by $a(x) = x$ for $x \in X$. Let the extension of a to βX be called $\hat{a}$. Show that $\hat{a}(u) = 0$ for some $u \in \beta X$.

4. For $g \in C[\beta X]$, $g = (g|X)^\wedge$ in the Gelfand representation of $C_1[X]$.

5. The Stone-Čech compactification of $(0, 1]$ is not $[0, 1]$. (This means, show that $\beta(0, 1]$ is not obtained by adding one point to $(0, 1]$.)

6. Suppose it known [Section 5] that the Gelfand representation of $C_1[X]$ is onto $C[\beta X]$. Deduce that X is dense in βX by this argument: If $g \in C[\beta X]$ with $g(x) = 0$ for $x \in X$, then $g = \hat{a}$ and $a = g|X = 0$, thus $g = 0$.

7. If X is not compact, βX cannot satisfy the first axiom of countability at any point $t \in \beta X \setminus X$. [Otherwise, construct $a \in C_1[X]$ which is not extendible by choosing $a(x_n) = (-1)^n$ and $x_n \to t$.]

8. Give an example of a compact separable nonmetrizable Hausdorff space. [$\beta(0, 1)$. See Problem 7.] Compare Section 13.3, Problem 37.

9. The generalized limit of Application 3 is not *translative;* that is, it is possible that $b_n = a_{n+1}$ for all n, yet $\lim b \neq \lim a$. [$a = \{(-1)^n\}$; $\lim a \neq 0$, since $a^2 = 1$; $\lim a = -\lim b$, since $a + b = 0$.]

10. Suppose that lim can be extended from real c to a positive linear functional L defined on real m. Show that for each $a \in m$, $\lim\inf a \leq L(a) \leq \lim\sup a$.

11. Accepting the fact that there is an extension of lim, as described in Problem 10, which is also translative [Appendix F], show that no such extension could be multiplicative. [See Problem 9.]

12. Let A be an $n \times n$ matrix such that for each k, $a_{kk} = 1$ and $\sum\{|a_{kr}|: r = 1, 2, \ldots, n; r \neq k\} < 1$. Show that A is nonsingular. [By Section 2, Fact (ii), with $\|A\| = \max\{\sum_{r=1}^{n}|a_{kr}|: k = 1, 2, \ldots, n\}$.]

13. In the hint to Problem 12, $\|A\|$ is the norm of A as an operator on E^n with $\|x\| = \max\{|x_k|: k = 1, 2, \ldots, n\}$ for $x \in E^n$. (Compare Section 4.4, Problem 39, the same result for an infinite matrix.)

14. Put some other norms on E^n and obtain other sufficient conditions for nonsingularity of a matrix as in Problems 12, 13 [for example, $\|x\| = \sum|x_k|$.]

15. Let z be a characteristic value of an $n \times n$ matrix A. Show that $|z| \leq \max\{\sum_{r=1}^{n}|a_{kr}|: k = 1, 2, \ldots, n\}$. [See the hint to Problem 12, and Section 2, Theorem 5, $(n = 1)$.]

16. Deduce the result of Section 1.2, Problem 21 by observing that the transform involved is that of a matrix A satisfying $\|A - 2I\| = 1$. Hence, by Section 2, Fact (ii), A has a conservative inverse and Section 1.2, Problem 20 may be applied. Apply this technique to Section 1.2, Problem 22, but first adjoin $2\delta^1$ as a new first row above A.

17. Let $\sum|t_n| < \infty$, $x \in s$, and suppose that $\{x_n + \sum_{k=1}^{n-1}t_k x_k\}$ is convergent. Show that x is convergent. [The given sequence is Jx for a certain matrix J. For some large integer p, replace the first p columns of J by, respectively, $\delta^1, \delta^2, \ldots, \delta^p$. The resulting matrix D will be a triangle satisfying $\|D - I\| < 1$ and Section 2, Fact (ii), and Section 1.2, Problem 20 may be applied.]

18. Let A be a regular triangle which is not of type M. Show that there exists a regular matrix B with $c_B = c_A$ and B not consistent with A. [Let $f \in c_A'$, $f = \lim_A$ on c but not everywhere in c_A. Then $f(x) = t \lim_A x + \sum t_k (Ax)_k$. Form J as in Problem 17 and set $B = JA$. This result is due to S. Mazur.]

19. Deduce the result of Problem 18, assuming that A is a regular matrix such that c is not dense in c_A.

20. Give an example of a compact Hausdorff space which contains a sequence with no convergent subsequence. [Consider $\{n\}$ in $\beta\omega$, and, for example, $f(k_n) = (-1)^n$.]

14.4 B^* Algebras

In this section we investigate algebras with an involution. The purpose is threefold. First, it turns out that, in the representation theory, this assumption leads to maps onto. Secondly, we are able to show how the commutative representation theory leads to results in the noncommutative case as well. We accomplish this by examining certain commutative subalgebras. Thirdly, we give a few technical details to show the reader some of the computations and techniques which are used in the theory. In order to have a definite goal, we shall conclude with the result [Section 5] that in a B^* algebra with identity, $1 + aa^*$ is always a unit. This result was proved by Kelley, Vaught, Fukamiya, and Kaplansky.

An *involution* on an algebra is a conjugate linear, antimultiplicative map of period 2 from the algebra to itself. This means, denoting the map by $a \rightarrow a^*$, that $(ta + b)^* = \bar{t}a^* + b^*$, $(ab)^* = b^*a^*$, and $a^{**} = a$, respectively, t being a scalar.

A complex Banach algebra with identity and involution satisfying $\|aa^*\| = \|a\|^2$ for all a is called a B^* *algebra*. The most obvious examples are $C_1[X]$, in which a^* is the complex conjugate of a; and $B[H]$, H a Hilbert space, in which a^* is the adjoint of a.

If $a = a^*$, we say that a is *self-adjoint;* 0 is obviously self-adjoint; so also is 1 [set $a = 1$, $b = 1^*$ in the identity $(ab)^* = b^*a^*$]. If a is a unit, so is a^*, and $(a^*)^{-1} = (a^{-1})^*$ [$a^*(a^{-1})^* = (a^{-1}a)^* = 1^* = 1$]. The identity $(a^*)^n = (a^n)^*$ for positive integer n is obvious. If a *commutes with* a^* (that is, $aa^* = a^*a$), a is said to be *normal*. Of course, a self-adjoint vector is normal. Finally, for $S \subset A$, let $S^* = \{a^* : a \in S\}$ and say that S is *self-adjoint* if $S^* = S$.

LEMMA 1.   *The involution is an isometry onto.*

We write $\|a\|^2 = \|aa^*\| \le \|a\| \cdot \|a^*\|$; thus, $\|a\| \le \|a^*\|$. From this, $\|a^*\| \le \|a^{**}\| = \|a\|$. The map is onto, since $a^{**} = a$.//

We now consider how one might embed certain members of a B^* algebra in a commutative subalgebra, that is, find a commutative subalgebra containing them.

LEMMA 2.   *Let a be a normal vector. Then the algebraic closure* B *of* $\{1, a, a^*\}$ *is commutative and self-adjoint. Thus it is a* B^* *algebra.*

That B is a subalgebra is proved as was Section 2, Fact (vii). Since each of 1, a, a^* commutes with the other two, the algebraic hull of $\{1, a, a^*\}$ is commutative. Since multiplication is continuous, [Section 2, Fact (i)], B is commutative. To see that B is self-adjoint, let H be the algebraic hull of $\{1, a, a^*\}$. We now use the fact that, for any isometric map f and set S, $f[\bar{S}] = \overline{f[S]}$, proved in Section 9.2, Corollary 1. Applying this to the involution (see Lemma 1), we have $B^* = (\bar{H})^* = \overline{(H^*)} = \bar{H} = B$.//

LEMMA 3.   *Let a be a normal vector. Then there exists a maximal commutative self-adjoint subalgebra* B *containing* a. *Furthermore,* B *is closed, contains 1, and contains its inverses, that is,* $b \in B$ *and* b *a unit, imply* $b^{-1} \in B$.

The adjective "maximal" as used here allows B to be the whole space, as opposed to its use in "maximal subspace" and "maximal ideal." Starting with the algebraic hull of

$\{1, a, a^*\}$, consider a maximal chain, ordered by containment, of commutative self-adjoint subalgebras, all including $\{1, a, a^*\}$. Let B be the union of this chain. Clearly B is a maximal commutative self-adjoint subalgebra. B is closed. $[\bar{B}$ is a commutative and self-adjoint subalgebra as in the proof of Lemma 2; also $\bar{B} \supset B$. Thus $\bar{B} = B$, since B is maximal.$]$

Next, let b be a unit and $b \in B$. For any $x \in B$, we have $b^{-1}x = xb^{-1}$, that is, b^{-1} *commutes with B*. $[$Certainly, $bx = xb$, since B is commutative. The result follows by Section 1, Problem 7.$]$ Moreover, $(b^{-1})^*$ commutes with B. $[(b^{-1})^* = (b^*)^{-1}$, and $b^* \in B$, since B is self-adjoint. The preceding argument now applies.$]$

Finally, b^{-1} is normal, since $b^{-1}(b^{-1})^* = b^{-1}(b^*)^{-1} = (b^*b)^{-1} = (bb^*)^{-1}$ $[$since b is normal, being, with b^*, a member of $B] = (b^*)^{-1}b^{-1} = (b^{-1})^*b^{-1}$. Thus, if $b^{-1} \notin B$ we would obtain, as a contradiction, a commutative self-adjoint algebra larger than B, namely, the algebraic hull of $\{B, b^{-1}, (b^{-1})^*\}.//$

Facts

In this list, A is a B^* algebra, a, b are vectors, z is a scalar, $\bar{z}$ is the complex conjugate of z.

(i) $z \in \sigma(a)$ if and only if $\bar{z} \in \sigma(a^*)$.

(ii) $r(a) = r(a^*)$, where r is the spectral radius.

(iii) If a is normal, $r(a) = \|a\|$.

(iv) The spectrum of a self-adjoint element is real.

(v) For commutative A, the Gelfand representation of A is an isometry into; in particular, A is semisimple. Moreover $(a^*)^\wedge = \bar{\hat{a}}$ and $(aa^*)^\wedge = |\hat{a}|^2$.

(vi) Let a be self-adjoint, $\|a\| \le 1$, and suppose that $\sigma(a)$ contains only real nonnegative numbers. Then $\|a - 1\| \le 1$.

(vii) If a is normal, $1 + aa^*$ is a unit.

(viii) Suppose that a, b are self-adjoint and that $\sigma(a)$, $\sigma(b)$ contain only real nonnegative numbers. Then the same is true of $\sigma(a + b)$.

(ix) For any $a \ne 0$, $\sigma(aa^*)$ is a set of real numbers at least one of which is positive.

Proofs

(i) Let $z \notin \sigma(a)$. Then $a - z$ is a unit. Hence $(a - z)^*$ is a unit; that is, $a^* - \bar{z}$ is a unit. Thus $\bar{z} \notin \sigma(a^*)$. Applying the same result to $\bar{z}$, a^*, instead of z, a, yields the converse.

(ii) This follows from Fact (i) and the definition of r.

(iii) Using $\|bb^*\| = \|b\|^2$ for $b = a^2$, aa^*, and a, we have

$$\|a^2\|^2 = \|a^2(a^*)^2\| = \|aa^*(aa^*)^*\| = \|aa^*\|^2 = \|a\|^4.$$

Thus $\|a^2\| = \|a\|^2$, and so $\|a\| = \|a^{2^n}\|^{2^{-n}}$ as in the proof of Section 2, Fact (xiii). The result follows from Section 2, Theorem 5.

(iv) *Case 1: The algebra is commutative.* Suppose that the conclusion is false. Let a be self-adjoint and with a nonreal complex number in its spectrum. We may assume $i \in \sigma(a)$. $[$Let $z = x + iy \in \sigma(a)$, x, y real, $y \ne 0$. Let $b = (a - x)/y$. Then b is self-adjoint and $i \in \sigma(b)$, since $b - i = (a - z)/y$ is not a unit.$]$ Now, let n be an arbitrary positive integer and let $b = a + in$. Then $i(1 + n) \in \sigma(b)$. Moreover, $- i(1 + n) \in \sigma(b^*)$, by Fact (i). Thus $(1 + n)^2 \leq r(b)r(b^*) = r(b)^2$ [Fact (ii)] $\leq \|b\|^2$ [Section 2, Fact (ix)] $= \|bb^*\| = \|a^2 + n^2\| \leq \|a^2\| + n^2$. Subtracting n^2 from the first and last terms yields $2n + 1 \leq \|a^2\|$, contradicting the fact that n is arbitrary.

Case 2: The algebra is not commutative. Let a be self-adjoint, and let B be the algebraic closure of $\{1, a\}$. By Lemma 2 and Case I, $\sigma_B(a)$ is real. But $\sigma(a) \subset \sigma_B(a)$ [Section 1, Problem 20].

(v) The isometry follows from Fact (iii), since every vector is normal. Next, given a, let $b = (a + a^*)/2$, $c = (a - a^*)/2i$. Then b, c are self-adjoint and $a = b + ic$, $a^* = b - ic$. Thus $(a^*)^\wedge = \hat{b} - i\hat{c} = \overline{\hat{b} + i\hat{c}}$ [since, by Fact (iv), $\hat{b}$, $\hat{c}$ are real functions] $= \bar{\hat{a}}$. Also $(aa^*)^\wedge = \hat{a}\bar{\hat{a}} = |\hat{a}|^2$.

(vi) We may assume that A is commutative. [By Lemma 3, a is contained in a commutative B^* algebra $B \subset A$ such that B contains its inverses. By Section 1, Problem 22, $\sigma(a) = \sigma_B(a)$.] We have $0 \leq x \leq 1$ for $x \in \sigma(a)$ [since $r(a) \leq \|a\| \leq 1$]. Thus, for $x \in \sigma(a - 1)$, $- 1 \leq x \leq 0$. It follows that $\|a - 1\| = r(a - 1) \leq 1$. [The equality is a consequence of Fact (iii); $(a - 1)$ is normal because A is commutative.]

(vii) Let B be the algebraic closure of $\{1, a, a^*\}$. By Lemma 2, B is a commutative B^* algebra. In the Gelfand representation, of B, $(aa^*)^\wedge = |\hat{a}|^2$ [Fact (v)] and so $- 1 \notin \sigma_B(aa^*)$ [$|\hat{a}(x)|^2 = - 1$ is impossible]. Thus $1 + aa^*$ is a unit in B, *a fortiori* in A.

(viii) We may assume $\|a\| \leq 1$, $\|b\| \leq 1$ [for we may divide both by the same large positive constant]. It follows from Fact (vi) that $\|a - 1\| \leq 1$, $\|b - 1\| \leq 1$; hence, $\|a + b - 2\| \leq \|a - 1\| + \|b - 1\| \leq 2$. Now $a + b$ is self-adjoint and so, by Fact (iv) $\sigma(a + b)$ is real. If $\sigma(a + b)$ contained a negative real number, say $- \epsilon$, $\epsilon > 0$, then $- 2 - \epsilon \in \sigma(a + b - 2)$ and so $\|a + b - 2\| \geq r(a + b - 2) \geq 2 + \epsilon$, contradicting the earlier inequality.

(ix) As in the proof of Fact (v), write $a = b + ic$, with b, c self-adjoint. Then $aa^* + a^*a = 2b^2 + 2c^2$. Suppose that $\sigma(aa^*)$ contains no positive numbers. Then $\sigma(- aa^*)$ is real [Fact (iv)] and contains only nonnegative numbers. But $a^*a = 2b^2 + 2c^2 + (- aa^*)$, and so, by Fact (viii), $\sigma(a^*a)$ contains only real nonnegative numbers. Thus $\sigma(aa^*) = \sigma(a^*a) = \{0\}$ [Section 1, Problem 12]. It now follows from Fact (iii) that $aa^* = 0$. Thus $\|a\|^2 = \|aa^*\| = 0$, and so $a = 0.//$

Problems on B* algebra 14.4

1. If $abb^* = 0$, then $ab = 0$. [$\|ab\|^2 = \|ab(ab)^*\|$.]
2. The product of two self-adjoint vectors is self-adjoint if and only if they commute.
3. If a commutes with b, then a^* commutes with b^*.
4. For any scalar homomorphism f, $f(a^*) = \overline{f(a)}$.
5. Not all vectors are self-adjoint.
6. "Normal" cannot be omitted in Fact (iii). $\left[a = \begin{pmatrix} 0 & 1 \\ 0 & 0 \end{pmatrix}. \right]$
7. Let $a = b + ic$ with b, c self-adjoint. Show that a is normal if and only if $bc = cb$.
8. Let a vector u be called *unitary* if $uu^* = u^*u = 1$. Show that if u is unitary, $\|ua\| = \|au\| = \|a\|$ for all a. In particular, $\|u\| = 1$.
9. Let a be self-adjoint, and let t be a real number greater than $\|a\|$. Let $b = a + i(t^2 - a^2)^{\frac{1}{2}}$ (see Section 2, Problem 4). Show that b/t is unitary.

10. For any self-adjoint a, we have $a = \lambda(u + u^*)$ for some positive λ and unitary u. ⟦Problem 9.⟧

11. Every vector can be written $\lambda(u + u^*) + i\mu(v + v^*)$, where u, v are unitary, and λ, μ are nonnegative real numbers. ⟦Write $a = b + ic$, with b, c self-adjoint, and apply Problem 10.⟧

12. If a vector commutes with every unitary vector, it commutes with every vector. ⟦Problem 11.⟧

13. Let a self-adjoint idempotent be called a *projection*. (In the language of Chapter 8, a perpendicular projection, see Section 8.6, Problem 22.) Let a, b be projections. Show that (a) $a + b$ is a projection if and only if $ab = 0$, (b) $a - b$ is a projection if and only if $ab = b$, (c) ab is a projection if and only if $ab = ba$. ⟦See Problem 2.⟧ Compare Section 1, Problem 8.

14. In E, identify all self-adjoint vectors, all normal vectors, all unitary vectors, and all projections.

15. If a is a nonzero projection, $\|a\| = 1$.

16. For projections a, b, define $a \geq b$ to mean $ab = b$. Show that (i) this introduces an antisymmetric partial ordering of the set P of projections. For projections a, b, c, show that (ii) $0 \leq a \leq 1$; (iii) $a \geq b$ if and only if $a - b \in P$; (iv) if $a + b \in P$, then $a + b = a \vee b$; (v) if $ab \in P$, then $ab = a \wedge b$, and $a + b - ab = a \vee b$; (vi) if $ab = 0$, then $a \wedge b = 0$; (vii) $ab = 2a$ implies $a = 0$; (viii) $a \leq b$, $c \leq b - a$ imply $ac = 0$ and $c \leq b$; (ix) $a \geq b$, $a \geq c$, $a = bc$ imply $b = c = a$; (x) $ab = 1$ implies $a = b = 1$.

17. If a is normal and $\sigma(a)$ is real, then a is self-adjoint.

18. A normal idempotent is a projection. ⟦Considering the algebraic closure of $\{1, a, a^*\}$, $(\hat{a})^2 = \hat{a}$; hence $\hat{a}$ is real, so a is self-adjoint.⟧

19. There is no normal nilpotent except 0. ⟦Fact (iii).⟧

20. If a is normal, $(1 + aa^*)^{-1}$ belongs to the algebraic closure of $\{1, a, a^*\}$.

21. Let $f \in C_1[X]$. Show that $1/(1 + |f|^2)$ lies in the algebraic closure of $\{1, f, \bar{f}\}$.

22. If a is self-adjoint, the spectrum of a contains either $\|a\|$ or $-\|a\|$. ⟦Facts (iii) and (iv).⟧

23. If a is normal, $\|a\|^2 \in \sigma(aa^*)$.

24. For any a, the series $\sum_{n=0}^{\infty}(ia)^n/n!$ is convergent and, if a is self-adjoint, its sum is unitary.

25. Suppose that $\|b + 1\| < 1$. Show that $\sum_{n=1}^{\infty}(1 - b)^n/n$ is convergent. Denote its sum by a. Show that $b = \sum_{n=0}^{\infty}a^n/n!$.

26. Let Φ be the algebra of all matrices A such that $\|A\| < \infty$ and let K be the subalgebra consisting of the conservative matrices. Show that K contains its inverses. ⟦Section 12.4, Problem 34.⟧

14.5 Unfinished business

In this section we give a brief sketch of the most immediate succeeding development. Some of the proofs are omitted. References are listed in Appendix B.

We have discussed the possibility that the Gelfand representation be one to one, continuous, homeomorphic, isometric. Obviously, the question of when it is onto ought to be discussed. The principal tool is the Stone-Weierstrass theorem. We state it without proof (see Appendix G).

THEOREM 1. THE STONE-WEIERSTRASS THEOREM. *Let* X *be a compact Hausdorff space and* A *a closed subalgebra of* $C[X]$ *which* (a) *is separating over* X, *and* (b) *contains, with each of its members, the complex conjugate of that member. Then, either* $A = C[X]$ *or* A *is a maximal ideal* I_X.

Of course, the first alternative holds if $1 \in A$. The theorem also holds for real $C[X]$, in which case condition (b) is superfluous.

The classical Weierstrass theorem is a corollary. ⟦Take $X = [0, 1]$, A the closure of the set of polynomials in real C.⟧

COROLLARY 1. *The Gelfand representation of a commutative* B* *algebra with identity is a congruence onto, thus such an algebra is* C[X] *for some compact Hausdorff space* X.

This follows from the Stone-Weierstrass theorem, Section 1, Problem 10 and Section 4, Fact (v).//

The great advantage of this result is that it allows us to deduce the existence of various vectors, in general B* algebras, not necessarily commutative, from their existence in $C[X]$. Consider one example: *Every self-adjoint vector whose spectrum contains no negative numbers has a square root; in particular, any vector of the form* aa* *has a square root.* 〚If a has the stated properties, let B be the algebraic closure of $\{1, a\}$. Then $B = C[X]$, $\hat{a}$ is a nonnegative real function; thus $(\hat{a})^{1/2} \in C[X]$ and, since the representation is onto, $(\hat{a})^{1/2} = \hat{b}$ for some $b \in B$. Obviously, $b^2 = a$, since $(b^2)^{\wedge} = \hat{b}^2 = \hat{a}$ and, since B is semisimple, so that the representation is one to one.〛

A second example is given in Corollary 2, which is the culmination of the development given in Section 4. A special case was proved in Section 8.6, Theorem 1.

COROLLARY 2. *In a* B* *algebra,* 1 + aa* *is always a unit.*

Let $b = aa^*$. Let B be the algebraic closure of $\{1, b\}$. By Section 4, Lemma 2, B is a commutative B* algebra with identity; hence $B = C[X]$, by Corollary 1. Define u, $v \in C[X]$ by $u = \hat{b} \vee 0$, $v = (-\hat{b}) \vee 0$ 〚$\hat{b}$ is a real function, by Section 4, Fact (iv)〛. Since the representation of B is onto, there exist c, $d \in B$ with $u = \hat{c}$, $v = \hat{d}$. Then c, d satisfy $cd = 0$ 〚since $\hat{c}\hat{d} = 0$〛; $b = c - d$ 〚since $\hat{b} = \hat{c} - \hat{d}$〛; thus, $da(da)^* = dbd = d(c - d)d = -d^3$. Consequently, $\sigma[da(da)^*]$ is the range of $-\hat{d}^3$, which contains no positive numbers since $\hat{d} = v$ is a function taking on only real nonnegative values. By Section 4, Fact (ix), $da = 0$, and so the identity just proved implies that $d^3 = 0$. Hence $v = 0$ 〚$v^3 = 0$, since $v = \hat{d}$; $v = 0$, since $C[X]$ has no nilpotent elements〛. From the definition of v, it follows that $\hat{b}(x) \geq 0$ for all $x \in X$; that is, $\sigma_B(b)$ contains only positive real numbers. In particular, $-1 \notin \sigma_B(b)$ so that $1 + b$ is a unit in B, *a fortiori* in A.//

The prototype of a noncommutative algebra is $B[H]$, the set of bounded operators on a Hilbert space H. A typical representation theorem is that *every* B* *algebra is congruent with a subalgebra of* B[H] *for some* H, *with the involution going over into the adjoint operation.* Briefly, one defines a *positive* linear functional f on a B* algebra A to be one such that $f(aa^*) \geq 0$ for all a.

We define $(a, b) = f(ab^*)$, f being a fixed positive linear functional; then (a, b) has all the properties of an inner product except, possibly, that $(a, a) = 0$ for some $a \neq 0$. Let $N(f) = \{a: (a, a) = 0\}$. Then $N(f)$ is a right ideal. 〚For example, if $a \in N(f)$, $(ab, ab) = f(abb^*a^*) = (a, bb^*a^*) = 0$, by Cauchy's inequality.〛 Let $H(f)$ be the completion of the inner-product space $A/N(f)$. It is a Hilbert space and the map $a \to a_f \in B[H(f)]$ given by $a_f(b) = f(ab^*)$ for $b \in A$ is a norm-reducing homomorphism of A into $B[H(f)]$ which carries the involution into the adjoint. We now form a direct sum of all $H(f)$, f a positive linear functional on A, and define a map from A into this sum by combining maps of the preceding type in an obvious way. The remainder of the proof consists of showing that a B* algebra has sufficiently many positive linear functionals that the representation is a congruence into.//

In the study of Banach algebras without identity, it is customary to ignore the possibility of adjoining an identity 〚Section 1, Problem 14〛 and proceed as follows (the idea is due to S. Perlis): Define a new operation on the algebra by the equation $a \circ b = a + b - ab$.

This operation is associative and has 0 as identity.   If the algebra has an identity we have $(1 - a)(1 - b) = 1 - a \circ b$; thus, the new operation can be made to play the role of multiplication.   (Observe that 1 acts like infinity in that $1 \circ a = 1$ for all a.)   In particular, $(1 - a)(1 - b) = 1$ if and only if $a \circ b = 0$, in which case a is called a *left quasi-inverse* for b. *Right quasi-inverse* and *quasi-inverse* are defined similarly.

The analogue of Section 2, Fact (ii), is that if $\|a\| < 1$, a has the quasi-inverse $- \Sigma_{n=1}^{\infty} a^n$.

Considering scalar homomorphisms f, if a has a quasi-inverse, $f(a) \neq 1$ $[0 = f(a + b - ab) = f(a) + f(b) - f(a)f(b) = 1$, if $f(a) = 1]$.

Thus the hyperplane $f = 1$ does not meet the unit cell and so $\|f\| \leq 1$ [Section 4.2, Fact (iii)].

In the remaining discussion we shall assume the algebra commutative.   Let H be the set of nonzero scalar homomorphisms.   Then, as we have just seen, H is a subset of the unit disk.

Modifying the proof of Section 2, Theorem 2, we obtain the result that $H \cup \{0\}$ is compact.   Thus H is locally compact.   It is then straightforward to prove that the Gelfand representation is into the space of all continuous functions on a locally compact space H which *vanish at infinity;* that is, for each $\epsilon > 0$, $\{f \in H: |\hat{a}(f)| \geq \epsilon\}$ is compact.   If, in addition, the algebra has an involution and satisfies $\|aa^*\| = \|a\|^2$, the Stone-Weierstrass theorem may be used to show that the Gelfand representation is onto.

For each $f \in H$, $f^{\perp}$ is a regular maximal ideal [Section 1, Problem 33].   Conversely, one proves that each regular maximal ideal is $f^{\perp}$ for some $f \in H$.   This is done by observing that, if I is a regular maximal ideal, A/I is a field, hence, one dimensional [Section 2, Corollary 1].

Example 1: The Fourier transform.   Let A be the space $L^1[R]$ of all complex functions a on R satisfying $\|a\| \equiv \int_{-\infty}^{\infty} |a(u)|\, du < \infty$.   Here, A is a Banach space and is made into a commutative Banach algebra by defining multiplication to be convolution, denoted by $*$, and defined by $a * b(t) = \int_{-\infty}^{\infty} a(u)b(t - u)\, du$.

Given any continuous linear functional f on A, there exists a continuous bounded complex function α on R such that, for $a \in A$, $f(a) = \int_{-\infty}^{\infty} a(u)\alpha(u)\, du$, and $\|f\| = \sup \{|\alpha(u)|: u \in R\}$ (see Appendix J).   Now, suppose that f is a nonzero scalar homomorphism on A. Then, for $a, b \in A$, we have $\int_{-\infty}^{\infty} \int_{-\infty}^{\infty} a(u)b(v)\alpha(u + v)\, du\, dv = f(ab)$ [in the integral, substitute $v = v$, $u = t - v$ and obtain $\int a* b(t)\, \alpha(t)\, dt] = f(a)f(b) = \iint a(u)b(v)\alpha(u)\alpha(v)\, du\, dv$.   Thus $\alpha(u + v) = \alpha(u)\alpha(v)$.

Thus, for positive integer n, $\alpha(nu) = \alpha(u)^n$ for all u.   Now $\alpha(1) \neq 0$ $[\alpha(u) = \alpha(1)\alpha(u - 1) = 0$ for all u if $\alpha(1) = 0]$ and $\alpha(0) = 1$ $[\alpha(1) = \alpha(0)\alpha(1)]$ so that $\alpha(- u)\alpha(u) = \alpha(0) = 1$ and then $\alpha(- u) = \alpha(u)^{-1}$; hence $\alpha(nu) = \alpha(u)^n$ for all integer n.   Next, let r be rational, $r = m/n$, then $\alpha(ru)^n = \alpha(nru) = \alpha(mu) = \alpha(u)^m$ and so $\alpha(ru) = \alpha(u)^r$.   It follows that $\alpha(r) = \alpha(1)^r = e^{\mu r}$ for some fixed μ, whenever r is rational; for $\alpha(1) = e^{\mu}$ since $\alpha(1) \neq 0$.   Since α is continuous, $\alpha(u) = e^{\mu u}$ for all $u \in R$.   Since sup $|\alpha(u)| = \|f\| \leq 1$, we have that μ is pure imaginary and so we may write $\alpha(u) = e^{-i\lambda u}$, λ real, and obtain $\hat{a}(f) = f(a) = \int_{-\infty}^{\infty} a(u)e^{-i\lambda u}\, du$, the Fourier transform of a.

Thus the Gelfand representation carries each member of A into its Fourier transform. It is a familiar fact, of course, that convolution goes over into pointwise multiplication. This says, here, that $(a * b)^{\hat{}} = \hat{a}\hat{b}$.

Problems 14.5

In this list, A has all the properties of a complex B^* algebra, except that it is not assumed to have an identity. If the spectrum is mentioned, A is assumed to have an identity. The statement $\sigma(a) \geq 0$ means that the spectrum of a is real and contains only nonnegative numbers.

1. If A has an identity, $z + aa^*$ is a unit for every scalar z which is not 0 or a negative real number.

2. Let A be commutative. For every nonzero scalar homomorphism f on A, $\|f\| = 1$. (Problem 3 shows that the B^* assumption cannot be dropped.) ⟦A is the set of continuous complex functions vanishing at infinity on H. For $f \in H$, there exists such a function which has its maximum at f.⟧

3. Assume that A does not have an identity. Define $\|a\|_1 = 2\|a\|$. Show that, with this new norm, A is a Banach algebra and for every scalar homomorphism f on A, $\|f\| \leq \frac{1}{2}$.

4. Deduce the Stone-Weierstrass theorem from its real case. ⟦Show that RA is separating.⟧

5. Real C is the algebraic closure of $\{1, a\}$, where a is any strictly monotone function. (Compare Section 2, Problem 25, which is obvious in this case.)

6. E^2, with its natural norm, cannot be given an involution which makes it a B^* algebra. ⟦E^2 is rotund, thus cannot be $C[H]$.⟧

7. A nonzero idempotent cannot have a quasi-inverse.

8. A nilpotent always has a quasi-inverse. ⟦Try $- a - a^2 - \cdots - a^{n-1}$.⟧

9. ab has a quasi-inverse if and only if ba has one. ⟦Section 1, Problem 12.⟧

10. The set of vectors with quasi-inverse is open. (Compare Section 2, Fact (iii). The proof is similar.)

11. The quasi-inverse is a continuous operation where it is defined. ⟦As in Section 2, Fact (v).⟧

12. $2 \circ 2 = 0$.

13. $a \circ b - b \circ a = ba - ab$.

14. $(a + b) \circ (c + d) = a \circ c + a \circ d + b \circ c + b \circ d - (a + b + c + d)$.

15. $a \circ \sum_{k=1}^{n} b_k = \sum_{k=1}^{n} a \circ b_k - (n - 1)a$.

16. $a \circ b + (- a) \circ b = 2b$.

17. It is possible for a nonzero vector a satisfying $a^3 = a$ to have a quasi-inverse. (Compare Problem 7.)

18. If a^n has a quasi-inverse for some positive integer n, then a has a quasi-inverse. However, the converse is false. ⟦$(- 1)^2$ has no quasi-inverse.⟧

19. If $\alpha_1, \alpha_2, \ldots, \alpha_n$ are the nth roots of 1, then

$$\frac{a}{\alpha_1} \circ \frac{a}{\alpha^2} \circ \cdots \circ \frac{a}{\alpha_n} = a^n.$$

20. Find all vectors in c_0 which have quasi-inverses.

21. Prove the statement in the text reading "the map $a \to a_f \in B[H(f)]$ given by $a_f(b) = f(ab^*)$ for $b \in A$ is a norm-reducing homomorphism which carries the involution into the adjoint."

22. If a is self-adjoint, and $\sigma(a) \geq 0$, then a has a square root which, moreover, belongs to the algebraic closure of $\{1, a\}$.

23. Let A have an identity. Let $a \geq 0$ mean that $\sigma(a) \geq 0$, and $a \geq b$ mean $a - b \geq 0$. (a) Show that A becomes an ordered linear space with antisymmetric order and that the positive cone is closed. (b) Show that $a \geq 0$ if and only if $a = bb^*$. Thus the definition of positive linear functional given here agrees with that of Section 2.7, Problem 27. ⟦Take $b = a^{1/2}$.⟧ (c) 1 is an order identity for A. (d) Every self-adjoint vector is the difference of two positive vectors. ⟦$2a = (1 + a)^2 - 1 - a^2$.⟧ (e) A positive linear functional is real on self-adjoint vectors. ⟦By (d).⟧ (f) A positive linear functional f satisfies $f(a^*) = \overline{f(a)}$.

24. Let A have an identity and let B be a B^* subalgebra of A. Show that B contains its inverses; that is, $b \in B$, b a unit in A imply $b^{-1} \in B$. ⟦$B = C[H]$.⟧

APPENDIX

Numbers in square brackets refer to entries in the list of references given in Appendix O.

A. Chapter 8 of [2] gives an excellent Readers' Guide, containing references for further study of most of the topics given in this book. In particular, it may be consulted for references for the study of Hilbert space. The Notes and Remarks at the end of each chapter of [3] are interesting and useful guides to the literature. Moreover, they seem to be complete.

B. Continuations of the material of Chapter 14 may be found in [4], [7], and [9].

C. The theory of uniform spaces is developed in Chapter 6 of [5] and in Chapter 4 of [8].

D. Proof that L^p, and l^p, $p > 1$, are uniformly convex is given in [1].

E. Schauder bases for C and L^p, $p \geq 1$, are given in [2], page 69, and in [11], respectively.

F. A generalized limit for all bounded sequences which is translative is given in [2], page 83. There is an elegant construction in [3], page 73, Problem 22.

G. Proofs of the Stone-Weierstrass theorem are given in [2], page 103, [3], page 272, and [7], page 9.

H. R. C. James has given an example of a nonreflexive Banach space which is congruent with its second conjugate, and whose natural embedding is of codimension 1 in its second conjugate. An account is given in [2], page 72.

I. A discussion of the duality of uniformly convex spaces, and uniformly even spaces is given in [8], pages 199–203. See also [2], pages 111–115.

J. The representation theorems for continuous linear functionals on C and L^1 are given in [10], Chapters 2 and 3.

K. For the most standard proof of the Hahn-Banach theorem, see [2], pages 9 and 11. The best generalization of a certain type is given in [2], page 95, Theorem 3.

L. The student interested in continuing the study of summability along the lines suggested in this book may refer to [12], and the articles of A. Wilansky and K. Zeller, in which other references are given. Consult the Mathematical Reviews beginning in 1950.

M. It is a very delightful experience to browse through the first several volumes of *Studia Mathematica* and the volumes of *Fundamenta Mathematicae* of the same period. There are many short and amusing articles on various points in functional analysis, written by those who breathed the exciting air of its creation.

N. An elementary presentation of the theory of distributions is given in [6].

O. The list below contains a few articles, of which specific mention has been made, and several books.   The books given contain discussions of, and references for all the directions for which this book is a point of departure.   Thus, such books as those of Banach and Bourbaki are present by implication.

1. J. A. Clarkson, "Uniformly convex spaces," *Trans. Am. Math. Soc.* **40** (1936), 396–414.

2. M. M. Day, *Normed Linear Spaces*, rev. ed. (New York: Academic Press, Inc., 1962).

3. N. Dunford and J. T. Schwartz, *Linear Operators*, Part I (New York: Interscience Publishers, Inc., 1958).

4. L. Gillman and M. Jerison, *Rings of Continuous Functions* (Princeton: D. Van Nostrand Co., Inc., 1960).

5. J. L. Kelley, *General Topology* (Princeton: D. Van Nostrand Co., Inc., 1955).

6. M. J. Lighthill, *Introduction to Fourier Analysis and Generalised Functions* (New York: Cambridge University Press, 1958).

7. L. H. Loomis, *An Introduction to Abstract Harmonic Analysis* (Princeton: D. Van Nostrand Co., Inc., 1953).

8. H. Nakano, *Topology and Linear Topological Spaces* (Tokyo: Maruzen Co., Ltd., 1951).

9. C. E. Rickart, *General Theory of Banach Algebras* (Princeton: D. Van Nostrand Co., Inc., 1960).

10. F. Riesz and B. Sz-Nagy, *Functional Analysis* (New York: Frederick Ungar Publishing Co., Inc., 1955).

11. J. Schauder, "Eine Eigenschaft des Haarschen Orthogonal-systemes," *Math. Z.* 28 (1928), 317–320.

12. K. Zeller, *Theorie der Limitierungsverfahren* (Berlin: Springer Verlag, 1958).

13. J. L. Kelley, I. Namioka, et al., *Linear Topological Spaces* (Princeton: D. Van Nostrand Co., Inc., 1963).

GLOSSARY

The entries are some of the more common words found in the literature. The definitions are given in the language of this book.

Almost open map: map carrying each nonempty open set onto a set which is somewhere dense.

B_0 space: locally convex Fréchet space.

Barreled space: t space.

Bijection: one-to-one and onto map.

Circled: balanced.

Complete (applied to orthonormal system): maximal.

Deficiency: codimension.

Determining: norming.

Duxial: subspace $S \subset A^*$ is called duxial if $\|a\|_S = \|a\|$ for all $a \in A$.

Equivalent: congruent.

Euclidean space: finite-dimensional inner product space.

Eigenvalue: characteristic value.

F space: locally convex Fréchet space.

Hausdorff maximal principle: axiom of transfinite induction.

Injection: one-to-one map.

Linearly ordered: totally ordered.

Latent value, latent root: characteristic value.

Maximal ideal space: carrier space.

Moore-Smith convergence: net convergence.

Norm: (sometimes) total paranorm.

Norm-determining: norming.

Normal matrix: (in summability) triangle.

Normed ring: Banach algebra.

Prehilbert space: inner-product space.

Proper value: characteristic value.

Pseudometric: semimetric.

Radial at x: contains a line segment in each direction passing through x.

Residual: having a complement which is of the first category.

Simply ordered: totally ordered.

Second countable, second axiom of countability: the assumption that a topology has a countable base.

Sfield: division ring.

Surjection: onto map.

Summability, pth power: $\int |f|^p < \infty$.

Topologically isomorphic: linearly homeomorphic.

Tonnelé, tunneled: t space.

Uniformly rotund: uniformly convex.

Unitary space: inner product space.

Vector space: linear space.

Zorn's lemma: a formulation of the axiom of transfinite induction.

INDEX

Symbols are given in the alphabetical listing where possible—otherwise at the end. Greek letters are listed alphabetically by their English spelling, for example, χ occurs in the C section.

a_k, 93
Ac, 62, 64, 205, 214, 259
Ax, 3
$(Ax)_n$, 3
Absolute G_δ, 80
Absolutely convergent, 84
Absorbing, 23
Additive, 18, 19, 79, 81, 94, 96
Adjoint, 98, 133
Affine, 28
Affine hull, 29
Affine mean, 29
Algebra, 251
Algebraic closure, 259
Algebraic hull, 259
Alc topology, 222
Almost all, 2
Analytic geometry, 122
Annihilator, 5, 95
Antisymmetric, 9
Approximate Characteristic value, 135
ARENS, R., 267, 248
Associated net, 148
Associated real linear space, 42
Automorphism, 113
Axiom of transfinite induction, 10

βX, 269
$B[H]$, 132, 272, 276, 290 (Table)
$B_1[H]$, 56, 62, 70, 71, 93, 290 (Table)
b property, 187
B^* algebra, 272
Baire category theorem, 78
Balanced, 22
Balanced hull, 177
Balanced closure, 177

Balloon, 30
Balloon topology, 173, 226, 249
Banach-Alaoglu theorem, 239, 240
Banach algebra, 259
Banach space, 78
Banach-Steinhaus closure theorem, 117, 200, 225
Base, 138
Basic, 89, 209
Basis, 86, 129, 207
Bessel's inequality, 127
Bidual, 250
Bilinear, 233
Biorthogonal, 5, 35, 87, 209, 221
DU BOIS-REYMOND, P., 118
Bornivore, 187
Bornological, 187
Boundary, 193
Bounded set, 178, 181, 194, 216
Bounded operator, 132
Bounded seminorm and function, 64
Boundedly complete, 212

χ, 93, 95, 231
c and c_0, 289
   algebra, 259
   basis, 86, 87, 88
   convergence and topology, 62, 71, 75, 84, 85, 153, 202, 203
   dual, 91, 92, 95, 102, 103
   norm, 122
   not a conjugate space, 105
   projections, 68
   subsets, 86, 207
C, $C^{(n)}$, $C^{(\infty)}$, 290
   algebra, 270
   basis, 87

C, dual, 96
  maps, 64, 206
  topology, 62, 203, 204, 208
$C[X]$, $C_1[X]$, 290
  algebra, 251, 259, 272
  ideals and scalar homomorphisms, 252, 254, 270
  representation, 256
  spectrum, 255
  topology, 56, 62, 270
c_A, 3, 76, 154, 228, 289 (Table)
$C(a, r)$, 60
carrier space, 261
category, 73, 78, 137
Cauchy's inequality, 121
Cauchy sequence and net, 76, 82, 147, 173, 194, 218
cell, 60
Center, 267
Chain, 9
Characteristic value and vector, 134
Circumference, 60
Closed function, 79, 195
Closed set, 60, 137
Closed-graph lemma, 197
Closed graph theorem, 200
Closed vs continuous, 196
Closure, 72, 137
Cluster point, 157
Codimension, 33
Coercive, 243, 258
Cofinal, 10, 156
Column-finite, 4
Commutative, 251
Compact, 160, 163, 165
Compact support, 43
Comparable, 9
Comparison of topologies, 64
Compatible, 234
Complementary, 32, 132
Complete, 76, 82, 84, 177
Completely regular, 140, 158
Completion, 79, 83, 129,
Cone, 30
Congruent, 81
Conical hull, 32
Conjugate linear, 120
Conjugate space, 90
Consecutive hulls, 11, 86, 177
Conservative, 4, 118
Consistent, 95, 231, 271
Containment (ordering by), 9
Contains its inverses, 257, 272, 278
Continuous, 61, 65, 137, 145, 155, 217, 241
Continuously embedded, 202
Conull, 93

Convergent
  filter, 148
  net, 144
  sequence, 61, 137
  series, 84
Convex, 23
Convex balanced closure, 177, 238
Convex balanced hull, 29
Convex hull, 27
Convolution, 268
Coordinates, 4, 87
COPPING, J., 232
Copy, 155
Coregular, 93
Countable Hamel basis, 106, 193
Countable product, 3
Cover, 160
Crisscross theorems, 21, 74

δ^n 4
$d(a,b)$, 60
$d(S,T)$, 61
$D(a,r)$, 60
d_A, 3, 228, 289 (Table)
DAY, M. M., 114
Dense, 73, 137
Dense cone, 10, 26, 32, 49
Derivative, 44, 64, 106, 198, 206, 218
Determining, 215
Diagonal, 154
Diameter, 61
Dimension, 17, 128
Dirac delta, 44
Directed set, 9
Dirichlet problem, 68
Discrete metric and topology, 55, 63, 136
Disk, 60
Distance, 60, 61
Distribution, 43
Division ring and algebra, 254
DIXMIER, J., 105
Dual, 62
Duality, 233

E, E^n, E^∞, 1, 63, 153, 202, 259, 289 (Table)
E_C, 55, 62, 64, 205, 214, 218, 290 (Table)
Empty set, 14, 15, 16, 22, 178
End, 164
Equicontinuous, 188, 200, 225, 242
Equivalent, 53, 73
Euclidean topology, 138, 139, 150, 152, 165
Evaluation map, 5
Eventually, 143
Existence of functions, 19, 67, 68
Expansion, 86
Extend linearly, 20

Extension of functions and subspaces, 21, 48, 65, 66, 68, 70, 71
Extreme point, 71

F, $F[X]$, 3, 4, 203, 205, 290 (Table)
FH space, 202, 270
FK space, 202, 203, 226ff
Factor, 3
Fatou's lemma, 212
Field, 254
Filter, 148, 160, 164, 166, 258
Finalizing, 156
Finite dimensional, 16, 35, 39, 101, 192, 193, 221, 236
Finite intersection property, 159, 160
Finiteness, 151, 173, 206
Finite product, 3
Finite sequence, 3
First countable, 138, 183
Fourier series, 118, 127, 131, 268
Fourier transform, 277
Fréchet combination, 54, 63, 79, 147, 149
Fréchet space, 78
Frequently, 143
FUKAMIYA, M., 272
Full intersection property, 160
Function, 1, 45
Functional, 19
Fundamental, 85, 220

$G(A)$, 259
G_δ, 74, 80, 84
G radical, 255
G semisimple, 255
Gauge, 58
Gelfand representation, 256, 264
Generalized limit, 270
Generated by, 138, 171
Gram-Schmidt process, 123
Graph, 195
Green's function, 69
GRYNBLYUM, M. M., 211

Hahn-Banach theorem, 65, 219
Hamel basis, 16
Hamel dimension, 17
Hausdorff space, 139
HAYMAN, W. K., 115
Heaviside distribution, 44
Helly's theorem, 103
Hermitian, 133
Hilbert space, 121
HILDEBRANDT, T. H., 94
Hölder's inequality, 6, 8
Homeomorphism, 72, 137

Homomorphism, 19, 253
Hyperplane, 37

I_x, 252
Ideal, 252
Ideal maximal subspace, 252, 262
Idempotent, 253
Identity, 251
Identity map, 19
Inclusion map, 19
Inclusion (ordering by), 9
Indiscrete, 63, 136
Infinite dimensional, 16
Inner product, 120
Inner product space, 121
Integral, 44, 94
Interior, 60, 73, 137, 141
Invariant semimetric, 61
Inverse, 11, 133, 252
Invertible, 133
Involution, 133, 272
Irreducible, 217
Isometry, 72, 84
Isomorphism, 19, 253
Isotone, 147

JAMES, R. C., 212
Jensen's inequality, 7
Joint continuity, 152, 155, 202
Jordan-von Neumann theorem, 124

KAPLANSKY, I., 272
KELLEY, J. L., 272
Kernel, 5, 256
KLEE, V., 84

l^p, 289
  algebra, 259, 268
  basis, 86
  dual, 91, 95, 101, 243
  norm, 121, 122, 180
  topology, 62, 153, 185, 202, 203
L^p, 290
  basis, 87, 208
  dual, 11, 114, 242
  norm, 121
  subsets, 132, 181
  topology, 62, 204
l_n, 87, 207
$L(A,B)$, 95
LAX, P. D., 68
Left ideal, 252
Legendre polynomials, 135
Lexicographic order, 9
Lie on one side of, or on opposite sides of, 47, 49
Lim, 5, 61

Lim$_A$, 4
Lim sup and inf, 147
Line, 23
Line segment, 23
Linear closure, 85
Linear combination, 14
Linear function or map, 18
Linear homeomorphism, 81
Linear metric and semimetric space, 61
Linear space, 13
Linear subspace, 13
Linear topological space, 167
Linear topology generated by a family of semi-norms, 171, 215
Linearly independent, 14
Little closed graph and open mapping theorems, 196
Local base, 138
Locally compact, 160
Locally complete, 80
Locally convex, 171, 180

M, 62, 116, 204, 208, 290 (Table)
m, 62, 75, 94, 95, 153, 166, 202, 203, 289 (Table)
Mackey-Arens theorem, 248
MACPHAIL, M. S., 229
MCSHANE, E. J., 110
Magnification, 27
Maximal chain, 10
Maximal group, 259, 267
Maximal ideal, 252
Maximal orthonormal set, 126, 131
Maximal subspace, 37, 175
Maximum, 10, 67
Mazur's theorem, 262
MAZUR, S., 94, 95, 262, 266, 271
Measure, 93
Metric, 60
Metrically bounded, 77
Metrizable, see semimetrizable
MILMAN, D., 109
Minimal T_1 topology, 142
Minkowski's inequality, 6
Monotone basis, 88
Most general function, 90
Multiplicative function, 253
Multiplicative limit, 270, 271
Multiplicative matrix, 95
Multiplicative property, 132, 259

N(*a,r*), 60
N(*T*), 135
NACHBIN, L., 65
Natural embedding, 36, 100, 234, 250
Natural homomorphism, 33, 177

Natural norm, paranorm, invariant metric, topology, 62, 203, 204
Natural subnet, 157
Neighborhood, 60, 137
Net, 143
Nilpotent, 253
Not a normed or metric space, 154, 155, 185, 206, 218
Norm, 56, 64
Norm decreasing and increasing, 99
Normable, see semimetrizable
Normal, 135, 140, 272
Normed space, 61
Norming, 105, 201, 246
Not a conjugate space, 105
Not locally convex spaces, 172, 180, 236
Nowhere absorbing, 23
Nowhere dense, 73, 137
Null sequence, 2

ω, 1, 289
One-sided ideal, 252
Open function or map, 73, 137
Open-mapping theorem, 199
Open set, 60, 136
Order ideal, 32
Order identity, 32
Ordered linear space, 32, 41, 71, 278
Orthogonal, 100, 107, 112, 123, 134
Orthogonal coefficients, 127
Orthogonal series, 129
Orthonormal, 123

π, See product
P_n, P_t, 4, 5
Parallel postulate, 26
Parallelogram law, 109, 124
Paranorm, 52
Parseval's relation, 127
Pathology, 64, 70, 87, 112, 118, 154, 181, 190, 205, 220
Perfect, 79
Perfectly separable, 243
PERLIS, S., 276
Perpendicular projection, 135
PETTIS, B. J., 109
Points, 5, 13
Pointwise bounded, 116
Pointwise convergent, 117
Pointwise topology, 152, 234
Polar, 236
Polynomials, 64, 71, 89, 106, 260
Poset, 9
Positive cone, 32
Positive distribution, 45

Positive linear functional, 32, 41, 43, 71, 276, 278
Primitive, 44
Product, 3, 151, 155, 168, 172, 181, 185, 234
Projection on a coordinate space, 5, 154
Projection on a subspace 34, 68, 105, 135, 201, 214, 257
Proper ideal, 252
Property α, 212
Pseudobounded, 182, 194, 242

Quasi-inverse, 277
Quotient, 33, 53, 96, 147, 177, 254, 260

R, R^n, R^∞, 1, 10, 259, 289 (Table)
R^+, 289
Rf, 1
$r(a)$, 255
r_A, 4, 42, 290
$R(T)$, 135
Radical, 265
Rank, 29
Rational homogeneous, 19
Real, 291
Real algebra, 251
Real linear function, 42
Real linear space, 13
Real span, 15
Real vs complex, 42, 49, 57, 71, 173, 188
Reducible, 217
Refine, 160
Reflexive order, 9
Reflexive space, 100, 109, 213, 244, 246
Regular ideal, 258
Regular matrix, 4
Regular operator, 133
Regular space, 139
Regularly closed, 242
Relative topology, 137, 146, 155, 163
Relatively absorbing, 49
Relatively strong, 249
Representation, 36, 151, 240. See also Gelfand representation and individual spaces such as L^p, Hilbert space, *FK* space
Resonance, 117
Reversible, 76, 228
Riemann-Lebesgue lemma, 128
Riemann mapping theorem, 68
RIESZ, F., 123
Riesz-Fischer theorem, 130
Ring, 251
RINGROSE, J. R., 246
Rotund, 107
Row-finite, 4, 42, 96, 207, 227
$\sigma(a)$, $\sigma(T)$, 133, 255
$\sigma_B(a)$, 257

$\sigma(A,\Phi)$, $\sigma(\Phi)$, 155, 169, 171, 172, 215
$\sigma(A,B)$, 235, 242, 248
$\sigma(A,A^\#)$, $\sigma(A^\#,A)$, 154, 181, 234, 249
$\sigma(A,A')$, $\sigma(A',A)$, 154, 187, 223, 224, 225, 234

ΣA_β, 156
s, 289
   basis, 86, 88
   coordinates, 64
   dual, 90, 95
   maps, 42, 95, 96, 201, 207
   product, 3, 153
   subsets, 64, 74, 166, 181, 191, 246
   topology, 55, 62, 84, 85, 153, 155, 173, 187, 218, 249
SH space, 207, 250
Saturated, 35
Scalar, 13
Scalar homomorphism, 253, 261
Schatz's apple, 23
Schauder basis, 86
Self-adjoint, 133, 272
Semicontinuous, 71, 74, 83, 119, 147, 164, 177, 212, 226
Semimetric, 60
Semimetrizable and seminormable, 137, 150, 183, 217, 242
Seminorm, 56
Seminormed space, 61
Semisimple, 255, 265
Separable, 75, 89, 130, 164, 214, 243
Separate continuity, 155, 202
Separated space, 176
Separated by functions and hyperplanes, 49, 139, 219
Separated by open sets, 139
Separating family of functions, 20
Separation axioms, 139
Sequence, 1, 2
Sequential convergence, 141, 142, 243
Sequentially closed, 142
Sequentially continuous, 142
Series, 84
Sesquilinear, 234
Sgn, 1
Silverman-Toeplitz conditions, 4, 118
Solution of equations, 21, 104
Somewhere absorbing, 23
Somewhere dense, 73, 137
Span, 15
Spectral radius, 255, 264, 265
Spectrum, 133, 255
Stone-Cech compactification, 269
Stone-Weierstrass theorem, 275
Strictly on one side of or on opposite sides of, 47
Strictly separated, 49

Strong topology, 246

Stronger paranorm, semimetric and topology, 53, 73, 137, 146

Sturm-Liouville, 134

Subadditive, 22, 189

Subbase, 138

Subcover, 160

Subnet, 156

Subspace, 13

Sum of 2 subspaces, 201

Summable series, 147

Summability (matrix), 3, 71, 119, 214, 275. See also χ, c_A, consistent, coercive, column-finite, conull, coregular, d_A, *FK* space, generalized limit, $\lim_A$, multiplicative matrix, perfect, r_A, regular matrix, reversible, row-finite, Silverman-Toeplitz conditions, translative, triangle, type *M*.

Sup topology, 139, 168, 172

Superfluous, 216

Support, 46

Symmetric, 22

τ (A,B), 247

t property, 224

t space, 224

T_0, T_1, etc. space, 139, 162

Table of Spaces, 289–291

Tail, 158

Tangent, 67

Term, 143

TOEPLITZ, O., 42

Topological divisor of zero, 267

Topological group, 177, 186, 193, 198

Topological space, 136

Topologically complete, 84

Topologically free, 208

Topology, 136

Total, 20, 53

Totally bounded, 164, 182, 192, 242

Totally ordered, 9

Transfer, 75, 76

Transfinite induction, 10

Transitive, 9

Translation, 22, 168

Translative, 271

Triangle, 4, 76, 89

Triangular inequality, 52, 56, 60

Trivial linear combination, 14

Trivial order, 9

True subset, 63

Two-sided ideal, 252

Tychonoff space, 140

Tychonoff's theorem, 165

Type *M*, 95

$u(a,b)$, 233

Ultrafilter, 166

Uniform boundedness principle, 116, 200, 223

Uniform continuity, 82

Uniformity, 193

Uniformly bounded, 116

Uniformly convex, 108, 246

Uniqueness of topology, 200

Unit, 133

Unitary, 274

Unit cell, disk and circumference, 63

Unit vector, 123

Universal net, 164

Urysohn's lemma, 140

VAUGHT, R. L., 272

Vector, 13

$w(A,A')$, $w(A,\Phi)$, $w(A,f)$, 149, 172. See also $\sigma(A,A')$, etc.

Weak convergence, 71, 111, 119, 129, 214, 243

Weak linear topology, 171

Weak star topology, 234

Weak topology, 149, 235

Weaker, see stronger

Weakly continuous, 201, 243

Weierstrass approximation theorem, 73, 275

Weighted mean, 26

WIENER, N., 269

$\star$, $\blacktriangle$, 2

$\bigcap$, 1

$f\,|\,S$, $f{\circ}g$, 1

$A \backslash B$, 1

A/B, 33

$A^{\#}$, A', A^*, 20, 62, 90

a^*, T^*, 98, 272

$!a!$, 62

$\|a\|$, $\|p\|$, $\|f\|$, 64

$\|A\|$, 4

$\|a\|_s$, $\|p\|_s$, $\|f\|_s$, 64, 83, 105

$\emptyset$, 1

$\hat{a}$, $\hat{A}$, 36

$f \wedge g$, $T \vee T'$, $\vee\Phi$, 56, 139

A^B, 291

$A^{(B)}$, 291

$a \perp b$, $a^{\perp}$, $S^{\perp}$, 122, 123

$f^{\perp}$, 5

$\bar{S}$, 72

S^i, 141

$\tilde{S}$, 1

S^0, 236

$\oplus$, 15

(A, T) 136

(A, Φ) 226

TABLE OF SPACES

SYMBOL	THE SET OF	NATURAL NORM OR PARANORM
ω	positive integers	
R	real numbers	
R^+	positive real numbers	
E	complex numbers	
R^n	n-tuples of real numbers	$\|x\| = \sum_{k=1}^{n} \sqrt{x_k^2}$
E^n	n-tuples of complex numbers	$\|x\| = \sum_{k=1}^{n} \sqrt{\|x_k\|^2}$
s	sequences	$!x! = \sum_{k=1}^{\infty} \frac{1}{2^k} \frac{\|x_k\|}{1 + \|x_k\|}$
c_0	null sequences	$\|x\| = \sup \|x_n\|$
c	convergent sequences	$\|x\| = \sup \|x_n\|$
m	bounded sequences	$\|x\| = \sup \|x_n\|$
l^p	sequences x such that $\Sigma\|x_k\|^p < \infty$	for $\|p\| \geq 1$, $\|x\| = (\Sigma\|x_k\|^p)^{1/p}$ for $0 < p < 1$, $!x! = \Sigma\|x_k\|^p$.
l	$(= l^1)$	
E^∞	finite sequences. (x is called *finite* if $x_n = 0$ for almost all n)	
R^∞	finite real sequences	
d_A	sequences x such that Ax exists (*Domain* of the matrix A)	See Section 12.4
c_A	sequences x such that $Ax \in c$ (*Convergence domain* of A)	If A is a triangle, $\|x\| = \sup \{\|(Ax)_n\|: n = 1,2, \ldots \}$ See Section 12.4
m_A	sequences x such that $Ax \in m$ (*Boundedness domain* of A)	See Section 12.4

r_A	sequences y such that $y = Ax$ for some $x \in d_A$ (*Range of A*)	
$F[H]$	complex functions on H, H a set	
F	($= F[H]$ with $H = [0,1]$, the closed unit interval)	
$B_1[H]$	bounded complex functions on H, H a set.	$\|f\| = \sup\{|f(h)| : h \in H\}$
$B[H]$	bounded operators on H, H a normed space,	See Section 8.6
$C[H]$	continuous complex functions on H, H a topological space	
C	($= C[H]$ with $H = [0,1]$)	
$C_1[H]$	bounded continuous complex functions on H, H a topological space	$\|f\| = \sup\{|f(h)| : h \in H\}$
$A^{\#}$	linear functionals on A, A a linear space	
A', A^*	continuous linear functionals on A, A a paranormed, or linear topological space	See Section 4.4, Definition 1.
$C^{(n)}$	real functions on $[0,1]$ with n continuous derivatives	$\|f\| = \sup\{|f^{(k)}(x)| : 0 \leq x \leq 1, 0 \leq k \leq n\}$
$C^{(\infty)}$	real functions on $[0,1]$ with infinitely many derivatives	$!f! = \sum_{n=0}^{\infty} \frac{1}{2^n} \cdot \frac{\|f\|_n}{1 + \|f\|_n}$, where $\|f\|_n = \sup\{|f^{(n)}(x)| : 0 \leq x \leq 1\}$
L^p	Lebesgue measurable functions f on $[0,1]$ such that $\int_0^1 |f|^p < \infty$	for $p \geq 1$, $\|f\| = \left(\int_0^1 |f|^p\right)^{1/p}$ for $0 < p < 1$, $!f! = \int_0^1 |f|^p$.
M	Lebesgue measurable functions on $[0,1]$	$!f! = \int_0^1 \frac{|f|}{1 + |f|}$
A_C	functions of a complex variable, analytic in the circle ($|z| < 1$), and continuous on ($|z| \leq 1$)	$\|f\| = \sup\{|f(z)| : |z| \leq 1\}$
E_C	entire functions (in the sense of the theory of functions of a complex variable)	$!f! = \sum_{n=0}^{\infty} \frac{1}{2^n} \cdot \frac{\|f\|_n}{1 + \|f\|_n}$, where $\|f\|_n = \sup\{|f(z)| : |z| \leq n\}$.

A^B	functions $f\colon B \to A$, A,B sets
$A^{(B)}$	functions $f\colon B \to A$ carrying all but finitely many $b \in B$ to 0
$\pi\{A_\beta\colon\beta \in B\}$	functions $f\colon B \to \cup\{A_\beta\colon\beta \in B\}$ such that $f(\beta) \in A_\beta$ for each $\beta \in B$
Real	This denotes the corresponding space of real objects. For example, real C is the space of continuous real functions on $[0,1]$; real s is the space of all real sequences.

Manufactured in the United States of America

ABOUT THE AUTHOR

Albert Wilansky is Professor of Mathematics at Lehigh University. He was educated in the public schools of St. John's, Newfoundland; the Memorial College of Newfoundland; and Dalhousie University in Halifax, Nova Scotia. He received his doctorate from Brown University in 1947.

Professor Wilansky has written numerous articles on the applications of functional analysis to the theory of summability, as well as many teaching notes and problems. He is Associate Editor of the *American Mathematical Monthly*, and Visiting Lecturer of the Mathematical Association of America. Professor Wilansky was consultant to the Frankford Arsenal in Philadelphia and was a Governor of the Mathematical Association of America.

DATE DUE

MR 7- '67			
MR 5 '68			
NOV 2 4 1984			
DEC 0 3 1999			
		PRINTED IN U.S.A.